Basic College Mathematics
Fifth Edition

> # Student's Solutions Manual

Basic College Mathematics

Fifth Edition

Lial • Salzman • Hestwood • Miller

Student's Solutions Manual

Prepared with the assistance of

Carmen Eldersveld

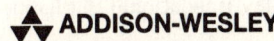
ADDISON-WESLEY

An imprint of Addison Wesley Longman, Inc.

Reading, Massachusetts • Menlo Park, California • New York • Harlow, England
Don Mills, Ontario • Sydney • Mexico City • Madrid • Amsterdam

Reproduced by Addison Wesley Educational Publishers from camera-ready copy supplied by the author.

Copyright © 1998 Addison Wesley Educational Publishers, Inc.

All rights reserved. No part of this publication may be reproduced, stored in a retrieval system, or transmitted, in any form or by any means, electronic, mechanical, photocopying, recording, or otherwise, without the prior written permission of the publisher. Printed in the United States of America.

ISBN 0-321-01317-4

2 3 4 5 6 7 8 9 10   CRS   00 99 98

PREFACE

This book provides complete solutions for all the margin exercises, section exercises numbered 3, 7, 11, ..., and all the chapter review, chapter test, and cumulative review exercises in *Basic College Mathematics*, Fifth Edition, by Margaret L. Lial, Stanley A. Salzman, Diana L. Hestwood, and Charles D. Miller. Some solutions are presented in more detail than others. Thus, you may need to refer to a similar exercise to find a solution that is presented in sufficient detail. As needed, artwork is provided to clarify and illustrate solutions.

The following people have made valuable contributions to the production of this *Student's Solutions Manual:* Judy Martinez, typist, and James McLaughlin, artist.

CONTENTS

CHAPTER 1 WHOLE NUMBERS

    1.1 Reading and Writing Whole Numbers 1
    1.2 Addition of Whole Numbers 2
    1.3 Subtraction of Whole Numbers 4
    1.4 Multiplication of Whole Numbers 6
    1.5 Division of Whole Numbers 9
    1.6 Long Division 12
    1.7 Rounding Whole Numbers 15
    1.8 Roots and Order of Operations 19
    1.9 Solving Application Problems 21
    Chapter 1 Review Exercises 24
    Chapter 1 Test 32

CHAPTER 2 MULTIPLYING AND DIVIDING FRACTIONS

    2.1 Basics of Fractions 35
    2.2 Mixed Numbers 36
    2.3 Factors 37
    2.4 Writing a Fraction in Lowest Terms 40
    2.5 Multiplication of Fractions 42
    2.6 Applications of Multiplication 43
    2.7 Dividing Fractions 44
    2.8 Multiplication and Division of Mixed Numbers 45
    Chapter 2 Review Exercises 48
    Chapter 2 Test 52
    Cumulative Review Exercises (Chapters 1-2) 53

CHAPTER 3 ADDING AND SUBTRACTING FRACTIONS

    3.1 Adding and Subtracting Like Fractions 57
    3.2 Least Common Multiples 58
    3.3 Adding Subtracting Unlike Fractions 61
    3.4 Adding and Subtracting Mixed Numbers 63
    3.5 Order Relations and the Order of Operations 66
    Chapter 3 Review Exercises 68
    Chapter 3 Test 73
    Cumulative Review Exercises (Chapters 1-3) 75

CHAPTER 4 DECIMALS

- 4.1 Reading and Writing Decimals ... 80
- 4.2 Rounding Decimals ... 81
- 4.3 Adding Decimals ... 84
- 4.4 Subtracting Decimals ... 85
- 4.5 Multiplying Decimals ... 87
- 4.6 Dividing Decimals ... 90
- 4.7 Writing Fractions as Decimals ... 94
- Chapter 4 Review Exercises ... 97
- Chapter 4 Test ... 103
- Cumulative Review Exercises (Chapters 1-4) ... 105

CHAPTER 5 RATIO AND PROPORTION

- 5.1 Ratios ... 110
- 5.2 Rates ... 112
- 5.3 Proportions ... 113
- 5.4 Solving Proportions ... 115
- 5.5 Applications of Proportions ... 118
- Chapter 5 Review Exercises ... 120
- Chapter 5 Test ... 126
- Cumulative Review Exercises (Chapters 1-5) ... 127

CHAPTER 6 PERCENT

- 6.1 Basics of Percent ... 132
- 6.2 Percents and Fractions ... 133
- 6.3 The Percent Proportion ... 136
- 6.4 Identifying the Parts in a Percent Problem ... 138
- 6.5 Using Proportions to Solve Percent Problems ... 139
- 6.6 The Percent Equation ... 143
- 6.7 Applications of Percent ... 145
- 6.8 Simple Interest ... 149
- 6.9 Compound Interest ... 151
- Chapter 6 Review Exercises ... 153
- Chapter 6 Test ... 160
- Cumulative Review Exercises (Chapters 1-6) ... 162

CHAPTER 7 MEASUREMENT

- 7.1 The English System ... 169
- 7.2 The Metric System—Length ... 172
- 7.3 The Metric System—Capacity and Weight (Mass) ... 174
- 7.4 Applications of Metric Measurement ... 176
- 7.5 Metric-English Conversions and Temperature ... 177
- Chapter 7 Review Exercises ... 178
- Chapter 7 Test ... 183
- Cumulative Review Exercises (Chapters 1-7) ... 184

CHAPTER 8 GEOMETRY

- 8.1 Basic Geometric Terms...189
- 8.2 Angles and Their Relationships..189
- 8.3 Rectangles and Squares..190
- 8.4 Parallelograms and Trapezoids..192
- 8.5 Triangles..194
- 8.6 Circles..195
- 8.7 Volume...198
- 8.8 Pythagorean Theorem..200
- 8.9 Similar Triangles...202
- Chapter 8 Review Exercises..204
- Chapter 8 Test..211
- Cumulative Review Exercises (Chapters 1-8)................................213

CHAPTER 9 BASIC ALGEBRA

- 9.1 Signed Numbers..218
- 9.2 Addition and Subtraction of Signed Numbers.............................219
- 9.3 Multiplication and Division of Signed Numbers.........................222
- 9.4 Order of Operations..224
- 9.5 Evaluating Expressions and Formulas..227
- 9.6 Solving Equations..229
- 9.7 Solving Equations with Several Steps...233
- 9.8 Applications...237
- Chapter 9 Review Exercises..240
- Chapter 9 Test..248
- Cumulative Review Exercises (Chapters 1-9)................................250

CHAPTER 10 STATISTICS

- 10.1 Circle Graphs..256
- 10.2 Bar Graphs and Line Graphs...258
- 10.3 Frequency Distributions and Histograms...................................259
- 10.4 Mean, Median, and Mode...259
- Chapter 10 Review Exercises..261
- Chapter 10 Test..263
- Cumulative Review Exercises (Chapters 1-10)..............................264

APPENDIX B 271

Chapter 1

WHOLE NUMBERS

1.1 Reading and Writing Whole Numbers

1.1 Margin Exercises

1. **(a)** 341
    4 is in the tens place.
   (b) 714
    4 is in the ones places.
   (c) 479
    4 is in the hundreds place.

2. The place value of each digit

   (a) 24,386
   ones: 6
   tens: 8
   hundreds: 3
   thousands: 4
   ten thousands: 2

   (b) 371,942
   ones: 2
   tens: 4
   hundreds: 9
   thousands: 1
   ten thousands: 7
   hundred thousands: 3

3. The digits in each period (group) of 3,251,609,328:

   (a) 3 is in the billions period.
   (b) 251 is in the millions period.
   (c) 609 is in the thousands period.
   (d) 328 is in the ones period.

4. **(a)** 46 is forty-six.
   (b) 68 is sixty-eight.
   (c) 293 is two hundred ninety-three.
   (d) 902 is nine hundred two.

5. **(a)** 7309 is seven thousand, three hundred nine.

   (b) 95,372 is ninety-five thousand, three hundred seventy-two.
   (c) 100,075,002 is one hundred million, seventy-five thousand, two.
   (d) 11,022,040,000 is eleven billion, twenty-two million, forty thousand.

6. **(a)** One thousand, four hundred thirty-seven is 1437.
   (b) Nine hundred seventy-one thousand, six is 971,006.
   (c) Eighty-two million, three hundred twenty-five is 82,000,325.

1.1 Section Exercises

3. 18,015
   1 is in the ten thousands place.
   0 is in the hundreds place.

7. 7,536,175
   millions: 7
   thousands: 536
   ones: 175

11. Evidence suggests that this is true. It is common to count using fingers.

15. 725,009 is seven hundred twenty-five thousand, nine.

19. Thirty-two thousand, five hundred twenty-six is 32,526.

23. Four thousand, twenty in digits is 4020.

27. Two hundred eighty million, four hundred eighty-nine thousand in digits is

    280,489,000.

1

1.2 Addition of Whole Numbers

1.2 Margin Exercises

1. (a) $3 + 4 = 7$; $4 + 3 = 7$

   (b) $9 + 9 = 18$

   (c) $7 + 8 = 15$; $8 + 7 = 15$

   (d) $6 + 9 = 15$; $9 + 6 = 15$

2. (a)
$$\begin{array}{rl} 5 & \\ 4 & 5+4=9 \\ 6 & 9+6=15 \\ 9 & 15+9=24 \\ +\ 2 & 24+2=26 \\ \hline 26 & \end{array}$$

   (b)
$$\begin{array}{rl} 7 & \\ 5 & 7+5=12 \\ 1 & 12+1=13 \\ 2 & 13+2=15 \\ +\ 6 & 15+6=21 \\ \hline 21 & \end{array}$$

   (c)
$$\begin{array}{rl} 9 & \\ 2 & 9+2=11 \\ 1 & 11+1=12 \\ 3 & 12+3=15 \\ +\ 4 & 15+4=19 \\ \hline 19 & \end{array}$$

   (d)
$$\begin{array}{rl} 3 & \\ 8 & 3+8=11 \\ 6 & 11+6=17 \\ 4 & 17+4=21 \\ +\ 8 & 21+8=29 \\ \hline 29 & \end{array}$$

3. (a) $\begin{array}{r} 25 \\ +\ 73 \\ \hline 98 \end{array}$ (b) $\begin{array}{r} 364 \\ +\ 532 \\ \hline 896 \end{array}$ (c) $\begin{array}{r} 42{,}305 \\ +\ 11{,}563 \\ \hline 53{,}868 \end{array}$

4. (a) $\begin{array}{r} \overset{1}{6}9 \\ +\ 26 \\ \hline 95 \end{array}$ (b) $\begin{array}{r} \overset{1}{7}6 \\ +\ 18 \\ \hline 94 \end{array}$

   (c) $\begin{array}{r} \overset{1}{5}6 \\ +\ 37 \\ \hline 93 \end{array}$ (d) $\begin{array}{r} \overset{1}{3}4 \\ +\ 49 \\ \hline 83 \end{array}$

5. (a) $\begin{array}{r} \overset{22}{481} \\ 79 \\ 38 \\ +\ 395 \\ \hline 993 \end{array}$ (b) $\begin{array}{r} \overset{1\ 21}{4\ 271} \\ 372 \\ 8\ 976 \\ +\ \ 162 \\ \hline 13{,}781 \end{array}$

   (c) $\begin{array}{r} \overset{22}{5}\overset{2}{7} \\ 4 \\ 392 \\ 804 \\ 51 \\ +\ \ 27 \\ \hline 1335 \end{array}$ (d) $\begin{array}{r} \overset{2\ 21}{7\ 821} \\ 435 \\ 72 \\ 305 \\ +\ 1\ 693 \\ \hline 10{,}326 \end{array}$

6. (a) $\begin{array}{r} 278 \\ 825 \\ 14 \\ 3 \\ 7 \\ +\ 9\ 275 \\ \hline 10{,}402 \end{array}$ (b) $\begin{array}{r} 3305 \\ 650 \\ 708 \\ 29 \\ 40 \\ 6 \\ +\ \ \ 3 \\ \hline 4741 \end{array}$ (c) $\begin{array}{r} 15{,}829 \\ 765 \\ 78 \\ 15 \\ 9 \\ 7 \\ +\ 13{,}179 \\ \hline 29{,}882 \end{array}$

7. The shortest distance from Lake Buena Vista to Conway is as follows.

   $\begin{array}{rl} 4 & \textit{To Resort Area} \\ 6 & \textit{Resort Area to Pine Castle} \\ 3 & \textit{Pine Castle to Belle Isle} \\ +\ 6 & \textit{Belle Isle to Conway} \\ \hline 19 & \text{miles} \end{array}$

8. The next shortest distance is as follows.

   $\begin{array}{rl} 5 & \textit{Orlando to Pine Hills} \\ 8 & \textit{Pine Hills to Altamonte Springs} \\ 5 & \textit{Altamonte Springs to Castleberry} \\ 6 & \textit{Castleberry to Bertha} \\ 7 & \textit{Bertha to Winter Park} \\ +\ 7 & \textit{Winter Park to Clear Lake} \\ \hline 38 & \text{miles} \end{array}$

9. (a) $\begin{array}{r} 32 \\ 8 \\ 5 \\ +\ 14 \\ \hline 59 \end{array}$ correct   (b) $\begin{array}{r} 872 \\ 539 \\ 46 \\ +\ 152 \\ \hline 1609 \end{array}$ correct

   (c) $\begin{array}{r} 79 \\ 218 \\ 7 \\ +\ 639 \\ \hline 943 \end{array}$ (953 is incorrect)

Section 1.2   Addition of Whole Numbers

(d) 21,892
         11,746
      + 43,925
        77,563   (79,563 is incorrect)

1.2 Section Exercises

3.   44
       + 53
         97

7.   258
         421
       + 320
         999

11. Line up: 274
                   302
                 + 421
                   997

15. Line up: 12,142
                    43,201
                  + 23,103
                    78,446

19. Line up: 38,204
                  + 21,020
                    59,224

23.   ¹
          58
        + 96
         154

The sum of the ones column is 14. Write 4 and carry 1 ten to the tens column. The sum of the tens column is 15. Write 5 in the tens column and 1 in the hundreds column.

27.   ¹
         73
       + 89
        162

31.   ¹
         746
       + 905
        1651

35.   ¹¹
         278
       + 135
         413

39.   ¹¹
         526
       + 884
        1410

43.   ¹ ¹¹
         7 896
       + 3 728
        11,624

The sum of ones column is 14. Write 4 and carry 1 ten to the tens column. The sum of the tens column is 12. Write 2 and carry 1 to the hundreds column. The sum of the hundreds column is 16. Write 6 and carry 1 to the thousands column. The sum of the thousands column is 11. Write 1 in the thousands column and 1 in the ten thousands column.

47.   ²²
         9 056
            78
         6 089
       +   731
        15,954

51.   ¹¹
           218
         7 022
           335
       + 9 283
        16,858

55.   ¹ ¹²
         2 109
            63
            16
             3
       + 9 887
        12,078

59.   ¹²
           413
            85
         9 919
           602
            31
       + 1 218
        12,268

63. Add up to check addition.

769
179
214
376
759   Incorrect – should be 769

67. Add up to check addition.

11,577
   678
 7 952
    56
   718
 2 173
11,377   Incorrect – should be 11,577

71. Changing the order in which numbers are added does not change the sum. You can add from bottom to top when checking addition.

75. The shortest distance between Thomasville and Murphy is through Rena and Austin.

  12   *Thomasville to Rena*
  15   *Rena to Austin*
+ 11   *Austin to Murphy*
  38   miles

79.   413   women
        + 286   men
          699   people

83. To find the perimeter add all 4 sides in any order.

$$\begin{array}{r}\overset{3}{9}8\\49\\98\\+\ 49\\\hline 294\quad\text{inches}\end{array}$$

1.3 Subtraction of Whole Numbers

1.3 Margin Exercises

1. **(a)** $4 + 3 = 7$:
   $7 - 3 = 4$ or $7 - 4 = 3$

   (b) $6 + 5 = 11$:
   $11 - 5 = 6$ or $11 - 6 = 5$

   (c) $15 + 22 = 37$:
   $37 - 15 = 22$ or $37 - 22 = 15$

   (d) $23 + 55 = 78$:
   $78 - 55 = 23$ or $78 - 23 = 55$

2. **(a)** $5 - 3 = 2$: $5 = 3 + 2$

   (b) $8 - 3 = 5$: $8 = 3 + 5$

   (c) $21 - 15 = 6$: $21 = 15 + 6$

   (d) $58 - 42 = 16$: $58 = 42 + 16$

3. **(a)** $\begin{array}{r}56\\-\ 31\\\hline 25\end{array}$ **(b)** $\begin{array}{r}38\\-\ 14\\\hline 24\end{array}$ **(c)** $\begin{array}{r}378\\-\ 235\\\hline 143\end{array}$

   (d) $\begin{array}{r}3927\\-\ 2614\\\hline 1313\end{array}$ **(e)** $\begin{array}{r}5464\\-\ 324\\\hline 5140\end{array}$

4. **(a)** $\begin{array}{r}65\\-\ 23\quad\textit{subtraction}\\\hline 42\quad\textit{problem}\end{array}$

   $\begin{array}{r}23\\+\ 42\quad\textit{addition}\\\hline 65\quad\textit{problem}\end{array}$

   42 is correct.

   (b) $\begin{array}{r}46\\-\ 32\quad\textit{subtraction}\\\hline 24\quad\textit{problem}\end{array}$

   $\begin{array}{r}32\\+\ 24\quad\textit{addition}\\\hline 54\quad\textit{problem}\end{array}$

   24 is incorrect.
   Rework.
   $\begin{array}{r}45\\-\ 32\\\hline 14\quad\text{is correct.}\end{array}$

   (c) $\begin{array}{r}374\\-\ 251\quad\textit{subtraction}\\\hline 113\quad\textit{problem}\end{array}$

   $\begin{array}{r}251\\+\ 113\quad\textit{addition}\\\hline 364\quad\textit{problem}\end{array}$

   364 is incorrect.
   Rework.
   $\begin{array}{r}374\\-\ 251\\\hline 123\quad\text{is correct.}\end{array}$

   (d) $\begin{array}{r}7531\\-\ 4301\quad\textit{subtraction}\\\hline 3230\quad\textit{problem}\end{array}$

   $\begin{array}{r}4301\\+\ 3230\quad\textit{addition}\\\hline 7531\quad\textit{problem}\end{array}$

   3230 is correct.

5. **(a)** $\begin{array}{r}\overset{5\ 17}{\cancel{6}\cancel{7}}\\-\ 3\ 8\\\hline 2\ 9\end{array}$ **(b)** $\begin{array}{r}\overset{8\ 17}{\cancel{9}\cancel{7}}\\-\ 2\ 9\\\hline 6\ 8\end{array}$

   (c) $\begin{array}{r}\overset{2\ 11}{\cancel{3}\cancel{1}}\\-\ 1\ 7\\\hline 1\ 4\end{array}$ **(d)** $\begin{array}{r}\overset{5\ 13}{8\cancel{6}\cancel{3}}\\-\ \ 4\ 7\\\hline 8\ 1\ 6\end{array}$

   (e) $\begin{array}{r}\overset{5\ 12}{7\cancel{6}\cancel{2}}\\-\ 1\ 5\ 7\\\hline 6\ 0\ 5\end{array}$

6. **(a)** $\begin{array}{r}\overset{2\ 15}{\cancel{3}\cancel{5}4}\\-\ \ 8\ 2\\\hline 2\ 7\ 2\end{array}$ **(b)** $\begin{array}{r}\overset{3\ 14 17}{\cancel{4}\cancel{5}\cancel{7}}\\-\ \ 6\ 8\\\hline 3\ 8\ 9\end{array}$

   (c) $\begin{array}{r}\overset{7\ 16 14}{\cancel{8}\cancel{7}\cancel{4}}\\-\ 4\ 8\ 6\\\hline 3\ 8\ 8\end{array}$ **(d)** $\begin{array}{r}\overset{1\ 3\ 12 17}{\cancel{1}\cancel{4}\cancel{3}\cancel{7}}\\-\ \ \ 9\ 8\ 8\\\hline \ \ \ 4\ 4\ 9\end{array}$

   (e) $\begin{array}{r}\overset{7\ 16 13}{\cancel{8}\cancel{7}\cancel{3}9}\\-\ 3\ 8\ 9\ 2\\\hline 4\ 8\ 4\ 7\end{array}$

Section 1.3 Subtraction of Whole Numbers 5

7. (a) $\overset{2\ 10}{\cancel{3}\cancel{0}8}$
     − 2 8 5
     ─────
        2 3

   (b) $\overset{\overset{9}{}}{1\cancel{10}6}\overset{}{\cancel{2}\cancel{0}\cancel{6}}$
     − 1 4 8
     ─────
        5 8

   (c) $\overset{4\ 10}{\cancel{5}\cancel{0}73}$
     − 1 6 3 2
     ───────
       3 4 4 1

8. (a) $\overset{\overset{9}{}}{3\cancel{10}15}\cancel{4}\cancel{0}\cancel{5}$
     − 2 6 7
     ─────
        1 3 8

   (b) $\overset{6\ 10}{3\ 7\ \cancel{0}}$
     − 1 6 3
     ─────
        2 0 7

   (c) $\overset{14\ 16}{\cancel{15}\cancel{17}\cancel{7}10}$ 1 5 7 0
     −   9 8 3
     ─────────
           5 8 7

   (d) $\overset{6\ \overset{9}{\cancel{10}}\ \overset{9}{\cancel{10}}\ 11}{7\ \cancel{0}\ \cancel{0}\ \cancel{1}}$
     − 5 1 9 3
     ───────
       1 8 0 8

   (e) $\overset{3\ \overset{9}{\cancel{10}}\ \overset{9}{\cancel{10}}\ 10}{\cancel{4}\ \cancel{0}\ \cancel{0}\ \cancel{0}}$
     − 1 7 8 2
     ───────
       2 2 1 8

9. (a)   425   57
       − 368   + 368
       ─────   ─────
          57   425

   Match: 57 is correct.

   (b)   670   241
       − 439   + 439
       ─────   ─────
         241   680   error

   No match

   Rework.   670   231
            − 439   + 439
            ─────   ─────
              231   670

   Match: 231 is correct.

   (c)   14,726   5 887
       − 8 839   + 8 839
       ───────   ───────
          5 887   14,726

   Match: 5887 is correct.

10. (a)   147   deliveries on Friday
        − 126   deliveries on Tuesday
        ─────
           21   more deliveries on Friday

    (b)   126   deliveries on Tuesday
        − 119   deliveries on Wednesday
        ─────
            7   more deliveries on Tuesday

1.3 Section Exercises

3.   97   Check: 64
    − 64   + 33
    ────   ────
      33   97

7.   335   Check: 213
   − 122   + 122
   ─────   ─────
     213   335

11. 6821   Check: 6211
   − 610   + 610
   ─────   ─────
     6211   6821

15. 6259   Check: 4148
   − 4148   + 2111
   ─────   ─────
     2111   6259

19. 46,253   Check: 41,110
   − 5 143   + 5 143
   ──────   ──────
     41,110   46,253

23.   89   Check: 63
    − 27   + 27
    ────   ────
      63   90   incorrect

  Rework.
      89
    − 27
    ────
      62   is the correct answer.

27. 3767   Check: 2456
   − 2456   + 1311
   ─────   ─────
     1311   3767   correct

31. $\overset{16}{\cancel{3}6}$
   − 2 8
   ────
       8

43. $\overset{\overset{17}{8}\overset{}{\cancel{18}}}{9\ \cancel{9}\ 8\ 8}$
   − 2 3 9 9
   ───────
     7 5 8 9

35. $\overset{3\ 15}{\cancel{4}\cancel{5}}$
   − 2 9
   ────
     1 6

47. $\overset{3\ 10}{\cancel{4}\cancel{0}}$
   − 3 7
   ────
        3

39. $\overset{6\ 11}{7\ \cancel{7}\ \cancel{1}}$
   − 2 5 2
   ─────
     5 1 9

51. $\overset{3\ \overset{9}{\cancel{10}}\ 17}{\cancel{4}\ \cancel{0}\ \cancel{7}}$
   − 3 9 9
   ─────
         8

55. $\overset{\overset{12}{8\,13}10}{\cancel{9}\cancel{3}\cancel{0}5}$
    -1530
    $\overline{7775}$

63. $\overset{\overset{14\ 9}{7\,15\,10\,13}}{\cancel{8}\cancel{5}\cancel{0}\cancel{3}}$
    -2816
    $\overline{5687}$

59. $\overset{1\overset{9}{10}10}{\cancel{2}\cancel{0}\cancel{0}6}$
    -1850
    $\overline{156}$

67. $\overset{\overset{9\ 9}{6\,5\,10\,10\,10}}{\cancel{6}\cancel{6},\cancel{0}\cancel{0}\cancel{0}}$
    $-34,444$
    $\overline{31,556}$

71.   4791   2853
    -2853 $+1938$
    $\overline{1938}$ $\overline{4791}$
       match   correct

75.   65,318   41,889
    $-23,429$ $+23,429$
    $\overline{41,889}$ $\overline{65,318}$
       match   correct

79. Possible answers are:
    $3+2=5$ could be changed to $5-2=3$ or $5-3=2$.
    $6-4=2$ could be changed to $2+4=6$ or $4+2=6$.

83.   254
    -133
    $\overline{121}$ passengers

87.   1821
    -1454
    $\overline{367}$ feet

91. $\overset{\overset{11}{5\,17\,15}}{12,\cancel{6}\cancel{2}\cancel{5}}$
    $-11,296$
    $\overline{1329}$

There are 1329 more students enrolled in fall semester classes.

95. Rewrite one hundred one thousand, five hundred dollars using digits.

    $\$101,500$
    $-44,000$
    $\overline{\$\,57,500}$

The general manager earns $57,500 more.

99. $\overset{\overset{12\ 14}{1\,13\,15\,12}}{1\cancel{2},\cancel{3}\cancel{5}\cancel{2}}$
    $-11,594$
    $\overline{758}$

On Tuesday, 758 more people visited the park.

1.4 Multiplication of Whole Numbers

1.4 Margin Exercises

1. (a) 6 *factor*   (b) 8 *factor*
       ×3 *factor*   ×4 *factor*
       ── ─────   ── ─────
       18 *product*   32 *product*

   (c) 7 *factor*   (d) 9 *factor*
       ×5 *factor*   ×3 *factor*
       ── ─────   ── ─────
       35 *product*   27 *product*

2. (a) $4 \times 7 = 28$ (b) $0 \times 9 = 0$

   (c) $8 \cdot 6 = 48$ (d) $5 \cdot 5 = 25$

   (e) $(3)(8) = 24$

3. (a) $(2 \times 3) \times 4$ (b) $(6 \times 1) \times 5$
       $6 \times 4 = 24$ $6 \times 5 = 30$

   (c) $(8 \times 3) \times 0$
       $24 \times 0 = 0$

4. (a) $\overset{1}{5}2$ (b) 79
       $\times\ 5$ $\times\ 0$
       ─────   ─────
       260   0

   (c) $\overset{5\,1}{8}62$ (d) $\overset{5\ 2}{2}\,831$
       $\times\ \ 9$ $\times\ \ \ 7$
       ─────   ──────
       7758   19,817

   (e) $\overset{1\,3}{4}\,714$
       $\times\ \ \ 8$
       ──────
       37,712

5. (a) 45×10

       45       $45 \times 10 = 450$
       ×1   *Attach* 0
       ──
       45

   (b) 102×100

       102      $102 \times 100 = 10{,}200$ *Attach* 00
       ×1
       ──
       102

Section 1.4   Multiplication of Whole Numbers

(c) 571 × 1000

$$\begin{array}{r} 571 \\ \times\ \ \ 1 \\ \hline 571 \end{array}$$ 571 × 1000 = 571,000   Attach 000

(e)
$$\begin{array}{r} 835 \\ \times\ \ 189 \\ \hline 7\,515 \\ 66\,80\ \ \\ 83\,5\ \ \ \ \\ \hline 157,815 \end{array}$$

6. (a) 14 × 50

$$\begin{array}{r} 14 \\ \times\ \ 5 \\ \hline 70 \end{array}$$ 14 × 50 = 700   Attach 0

9. (a)
$$\begin{array}{r} 28 \\ \times\ \ 60 \\ \hline 1680 \end{array}$$ 6 × 28 = 168
1 zero
Insert 0

(b) 68 × 400

$$\begin{array}{r} 68 \\ \times\ \ \ 4 \\ \hline 272 \end{array}$$ 68 × 400 = 27,200   Attach 00

(b)
$$\begin{array}{r} 817 \\ \times\ \ \ 30 \\ \hline 24,510 \end{array}$$ 3 × 817 = 2451
1 zero
Insert 0

(c) 180   1 zero   18 × 3 = 54
× 30   1 zero
5400   Attach 00

(c)
$$\begin{array}{r} 481 \\ \times\ \ 206 \\ \hline 2\,886 \\ 96\,20\ \ \\ \hline 99,086 \end{array}$$ 2 × 481 = 962
Insert 0

(d) 6 100   2 zeros   61 × 9 = 549
×   90   1 zero
549,000   Attach 000

(d)
$$\begin{array}{r} 3526 \\ \times\ \ 6002 \\ \hline 7\,052 \\ 21\,156\,00\ \ \ \\ \hline 21,163,052 \end{array}$$ 6 × 3526 = 21,156
Insert 00

(e)   800   2 zeros   8 × 2 = 16
× 200   2 zeros
160,000   Attach 0000

10. (a)
$$\begin{array}{r} 289 \\ \times\ \ 12 \\ \hline 578 \\ 289\ \ \\ \hline 3468 \end{array}$$

The total cost of 289 redwood planters is $3468.

7. (a)
$$\begin{array}{r} 35 \\ \times\ \ 54 \\ \hline 140 \\ 175\ \ \\ \hline 1890 \end{array}$$ Add

(b)
$$\begin{array}{r} 76 \\ \times\ \ 49 \\ \hline 684 \\ 304\ \ \\ \hline 3724 \end{array}$$ Add

(b)
$$\begin{array}{r} 180 \\ \times\ \ 42 \\ \hline 360 \\ 720\ \ \\ \hline 7560 \end{array}$$

The total cost of 180 cordless drills is $7560.

8. (a)
$$\begin{array}{r} 38 \\ \times\ \ 15 \\ \hline 190 \\ 38\ \ \\ \hline 570 \end{array}$$

(b)
$$\begin{array}{r} 31 \\ \times\ \ 43 \\ \hline 93 \\ 124\ \ \\ \hline 1333 \end{array}$$

(c)
$$\begin{array}{r} 67 \\ \times\ \ 59 \\ \hline 603 \\ 335\ \ \\ \hline 3953 \end{array}$$

(d)
$$\begin{array}{r} 234 \\ \times\ \ 73 \\ \hline 702 \\ 16\,38\ \ \\ \hline 17,082 \end{array}$$

(c)
$$\begin{array}{r} 8218 \\ \times\ \ \ \ 15 \\ \hline 41\,090 \\ 82\,18\ \ \\ \hline 123,270 \end{array}$$

The total cost of 15 forklifts is $123,270.

1.4 Section Exercises

3. $9 \times 1 \times 7$

$(9 \times 1) \times 7 = 9 \times 7 = 63$
or
$9 \times (1 \times 7) = 9 \times 7 = 63$

7. $4 \cdot 1 \cdot 6$

$(4 \cdot 1) \cdot 6 = 4 \cdot 6 = 24$
or
$4 \cdot (1 \cdot 6) = 4 \cdot 6 = 24$

11. (3)(0)(7)

$(3)(0)(7)$
$(3)(0) = 0 \cdot (7) = 0$

The product of any number and 0 is 0.

15.
$$\begin{array}{r} \scriptstyle 3 \\ 35 \\ \times\ \ 7 \\ \hline 245 \end{array}$$

$7 \cdot 5 = 35$ *Write 5, carry 3 tens*
$7 \cdot 3 = 21$ *Add 3 to get 24*
Write 24

19.
$$\begin{array}{r} 512 \\ \times\ \ 4 \\ \hline 2048 \end{array}$$

$4 \cdot 2 = 8$ *Write 8*
$4 \cdot 1 = 4$ *Write 4*
$4 \cdot 5 = 20$ *Write 20*

23.
$$\begin{array}{r} \scriptstyle 21\ \\ 2153 \\ \times\ \ 4 \\ \hline 8612 \end{array}$$

$4 \cdot 3 = 12$ *Write 2, carry 1*
$4 \cdot 5 = 20$ *Add 1 to get 21*
Write 1, carry 2
$4 \cdot 1 = 4$ *Add 2 to get 6*
Write 6
$4 \cdot 2 = 8$ *Write 8*

27.
$$\begin{array}{r} \scriptstyle 141\ \\ 3182 \\ \times\ \ \ \ 6 \\ \hline 19{,}092 \end{array}$$

$6 \cdot 2 = 12$ *Write 2, carry 1*
$6 \cdot 8 = 48$ *Add 1 to get 49*
Write 9, carry 4
$6 \cdot 1 = 6$ *Add 4 to get 10*
Write 0, carry 1
$6 \cdot 3 = 18$ *Add 1 to get 19*
Write 19

31.
$$\begin{array}{r} 20 \\ \times\ \ 6 \\ \hline \end{array} \qquad \begin{array}{r} 2 \\ \times\ \ 6 \\ \hline 12 \end{array} \qquad \begin{array}{r} 20 \\ \times\ \ 6 \\ \hline 120 \end{array}$$
Attach 1 zero

35.
$$\begin{array}{r} 740 \\ \times\ \ 3 \\ \hline \end{array} \qquad \begin{array}{r} 74 \\ \times\ \ 3 \\ \hline 222 \end{array} \qquad \begin{array}{r} 740 \\ \times\ \ 3 \\ \hline 2220 \end{array}$$
Attach 1 zero

39.
$$\begin{array}{r} 125 \\ \times\ \ 30 \\ \hline \end{array} \qquad \begin{array}{r} 125 \\ \times\ \ 3 \\ \hline 375 \end{array} \qquad \begin{array}{r} 125 \\ \times\ \ 30 \\ \hline 3750 \end{array}$$
Attach 1 zero

43.
$$\begin{array}{r} 900 \\ \times\ 300 \\ \hline \end{array} \qquad \begin{array}{r} 9 \\ \times\ \ 3 \\ \hline 27 \end{array} \qquad \begin{array}{r} 900 \\ 300 \\ \hline 270{,}000 \end{array}$$
Attach 1 zero

47. $970 \cdot 50$
$$\begin{array}{r} 97 \\ \times\ \ 5 \\ \hline 485 \end{array}$$

$970 \cdot 50 = 48{,}500$
Attach 2 zeros

51. $9700 \cdot 200$
$$\begin{array}{r} 97 \\ \times\ \ 2 \\ \hline 194 \end{array}$$

$9700 \cdot 200 = 1{,}940{,}000$
Attach 4 zeros

55.
$$\begin{array}{rl} 68 & \\ \times\ \ 22 & \\ \hline 136 & \leftarrow 68 \times 2 \\ \underline{136\ \ } & \leftarrow 68 \times 20 \text{ (0 not written)} \\ 1496 & \end{array}$$

Section 1.5 Division of Whole Numbers

59. (58)(41)

$$\begin{array}{r}58\\ \times\ 41\\ \hline 58\\ 232\ \\ \hline 2378\end{array}$$

63. (32)(475)

$$\begin{array}{r}475\\ \times\ \ 32\\ \hline 950\\ 14\ 25\ \\ \hline 15,200\end{array}$$

67. (44)(331)

$$\begin{array}{r}331\\ \times\ \ \ 44\\ \hline 1\ 324\\ 13\ 24\ \\ \hline 14,564\end{array}$$

71.
$$\begin{array}{r}538\\ \times\ \ \ 342\\ \hline 1\ 076\\ 21\ 52\ \ \\ 161\ 4\ \ \ \\ \hline 183,996\end{array}$$

75.
$$\begin{array}{r}215\\ \times\ \ \ 307\\ \hline 1\ 505\\ 0\ 00\ \ \\ 64\ 5\ \ \ \\ \hline 66,005\end{array}$$

79.
$$\begin{array}{r}6\ 310\\ \times\ \ \ 3\ 078\\ \hline 50\ 480\\ 441\ 70\ \ \\ 18\ 930\ 0\ \ \ \\ \hline 19,422,180\end{array}$$

83. To multiply by 10, 100, or by 1000 just add the number of zeros to the number you are multiplying and that is your answer.
For example:
$9 \cdot 10 = 90, 18 \cdot 100 = 1800$, and $27 \cdot 1000 = 27,000$.

87. 12 tomato plants per flat
$$\begin{array}{r}\underline{18}\ \text{flats}\\ 96\\ \times\ 12\ \\ \hline 216\ \text{plants}\end{array}$$

91. 16 gallons of paint at $18 per gallon
$$\begin{array}{r}18\\ \times\ \ 16\\ \hline 108\\ \underline{18\ \ }\\ 288\end{array}$$
The total cost is $288.

95. 108 sets of wrenches at $37 per set
$$\begin{array}{r}108\\ \times\ \ 37\\ \hline 756\\ \underline{324\ \ }\\ 3996\end{array}$$
The total cost is $3996.

99.
$$\begin{array}{r}122\\ +\ 53\\ \hline 175\ \text{joggers}\end{array}$$

103.
$$\begin{array}{rl}440 & \to\ 4\ \text{tires at \$110 each}\\ 98 & \to\ 2\ \text{seat covers at \$49 each}\\ +\ \ 18 & \to\ 6\ \text{socket wrenches at \$3 each}\\ \hline 556\end{array}$$
The total amount spent is $556.

1.5 Division of Whole Numbers

1.5 Margin Exercises

1. (a) $48 \div 6 = 8$: $6\overline{)48}^{\,8}$, $\dfrac{48}{6} = 8$

   (b) $24 \div 6 = 4$: $6\overline{)24}^{\,4}$, $\dfrac{24}{6} = 4$

   (c) $9\overline{)36}^{\,4}$: $36 \div 9 = 4$, $\dfrac{36}{9} = 4$

   (d) $\dfrac{42}{6} = 7$: $42 \div 6 = 7$, $6\overline{)42}^{\,7}$

2. (a) $10 \div 2 = 5$
   dividend: 10
   divisor: 2
   quotient: 5

   (b) $30 \div 5 = 6$
   dividend: 30
   divisor: 5
   quotient: 6

   (c) $\dfrac{28}{7} = 4$
   dividend: 28
   divisor: 7
   quotient: 4

   (d) $2\overline{)36}^{\,18}$
   dividend: 36
   divisor: 2
   quotient: 18

3. (a) $0 \div 9 = 0$ (b) $\dfrac{0}{8} = 0$

   (c) $\dfrac{0}{36} = 0$ (d) $57\overline{)0}^{\,0}$

4. (a) $6\overline{)18}^{3}$ (b) $\frac{28}{4} = 7$

$3 \cdot 6 = 18$ $4 \cdot 7 = 28$

(c) $48 \div 8 = 6$
$6 \cdot 8 = 48$

5. (a) $\frac{8}{0}$ undefined

(b) $\frac{0}{8} = 0$ (c) $0\overline{)32}$ undefined

(d) $32\overline{)0}^{0}$ (e) $100 \div 0$ undefined

(f) $0 \div 100 = 0$

6. (a) $5 \div 5 = 1$ (b) $14\overline{)14}^{1}$

(c) $\frac{37}{37} = 1$

7. (a) $2\overline{)18}^{9}$ (b) $3\overline{)39}^{13}$

(c) $4\overline{)88}^{22}$ (c) $2\overline{)462}^{231}$

8. (a) $2\overline{)225}^{112\ R1}$ (b) $3\overline{)275}^{91\ R2}$

(c) $4\overline{)5^{1}3^{1}8}^{134\ R2}$ (d) $\frac{819}{5}$

$5\overline{)8^{3}1^{1}9}^{163\ R4}$

9. (a) $5\overline{)9^{4}3^{3}7}^{187\ R2}$ (b) $\frac{675}{7}$

$7\overline{)67^{4}5}^{96\ R3}$

(c) $3\overline{)188^{2}5}^{628\ R1}$ (d) $8\overline{)11^{3}3^{1}5}^{141\ R7}$

10. (a) $3\overline{)115}^{38\ R1}$

divisor × quotient + remainder = dividend
↓ ↓ ↓ ↓
3 × 38 + 1
114 + 1 = 115

The answer is correct.

(b) $8\overline{)739}^{92\ R2}$

divisor × quotient + remainder = dividend
↓ ↓ ↓ ↓
8 × 92 + 2
736 + 2 = 738
↑
incorrect

$8\overline{)73^{1}9}^{92\ R3}$ The correct answer is 92 R3.

(c) $4\overline{)1312}^{328}$

divisor × quotient + remainder = dividend
↓ ↓ ↓ ↓
4 × 328 + 0 = 1312

The answer is correct.

(d) $5\overline{)2383}^{476\ R3}$

divisor × quotient + remainder = dividend
↓ ↓ ↓ ↓
5 × 476 + 3
2380 + 3 = 2383

The answer is correct.

11. (a) 612:
ends in 2, divisible by 2

(b) 315:
ends in 5, not divisible by 2

(c) 2714:
ends in 4, divisible by 2

(d) 36,000:
ends in 0, divisible by 2

12. (a) 836:
$8 + 3 + 6 = 17$, not divisible by 3

Section 1.5 Division of Whole Numbers

(b) 7545:
$7+5+4+5 = 21$,
divisible by 3

(c) 242,913:
$2+4+2+9+1+3 = 21$,
divisible by 3

(d) 102,484:
$1+0+2+4+8+4 = 19$
not divisible by 3

13. (a) 160: ends in 0, divisible by 5

(b) 635: ends in 5, divisible by 5

(c) 3381: ends in 1, not divisible by 5

(d) 108,605: ends in 5, divisible by 5

14. (a) 290: ends in 0, divisible by 10

(b) 218: ends in 8, not divisible by 10

(c) 2020: ends in 0, divisible by 10

(d) 11,670: ends in 0, divisible by 10

1.5 Section Exercises

3. $\dfrac{45}{9} = 5$: $9\overline{)45}^{\,5}$ $\quad 45 \div 9 = 5$

7. $8 \div 8 = 1$

11. $24 \div 0$ is undefined.

15. $12\overline{)0} = 0$ *Zero divided by any non-zero number is zero*

19. $\dfrac{0}{3} = 0$

23. $4\overline{)10^28}^{\,27}$ Check: $\begin{array}{r} 27 \\ \times\; 4 \\ \hline 108 \end{array}$

27. $4\overline{)243^32}^{\,608}$ Check: $4 \times 608 = 2432$

31. $6\overline{)9^31^13^17}^{\,1522\ R5}$

Check: $6 \times 1522 + 5 = 9132 + 5 = 9137$

35. $4\overline{)4024}^{\,1006}$

Check: $4 \times 1006 = 4024$

39. $6\overline{)4867}^{\,811\ R1}$

Check: $6 \times 811 + 1 = 4866 + 1 = 4867$

43. $4\overline{)29{,}^1 29^18}^{\,7\ 324\ R2}$

Check: $7324 \times 4 + 2 = 29{,}296 + 2 = 29{,}298$

47. $\dfrac{26{,}684}{4}$

$4\overline{)26{,}^2 6^284}^{\,6\ 671}$

Check: $4 \times 6671 = 26{,}684$

51. $7\overline{)71{,}^1 7^37^26}^{\,10{,}253\ R5}$

Check: $10{,}253 \times 7 + 5 = 71{,}771 + 5 = 71{,}776$

55. $4\overline{)218}^{\,54\ R2}$

Check:

$4 \times 54 + 2 = 216 + 2 = 218$ *correct*

59. $7\overline{)4692}^{\,650\ R2}$

Check: $7 \times 650 + 2 = 4550 + 2 = 4552$ *incorrect*

Rework:

$7\overline{)46^492}^{\,670\ R2}$

Check:

$7 \times 670 + 2 = 4690 + 2$
$ = 4692$ *correct*

63. $6\overline{)18{,}023}^{\,3003\ R5}$

Check:

$6 \times 3003 + 5 = 18{,}018 + 5$
$ = 18{,}023$ *correct*

67. $9\overline{)86{,}655}^{\,9\ 628\ R7}$

Check:

$9 \times 9628 + 7 = 86{,}652 + 7$
$ = 86{,}659$ *incorrect*

Rework.

$$9)\overline{86,^56^25^75} \quad \begin{array}{c} 9\ 6\ 2\ 8\ \ R3 \end{array}$$

Check:

$$9 \times 9628 + 3 = 86,652 + 3$$
$$= 86,655 \ correct$$

71. Multiply the quotient by the divisor and add any remainder. The result should be the dividend.

75. $6)\overline{\$9^39,^3600}$ $\quad \$1\ 6,\ 600$

Each van costs $16,600.

79. $36)\overline{73^180}$ $\quad 2\ 05$

205 acres can be fertilized.

83. 30 is: · divisible (✓) by 2, since it ends in 0.
· divisible (✓) by 3, since $3 + 0 = 3$ which is divisible by 3.
· divisible (✓) by 5, since it ends in 0.
· divisible (✓) by 10, since it ends in 0.

87. 445 is: · not divisible (×) by 2, since it does not end in 0, 2, 4, 6, or 8.
· not divisible (×) by 3, since $4 + 4 + 5 = 13$ which is not divisible by 3.
· divisible (✓) by 5, since it ends in 5.
· not divisible (×) by 10, since it does not end in 0.

91. 5166: divisible (✓) by 2, since it ends in 6.
· divisible (✓) by 3, since $5 + 1 + 6 + 6 = 18$ which is divisible by 3.
· not divisible (×) by 5, since it does not end in 0 or 5.
· not divisible (×) by 10, since it does not end in 0.

95. Kaci Salmon earns $36,540 in one year. Since there are 12 months in one year,

$$\$36,540 \div 12 = \$3045$$

are the earnings for each month.
For three months the earnings would be

$$3 \times \$3045 = \$9135.$$

1.6 Long Division

1.6 Margin Exercises

1. (a)
$$\begin{array}{r} 71 \\ 25)\overline{1775} \\ \underline{175} \quad \leftarrow 7 \times 25 \\ 25 \\ \underline{25} \quad \leftarrow 1 \times 25 \\ 0 \end{array}$$

(b)
$$\begin{array}{r} 82 \\ 26)\overline{2132} \\ \underline{208} \quad \leftarrow 8 \times 26 \\ 52 \\ \underline{52} \quad \leftarrow 2 \times 26 \\ 0 \end{array}$$

(c)
$$\begin{array}{r} 45 \\ 51)\overline{2295} \\ \underline{204} \quad \leftarrow 4 \times 51 \\ 255 \\ \underline{255} \quad \leftarrow 5 \times 51 \\ 0 \end{array}$$

(d)
$$\begin{array}{r} 78 \\ 84)\overline{6552} \\ \underline{588} \quad \leftarrow 7 \times 84 \\ 672 \\ \underline{672} \quad \leftarrow 8 \times 84 \\ 0 \end{array}$$

2. (a)
$$\begin{array}{r} 42 \\ 56)\overline{2352} \\ \underline{224} \quad \leftarrow 4 \times 56 \\ 112 \\ \underline{112} \quad \leftarrow 2 \times 56 \\ 0 \end{array}$$

Section 1.6   Long Division

(b) $\overline{}$ 42   R3
     38)1599
     $\underline{152}$ ← 4 × 38
      79
     $\underline{76}$ ← 2 × 28
      3

(c) $\overline{}$ 83 R21
     65)5416
     $\underline{520}$ ← 8 × 65
      216
     $\underline{195}$ ← 3 × 65
      21

(d) $\overline{}$ 74 R63
     89)6649
     $\underline{623}$ ← 7 × 89
      419
     $\underline{356}$ ← 4 × 89
      63

3. (a) $\overline{}$ 130 R7
       24)3127
       $\underline{24}$ ← 1 × 24
        72
       $\underline{72}$ ← 3 × 24
        07
       $\underline{0}$ ← 0 × 24
        7

   (b) $\overline{}$ 205
       52)10,660
       $\underline{10\,4}$ ← 2 × 52
        260
       $\underline{260}$ ← 5 × 52
        0

   (c) $\overline{}$ 408 R21
       39)15,933
       $\underline{15\,6}$ ← 4 × 39
        333
       $\underline{312}$ ← 8 × 39
        21

(d) $\overline{}$ 300 R62
     78)23,462
     $\underline{23\,4}$ ← 3 × 78
      62

4. (a) $5\underline{0} \div 1\underline{0} = 5$
       One zero is dropped.

   (b) $18\underline{00} \div 1\underline{00} = 18$
       Two zeros are dropped.

   (c) $305,\underline{000} \div 1\underline{000} = 305$
       Three zeros are dropped.

5. (a) 60)7200
       Drop 1 zero from divisor
       and 1 zero from dividend.

       $\overline{}$ 120
       6)720
       $\underline{6}$
        12
       $\underline{12}$
        0
       $\underline{0}$
        0

       The quotient is 120.

   (b) 130)131,040
       Drop 1 zero from divisor
       and 1 zero from dividend.

       $\overline{}$ 1 008
       13)13,104
       $\underline{13}$
        104
       $\underline{104}$
        0

       The quotient is 1008.

   (c) 2600)195,000
       Drop 2 zeros from divisor
       and 2 zeros from dividend.

       $\overline{}$ 75
       26)1950
       $\underline{182}$
        130
       $\underline{130}$
        0

       The quotient is 75.

6. (a)
$$\begin{array}{r}43\\18{\overline{\smash{\big)}\,774}}\\\underline{72}\\54\\\underline{54}\\0\end{array}$$

$$\begin{array}{r}43\\\times18\\\hline 344\\\underline{43}\\774\end{array}$$ ← *correct*

Multiply the quotient and the divisor

(b)
$$\begin{array}{r}42\text{R}178\\426{\overline{\smash{\big)}\,19{,}170}}\\\underline{1704}\\1130\\\underline{952}\\178\end{array}$$

$$\begin{array}{r}426\\\times42\\\hline 852\\\underline{1704}\\17{,}892\\+178\\\hline 18{,}070\end{array}$$

The result does not match dividend. Rework.

$$\begin{array}{r}45\\426{\overline{\smash{\big)}\,19{,}170}}\\\underline{1704}\\2130\\\underline{2130}\\0\end{array}$$

(c)
$$\begin{array}{r}57\text{R}18\\515{\overline{\smash{\big)}\,29{,}316}}\\\underline{2570}\\3616\\\underline{3598}\\18\end{array}$$

$$\begin{array}{r}514\\\times57\\\hline 3598\\\underline{2570}\\29{,}298\\+18\\\hline 29{,}316\end{array}$$ ← *correct*

Multiply the divisor and quotient

Add the remainder

1.6 Section Exercises

3. $18{\overline{\smash{\big)}\,4500}}$

2;   25;   250

$$\begin{array}{r}2\\18{\overline{\smash{\big)}\,4500}}\end{array}$$

2 goes over the 5, because $\frac{45}{18}$ is about 2. The answer must then be a three digit number or 250.

7. $52{\overline{\smash{\big)}\,68{,}025}}$

13;   130 R1;   1308 R9

$$\begin{array}{r}1\\52{\overline{\smash{\big)}\,68{,}025}}\end{array}$$

1 goes over the 8, because $\frac{68}{52}$ is about 1. The answer must then be a four digit number or 1308 R9.

11. $523{\overline{\smash{\big)}\,470{,}800}}$

9 R100;   90 R100;   900 R100

$$\begin{array}{r}9\\523{\overline{\smash{\big)}\,470{,}800}}\end{array}$$

9 goes over the 8, because $\frac{4708}{523}$ is about 9. The answer must then be a three digit number or 900 R100.

15.
$$\begin{array}{r}236\text{R}29\\47{\overline{\smash{\big)}\,11{,}121}}\\\underline{94}\\172\\\underline{141}\\311\\\underline{282}\\29\end{array}$$

Check:
$$\begin{array}{r}236\\\times47\\\hline 1652\\\underline{944}\\11092\\+29\\\hline 11{,}121\end{array}$$

19.
$$\begin{array}{r}1239\text{R}15\\63{\overline{\smash{\big)}\,78{,}072}}\\\underline{63}\\150\\\underline{126}\\247\\\underline{189}\\582\\\underline{567}\\15\end{array}$$

Check:
$$\begin{array}{r}1239\\\times63\\\hline 3717\\\underline{7434}\\78{,}057\\+15\\\hline 78{,}072\end{array}$$

23.
$$\begin{array}{r}850\\420{\overline{\smash{\big)}\,357{,}000}}\\\underline{3360}\\2100\\\underline{2100}\\00\\\underline{00}\\0\end{array}$$

Check:
$$\begin{array}{r}850\\\times420\\\hline 17000\\\underline{3400}\\357{,}000\end{array}$$

27. $28\overline{)18,424}$ 658 R9

Check:

```
      658
    ×  28
    5 264
   13 16
   18,424
   +    9
   18,433   incorrect
```

Rework.

```
         658
    28)18,424
       16 8
        1 62
        1 40
          224
          224
            0
```

Correct answer is 658.

31. When dividing by 10, 100, or 1000 drop the same number of zeros from the dividend and the divisor. One example is

$$2500 \div 100 = 25 \div 1 = 25.$$

35. First, add the number of gold and silver medals.

```
     604
   + 604
    1208
```

Subtract the sum from the total number of medals.

```
    1838
  − 1208
     630
```

There were 630 bronze medals.

39.
```
     42   circuits in 1 hour
   ×  8   hours per day
    336   circuits in 1 day
   ×  5   days in a work week
   1680   total circuits
```

1.7 Rounding Whole Numbers

1.7 Margin Exercises

1. (a) 746 (nearest ten)

   7$\underline{4}$6

   Underline the tens place.
   746 is closer to 750.

   (b) 2412 (nearest thousand)

   $\underline{2}$412

   Underline the thousands place.
   2412 is closer to 2000.

   (c) 89,512 (nearest hundred)

   89,$\underline{5}$12

   Underline the hundreds place.
   89,512 is closer to 89,500

   (d) 546,325 (nearest ten thousand)

   5$\underline{4}$6,325

   Underline the ten thousands place.
   546,325 is closer to 550,000.

2. (a) 34

   $\underline{3}$4 Next digit is 4 or less.

   Underline tens place. Change the digit to the right of the underlined place to zero.
   34 rounded to the nearest ten is 30.

   (b) 71

   $\underline{7}$1 Next digit is 4 or less.

   Underline tens place. Leave as 7 as 7.
   All digits to the right of the underlined place are changed to 0.
   71 rounded to the nearest ten is 70.

   (c) 143

   1$\underline{4}$3 Next digit is 4 or less.

   Leave 4 as 4.
   All digits to the right of the underlined place are changed to 0.
   143 rounded to the nearest ten is 140.

   (d) 5732

   57$\underline{3}$2 Next digit is 4 or less.

   Leave 3 as 3.

All digits to the right of the underlined place are changed to 0.

5732 rounded to the nearest ten is 5730.

3. (a) 1725

   1̲725   Next digit is 5 or more.

   Change 1 to 2.
   All digits to right of the underlined place are changed to zeros.
   1725 rounded to the nearest thousand is 2000.

   (b) 6511

   6̲511   Next digit is 5 or more.

   Change 6 to 7.
   All digits to the right of the underlined place are changed to zeros.
   6511 rounded to the nearest thousand is 7000.

   (c) 56,899

   56̲,899   Next digit is 5 or more.

   Change 6 to 7.
   All digits to the right of the underlined place are changed to zeros.
   56,899 rounded to the nearest thousand is 57,000.

   (d) 82,608

   82̲,608   Next digit is 5 or more.

   Change 2 to 3.
   All digits to the right of the underlined place are changed to zeros.
   82,608 rounded to the nearest thousand is 83,000.

4. (a) 6536 to the nearest ten

   653̲6   Next digit is 5 or more.

   Change 3 to 4.
   All digits to the right of the underlined place are changed to zeros.
   6536 rounded to the nearest ten is 6540.

   (b) 3427 to the nearest hundred

   34̲27   Next digit is 4 or less.

   Leave 4 as 4.
   All digits to the right of the underlined place are changed to zeros.
   3427 rounded to the nearest hundred is 3400.

   (c) 73,077 to the nearest hundred

   73,0̲77   Next digit is 5 or more.

   Change 0 to 1.
   All digits to the right of the underlined place are changed to zeros.
   73,077 rounded to the nearest hundred is 73,100.

   (d) 61,968 to the nearest hundred

   61,9̲68   Next digit is 5 or more.

   Change 9 to 10. Write 0 carry 1.
   All digits to the right of the underlined place are changed to zeros.
   61,968 rounded to the nearest hundred is 62,000.

5. (a) 14,671 to the nearest ten thousand

   1̲4,671

   Ten thousands place does not change because the digit to the right is 4 or less.
   All digits to the right of the underlined place are changed to zeros.
   14,671 rounded to the nearest ten thousand is 10,000.

   (b) 724,518,715 to the nearest million

   724̲,518,715

   Change 4 to 5 because the digit to the right is 5 or more.
   All digits to the right of the underlined place are changed to zeros.
   725,518,715 rounded to the nearest million is 725,000,000.

6. (a) to the nearest ten:

   15̲6 ← Change 6 to zero.
   Tens place (5 + 1 = 6) changes.
   156 rounded to the nearest ten is 160.

   to the nearest hundred:

   1̲56   Next digit is 5 or more.
   Hundreds place (1 + 1 = 2) changes.
   All digits to the right of the underlined places are changed to zeros.
   156 rounded to the nearest hundred is 200.

   (b) to the nearest ten:

   64̲9   Next digit is 5 or more.
   Tens place (4 + 1 = 5) changes.
   649 rounded to the nearest ten is 650.

   to the nearest hundred:

   6̲49   Next digit is 4 or less.

Section 1.7 Rounding Whole Numbers

Hundreds place stays the same.
649 rounded to the nearest hundred is 600.

(c) to the nearest ten:

98<u>0</u>9   Next digit is 5 or more.

Tens place $(0 + 1 = 1)$ changes.
9809 rounded to the nearest ten is 9810.

to the nearest hundred:

9<u>8</u>09   Next digit is 4 or less.
Hundreds place stays the same.
9809 rounded to the nearest hundred is 9800.

7. (a) to the nearest ten:

10<u>7</u>6   Next digit is 5 or more.
Tens place $(7 + 1 = 8)$ changes.
1076 rounded to the nearest ten is 1080.

to the nearest hundred:

1<u>0</u>76   Next digit is 5 or more.
Hundreds place $(0 + 1 = 1)$ changes.
1076 rounded to the nearest hundred is 1100.

to the nearest thousand:

<u>1</u>076   Next digit is 4 or less.
Thousands place stays the same.
1076 rounded to the nearest thousand is 1000.

(b) to the nearest ten:

37,4<u>5</u>4   Next digit is 4 or less.
Tens place stays the same.
37,454 rounded to the nearest ten is 37,450.

to the nearest hundred:

37,<u>4</u>54   Next digit is 5 or more.
Hundreds place $(4 + 1 = 5)$ changes.
37,454 rounded to the nearest hundred is 37,500.

to the nearest thousand:

3<u>7</u>,454   Next digit is 4 or less.
Thousands place stays the same.
37,454 rounded to the nearest thousand is 37,000.

(c) to the nearest ten:

178,4<u>1</u>9   Next digit is 5 or more.
Tens place $(1 + 1 = 2)$ changes.
178,419 rounded to the nearest ten is 178,420.

to the nearest hundred:

178,<u>4</u>19   Next digit is 4 or less.

Tens place stays the same.
178,419 rounded to the nearest hundred is 178,400.

to the nearest thousand:

17<u>8</u>,419   Next digit is 4 or less.
Thousands place stays the same.
178,419 rounded to the nearest thousand is 178,000.

8. (a)

```
    18      20
    73      70    rounded to the
    57      60    nearest ten
  + 34    + 30
          ────
           180    estimated answer
```

(b)

```
    44      40    rounded to the
  − 18    − 20    nearest ten
          ────
            20    estimated answer
```

(c)

```
    37      40    rounded to the
  × 84    × 80    nearest ten
          ────
          3200    estimated answer
```

9. (a)

```
   175     200
   618     600    rounded to the
   739     700    nearest hundred
 + 865   + 900
         ─────
          2400    estimated answer
```

(b)

```
   739     700    rounded to the
 − 361   − 400    nearest hundred
         ─────
           300    estimated answer
```

(c)

```
    723         700      rounded to the
  × 478       × 500      nearest hundred
              ───────
              350,000    estimated answer
```

10. (a)

```
       36
     3852
      749
   + 5474
   ──────
       40     all digits changed to
     4000     zero except first digit
      700     which is rounded
   + 5000
   ──────
     9740     estimated answer
```

(b)   2583
       − 765

       3000   first digit rounded; all
    −   800   others changed to zero
       2200   estimated answer

(c)   639
        ×   55

         600   only one nonzero
       × 60   digit remains
      36,000   estimated answer

1.7 Section Exercises

3. 1085 rounded to the nearest ten: ≈ 1090

10$\underline{8}$5   Next digit is 5 or more.

Tens place changes (8 + 1 = 9). All digits to the right of the underlined place change to 0.

7. 86,813 rounded to the nearest hundred: ≈ 86,800

86,$\underline{8}$13   Next digit is 4 or less.

Hundreds place does not change. All digits to the right of the underlined place change to 0.

11. 5996 rounded to the nearest hundred: ≈ 6000

5$\underline{9}$96   Next digit is 5 or more.

Hundreds place changes (9 + 1 = 10; carry 1). All digits to the right of the underlined place change to 0.

15. 78,499 rounded to the nearest thousand: ≈ 78,000

7$\underline{8}$,499   Next digit is 4 or less.

Thousands place does not change. All digits to the right of the underlined place change to 0.

19. 53,182 rounded to the nearest thousand: ≈ 53,000

5$\underline{3}$,182   Next digit is 4 or less.

Thousands place does not change. All digits to the right of the underlined place change to 0.

23. 8,906,422 rounded to the nearest million: ≈ 9,000,000

$\underline{8}$,906,422   Next digit is 5 or more.

Millions place changes (8 + 1 = 9). All digits to the right of the underlined place change to 0.

27. To the nearest ten
  44$\underline{8}$3   Next digit is 4 or less. The digit to the right of the underlined place changes to 0. Leave 8 as 8.

  ≈ 4480

To the nearest hundred
  4$\underline{4}$83   Next digit is 5 or more. All digits to the right of the underlined place are changed to zeros. Add 1 to 4.

  ≈ 4500

To the nearest thousand
  $\underline{4}$483   Next digit is 4 or less. All digits to the right of the underlined place are changed to zeros. Leave 4 as 4.

  ≈ 4000

31. To the nearest ten
  31$\underline{3}$2   Next digit is 4 or less. All digits to the right of the underlined place are changed to zeros. Leave 3 as 3.

  ≈ 3130

To the nearest hundred
  3$\underline{1}$32   Next digit is 4 or less. All digits to the right of the underlined place are changed to zeros. Leave 1 as 1.

  ≈ 3100

To the nearest thousand
  $\underline{3}$132   Next digit is 4 or less. All digits to the right of the underlined place are changed to zeros. Leave 3 as 3.

  ≈ 3000

35. To the nearest ten

26,2<u>9</u>2   Next digit is 4 or less.
All digits to the right
of the underlined place
are changed to zeros.
Leave 9 as 9.

$\approx 26{,}290$

To the nearest hundred

26,<u>2</u>92   Next digit is 5 or more.
All digits to the right
of the underlined place
are changed to zeros.
Add 1 to 2.

$\approx 26{,}300$

To the nearest thousand

2<u>6</u>,292   Next digit is 4 or less.
All digits to the right
of the underlined place
are changed to zeros.
Leave 6 as 6.

$\approx 26{,}000$

39. *Step* 1 Locate the place to be rounded and underline it.

Step 2 Look only at the next digit to the right. If this digit is 5 or more, increase it by 1.

Step 3 Change all digits to the right of the underlined place to zeros.

43.

estimate	exact
100	97
− 30	− 26
70	71

47.

estimate	exact
800	786
800	823
300	342
+ 700	+ 684
2600	2635

51.

estimate	exact
400	368
× 400	× 436
160,000	2 208
	11 04
	147 2
	160,448

55.

estimate	exact
700	681
− 300	− 316
400	365

59. Perhaps the best explanation is that 648 is closer to 650 than 640, but 648 is closer to 600 than to 700.

63. To the nearest hundred thousand

$5,465,485,\underline{3}62,159

The next digit is 5 or more.
All digits to the right of the underlined place are changed to zeros.
Add 1 to 3.

$\approx \$5{,}465{,}485{,}400{,}000$

To the nearest hundred million

$5,465,<u>4</u>85,362,159

The next digit is 5 or more.
All digits to the right of the underlined place are changed to zeros.
Add 1 to 4.

$\approx \$5{,}465{,}500{,}000{,}000$

To the nearest billion

$5,46<u>5</u>,485,362,159

The next digit is 4 or less.
All digits to the right of the underlined place are changed to zeros.
Leave 5 as 5.

$\approx \$5{,}465{,}000{,}000{,}000$

1.8 Roots and Order of Operations

1.8 Margin Exercises

1. (a) 3^2: exponent, 2; base, 3
$3^2 = 3 \times 3 = 9$

(b) 6^3: exponent, 3; base, 6
$6^3 = 6 \times 6 \times 6 = 216$

(c) 2^4: exponent, 4; base, 2
$2^4 = 2 \times 2 \times 2 \times 2 = 16$

(d) 3^4: exponent, 4; base, 3
$3^4 = 3 \times 3 \times 3 \times 3 = 81$

2. (a) Because
$$2^2 = 4, \sqrt{4} = \sqrt{2 \cdot 2} = \sqrt{2^2} = 2.$$

(b) Because
$$6^2 = 36, \sqrt{36} = \sqrt{6 \cdot 6} = \sqrt{6^2} = 6.$$

(c) Because
$$9^2 = 81, \sqrt{81} = \sqrt{9 \cdot 9} = \sqrt{9^2} = 9.$$

(d) Because
$$15^2 = 15, \sqrt{225} = \sqrt{15 \cdot 15} = \sqrt{15^2} = 15.$$

(e) Because
$$1^2 = 1, \sqrt{1} = \sqrt{1 \cdot 1} = \sqrt{1^2} = 1.$$

3. (a)
$3 + 8 + 2^2$ *Evaluate exponent*
$3 + 8 + 2 \cdot 2$ *Multiply*
$3 + 8 + 4$ *Add*
$11 + 4 = 15$

(b)
$3^2 + 2^3$ *Evaluate exponents*
$3 \cdot 3 + 2 \cdot 2 \cdot 2$ *Multiply from left to right*
$9 + 8 = 17$ *Add*

(c)
$5 \cdot 8 \div 20 - 1$ *Multiply*
$40 \div 20 - 1$ *Divide*
$2 - 1 = 1$ *Subtract last*

(d)
$40 \div 5 \div 2$ *Divide from left to right*
$8 \div 2 = 4$

(e)
$8 + (14 \div 2) \cdot 6$ *Work inside parentheses*
$8 + 7 \cdot 6$ *Multiply*
$8 + 42 = 50$ *Add last*

4. (a)
$8 - 3 + 4^2$ *Exponent*
$8 - 3 + 16$ *Subtract*
$5 + 16 = 21$ *Add*

(b)
$2^2 + 3^2 - (5 \cdot 2)$ *Parentheses*
$2^2 + 3^2 - 10$ *Exponents*
$4 + 9 - 10$ *Add*
$13 - 10 = 3$ *Subtract*

(c)
$2 \cdot \sqrt{81} - 6 \cdot 2$ *Square root*
$2 \cdot 9 - 6 \cdot 2$ *Multiply*
$18 - 12 = 6$ *Subtract*

(d)
$20 \div 2 + (7 - 5)$ *Parentheses*
$20 \div 2 + 2$ *Divide*
$10 + 2 = 12$ *Add*

(e)
$15 \cdot \sqrt{9} - 8 \cdot \sqrt{4}$ *Square root*
$15 \cdot 3 - 8 \cdot 2$ *Multiply*
$45 - 16 = 29$ *Subtract*

1.8 Section Exercises

3. From the table,
$$4^2 = 16, \text{ so } \sqrt{16} = 4.$$

7. From the table,
$$11^2 = 121, \text{ so } \sqrt{121} = 11.$$

11. Exponent is 2; base is 6.
$$6^2 = 6 \cdot 6 = 36$$

15. Exponent is 2; base is 15.
$$15^2 = 15 \cdot 15 = 225$$

19. $15^2 = 15 \cdot 15 = 225$, so
$$\sqrt{225} = 15.$$

23. $40^2 = 40 \cdot 40 = 1600$, so
$$\sqrt{1600} = \sqrt{40 \cdot 40} = 40.$$

27. A perfect square is the square of a whole number. The number 25 is the square of 5 because $5 \cdot 5 = 25$. The number 50 is not a perfect square. There is no whole number that can be squared to get 50.

31.
$6 \cdot 5 - 4$ *Multiply*
$30 - 4 = 26$ *Subtract*

35.
$25 \div 5(8 - 4)$ *Parentheses*
$25 \div 5(4)$ *Divide*
$5(4) = 20$ *Multiply*

39.
$4 \cdot 1 + 8(9 - 2) + 3$ *Parentheses*
$4 \cdot 1 + 8 \cdot 7 + 3$ *Multiply*
$4 + 56 + 3 = 63$ *Divide*

Section 1.9 Solving Application Problems

43. $\;5 \cdot \sqrt{100} - 7 \cdot 2\quad$ *Square root*
    $5 \cdot 10 - 7 \cdot 2\quad$ *Multiply*
    $50 - 14 = 36\quad$ *Subtract*

47. $\;2^3 + 3^2 + (14 - 4) \cdot 3\quad$ *Parentheses*
    $2^3 \cdot 3^2 + 10 \cdot 3\quad$ *Exponents*
    $8 \cdot 9 + 10 \cdot 3\quad$ *Multiply*
    $72 + 30 = 102\quad$ *Add*

51. $\;3^2 + 6^2 + (30 - 21) \cdot 2\quad$ *Parentheses*
    $3^2 + 6^2 + 9 \cdot 2\quad$ *Exponents*
    $9 + 36 + 9 \cdot 2\quad$ *Multiply*
    $9 + 36 + 18 = 63\quad$ *Add*

55. $\;7 \cdot 2 + 8(2 \cdot 3) - 4\quad$ *Parentheses*
    $7 \cdot 2 + 8(6) - 4\quad$ *Multiply*
    $14 + 48 - 4\quad$ *Add*
    $62 - 4 = 58\quad$ *Subtract*

59. $\;6 \cdot (5 - 1) + \sqrt{4}\quad$ *Square root*
    $6 \cdot (5 - 1) + 2\quad$ *Parentheses*
    $6 \cdot 4 + 2\quad$ *Multiply*
    $24 + 2 = 26\quad$ *Add*

63. $\;5^2 \cdot 2^2 + (8 - 4) \cdot 2\quad$ *Parentheses*
    $5^2 \cdot 2^2 + 4 \cdot 2\quad$ *Exponents*
    $25 \cdot 4 + 4 \cdot 2\quad$ *Multiply*
    $100 + 8 = 108\quad$ *Add*

67. $\;5 \cdot \sqrt{36} - 7(7 - 4)\quad$ *Parentheses*
    $5 \cdot \sqrt{36} - 7 \cdot 3\quad$ *Square root*
    $5 \cdot 6 - 7 \cdot 3\quad$ *Multiply*
    $30 - 21 = 9\quad$ *Subtract*

71. $\;8 + 5 \div 5 + 7 + \frac{0}{3}\quad$ *Divide*
    $8 + 1 + 7 + \frac{0}{3}\quad$ *Add from*
    $9 + 7 + \frac{0}{3}\quad$ *left to right*
    $16 + \frac{0}{3} = 16$

75. $\;3 \cdot \sqrt{25} - 4 \cdot \sqrt{9}\quad$ *Square root*
    $3 \cdot 5 - 4 \cdot 3\quad$ *Multiply*
    $15 - 12 = 3\quad$ *Subtract*

79. $\;15 \div 3 \cdot 2 \cdot 6 \div (14 - 11)\quad$ *Parentheses*
    $15 \div 3 \cdot 2 \cdot 6 \div 3\quad$ *Divide from*
    $5 \cdot 2 \cdot 6 \div 3\quad$ *left to right*
    $10 \cdot 2 = 20\quad$ *Multiply*

83. $\;5 \div 1 \cdot 10 \cdot 4 \div (17 - 9)\quad$ *Parentheses*
    $5 \div 1 \cdot 10 \cdot 4 \div 8\quad$ *Multiply and*
    $5 \cdot 10 \cdot 4 \div 8\quad$ *divide from*
    $50 \cdot 4 \div 8\quad$ *left to*
    $200 \div 8 = 25\quad$ *right*

87. $\;1 + 3 - 2 \cdot \sqrt{1} + 3 \cdot \sqrt{121} - 5 \cdot 3$
    $1 + 3 - 2 \cdot 1 + 3 \cdot 11 - 5 \cdot 3$
    $1 + 3 - 2 + 33 - 15$
    $4 - 2 + 33 - 15$
    $2 + 33 - 15$
    $35 - 15 = 20$

1.9 Solving Application Problems

1.9 Margin Exercises

1. **(a)** an hourly wage: $2; $<u>7</u>; $60

   (b) a score on a 100-point test:
   6; 20; <u>74</u>; 109

   (c) the cost of heart bypass surgery:
   $500; <u>$50,000</u>; $5,000,000

2. **(a)** *Step 1* The total number of fossils is given, and the number each person receives must be found.

   Step 2 "Divided equally" indicates division.

   Step 3 80 fossils divided equally among 4 people gives an estimate of 20 fossils.

   Step 4 $\quad 4\overline{)84}^{\,21}$

   Check:

   $\quad 21\quad$ amount received by each person
   $\underline{\times\ \ 4}\quad$ number of people
   $\quad 84\quad$ total fossils

   The answer is reasonable.

   Each person receives 21 fossils.

   (b) *Step 1* The number of sales leads and sales people is given, and the number each person receives must be found.

   Step 2 "Divide equally" indicates division.

   Step 3 About 240 sales leads divided by 10 gives an estimate of 24.

   Step 4 $\quad 12\overline{)264}^{\,22}$

   Check:

   $\quad 22\quad$ amount received by each person
   $\underline{\times\ 12}\quad$ number of people
   $\ 264\quad$ total sales leads

   The answer is reasonable.

   Each person gets 22 sales leads.

3. (a) *Step* 1   The number of points on examinations and quizzes is given. The total number of points must be found.

Step 2   "Her total points" indicates addition.

Step 3   Rounding each score to the nearest ten gives 90, 80, 80, 100, 20, 10, 20, and 10. The sum of these scores gives an estimate of 410 points.

Step 4
```
      92
      81
      83
      98
      15
      14
      15
    + 12
     410
```
The answer is reasonable.
Her total is 410 points.

(b) *Step* 1   The customer contacts for each day are given. The total number of contacts for the week must be found.

Step 2   "Total" indicates addition.

Step 3   Rounding each day's contacts to the nearest ten gives 80, 60, 120, 100, and 200. The sum gives an estimate of 560 customer contacts.

Step 4
```
       78
       64
      118
      102
    + 196
      558
```
The answer is reasonable.
A check shows the answer is correct.

Stephanie had 558 customer contacts for the week.

4. (a) *Step* 1   The number of square feet for the home and the apartment is given. The difference must be found.

Step 2   "Difference" indicates subtraction.

Step 3   Rounding each number of square feet to the nearest hundred gives 1500 and 1000.

Subtracting these numbers gives 500 square feet.

Step 4   1450   Check: 980
           − 980   + 470
              470   1450

The answer is reasonable.

The difference in the number of square feet is 470 square feet.

(b) *Step* 1   There are 19,805 employees and 3980 employees will experience layoff.

Step 2   The wording "how many employees remain" indicates subtraction.

Step 3   The total number of employees is about 20,000. About 4000 employees are laid off. A reasonable amount of employees remaining is

$$20,000 - 4000 = 16,000.$$

Step 4   19,805   Check: 15,825
            − 3 980   + 3 980
              15,825   19,805

The answer is reasonable.

15,825 employees remain.

5. (a) *Step* 1   The amount that she receives for each car sold, the number of cars sold, and the sales expense are given. The amount remaining must be found.

Step 2   "Each" indicates a total must be found. Since she is paid the same amount for each sale, multiply. Then subtract expenses.

Step 3   Estimate that she is paid about $300 for each car sale or 5 × $300 = $1500.
Expenses are about $300.
Subtracting these numbers gives $1500 − $300 = $1200.

Step 4 $315 $1575
            ×   5   − 280
            $1575 $1295

The answer is reasonable.

The amount remaining is $1295.

(b) *Step* 1   The number of cars entering in a 4-hour period and the number of cars leaving are given. The number remaining must be found.

Step 2   "Each" indicates a total must be found. Since the number each hour is the same, multiply. Subtract to find the number remaining.

Step 3   Estimate that about 130 cars enter each hour. In 4 hours about 520 cars enter. Subtract

Section 1.9 Solving Application Problems

the number of cars that leave. A reasonable estimate is $520 - 270 = 250$.

Step 4
$$\begin{array}{r} 125 \\ \times\ \ 4 \\ \hline 500 \end{array} \qquad \begin{array}{r} 500 \\ -\ 271 \\ \hline 229 \end{array}$$

The answer is reasonable.

Check:
$$\begin{array}{r} 271 \\ +\ 229 \\ \hline 500 \end{array} \qquad 4\overline{)500}^{\ 125}$$

There are 229 cars remaining in the lot.

1.9   Section Exercises

3. *Step* 1 Find how many types of cereal that the supermarket sells.

Step 2 "All but 62 types" indicates subtraction.

Step 3 The total number should be about $200 - 60 = 140$ types.

Step 4 Subtract:
$$\begin{array}{r} 200 \\ -\ 62 \\ \hline 138 \end{array} \qquad \text{Check:} \begin{array}{r} 138 \\ +\ 62 \\ \hline 200 \end{array}$$

The supermarket sells 138 types of cereal.

7. *Step* 1 Find the number of toys each child will receive.

Step 2 "Same number of toys to each" indicates division.

Step 3 3000 divided by 700 gives an estimate of about 4 toys.

Step 4
$$657\overline{)2628}^{\ \ \ 4} \qquad \text{Check:} \begin{array}{r} 657 \\ \times\ \ 4 \\ \hline 2628 \end{array}$$
$$\underline{2628}$$
$$0$$

Each child will receive 4 toys.

11. *Step* 1 Find the amount saved for five months.

Step 2 Use multiplication to find the amount.

Step 3 The amount saved is about $10 per month making the total $50 ($5 \times \$10$).

Step 4
$$\begin{array}{r} \$14 \\ \times\ \ 5 \\ \hline \$70 \end{array} \qquad \text{Check:} \quad 5\overline{)70}^{\ \ 14}$$
$$\underline{5}$$
$$20$$
$$\underline{20}$$
$$0$$

The answer is reasonable.

The amount saved in five months is $70.

15. *Step* 1 Find her monthly savings.

Step 2 Her monthly take home pay and expenses are given. Expenses must be totaled. "Remainder" indicates subtraction.

Step 3 Estimate expenses:

$\$2000 - \$500 - \$300 - \$300 - \$200 - \$200 = \$500$.

Step 4
$$\begin{array}{r} \$450 \\ 325 \\ 320 \\ 182 \\ +\ 150 \\ \hline \$1427 \end{array} \qquad \begin{array}{r} \$1620 \\ -\ 1427 \\ \hline \$193 \end{array}$$

Check:
$$\begin{array}{r} \$1427 \\ +\ \ 193 \\ \hline \$1620 \end{array}$$

Her monthly savings are $193.

19. *Step* 1 Find the total cost of all Safety and Security Items.

Step 2 Add each cost to find the total cost.

Step 3 Estimate: $\$500 + \$800 + \$100 + \$100 + \$100 = \$1600$

Step 4
$$\begin{array}{r} \$475 \\ 780 \\ 130 \\ 115 \\ +\ 135 \\ \hline \$1635 \end{array}$$

The total cost is $1635.

23. *Step* 1 The number and cost of wheelchairs and recorder-players are given and the total cost of all items must be found.

Step 2 Find the cost of all wheelchairs and the cost of all recorder-players. Then add these costs to get the total cost.

Step 3 The cost of the wheelchairs is about $6000 ($\$1000 \times 6$).

The cost of the recorder-players is about $18,000 ($\$900 \times 20$).

Estimate: $\$6000 + \$18,000 = \$24,000$

Step 4 Cost of wheelchairs

$$\begin{array}{r}\$1256\\\times\quad 6\\\hline\$7536\end{array}$$

Cost of recorder-players

$$\begin{array}{r}\$895\\\times\quad 15\\\hline 4\;475\\8\;95\\\hline\$13,425\end{array}$$

The total cost is $13,425 + $7536 = $20,961.

27. Estimating the answer can help you avoid careless mistakes like decimal errors and calculation errors. Examples of reasonable answers in daily life might be a $20 bag of groceries, $15 to fill the gas tank, or $45 for a phone bill.

31. *Step* 1 Find the final weight of the car.

Step 2 To find the weight of the car without the first engine, subtract. Then add the weight of the second engine to that amount.

Step 3 2000 − 600 = 1400

1400 + 600 gives an estimate of 2000 pounds.

Step 4
$$\begin{array}{rr}2425 & 1843\\-\;\;582 & +\;\;634\\\hline 1843 & 2477\end{array}$$

The car weighs 2477 pounds after the engine change.

35. *Step* 1 Find how many vending machines the company has at the end of the month.

Step 2 Subtract the machines that were distributed and add those that were returned to the total number of machines on hand.

Step 3 A reasonable answer would be

330 − 40 − 20 − 80 + 20 + 40 + 100 = 350.

Estimate about 350 were on hand.

Step 4
$$\begin{array}{rrrr}35 & 15 & 325 & 191\\23 & 38 & -\;134 & +\;161\\+\;76 & +\;108 & \overline{191} & \overline{352}\\\hline 134 & 161 & & \end{array}$$

The company has 352 machines.

Chapter 1 Review Exercises

1. <u>4</u> 621
thousands: 4
ones: 621

2. 87,<u>328</u>
thousands: 87
ones: 328

3. 105,<u>724</u>
thousands: 105
ones: 724

4. <u>1</u>,<u>768</u>,<u>710</u>,<u>618</u>
billions: 1
millions: 768
thousands: 710
ones: 618

5. 725 is seven hundred twenty-five.

6. 12,412 is twelve thousand, four hundred twelve.

7. 319,215 is three hundred nineteen thousand, two hundred fifteen.

8. 62,500,005 is sixty-two million, five hundred thousand, five.

9. Four thousand, four is 4004.

10. Two hundred million, four hundred fifty-five is 200,000,455.

11.
$$\begin{array}{r}\overset{1}{7}4\\+\;18\\\hline 92\end{array}$$

12.
$$\begin{array}{r}35\\+\;78\\\hline 113\end{array}$$

13.
$$\begin{array}{r}\overset{1\;1}{807}\\4606\\+\;\;\;51\\\hline 5464\end{array}$$

14.
$$\begin{array}{r}\overset{\;\;1}{8\;215}\\9\\+\;7\;433\\\hline 15,657\end{array}$$

15.
$$\begin{array}{r}\overset{1\;1}{1108}\\566\\7201\\+\;\;304\\\hline 9179\end{array}$$

16.
$$\begin{array}{r}\overset{11}{187}\\5543\\246\\+\;1003\\\hline 6979\end{array}$$

17.
$$\begin{array}{r}\overset{11\;33}{5\;732}\\11,069\\37\\1\;595\\+\;22,169\\\hline 40,602\end{array}$$

18.
$$\begin{array}{r}\overset{1\;31}{3\;451}\\12,286\\43\\1\;291\\+\;32,784\\\hline 49,855\end{array}$$

Chapter 1 Review Exercises

19. $\begin{array}{r}34\\-12\\\hline 22\end{array}$ Check: $\begin{array}{r}12\\+22\\\hline 34\end{array}$

20. $\begin{array}{r}56\\-35\\\hline 21\end{array}$ Check: $\begin{array}{r}35\\+21\\\hline 56\end{array}$

21. $\begin{array}{r}{\scriptstyle 1\,12\,18}\\\cancel{2}\cancel{3}\cancel{8}\\-199\\\hline 39\end{array}$ Check: $\begin{array}{r}{\scriptstyle 11}\\199\\+\ 39\\\hline 238\end{array}$

22. $\begin{array}{r}{\scriptstyle 4\,16\,13}\\\cancel{5}\cancel{7}\cancel{3}\\-389\\\hline 184\end{array}$ Check: $\begin{array}{r}{\scriptstyle 11}\\389\\+184\\\hline 573\end{array}$

23. $\begin{array}{r}{\scriptstyle 3\,13\,7\,10}\\\cancel{4}\cancel{3}\cancel{8}\cancel{0}\\-\ 577\\\hline 3803\end{array}$ Check: $\begin{array}{r}{\scriptstyle 1\ \ 1}\\3803\\+\ 577\\\hline 4380\end{array}$

24. $\begin{array}{r}{\scriptstyle 4\,12\,11\,10}\\\cancel{5}\cancel{2}\cancel{1}\cancel{0}\\-\ 883\\\hline 4327\end{array}$ Check: $\begin{array}{r}{\scriptstyle 111}\\4327\\+\ 883\\\hline 5210\end{array}$

25. $\begin{array}{r}{\scriptstyle 1\,12\,11\,10}\\\cancel{2}\cancel{2}\cancel{1}\cancel{0}\\-1986\\\hline 224\end{array}$ Check: $\begin{array}{r}{\scriptstyle 111}\\1986\\+\ 224\\\hline 2210\end{array}$

26. $\begin{array}{r}{\scriptstyle 8\ 16\ 9\ 17\,10\,14}\\\cancel{9}\cancel{9}\cancel{7}\cancel{0}\cancel{4}\\-73{,}838\\\hline 25{,}866\end{array}$ Check: $\begin{array}{r}{\scriptstyle 1\ \ 11}\\25{,}866\\+73{,}838\\\hline 99{,}704\end{array}$

27. $\begin{array}{r}5\\\times 5\\\hline 25\end{array}$

28. $\begin{array}{r}8\\\times 0\\\hline 0\end{array}$

29. $7 \times 3 = 21$

30. $8 \times 8 = 64$

31. $(6)(7) = 42$

32. $(4)(9) = 36$

33. $7 \cdot 8 = 56$

34. $9 \cdot 9 = 81$

35. $2 \times 4 \times 6$
$(2 \times 4) \times 6$
$8 \times 6 = 48$

36. $9 \times 1 \times 5$
$(9 \times 1) \times 5$
$9 \times 5 = 45$

37. $4 \times 4 \times 3$
$(4 \times 4) \times 3$
$16 \times 3 = 48$

38. $2 \times 2 \times 2$
$(2 \times 2) \times 2$
$4 \times 2 = 8$

39. $(8)(0)(6) = 0$
Any number times 0 equals 0.

40. $(8)(8)(1)$
$64 \cdot 1 = 64$

41. $6 \cdot 1 \cdot 8$
$(6 \cdot 1) \cdot 8$
$6 \cdot 8 = 48$

42. $7 \cdot 7 \cdot 0$
Any number times 0 equals 0.

43. $\begin{array}{r}{\scriptstyle 1}\\43\\\times\ \ 4\\\hline 172\end{array}$

44. $\begin{array}{r}{\scriptstyle 1}\\62\\\times\ \ 7\\\hline 434\end{array}$

45. $\begin{array}{r}{\scriptstyle 7}\\58\\\times\ \ 9\\\hline 522\end{array}$

46. $\begin{array}{r}98\\\times\ \ 1\\\hline 98\end{array}$

47. $\begin{array}{r}{\scriptstyle 25}\\639\\\times\ \ \ 6\\\hline 3834\end{array}$

48. $\begin{array}{r}{\scriptstyle 5}\\781\\\times\ \ \ 7\\\hline 5467\end{array}$

49. $\begin{array}{r}{\scriptstyle 113}\\1349\\\times\ \ \ \ 4\\\hline 5396\end{array}$

50. $\begin{array}{r}{\scriptstyle 31}\\9163\\\times\ \ \ \ 5\\\hline 45{,}815\end{array}$

51. $\begin{array}{r}{\scriptstyle 11}\\7259\\\times\ \ \ \ 2\\\hline 14{,}518\end{array}$

52. $\begin{array}{r}{\scriptstyle 22}\\5440\\\times\ \ \ \ 6\\\hline 32{,}640\end{array}$

53. $\begin{array}{r}{\scriptstyle 1\ \ 2}\\93{,}105\\\times\ \ \ \ \ 5\\\hline 465{,}525\end{array}$

54. $\begin{array}{r}{\scriptstyle 16\ 52}\\21{,}873\\\times\ \ \ \ \ 8\\\hline 174{,}984\end{array}$

55. $\begin{array}{r}{\scriptstyle 3}\\34\\\times\ 18\\\hline 272\\34\ \ \\\hline 612\end{array}$

56. $\begin{array}{r}{\scriptstyle 1}\\52\\\times\ 36\\\hline 312\\156\ \ \\\hline 1872\end{array}$

57.
$$\begin{array}{r}\overset{1}{98}\\ \times\ 12\\ \hline 196\\ 98\ \\ \hline 1176\end{array}$$

58.
$$\begin{array}{r}\overset{5}{\underset{}{\overset{4}{68}}}\\ \times\ 75\\ \hline 340\\ 476\ \\ \hline 5100\end{array}$$

59.
$$\begin{array}{r}\overset{1\,1}{655}\\ \times\ 21\\ \hline 655\\ 13\,10\ \\ \hline 13,755\end{array}$$

63.
$$\begin{array}{rl}\$15 & \text{cost per CD}\\ \times\ 20 & \text{CD's}\\ \hline \$300 & \text{total cost}\end{array}$$

64.
$$\begin{array}{rl}\overset{3}{\$14} & \text{cost per shirt}\\ \times\ 48 & \text{T-shirts}\\ \hline 112\\ 56\ \\ \hline \$672 & \text{total cost}\end{array}$$

65.
$$\begin{array}{rl}\overset{33}{\underset{}{\overset{66}{278}}} & \text{batteries}\\ \times\ \$48 & \text{cost per battery}\\ \hline 2\,224\\ 11\,12\ \\ \hline \$13,344 & \text{total cost}\end{array}$$

66.
$$\begin{array}{rl}\overset{67}{168} & \text{welders}\\ \times\ \$9 & \text{cost per mask}\\ \hline \$1512 & \text{total cost}\end{array}$$

67.
$$\begin{array}{rrr}320 & 32 & 320\\ \times\ 60 & \times\ 6 & \times\ 60\\ \hline & 192 & 19,200\ \ Attach\\ & & 2\ zeros\end{array}$$

68.
$$\begin{array}{rrr}280 & 28 & 280\\ \times\ 90 & \times\ 9 & \times\ 90\\ \hline & 252 & 25,200\ \ Attach\\ & & 2\ zeros\end{array}$$

60.
$$\begin{array}{r}\overset{6\,1}{392}\\ \times\ 77\\ \hline 2\,744\\ 27\,44\ \\ \hline 30,184\end{array}$$

61.
$$\begin{array}{r}4051\\ \times\ 219\\ \hline 887,169\end{array}$$

62.
$$\begin{array}{r}1527\\ \times\ 328\\ \hline 500,856\end{array}$$

69.
$$\begin{array}{rrr}517 & 517 & 517\\ \times\ 400 & \times\ 4 & \times\ 400\\ \hline & 2068 & 206,800\ \ Attach\\ & & 2\ zeros\end{array}$$

70.
$$\begin{array}{rrr}752 & 752 & 752\\ \times\ 400 & \times\ 4 & \times\ 400\\ \hline & 3008 & 300,800\ \ Attach\\ & & 2\ zeros\end{array}$$

71.
$$\begin{array}{rrr}16,000 & 16 & 16,000\\ \times\ 8000 & \times\ 8 & \times\ 8000\\ \hline & 128 & 128,000,000\ \ Attach\\ & & 6\ zeros\end{array}$$

72.
$$\begin{array}{rrr}43,000 & 430 & 43,000\\ \times\ 2100 & \times\ 21 & \times\ 21\\ \hline & 903 & 90,300,000\ \ Attach\\ & & 5\ zeros\end{array}$$

73. $12 \div 4 = 3$

74. $36 \div 6 = 6$

75. $42 \div 7 = 6$

76. $18 \div 9 = 2$

77. $\dfrac{72}{8} = 72 \div 8 = 9$

78. $\dfrac{36}{9} = 36 \div 9 = 4$

79. $\dfrac{54}{6} = 54 \div 6 = 9$

80. $\dfrac{0}{6} = 0 \div 6 = 0$

81. $\dfrac{125}{0}$ undefined

82. $\dfrac{0}{35} = 0 \div 35 = 0$

83. $\dfrac{64}{8} = 64 \div 8 = 8$

84. $\dfrac{81}{9} = 81 \div 9 = 9$

85.
$$\begin{array}{r}10\ 8\\ 4\overline{)43^{3}2}\end{array}\quad \text{Check:}\quad \begin{array}{r}108\\ \times\ 4\\ \hline 432\end{array}$$

86.
$$\begin{array}{r}2\ 4\\ 9\overline{)21^{3}6}\end{array}\quad \text{Check:}\quad \begin{array}{r}\overset{3}{24}\\ \times\ 9\\ \hline 216\end{array}$$

87.
$$\begin{array}{r}6\ 2\ 51\\ 9\overline{)56,^{2}2^{4}59}\end{array}\quad \text{Check:}\quad \begin{array}{r}\overset{24}{6251}\\ \times\ 9\\ \hline 56,259\end{array}$$

Chapter 1 Review Exercises

88.
$$352$$
$$76\overline{)26{,}752}$$
$$\underline{22\ 8}$$
$$3\ 95$$
$$\underline{3\ 80}$$
$$152$$
$$\underline{152}$$
$$0$$

Check:
$$352$$
$$\underline{\times\ \ 76}$$
$$2\ 112$$
$$\underline{24\ 64\ \ }$$
$$26{,}752$$

89. $2704 \div 18$

$$150\ \ \text{R4}$$
$$18\overline{)2704}$$
$$\underline{18}$$
$$\ 90$$
$$\ \underline{90}$$
$$\ \ 04$$
$$\ \ \underline{00}$$
$$\ \ \ \ 4$$

Check:
$$150$$
$$\underline{\times\ \ \ 18}$$
$$1200$$
$$\underline{150\ \ }$$
$$2700$$
$$\underline{+\ \ \ \ \ 4}$$
$$2704$$

90. $15{,}525 \div 125$

$$124\ \ \text{R25}$$
$$125\overline{)15{,}525}$$
$$\underline{12\ 5}$$
$$\ \ 3\ 02$$
$$\ \ \underline{2\ 50}$$
$$\ \ \ \ \ 525$$
$$\ \ \ \ \ \underline{500}$$
$$\ \ \ \ \ \ \ 25$$

Check:
$$124$$
$$\underline{\times\ \ 125}$$
$$620$$
$$2\ 48\ \ $$
$$\underline{12\ 4\ \ \ \ }$$
$$15{,}500$$
$$\underline{+\ \ \ \ \ 25}$$
$$15{,}525$$

91. 318 to the nearest ten: ≈ 320

3$\underline{1}$8   Next digit is 5 or more.

Tens place changes $(1 + 1 = 2)$. The digit next to the underlined place changes to 0.

92. 14,309 to the nearest hundred: $\approx 14{,}300$

14,$\underline{3}$09   Next digit is 4 or less.

Hundreds place does not change. All digits to the right of the underlined place change to 0.

93. 19,721 to the nearest thousand: $\approx 20{,}000$

1$\underline{9}$,721   Next digit is 5 or more.

Thousands place changes $(9 + 1 = 10$; write 0 carry 1). All digits to the right of the underlined place change to 0.

94. 67,485 to the nearest ten thousand: $\approx 70{,}000$

$\underline{6}$7,485   Next digit is 5 or more.

Ten thousands place changes $(6 + 1 = 7)$. All digits to the right of the underlined place change to 0.

95. 2397 to the nearest ten: ≈ 2400

23$\underline{9}$7   Next digit is 5 or more.

Tens place changes $(9 + 1 = 10$; write 0, carry 1). The digit to the right of the underlined place changes to 0.

2397 to the nearest hundred ≈ 2400

2$\underline{3}$97   Next digit is 5 or more.

Hundreds place changes $(3 + 1 = 4)$. All digits to the right of the underlined place change to 0.

2397 to the nearest thousand: ≈ 2000

$\underline{2}$397   Next digit is 4 or less.

Thousands place does not change. All digits to the right of the underlined place change to 0.

96. 20,065 to the nearest ten: $\approx 20{,}070$

20,0$\underline{6}$5   Next digit is 5 or more.

Tens place changes $(6 + 1 = 7)$. The digit to the right of the underlined place changes to 0.

20,065 to the nearest hundred: $\approx 20{,}100$

20,$\underline{0}$65   Next digit is 5 or more.

Hundreds place changes $(0 + 1 = 1)$. All digits to the right of the underlined place change to 0.

20,065 to the nearest thousand: $\approx 20{,}000$

2$\underline{0}$,065   Next digit is 4 or less.

Thousands place does not change. All digits to the right of the underlined place change to 0.

97. 98,201 to the nearest ten: ≈ 98,200

 98,2<u>0</u>1   Next digit is 4 or less.

 Tens place does not change. The digit to the right of the underlined place changes to 0.

 98,201 to the nearest hundred: ≈ 98,200

 98,<u>2</u>01   Next digit is 4 or less.

 Hundreds place does not change. All digits to the right of the underlined place change to 0.

 98,201 to the nearest thousand: ≈ 98,000

 9<u>8</u>,201   Next digit is 4 or less.

 Thousands place does not change. All digits to the right of the underlined place change to 0.

98. 352,118 to the nearest ten: ≈ 352,120

 352,1<u>1</u>8   Next digit is 5 or more.

 Tens place changes (1 + 1 = 2). The digit next to the underlined place changes to 0.

 352,118 to the nearest hundred: ≈ 352,100

 352,<u>1</u>18   Next digit is 4 or less.

 Hundreds place does not change. All digits to the right of the underlined place change to 0.

 352,118 to the nearest thousand: ≈ 352,000

 35<u>2</u>,118   Next digit is 4 or less.

 Thousands place does not change. All digits to the right of the underlined place change to 0.

99. From the table,
$$6^2 = 36, \text{ so } \sqrt{36} = 6.$$

100. From the table,
$$7^2 = 49, \text{ so } \sqrt{49} = 7.$$

101. From the table,
$$12^2 = 144, \text{ so } \sqrt{144} = 12.$$

102. From the table,
$$14^2 = 196, \text{ so } \sqrt{196} = 14.$$

103. Exponent is 2; base is 3.
$$3^2 = 3 \cdot 3 = 9$$

104. Exponent is 3; base is 2.
$$2^3 = 2 \cdot 2 \cdot 2 = 8$$

105. Exponent is 3; base is 5.
$$5^3 = 5 \cdot 5 \cdot 5 = 125$$

106. Exponent is 5; base is 4.
$$4^5 = 4 \cdot 4 \cdot 4 \cdot 4 \cdot 4 = 1024$$

107. $9^2 - 9$ *Exponent*
 $81 - 9 = 72$ *Subtract*

108. $3^2 - 5$ *Exponent*
 $9 - 5 = 4$ *Subtract*

109. $2 \cdot 3^2 \div 2$ *Exponent*
 $2 \cdot 9 \div 2$ *Multiply*
 $18 \div 2 = 9$ *Divide*

110. $9 \div 1 \cdot 2 \cdot 2 \div (11 - 2)$ *Parentheses*
 $9 \div 1 \cdot 2 \cdot 2 \div 9$ *Divide and*
 $9 \cdot 2 \cdot 2 \div 9$ *multiply*
 $18 \cdot 2 \div 9$ *from left*
 $36 \div 9 = 4$ *to right*

111. $\sqrt{9} + 2 \cdot 3$ *Square root*
 $3 + 2 \cdot 3$ *Multiply*
 $3 + 6 = 9$ *Add*

112. $6 \cdot \sqrt{16} - 6 \cdot \sqrt{9}$ *Square roots*
 $6 \cdot 4 - 6 \cdot 3$ *Multiply*
 $24 - 18 = 6$ *Subtract*

113. *Step 1* Find total cost.

 Step 2 We know how many shovels there are and how much each one costs. Number of shovels × cost of each = total cost.

 Step 3 A reasonable answer is
$$50 \times \$10 = \$500.$$

 Step 4 48 × $11 = $528

 Check: $528 ÷ 48 = $11

114. *Step 1* Find the total revolutions.

 Step 2 We know the revolutions per minute and the number of minutes.
 Number of revolutions × minutes = total revolutions

Chapter 1 Review Exercises

Step 3 A reasonable answer is
$1000 \times 60 = 60{,}000$ revolutions.

Step 4 $1400 \times 60 = 84{,}000$ revolutions

Check: $84{,}000 \div 60 = 1400$

115. *estimate* *exact*

$$\begin{array}{r} 100 \\ \times\ \ 6 \\ \hline 600\ \text{cups} \end{array} \qquad \begin{array}{r} 120\ \text{cups} \\ \times\ \ \ 6\ \text{pots} \\ \hline 720\ \text{cups} \end{array}$$

116. *estimate*

$$\begin{array}{r} 6000 \\ \times\ \ \ 30 \\ \hline 180{,}000\ \text{brackets} \end{array}$$

exact

$$\begin{array}{r} 6000\ \text{brackets} \\ \times\ \ \ 30\ \text{drums} \\ \hline 180{,}000\ \text{brackets} \end{array} \quad \textit{Attach 4 zeros}$$

117. *estimate*

$$\begin{array}{r} 2000 \\ \times\ \ \ 10 \\ \hline 20{,}000\ \text{hours} \end{array}$$

exact

$$\begin{array}{r} 2000\ \text{hours per home} \\ \times\ \ \ 12\ \text{homes} \\ \hline 24{,}000\ \text{hours} \end{array} \quad \textit{Attach 3 zeroes}$$

118. *estimate* *exact*

$$\begin{array}{r} 80 \\ \times\ \ 5 \\ \hline 400\ \text{miles} \end{array} \qquad \begin{array}{r} 80\ \text{miles per hour} \\ \times\ \ 5\ \text{hours} \\ \hline 400\ \text{miles} \end{array}$$

119. *Step* 1 Find the total cost to admit adults and children.

Step 2 Multiply the number of adults times the adult admission fee and the number of children by the admission fee for children. Add to find the total fee.

Step 3 Estimate:

$$(\$20 \times 20) + (\$10 \times 30) = \$700$$

Step 4 Adults: Children:

$$\begin{array}{r} \$15 \\ \times\ \ 18 \\ \hline \$270 \end{array} \qquad \begin{array}{r} \$12 \\ \times\ \ 26 \\ \hline 72 \\ 24 \\ \hline \$312 \end{array}$$

Total:

$$\begin{array}{r} \$270 \\ +\ \ 312 \\ \hline \$582 \end{array}$$

The total cost is $582.

120. *Step* 1 Find the total monthly collections.

Step 2 We know the number of daily customers and the daily rate. We know the number of weekend-only customers and the rate.
Number of customers $\times$ daily rate + number of customers $\times$ weekend rate = total collections

Step 3 Reasonable answer:

$$= (60 \times \$20) + (20 \times \$10) = \$1400$$

Step 4 $(56 \times \$15) + (23 \times \$8)$
$= \$840 + \$184 = \$1024$

The total monthly collections are $1024.

121. *Step* 1 Find the differences between the cost of the two mowers.

Step 2 Difference indicates subtraction.

Step 3 A reasonable answer is

$$\$400 - \$200 = \$200.$$

Step 4 $\begin{array}{r} \$350 \\ -\ \ 170 \\ \hline \$180 \end{array}$

The difference in price is $180.

Check: $\$170 + \$180 = \$350$

122. *Step* 1 Find the new account balance.

Step 2 We know the amount of the check and the old balance.
Old balance $-$ check amount = new balance

Step 3 A reasonable answer:

$$\$400 - \$100 = \$300$$

Step 4 $382 - 135 = 247$

Check: $247 + 135 = 382$

She has $247 in her account.

123. *Step 1*   Find out how many pounds of pork are needed.

Step 2   We know the total number of cans and we must divide that total by 175 since each group of 175 cans requires 1 pound of pork. The number of groups × 1 pound = total pounds.

Step 3   A reasonable answer:

$$\frac{9000}{200} = 45 \text{ pounds}$$

Step 4 $\frac{8750}{175} = 50$

Check: 1 pound · 50 = 50 pounds, 50 · 175 cans = 8750 cans

50 pounds of pork are needed.

124. *Step 1*   Find how many hours it takes to produce all the plates.

Step 2   We know the total number of plates and we know how many are produced each hour.

$$\frac{\text{total number}}{\text{number per hour}} = \text{total hours}$$

Step 3   A reasonable answer:
30,000 ÷ 1000 = 30 hours

Step 4 $\frac{30,888}{936} = 33$ hours

Check: $33 \cdot 936 = 30,888$

It will take 33 hours.

125. *Step 1*   Find the total acres fertilized.

Step 2   We know the total amount of fertilizer and how much each acre needs.
Total pounds ÷ pounds needed per acre = total acres

Step 3   A reasonable answer:
6000 ÷ 300 = 20 acres

Step 4   5750 ÷ 250 = 23 acres

Check: 23 · 250 = 5750

23 acres can be fertilized.

126. *Step 1*   Find the number of homes that can be fenced.

Step 2   Divide the number of feet of fencing available by the number of feet needed for each home.

Step 3   Estimate: $\frac{6000}{200} = 30$ homes

Step 4 $\frac{5760}{180}$

```
      32
18)576
      54
      36
      36
       0
```

Check:
```
       32
      × 18
      256
       32
     5760   Attach zero
```

32 homes can be fenced.

127. $\begin{array}{r} 47 \\ \times\ 6 \\ \hline 282 \end{array}$ 128. $\begin{array}{r} 78 \\ \times\ 7 \\ \hline 546 \end{array}$

129. $\begin{array}{r} 182 \\ -\ 75 \\ \hline 107 \end{array}$ Check: $\begin{array}{r} 75 \\ +\ 107 \\ \hline 182 \end{array}$

130. $\begin{array}{r} 716 \\ -\ 153 \\ \hline 563 \end{array}$ 131. $\begin{array}{r} 662 \\ +\ 379 \\ \hline 1041 \end{array}$

132. $\begin{array}{r} 352 \\ +\ 678 \\ \hline 1030 \end{array}$

133. $\begin{array}{r} 38{,}140 \\ -\ 6\ 078 \\ \hline 32{,}0\ 6\ 2 \end{array}$ Check: $\begin{array}{r} 6\ 078 \\ +\ 32{,}062 \\ \hline 38{,}140 \end{array}$

134. $\begin{array}{r} 29{,}156 \\ -\ 4\ 209 \\ \hline 24{,}947 \end{array}$ 135. $21 \div 7 = 3$

136. $\frac{42}{6} = 7$ $(7 \cdot 6 = 42)$

Chapter 1 Review Exercises

137.
$\overset{12\ 22}{7\ 218}$
3
18
1 791
82,623
+ 1 982
―――――
93,635

138.
$\overset{1212}{3812}$
5
22
1 836
75 134
+ 2 369
―――――
83,178

139. $\frac{8}{0}$ is undefined.
Division by 0 is not possible

140. $\frac{6}{1} = 6$ ($6 \cdot 1 = 6$)

141. $55,200 \div 4 = 13,800$

138 *Attach 2 zeros*
$4\overline{)552}$

142. $18,440 \div 8 = 2305$
$2\ \ 30\ 5$
$8\overline{)18{,}^2 44^40}$

143.
8430
× 128
―――――
67 440
168 60
843 0
―――――
1,079,040

144.
38,571
× 3
―――――
115,713

145.
108
$34\overline{)3672}$
34
―――
27
0
―――
272
272
―――
0

146.
207
$68\overline{)14{,}076}$
$13\ 6$
―――
47
0
―――
476
476
―――
0

147. 286,753 is two hundred eighty-six thousand, seven hundred fifty-three.

148. 108,210 is one hundred eight thousand, two hundred ten.

149. 3349 to the nearest hundred: ≈ 3300

3<u>3</u>49   Next digit is 4 or less.

Hundreds place does not change. All digits to the right of the underlined place change to 0.

150. 200,498 to the nearest thousand: ≈ 200,000

20<u>0</u>,498   Next digit is 4 or less.

Thousands place does not change. All digits to the right of the underlined place change to 0.

151. From the table,
$$5^2 = 25, \text{ so } \sqrt{25} = 5.$$

152. From the table,
$$10^2 = 100, \text{ so } \sqrt{100} = 10.$$

153.
$165   cost per pair
× 36   pairs
―――――
990
495
―――――
$5940   total cost

154.
$520   cost per refrigerator
× 65   refrigerators
―――――
2 600
31 20
―――――
$33,800   total cost

155.
185   shirts
× $12   cost per shirt
―――――
370
185
―――――
$2220   total cost

156.
607   boxes
× $26   cost per box
―――――
3 642
12 14
―――――
$15,782   total cost

157.
52   cards per deck
× 9   decks
―――――
468   total cards

158.
238   cartons
× 12   textbooks
―――――
476
238
―――――
2856   textbooks

159.
$380
− 100
―――――
$280

A "push-type" mower costs $280.

160. $115,280
          − 87,340
          ———
          $27,940

They must raise $27,940.

161. First, find the rental fee.

4 − person	6 × $28 =	$168
6 − person	15 × $38 =	570
10 − person	10 × $70 =	700
12 − person	3 × $75 =	225
16 − person	2 × $85 =	+ 170
		$1883

Then find the launch fee.

6 × $2 =	$12
15 × $2 =	30
10 × $2 =	20
3 × $2 =	6
2 × $2 =	+ 4
	$72

Add the totals.

$1833
+ 72
———
$1905

Total receipts were $1905.

162. First, find the rental fee.

38 × $28 =	$1 064
73 × $38 =	2 774
58 × $70 =	4 060
34 × $75 =	2 550
18 × $85 =	+ 1 530
	$11,978

Then find the launch fee.

38 × $2 =	$ 76
73 × $2 =	146
58 × $2 =	116
34 × $2 =	68
18 × $2 =	+ 36
	$442

Add the totals.

$11,978
+ 442
———
$12,420

Total receipts were $12,420.

Chapter 1 Test

1. 8208 is eight thousand, two hundred eight.

2. 75,065 is seventy-five thousand, sixty five.

3. One hundred thirty-eight thousand, eight is 138,008.

4.
```
    21
   1984
     65
  4 283
 + 7 561
 ———————
 12,893
```

5.
```
  11 12
 17,063
      7
     12
   1505
  93,710
 +   333
 ————————
 112,630
```

6.
```
  6 9 9 12
  7 0 0 2
 − 3 9 5 4
 —————————
   3 0 4 8
```

7.
```
  4 9 15 12
  5 0 6 2
 − 1 9 7 8
 —————————
   3 0 8 4
```

8. 5 × 7 × 4
(5 × 7) × 4 = 35 × 4 = 140
or
5 × (7 × 4) = 5 × 28 = 140

9. 57 · 3000
```
   57
 ×  3
 ————
  171
```
57 · 3000 = 171,000
Attach 3 zeros

10. (85)(21)   Check:
```
    85           85
 ×  21       21)1785
 ————          168
    85         ———
   170         105
 ————          105
  1785         ———
                 0
```

11.
```
                              7 381
     7381       Check:  603)4,450,743
  ×   603                    4 428 6
 ——————                      ———————
  22 143
  00 00
  4 428 6
 ————————
 4,450,743
```

Chapter 1 Test

12.
```
            7 747
    16)123,952
        112
         11 9
         11 2
            75
            64
           112
           112
             0
```
Check:
```
        7747
    ×     16
       46 482
       77 47
      123,952
```

13. $\frac{791}{0}$ is undefined.

   Division by zero is not possible

14.
```
           458
   84)38,472
       33 6
        4 87
        4 20
          672
          672
            0
```
Check:
```
         458
    ×     84
        1 832
       36 64
       38,472
```

15.
```
          160
  280)44,800
      28 0
      16 80
      16 80
          00
           0
           0
```

16. 4756 to the nearest ten: ≈ 4760

   47<u>5</u>6   Next digit is 5 or more.

   Tens place changes (5 + 1 = 6). The digit next to the underlined place changes to 0.

17. 67,509 to the nearest thousand: ≈ 68,000

   6<u>7</u>,509   Next digit is 5 or more.

   Thousands place changes (7 + 1 = 8). All digits to the right of the underlined place change to 0.

18. $5^2 + 2 \times 5$ *Exponent*
     $25 + 2 \times 5$ *Multiply*
     $25 + 10 = 35$ *Add*

19. $7 \cdot \sqrt{64} - 14 \cdot 2$
     $7 \cdot 8 - 14 \cdot 2$ *Multiply from*
     $56 - 14 \cdot 2$ *left to right*
     $56 - 28 = 28$ *Subtract*

20. *estimate*: $500+$500+$500+$400−$800 = $1100

   exact:

   Add the rent collected.

```
      $485
       500
       515
   +   425
     $1925
```

   Subtract expenses.

```
     $1925
   −   785
     $1140    total amount
```

21. *estimate*: 60,000 ÷ 500 = 120 days

   exact

   Divide the total number of personal computers by the number of personal computers assembled each day.

```
           118
   472)55,696
       47 2
        8 49
        4 72
        3 776
        3 776
            0
```

   It would take 118 work days.

22. *estimate*: $1000 − $700 − $200 − $70 = $30

   exact: $1108 − $690 − $185 − $68 = $165

23. *estimate*: (100 × 4) + (100 × 4) = 800 ovens

   exact:

118	self-cleaning ovens per hour
× 4	hours
472	self-cleaning ovens

139	standard ovens per hour
× 4	hours
556	standard ovens

472	self-cleaning ovens
+ 556	standard ovens
1028	total ovens

24. (1) Locate the place to be rounded and underline it.
(2) Look only at the next digit to the right. If this digit is 4 or less, do not change the underlined digit. If the digit is 5 or more, increase the underlined digit by 1.
(3) Change all digits to the right of the underlined place to zeros.

Each person's example will vary.

25. (1) Read the problem carefully.
(2) Work out a plan.
(3) Estimate a reasonable answer.
(4) Solve the problem being certain to check your work.

Chapter 2

MULTIPLYING AND DIVIDING FRACTIONS

2.1 Basics of Fractions

2.1 Margin Exercises

1. **(a)** The figure has 5 equal parts.
   3 parts are shaded;
   $$\frac{3}{5}$$
   2 parts are unshaded.
   $$\frac{2}{5}$$

   (b) The figure has 6 equal parts.
   1 part is shaded;
   $$\frac{1}{6}$$
   5 parts are unshaded.
   $$\frac{5}{6}$$

   (c) The figure has 8 equal parts.
   7 parts are shaded;
   $$\frac{7}{8}$$
   1 part is unshaded.
   $$\frac{1}{8}$$

2. **(a)** An area equal to 8 of the $\frac{1}{7}$ parts is shaded.
   $$\frac{8}{7}$$

   (b) An area equal to 7 of the $\frac{1}{4}$ parts is shaded.
   $$\frac{7}{4}$$

3. **(a)** $\frac{2}{3}$ ←numerator
   ←denominator

   (b) $\frac{1}{4}$ ←numerator
   ←denominator

   (c) $\frac{8}{5}$ ←numerator
   ←denominator

   (d) $\frac{5}{2}$ ←numerator
   ←denominator

   See the margin exercise art in the textbook.

4. **(a)** $\frac{3}{4}, \frac{5}{7}, \frac{1}{2}$ *Proper fractions, numerator smaller than denominator*

   (b) $\frac{8}{7}, \frac{6}{6}, \frac{2}{1}$ *Improper fractions, numerator equal to or greater than denominator*

2.1 Section Exercises

3. The figure has 3 equal parts.
   Two parts are shaded.
   $$\frac{2}{3}$$
   One part is unshaded.
   $$\frac{1}{3}$$

7. There are 11 coins and 2 are dimes.
   $$\frac{2}{11}$$

11. There are 71 cars that make up a freight train.
    $71 - 58 = 13$ are *not* boxcars.
    $$\frac{13}{71}$$

15. $\frac{12}{7}$ ← numerator
    ← denominator

19. Proper fractions:
    $$\frac{3}{4}, \frac{9}{11}, \frac{7}{15}$$
    Improper fractions:
    $$\frac{3}{2}, \frac{5}{5}, \frac{19}{18}$$

23. The fraction $\frac{9}{16}$ represents *9* of the *16* equal parts into which a whole is divided.

27. $7 \cdot 2 \cdot 0$
    $14 \cdot 0 = 0$

31. $209 \div 11 = 19$

    $$\begin{array}{r} 19 \\ 11\overline{)209} \\ \underline{11} \\ 99 \\ \underline{99} \\ 0 \end{array}$$

2.2 Mixed Numbers

2.2 Margin Exercises

1. **(a)** The figure shows 1 whole object with 3 equal parts, all shaded, and a second whole with 2 parts shaded so 5 parts are shaded in all.

$$1\tfrac{2}{3} = \tfrac{5}{3}$$

(b) The figure shows 2 wholes with 4 equal parts, all shaded, and a third whole with one part shaded so 9 parts are shaded in all.

$$2\tfrac{1}{4} = \tfrac{9}{4}$$

2. **(a)** $3\tfrac{2}{3}$ $3 \cdot 3 = 9$
 $3\tfrac{2}{3}$ $9 + 2 = 11$
 $3\tfrac{2}{3} = \tfrac{11}{3}$

 (b) $4\tfrac{3}{8}$ $4 \cdot 8 = 32$
          $32 + 3 = 35$
 $4\tfrac{3}{8} = \tfrac{35}{8}$

 (c) $5\tfrac{3}{4}$ $5 \cdot 4 = 20$
 $5\tfrac{3}{4}$ $20 + 3 = 23$
 $5\tfrac{3}{4} = \tfrac{23}{4}$

 (d) $8\tfrac{5}{6}$ $8 \cdot 6 = 48$
 $8\tfrac{5}{6}$ $48 + 5 = 53$
 $8\tfrac{5}{6} = \tfrac{53}{6}$

3. **(a)** $\tfrac{5}{2}$ $2 \leftarrow$ whole number
 $2\overline{)5}$
 $\underline{4}$
 $1 \leftarrow$ remainder
 $\tfrac{5}{2} = 2\tfrac{1}{2}$

 (b) $\tfrac{15}{4}$ $3 \leftarrow$ whole number
 $4\overline{)15}$
 $\underline{12}$
 $3 \leftarrow$ remainder
 $\tfrac{15}{4} = 3\tfrac{3}{4}$

 (c) $\tfrac{35}{5}$ $7 \leftarrow$ whole number
 $5\overline{)35}$
 $\underline{35}$
 $0 \leftarrow$ remainder
 $\tfrac{35}{5} = 7$

 (d) $\tfrac{75}{8}$ $9 \leftarrow$ whole number
 $8\overline{)75}$
 $\underline{72}$
 $3 \leftarrow$ remainder
 $\tfrac{75}{8} = 9\tfrac{3}{8}$

2.2 Section Exercises

3. $2\tfrac{3}{4}$ $2 \cdot 4 = 8$
       $8 + 3 = 11$
 $2\tfrac{3}{4} = \tfrac{11}{4}$

7. $6\tfrac{3}{4}$ $6 \cdot 4 = 24$
       $24 + 3 = 27$
 $6\tfrac{3}{4} = \tfrac{27}{4}$

11. $6\tfrac{1}{3}$ $6 \cdot 3 = 18$
       $18 + 1 = 19$
 $6\tfrac{1}{3} = \tfrac{19}{3}$

15. $10\tfrac{3}{4}$ $10 \cdot 4 = 40$
        $40 + 3 = 43$
 $10\tfrac{3}{4} = \tfrac{43}{4}$

19. $8\tfrac{4}{5}$ $8 \cdot 5 = 40$
       $40 + 4 = 44$
 $8\tfrac{4}{5} = \tfrac{44}{5}$

23. $22\tfrac{7}{8}$ $22 \cdot 8 = 176$
        $176 + 7 = 183$
 $22\tfrac{7}{8} = \tfrac{183}{8}$

27. $17\tfrac{14}{15}$ $17 \cdot 15 = 255$
         $255 + 14 = 269$
 $17\tfrac{14}{15} = \tfrac{269}{15}$

Section 2.3   Factors

31. $\dfrac{8}{3}$

$$\begin{array}{r} 2 \leftarrow \text{whole number} \\ 3\overline{)8} \\ \underline{6} \\ 2 \leftarrow \text{remainder} \end{array}$$

$\dfrac{8}{3} = 2\dfrac{2}{3}$

35. $\dfrac{60}{12}$

$$\begin{array}{r} 5 \leftarrow \text{whole number} \\ 12\overline{)60} \\ \underline{60} \\ 0 \leftarrow \text{remainder} \end{array}$$

$\dfrac{60}{12} = 5$

39. $\dfrac{19}{4}$

$$\begin{array}{r} 4 \leftarrow \text{whole number} \\ 4\overline{)19} \\ \underline{16} \\ 3 \leftarrow \text{remainder} \end{array}$$

$\dfrac{19}{4} = 4\dfrac{3}{4}$

43. $\dfrac{58}{5}$

$$\begin{array}{r} 11 \leftarrow \text{whole number} \\ 5\overline{)58} \\ \underline{5} \\ 8 \\ \underline{5} \\ 3 \leftarrow \text{remainder} \end{array}$$

$\dfrac{58}{5} = 11\dfrac{3}{5}$

47. $\dfrac{50}{7}$

$$\begin{array}{r} 7 \leftarrow \text{whole number} \\ 7\overline{)50} \\ \underline{49} \\ 1 \leftarrow \text{remainder} \end{array}$$

$\dfrac{50}{7} = 7\dfrac{1}{7}$

51. $\dfrac{123}{4}$

$$\begin{array}{r} 30 \leftarrow \text{whole number} \\ 4\overline{)123} \\ \underline{12} \\ 3 \\ \underline{0} \\ 3 \leftarrow \text{remainder} \end{array}$$

$\dfrac{123}{4} = 30\dfrac{3}{4}$

55. Multiply the denominator by the whole number and add the numerator. The result becomes the new numerator which is placed over the original denominator.

$$2\dfrac{1}{2} = \dfrac{2 \times 2 + 1}{2} = \dfrac{5}{2}$$

59. $333\dfrac{1}{3}$ $333 \cdot 3 = 999$
$999 + 1 = 1000$

$333\dfrac{1}{3} = \dfrac{1000}{3}$

63. $4^2 + 2^2$ *Exponents*
$16 + 4 = 20$

67. $6 \cdot 3^2 - 5$ *Exponent*
$6 \cdot 9 - 5$ *Multiply*
$54 - 5 = 49$ *Subtract*

2.3 Factors

2.3 Margin Exercises

1. (a) Factorizations of 9:
$1 \cdot 9 = 9$ $3 \cdot 3 = 9$
The factors are 1, 3, and 9.

(b) Factorizations of 18:
$1 \cdot 18 = 18$ $2 \cdot 9 = 18$
$3 \cdot 6 = 18$
The factors are 1, 2, 3, 6, 9, and 18.

(c) Factorizations of 36:
$1 \cdot 36 = 36$ $2 \cdot 18 = 36$
$3 \cdot 12 = 36$ $4 \cdot 9 = 36$
$6 \cdot 6 = 36$
The factors are 1, 2, 3, 4, 6, 9, 12, 18, and 36.

(d) Factorizations of 80:
$1 \cdot 80 = 80$ $2 \cdot 40 = 80$
$4 \cdot 20 = 80$ $5 \cdot 16 = 80$
$8 \cdot 10 = 80$
The factors are 1, 2, 4, 5, 8, 10, 16, 20, 40, and 80.

2. 2, 5, 11, 13, and 19 each have no factor other than themselves or 1; 4, 6, 8, 10, 28, 36, and 42 each have a factor of 2; 21, 27, and 33 have a factor of 3.
So 4, 6, 8, 10, 21, 27, 28, 33, 36, and 42 are composite.

3. 2, 3, 7, 13, 19, and 29 are prime because they are divisible only by themselves and 1.

4. (a) $8 \div 2 = 4$
$4 \div 2 = 2$ *prime*
$8 = 2 \cdot 2 \cdot 2$

(b) $14 \div 2 = 7$ *prime*
$14 = 2 \cdot 7$

(c) $18 \div 2 = 9$
$9 \div 3 = 3$ *prime*
$18 = 2 \cdot 3 \cdot 3$

(d) $30 \div 2 = 15$
$15 \div 3 = 5$ *prime*
$30 = 2 \cdot 3 \cdot 5$

5. (a) $2 \overline{) 18}^{\,9}$

$3 \overline{) 9}^{\,3}$

$3 \overline{) 3}^{\,1}$ *quotient is* 1

$18 = 2 \cdot 3 \cdot 3 = 2 \cdot 3^2$

(b) $2 \overline{) 36}^{\,18}$

$2 \overline{) 18}^{\,9}$

$3 \overline{) 9}^{\,3}$

$3 \overline{) 3}^{\,1}$ *quotient is* 1

$36 = 2 \cdot 2 \cdot 3 \cdot 3 = 2^2 \cdot 3^2$

(c) $2 \overline{) 60}^{\,30}$

$2 \overline{) 30}^{\,15}$

$3 \overline{) 15}^{\,5}$

$5 \overline{) 5}^{\,1}$

$60 = 2 \cdot 2 \cdot 3 \cdot 5 = 2^2 \cdot 3 \cdot 5$

(d) $2 \overline{) 126}^{\,63}$

$3 \overline{) 63}^{\,21}$

$3 \overline{) 21}^{\,7}$

$7 \overline{) 7}^{\,1}$

$126 = 2 \cdot 3 \cdot 3 \cdot 7 = 2 \cdot 3^2 \cdot 7$

6. (a) $2 \overline{) 50}^{\,25}$

$5 \overline{) 25}^{\,5}$

$5 \overline{) 5}^{\,1}$

$50 = 2 \cdot 5 \cdot 5 = 2 \cdot 5^2$

(b) $2 \overline{) 88}^{\,44}$

$2 \overline{) 44}^{\,22}$

$2 \overline{) 22}^{\,11}$

$11 \overline{) 11}^{\,1}$

$88 = 2 \cdot 2 \cdot 2 \cdot 11 = 2^3 \cdot 11$

(c) $2 \overline{) 90}^{\,45}$

$3 \overline{) 45}^{\,15}$

$3 \overline{) 15}^{\,5}$

$5 \overline{) 5}^{\,1}$

$90 = 2 \cdot 3 \cdot 3 \cdot 5 = 2 \cdot 3^2 \cdot 5$

Section 2.3   Factors

(d)
$$\frac{75}{2\overline{)150}}$$

$$\frac{25}{3\overline{)75}}$$

$$\frac{5}{5\overline{)25}}$$

$$\frac{1}{5\overline{)5}}$$

$150 = 2 \cdot 3 \cdot 5 \cdot 5 = 2 \cdot 3 \cdot 5^2$

(e)
$$\frac{140}{2\overline{)280}}$$

$$\frac{70}{2\overline{)140}}$$

$$\frac{35}{2\overline{)70}}$$

$$\frac{7}{5\overline{)35}}$$

$$\frac{1}{7\overline{)7}}$$

$280 = 2 \cdot 2 \cdot 2 \cdot 5 \cdot 7 = 2^3 \cdot 5 \cdot 7$

7. (a)

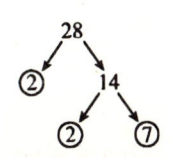

$28 = 2 \cdot 2 \cdot 7 = 2^2 \cdot 7$

(b)

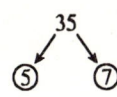

$35 = 5 \cdot 7$

(c)

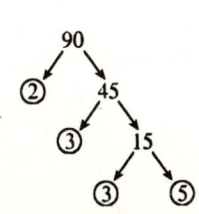

$90 = 2 \cdot 3 \cdot 3 \cdot 5 = 2 \cdot 3^2 \cdot 5$

2.3   Section Exercises

3. Factorizations of 6:
$$1 \cdot 6 = 6$$
$$2 \cdot 3 = 6$$

The factors of 6 are 1, 2, 3, and 6.

7. Factorizations of 18:
$$1 \cdot 18 = 18 \quad 2 \cdot 9 = 18$$
$$3 \cdot 6 = 18$$

The factors of 18 are 1, 2, 3, 6, 9, and 18.

11. Factorizations of 64:
$$1 \cdot 64 = 64 \quad 2 \cdot 32 = 64$$
$$4 \cdot 16 = 64 \quad 8 \cdot 8 = 64$$

The factors of 64 are 1, 2, 4, 8, 16, 32, and 64.

15. 2 is prime. It is divisible only by 2 and 1.

19. 11 is prime. It is only divisible by itself and 1.

23. 25 is divisible by 5. 25 is composite.

27. 45 is divisible by 3 and 5. 45 is composite.

31.

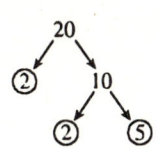

$20 = 2 \cdot 2 \cdot 5 = 2^2 \cdot 5$

35.

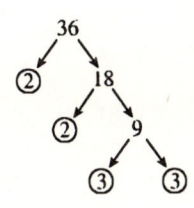

$36 = 2 \cdot 2 \cdot 3 \cdot 3 = 2^2 \cdot 3^2$

39.

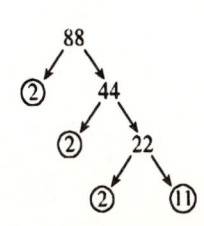

$88 = 2 \cdot 2 \cdot 2 \cdot 11 = 2^3 \cdot 11$

43.

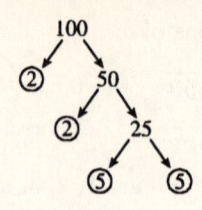

[factor tree: 100 → 2, 50; 50 → 2, 25; 25 → 5, 5]

$100 = 2 \cdot 2 \cdot 5 \cdot 5 = 2^2 \cdot 5^2$

47.

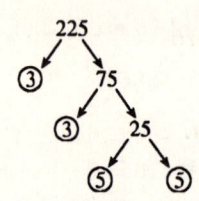

[factor tree: 225 → 3, 75; 75 → 3, 25; 25 → 5, 5]

$225 = 3 \cdot 3 \cdot 5 \cdot 5 = 3^2 \cdot 5^2$

51.

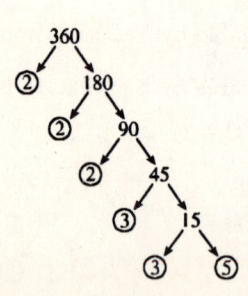

[factor tree: 360 → 2, 180; 180 → 2, 90; 90 → 2, 45; 45 → 3, 15; 15 → 3, 5]

$360 = 2 \cdot 2 \cdot 2 \cdot 3 \cdot 3 \cdot 5 = 2^3 \cdot 3^2 \cdot 5$

55. $2^3 = 2 \cdot 2 \cdot 2 = 8$

59. $3^4 = 3 \cdot 3 \cdot 3 \cdot 3 = 81$

63. $5^3 \cdot 3^2 = 5 \cdot 5 \cdot 5 \cdot 3 \cdot 3 = 125 \cdot 9 = 1125$

67.

[factor tree: 280 → 2, 140; 140 → 2, 70; 70 → 2, 35; 35 → 5, 7]

$280 = 2 \cdot 2 \cdot 2 \cdot 5 \cdot 7 = 2^3 \cdot 5 \cdot 7$

71.

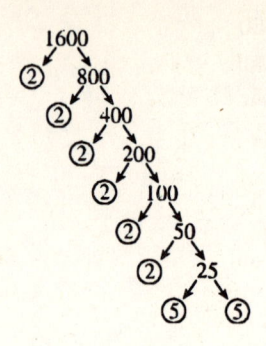

[factor tree: 1600 → 2, 800; 800 → 2, 400; 400 → 2, 200; 200 → 2, 100; 100 → 2, 50; 50 → 2, 25; 25 → 5, 5]

$1600 = 2 \cdot 2 \cdot 2 \cdot 2 \cdot 2 \cdot 2 \cdot 5 \cdot 5 = 2^6 \cdot 5^2$

75. $6 \cdot 1 \cdot 8$
$(6 \cdot 1) \cdot 8 = 6 \cdot 8 = 48$
or
$6 \cdot (1 \cdot 8) = 6 \cdot 8 = 48$

79. $5 \overline{)13^3 5}\ \ \ \ 2\ 7$ $135 \div 5 = 27$

2.4 Writing a Fraction in Lowest Terms

2.4 Margin Exercises

1. (a) 14, 20; 2
    $14 = 2 \cdot 7 \quad\quad 20 = 2 \cdot 10$
    Yes.

  (b) 32, 48; 16
    $32 = 2 \cdot 16 \quad\quad 48 = 3 \cdot 16$
    Yes.

  (c) 24, 36; 8
    $24 = 8 \cdot 3$ but 8 is not factor of 36
    No.

  (d) 56, 73; 1
    $56 = 56 \cdot 1 \quad\quad 73 = 73 \cdot 1$
    Yes.

2. (a) $\dfrac{2}{3}$

    2 and 3 have no common factor other than 1.
    Yes.

  (b) $\dfrac{4}{16}$

    4 and 16 have a common factor 4.
    No.

Section 2.4 Writing a Fraction in Lowest Terms

(c) $\dfrac{9}{11}$

9 and 11 have no common factor other than 1.
Yes.

(d) $\dfrac{15}{51}$

15 and 51 have a common factor 3.
No.

3. (a) $\dfrac{5}{10} = \dfrac{5 \div 5}{10 \div 5} = \dfrac{1}{2}$

(b) $\dfrac{9}{12} = \dfrac{9 \div 3}{12 \div 3} = \dfrac{3}{4}$

(c) $\dfrac{24}{30} = \dfrac{24 \div 6}{30 \div 6} = \dfrac{4}{5}$

(d) $\dfrac{15}{40} = \dfrac{15 \div 5}{40 \div 5} = \dfrac{3}{8}$

(e) $\dfrac{32}{80} = \dfrac{32 \div 16}{80 \div 16} = \dfrac{2}{5}$

4. (a) $\dfrac{16}{48} = \dfrac{\cancel{2} \cdot \cancel{2} \cdot \cancel{2} \cdot \cancel{2}}{\cancel{2} \cdot \cancel{2} \cdot \cancel{2} \cdot \cancel{2} \cdot 3} = \dfrac{1}{3}$

(b) $\dfrac{28}{60} = \dfrac{\cancel{2} \cdot \cancel{2} \cdot 7}{\cancel{2} \cdot \cancel{2} \cdot 3 \cdot 5} = \dfrac{1 \cdot 1 \cdot 7}{1 \cdot 1 \cdot 3 \cdot 5} = \dfrac{7}{15}$

(c) $\dfrac{74}{111} = \dfrac{2 \cdot \cancel{37}}{3 \cdot \cancel{37}} = \dfrac{2}{3}$

(d) $\dfrac{124}{340} = \dfrac{\cancel{2} \cdot \cancel{2} \cdot 31}{\cancel{2} \cdot \cancel{2} \cdot 5 \cdot 17} = \dfrac{1 \cdot 1 \cdot 31}{1 \cdot 1 \cdot 5 \cdot 17} = \dfrac{31}{85}$

5. (a) $\tfrac{1}{2}$ and $\tfrac{2}{4}$

$\dfrac{1 \times 8}{2 \times 8} = \dfrac{8}{16} \qquad \dfrac{2 \times 4}{4 \times 4} = \dfrac{8}{16}$

$\tfrac{1}{2}$ and $\tfrac{2}{4}$ are equivalent because they both equal $\tfrac{8}{16}$.

(b) $\tfrac{3}{4}$ and $\tfrac{2}{3}$

$\dfrac{3}{4} \qquad \dfrac{2}{3} \qquad \begin{array}{l} 4 \cdot 2 = 8 \\ 3 \cdot 3 = 9 \end{array}$

The cross products are not equal, so the fractions are not equivalent.

(c) $\dfrac{6}{50}$ and $\dfrac{9}{75}$

$\dfrac{6}{50} \qquad \dfrac{9}{75} \qquad \begin{array}{l} 9 \cdot 50 = 450 \\ 6 \cdot 75 = 450 \end{array}$

The cross products are equal, so the fractions are equivalent.

(d) $\dfrac{12}{22}$ and $\dfrac{18}{32}$

$\dfrac{12}{22} \qquad \dfrac{18}{32} \qquad \begin{array}{l} 22 \cdot 18 = 396 \\ 12 \cdot 32 = 384 \end{array}$

The cross products are not equal, so the fractions are not equivalent.

2.4 Section Exercises

3. $\dfrac{32}{48} = \dfrac{32 \div 16}{48 \div 16} = \dfrac{2}{3}$

7. $\dfrac{36}{42} = \dfrac{36 \div 6}{42 \div 6} = \dfrac{6}{7}$

11. $\dfrac{180}{210} = \dfrac{180 \div 30}{210 \div 30} = \dfrac{6}{7}$

15. $\dfrac{12}{600} = \dfrac{12 \div 12}{600 \div 12} = \dfrac{1}{50}$

19. $\dfrac{60}{108} = \dfrac{60 \div 12}{108 \div 12} = \dfrac{5}{9}$

23. $\dfrac{35}{40} = \dfrac{\cancel{5} \cdot 7}{2 \cdot 2 \cdot 2 \cdot \cancel{5}} = \dfrac{7 \cdot 1}{2 \cdot 2 \cdot 2 \cdot 1} = \dfrac{7}{8}$

27. $\dfrac{36}{12} = \dfrac{\cancel{2} \cdot \cancel{2} \cdot 3 \cdot \cancel{3}}{\cancel{2} \cdot \cancel{2} \cdot \cancel{3}} = \dfrac{1 \cdot 1 \cdot 3 \cdot 1}{1 \cdot 1 \cdot 1} = 3$

31. $\dfrac{1}{2}$ and $\dfrac{17}{34} \qquad \begin{array}{l} 2 \cdot 17 = 34 \\ 1 \cdot 34 = 34 \end{array}$

The cross products are equal, so the fractions are equivalent.

35. $\dfrac{15}{24}$ and $\dfrac{35}{52} \qquad \begin{array}{l} 15 \cdot 52 = 780 \\ 24 \cdot 35 = 840 \end{array}$

The cross products are not equal, so the fractions are not equivalent.

39. $\dfrac{7}{52}$ and $\dfrac{9}{40} \qquad \begin{array}{l} 9 \cdot 52 = 468 \\ 7 \cdot 40 = 280 \end{array}$

The cross products are not equal, so the fractions are not equivalent.

43. A fraction is in lowest terms when the numerator and the denominator have no common factors other than 1. Three examples are $\frac{1}{2}$, $\frac{3}{8}$, and $\frac{2}{3}$.

47. $\dfrac{356}{178} = \dfrac{356 \div 178}{178 \div 178} = \dfrac{2}{1} = 2$

51. Factorizations of 64:

$$1 \cdot 64 \quad 2 \cdot 32$$
$$4 \cdot 16 \quad 8 \cdot 8$$

The factors of 64 are 1, 2, 4, 8, 16, 32, and 64.

2.5 Multiplication of Fractions

2.5 Margin Exercises

1. $\frac{1}{4}$ of $\frac{1}{2}$ as read from the figures is the shaded part of the second figure. One of eight equal parts is shaded, or $\frac{1}{8}$.

$$\frac{1}{4} \cdot \frac{1}{2} = \frac{1}{8}$$

2. (a) $\dfrac{3}{4} \cdot \dfrac{1}{2} = \dfrac{3 \cdot 1}{4 \cdot 2} = \dfrac{3}{8}$

(b) $\dfrac{2}{5} \cdot \dfrac{2}{3} = \dfrac{2 \cdot 2}{5 \cdot 3} = \dfrac{4}{15}$

(c) $\dfrac{1}{4} \cdot \dfrac{5}{9} \cdot \dfrac{1}{2} = \dfrac{1 \cdot 5 \cdot 1}{4 \cdot 9 \cdot 2} = \dfrac{5}{72}$

(d) $\dfrac{1}{2} \cdot \dfrac{3}{4} \cdot \dfrac{3}{8} = \dfrac{1 \cdot 3 \cdot 3}{2 \cdot 4 \cdot 8} = \dfrac{9}{64}$

3. (a) $\dfrac{\cancel{3}^{1}}{\cancel{4}_{2}} \cdot \dfrac{\cancel{2}^{1}}{\cancel{3}_{1}} = \dfrac{1 \cdot 1}{2 \cdot 1} = \dfrac{1}{2}$

(b) $\dfrac{\cancel{6}^{2}}{\cancel{11}_{1}} \cdot \dfrac{\cancel{33}^{3}}{\cancel{21}_{7}} = \dfrac{2 \cdot 3}{1 \cdot 7} = \dfrac{6}{7}$

(c) $\dfrac{\cancel{20}^{1}}{4} \cdot \dfrac{\cancel{3}^{1}}{\cancel{10}_{2}} \cdot \dfrac{1}{\cancel{3}_{1}} = \dfrac{1 \cdot 1 \cdot 1}{4 \cdot 2 \cdot 1} = \dfrac{1}{8}$

(d) $\dfrac{\cancel{18}^{1}}{17} \cdot \dfrac{1}{\cancel{36}_{\cancel{2}_{1}}} \cdot \dfrac{\cancel{2}^{1}}{3} = \dfrac{1 \cdot 1 \cdot 1}{17 \cdot 1 \cdot 3} = \dfrac{1}{51}$

4. (a) $8 \cdot \dfrac{1}{8} = \dfrac{\cancel{8}^{1} \cdot 1}{1 \cdot \cancel{8}_{1}} = \dfrac{1}{1} = 1$

(b) $12 \cdot \dfrac{3}{4} \cdot \dfrac{5}{3} = \dfrac{\cancel{12}^{3} \cdot \cancel{3}^{1} \cdot 5}{\cancel{4}_{1} \cdot \cancel{3}_{1}} = 15$

(c) $\dfrac{7}{10} \cdot 50 = \dfrac{7}{\cancel{10}_{1}} \cdot \dfrac{\cancel{50}^{5}}{1} = \dfrac{7 \cdot 5}{1 \cdot 1} = \dfrac{35}{1} = 35$

(d) $\dfrac{5}{11} \cdot 99 \cdot \dfrac{3}{25} = \dfrac{\cancel{5}^{1}}{\cancel{11}_{1}} \cdot \dfrac{\cancel{99}^{9}}{1} \cdot \dfrac{3}{\cancel{25}_{5}}$

$\qquad = \dfrac{1 \cdot 9 \cdot 3}{1 \cdot 1 \cdot 5}$

$\qquad = \dfrac{27}{5}$ or $5\dfrac{2}{5}$

5. (a) $area = length \cdot width$

$\qquad = \dfrac{\cancel{2}^{1}}{4} \cdot \dfrac{1}{\cancel{2}_{1}}$

$\qquad = \dfrac{1}{4}$ square yard

(b) $area = length \cdot width$

$\qquad = \dfrac{7}{8} \cdot \dfrac{1}{3}$

$\qquad = \dfrac{7}{24}$ square inch

(c) $area = length \cdot width$

$\qquad = \dfrac{7}{\cancel{8}_{1}} \cdot \dfrac{\cancel{8}^{1}}{8}$

$\qquad = \dfrac{7}{8}$ square mile

2.5 Section Exercises

3. $\dfrac{2}{5} \times \dfrac{2}{3} = \dfrac{2 \cdot 2}{5 \cdot 3} = \dfrac{4}{15}$

7. $\dfrac{5}{6} \cdot \dfrac{12}{25} \cdot \dfrac{3}{4} = \dfrac{\cancel{5}^{1}}{\cancel{6}_{1}} \cdot \dfrac{\cancel{12}^{\cancel{2}^{1}}}{\cancel{25}_{5}} \cdot \dfrac{3}{\cancel{4}_{2}} = \dfrac{1 \cdot 1 \cdot 3}{1 \cdot 5 \cdot 2} = \dfrac{3}{10}$

11. $\dfrac{9}{22} \cdot \dfrac{11}{16} = \dfrac{9}{\cancel{22}_{2}} \cdot \dfrac{\cancel{11}^{1}}{16} = \dfrac{9}{32}$

15. $\dfrac{14}{25} \cdot \dfrac{65}{48} \cdot \dfrac{15}{28} = \dfrac{\cancel{14}^{1}}{\cancel{25}_{5}} \cdot \dfrac{\cancel{65}^{13}}{\cancel{48}_{16}} \cdot \dfrac{\cancel{15}^{5}}{\cancel{28}_{2}} = \dfrac{1 \cdot 13 \cdot 1}{1 \cdot 16 \cdot 2} = \dfrac{13}{32}$

Section 2.6 Applications of Multiplication

19. $5 \cdot \dfrac{3}{5} = \dfrac{\cancel{5}^{1}}{1} \cdot \dfrac{3}{\cancel{5}_{1}} = 3$

23. $32 \cdot \dfrac{3}{8} = \dfrac{\cancel{32}^{4} \cdot 3}{1 \cdot \cancel{8}_{1}} = 12$

27. $100 \cdot \dfrac{21}{50} \cdot \dfrac{3}{4} = \dfrac{\cancel{100}^{\cancel{2}^{1}}}{1} \cdot \dfrac{21}{\cancel{50}_{1}} \cdot \dfrac{3}{\cancel{4}_{2}} = \dfrac{63}{2} = 31\tfrac{1}{2}$

31. $\dfrac{3}{4} \cdot 363 = \dfrac{3 \cdot 363}{4 \cdot 1} = \dfrac{1089}{4} = 272\tfrac{1}{4}$

35. $\dfrac{54}{38} \cdot 684 \cdot \dfrac{5}{6} = \dfrac{\cancel{54}^{9}}{\cancel{38}_{1}} \cdot \dfrac{\cancel{684}^{18}}{1} \cdot \dfrac{5}{\cancel{6}_{1}}$

$= \dfrac{9 \cdot 18 \cdot 5}{1 \cdot 1 \cdot 1}$

$= \dfrac{810}{1} = 810$

39. Multiply the length and width.

$\dfrac{3}{4} \cdot 12 = \dfrac{3}{\cancel{4}_{1}} \cdot \dfrac{\cancel{12}^{3}}{1} = 9$

The area is 9 square yards.

43. Multiply the numerators and multiply the denominators. An example is

$\dfrac{3}{4} \cdot \dfrac{1}{2} = \dfrac{3 \cdot 1}{4 \cdot 2} = \dfrac{3}{8}.$

47. Multiply the length and the width.

$2 \cdot \dfrac{1}{2} = \dfrac{\cancel{2}^{1}}{1} \cdot \dfrac{1}{\cancel{2}_{1}} = 1$ square mile

51. Multiply to find the number of cars that enter the garage in a 365-day year.

```
      795
    × 365
    3 975
    47 70
   238 5
   290,175
```

In a 365-day year, 290,175 cars enter the garage.

2.6 Applications of Multiplication

2.6 Margin Exercises

1. (a) Find the number of extended warranties sold by multiplying $\tfrac{1}{3}$ and 8397.

$\dfrac{1}{3} \cdot 8397 = \dfrac{1}{\cancel{3}_{1}} \cdot \dfrac{\cancel{8397}^{2799}}{1}$

$= 2799$

They sold 2799 extended warranties.

(b) To find her retirement income, multiply $\tfrac{5}{8}$ and $48,000.

$\dfrac{5}{8} \cdot 48,000 = \dfrac{5}{\cancel{8}_{1}} \cdot \dfrac{\cancel{48,000}^{6000}}{1} = 30,000$

She will receive $30,000 as retirement income.

2. The number paid by the third party is $\tfrac{3}{16}$ of 2816.

$\dfrac{3}{16} \cdot 2816 = \dfrac{3}{\cancel{16}_{1}} \cdot \dfrac{\cancel{2816}^{176}}{1} = 528$

The third party paid for 528 prescriptions.

3. Find $\tfrac{3}{4}$ of $\tfrac{1}{3}$.

$\dfrac{3}{4} \cdot \dfrac{1}{3} = \dfrac{\cancel{3}^{1}}{4} \cdot \dfrac{1}{\cancel{3}_{1}} = \dfrac{1}{4}$

In this community, $\tfrac{1}{4}$ of the residents speak Spanish.

2.6 Section Exercises

3. Multiply the length and width.

$\dfrac{4}{3} \cdot \dfrac{1}{2} = \dfrac{\cancel{4}^{2} \cdot 1}{3 \cdot \cancel{2}_{1}} = \dfrac{2}{3}$

The area of the rectangle is $\tfrac{2}{3}$ square foot.

7. Erica needs to earn $\tfrac{5}{8}$ of $2800 during the summer.

$\dfrac{5}{8} \cdot 2800 = \dfrac{5 \cdot \cancel{2800}^{350}}{\cancel{8}_{1} \cdot 1} = 1750$

She earns $1750 during the summer.

11. $\frac{5}{12}$ of the 780 runners are women.

$$\frac{5}{12} \cdot 780 = \frac{5 \cdot \cancel{780}^{65}}{\cancel{12} \cdot 1} = 325$$

325 runners are women.

15. From Exercise 13 the total income is $38,000. The circle graph shows that $\frac{1}{5}$ of the income is for rent.

$$\frac{1}{5} \cdot 38,000 = \frac{1}{\cancel{5}} \cdot \frac{\cancel{38,000}^{7600}}{1} = 7600$$

The amount of their rent is $7600.

19. The correct solution is

$$\frac{9}{10} \times \frac{20}{21} = \frac{\cancel{9}^3}{\cancel{10}} \cdot \frac{\cancel{20}^2}{\cancel{21}_7} = \frac{6}{7}.$$

23. First multiply $\frac{2}{3}$ and 27,000 to find the number of her votes from senior citizens.

$$\frac{2}{3} \cdot 27,000 = \frac{2}{\cancel{3}} \cdot \frac{\cancel{27,000}^{9000}}{1} = 18,000$$

To find the votes from other than senior citizens, subtract:

$$27,000 - 18,000 = 9000 \text{ votes.}$$

27. Each carton contains 18 test kits.
We must find out how many eighteens there are in 1332, and this is done by division.

$$\begin{array}{r} 74 \\ 18\overline{)1332} \\ \underline{126} \\ 72 \\ \underline{72} \\ 0 \end{array}$$

74 cartons are needed.

2.7 Dividing Fractions

2.7 Margin Exercises

1. (a) $\frac{1}{4} \div \frac{3}{4} = \frac{1}{4} \cdot \frac{4}{3} = \frac{1 \cdot \cancel{4}^1}{\cancel{4} \cdot 3} = \frac{1}{3}$

(b) $\frac{3}{8} \div \frac{5}{8} = \frac{3}{8} \cdot \frac{8}{5} = \frac{3 \cdot \cancel{8}^1}{\cancel{8} \cdot 5} = \frac{3}{5}$

(c) $\frac{\frac{9}{10}}{\frac{3}{5}} = \frac{9}{10} \div \frac{3}{5} = \frac{9}{10} \cdot \frac{5}{3} = \frac{\cancel{9}^3 \cdot \cancel{5}^1}{\cancel{10}_2 \cdot \cancel{3}_1} = \frac{3}{2} = 1\frac{1}{2}$

(d) $\frac{\frac{5}{6}}{\frac{25}{24}} = \frac{5}{6} \div \frac{25}{24} = \frac{\cancel{5}^1 \cdot \cancel{24}^4}{\cancel{6}_1 \cdot \cancel{25}_5} = \frac{4}{5}$

2. (a) $6 \div \frac{2}{3} = \frac{6}{1} \cdot \frac{3}{2} = \frac{\cancel{6}^3 \cdot 3}{1 \cdot \cancel{2}_1} = 9$

(b) $9 \div \frac{3}{4} = \frac{9}{1} \cdot \frac{4}{3} = \frac{\cancel{9}^3 \cdot 4}{1 \cdot \cancel{3}_1} = 12$

(c) $\frac{7}{8} \div 3 = \frac{7}{8} \div \frac{3}{1} = \frac{7}{8} \cdot \frac{1}{3} = \frac{7}{24}$

(d) $\frac{7}{10} \div 3 = \frac{7}{10} \div \frac{3}{1} = \frac{7}{10} \cdot \frac{1}{3} = \frac{7}{30}$

3. (a) Divide the amount of cleaner (18 quarts) by the size of the spray bottle $\left(\frac{2}{3} \text{ quart}\right)$.

$$18 \div \frac{2}{3} = \frac{\cancel{18}^9}{1} \cdot \frac{3}{\cancel{2}_1} = \frac{9 \cdot 3}{1 \cdot 1} = 27$$

The spray bottle can be filled 27 times.

(b) Divide the amount of iced tea (24 quarts) by the size of the glass $\left(\frac{3}{4} \text{ quart}\right)$.

$$24 \div \frac{3}{4} = \frac{\cancel{24}^8}{1} \cdot \frac{4}{\cancel{3}_1} = \frac{8 \cdot 4}{1 \cdot 1} = 32$$

32 glasses can be filled.

4. (a) Divide the fraction of total revenue that the lottery pays by the number of winners.

$$\frac{7}{8} \div 14 = \frac{7}{8} \div \frac{14}{1} = \frac{\cancel{7}^1}{8} \cdot \frac{1}{\cancel{14}_2} = \frac{1}{16}$$

Each winner receives $\frac{1}{16}$ of the total revenue.

(b) This problem can be solved by dividing $\frac{1}{3}$ by 4.

$$\frac{1}{3} \div 4 = \frac{1}{3} \div \frac{4}{1} = \frac{1}{3} \cdot \frac{1}{4} = \frac{1}{12}$$

Each student will receive $\frac{1}{12}$ of the scholarship money.

2.7 Section Exercises

3. $\dfrac{7}{8} \div \dfrac{1}{3} = \dfrac{7}{8} \cdot \dfrac{3}{1} = \dfrac{21}{8} = 2\dfrac{5}{8}$

7. $\dfrac{7}{12} \div \dfrac{14}{15} = \dfrac{\cancel{7}^{1}}{\cancel{12}_{4}} \cdot \dfrac{\cancel{15}^{5}}{\cancel{14}_{2}} = \dfrac{1 \cdot 5}{4 \cdot 2} = \dfrac{5}{8}$

11. $\dfrac{\frac{36}{35}}{\frac{15}{14}} = \dfrac{36}{35} \div \dfrac{15}{14} = \dfrac{\cancel{36}^{12}}{\cancel{35}_{5}} \cdot \dfrac{\cancel{14}^{2}}{\cancel{15}_{5}} = \dfrac{12 \cdot 2}{5 \cdot 5} = \dfrac{24}{25}$

15. $\dfrac{15}{\frac{2}{3}} = 15 \div \dfrac{2}{3} = \dfrac{15}{1} \div \dfrac{2}{3} = \dfrac{15}{1} \cdot \dfrac{3}{2} = \dfrac{45}{2} = 22\dfrac{1}{2}$

19. $\tfrac{8}{9}$ of an acre divided into 4 parts:

$\dfrac{8}{9} \div 4 = \dfrac{8}{9} \div \dfrac{4}{1} = \dfrac{\cancel{8}^{2}}{9} \cdot \dfrac{1}{\cancel{4}_{1}} = \dfrac{2 \cdot 1}{9 \cdot 1} = \dfrac{2}{9}$

Each child will get $\tfrac{2}{9}$ of an acre.

23. Divide the amount of eye drops by the amount needed for each dispenser.

$11 \div \dfrac{1}{8} = \dfrac{11}{1} \div \dfrac{1}{8} = \dfrac{11}{1} \cdot \dfrac{8}{1} = 88$

88 dispensers can be filled.

27. Divide the number of pounds of chocolate chips by the amount needed for each batch.

$9 \div \dfrac{3}{4} = \dfrac{9}{1} \div \dfrac{3}{4} = \dfrac{\cancel{9}^{3}}{1} \cdot \dfrac{4}{\cancel{3}_{1}} = \dfrac{12}{1} = 12$

You can make 12 batches of cookies.

31. The airplane has flown 756 miles which is $\tfrac{7}{8}$ of the distance to Phoenix.
To find the total distance, divide.

$756 \div \dfrac{7}{8} = \dfrac{\cancel{756}^{108}}{1} \cdot \dfrac{8}{\cancel{7}_{1}} = 864$ miles.

Since the airplane has already flown 756 miles, it must fly

$864 - 756 = 108$ miles.

35. $2\dfrac{3}{8}$ $2 \cdot 8 = 16$
$16 + 3 = 19$
$2\dfrac{3}{8} = \dfrac{19}{8}$

39. $120\dfrac{4}{5}$ $120 \cdot 5 = 600$
$600 + 4 = 604$
$120\dfrac{4}{5} = \dfrac{604}{5}$

2.8 Multiplication and Division of Mixed Numbers

2.8 Margin Exercises

1. (a) $2\dfrac{3}{4}$

$2\dfrac{3}{4}$ ← 3 is more than 2
      ← half of 4 is 2

$2\dfrac{3}{4}$ rounds up to 3.

(b) $6\dfrac{3}{8}$

$6\dfrac{3}{8}$ ← 3 is less than 4
      ← half of 8 is 4

$6\dfrac{3}{8}$ rounds to 6.

(c) $4\dfrac{2}{3}$

$4\dfrac{2}{3}$ ← 2 is more than $1\dfrac{1}{2}$
      ← half of 3 is $1\dfrac{1}{2}$

$4\dfrac{2}{3}$ rounds to 5.

(d) $1\dfrac{7}{10}$

$1\dfrac{7}{10}$ ← 7 is more than 5
       ← half of 10 is 5

$1\dfrac{7}{10}$ rounds to 2.

(e) $3\dfrac{1}{2}$

$3\dfrac{1}{2}$ ← 1 is the same as 1
      ← half of 2 is 1

$3\dfrac{1}{2}$ rounds to 4.

(f) $5\dfrac{4}{9}$

$5\dfrac{4}{9}$ ← 4 is less than $4\dfrac{1}{2}$
      ← half of 9 is $4\dfrac{1}{2}$

$5\dfrac{4}{9}$ rounds to 5.

2. (a) $2\dfrac{1}{4} \cdot 7\dfrac{1}{3}$

estimate

$2\dfrac{1}{4}$ rounds to 2. $7\dfrac{1}{3}$ rounds to 7.

$2 \cdot 7 = 14$

exact

$2\dfrac{1}{4} \cdot 7\dfrac{1}{3} = \dfrac{9}{4} \cdot \dfrac{22}{3}$

$= \dfrac{\cancel{9}^{3}}{\cancel{4}_{2}} \cdot \dfrac{\cancel{22}^{11}}{\cancel{3}_{1}}$

$= \dfrac{33}{2} = 16\dfrac{1}{2}$

(b) $4\frac{1}{2} \cdot 1\frac{2}{3}$

estimate

$4\frac{1}{2}$ rounds to 5. $1\frac{2}{3}$ rounds to 2.

$$5 \cdot 2 = 10$$

exact

$$4\frac{1}{2} \cdot 1\frac{2}{3} = \frac{9}{2} \cdot \frac{5}{3} = \frac{\cancel{9}^3}{2} \cdot \frac{5}{\cancel{3}_1} = \frac{15}{2} = 7\frac{1}{2}$$

(c) $3\frac{3}{5} \cdot 4\frac{4}{9}$

estimate

$3\frac{3}{5}$ rounds to 4. $4\frac{4}{9}$ rounds to 4.

$$4 \cdot 4 = 16$$

exact

$$3\frac{3}{5} \cdot 4\frac{4}{9} = \frac{18}{5} \cdot \frac{40}{9} = \frac{\cancel{18}^2}{\cancel{5}_1} \cdot \frac{\cancel{40}^8}{\cancel{9}_1} = 16$$

(d) $3\frac{1}{5} \cdot 5\frac{3}{8}$

estimate

$3\frac{1}{5}$ rounds to 3. $5\frac{3}{8}$ rounds to 5.

$$3 \cdot 5 = 15$$

exact

$$3\frac{1}{5} \cdot 5\frac{3}{8} = \frac{16}{5} \cdot \frac{43}{8} = \frac{\cancel{16}^2}{5} \cdot \frac{43}{\cancel{8}_1} = \frac{86}{5} = 17\frac{1}{5}$$

3. (a) $6\frac{1}{4} \div 3\frac{1}{3}$

estimate

$6\frac{1}{4}$ rounds to 6. $3\frac{1}{3}$ rounds to 3.

$$6 \div 3 = 2$$

exact

$$6\frac{1}{4} \div 3\frac{1}{3} = \frac{25}{4} \div \frac{10}{3} = \frac{\cancel{25}^5}{4} \cdot \frac{3}{\cancel{10}_2}$$

$$= \frac{15}{8} = 1\frac{7}{8}$$

(b) $3\frac{3}{8} \div 2\frac{4}{7}$

estimate

$3\frac{3}{8}$ rounds to 3. $2\frac{4}{7}$ rounds to 3.

$$3 \div 3 = 1$$

exact

$$3\frac{3}{8} \div 2\frac{4}{7} = \frac{27}{8} \div \frac{18}{7} = \frac{\cancel{27}^3}{8} \cdot \frac{7}{\cancel{18}_2}$$

$$= \frac{21}{16} = 1\frac{5}{16}$$

(c) $8 \div 5\frac{1}{3}$

estimate

8 rounds to 8. $5\frac{1}{3}$ rounds to 5.

$$8 \div 5 = 1\frac{3}{5}$$

exact

$$8 \div 5\frac{1}{3} = \frac{8}{1} \div \frac{16}{3} = \frac{\cancel{8}^1}{1} \cdot \frac{3}{\cancel{16}_2} = \frac{3}{2} = 1\frac{1}{2}$$

(d) $4\frac{1}{2} \div 6$

estimate

$4\frac{1}{2}$ rounds to 5. 6 rounds to 6.

$$5 \div 6 = \frac{5}{6}$$

exact

$$4\frac{1}{2} \div 6 = \frac{9}{2} \div \frac{6}{1} = \frac{\cancel{9}^3}{2} \cdot \frac{1}{\cancel{6}_2} = \frac{3}{4}$$

4. (a) Multiply the number of dresses by the amount of material needed for each dress.

estimate

$2\frac{3}{4}$ rounds to 3. 7 rounds to 7.

$$3 \times 7 = 21$$

exact

$$2\frac{3}{4} \cdot 7 = \frac{11}{4} \cdot \frac{7}{1} = \frac{77}{4} = 19\frac{1}{4}$$

For 7 dresses $19\frac{1}{4}$ yards of material is needed.

(b) Multiply the amount that she earns per hour by the number of hours that she worked.

estimate

$9\frac{1}{4}$ rounds to 9. $6\frac{1}{2}$ rounds to 7.

$$9 \cdot 7 = 63$$

exact

$$9\frac{1}{4} \cdot 6\frac{1}{2} = \frac{37}{4} \cdot \frac{13}{2} = \frac{481}{8} = 60\frac{1}{8}$$

Clare would earn $\$60\frac{1}{8}$.

Section 2.8 Multiplication and Division of Mixed Numbers

5. (a) Divide the number of pounds of metal by the number of pounds needed for each airplane.

estimate

$28\frac{1}{2}$ rounds to 29. $2\frac{3}{8}$ rounds to 2.

$$29 \div 2 = 14\frac{1}{2}$$

exact

$$28\frac{1}{2} \div 2\frac{3}{8} = \frac{\cancel{57}^{3}}{\cancel{2}_{1}} \cdot \frac{\cancel{8}^{4}}{\cancel{19}_{1}} = 12$$

12 airplanes could be built.

(b) Divide the total amount of money by the student rate per hour.

estimate

150 rounds to 150. $6\frac{1}{4}$ rounds to 6.

$$150 \div 6 = 25$$

exact

$$150 \div 6\frac{1}{4} = \frac{\cancel{150}^{6}}{1} \cdot \frac{4}{\cancel{25}_{1}} = 24$$

24 hours of student help can be paid.

2.8 Section Exercises

3. $1\frac{2}{3} \cdot 2\frac{7}{10}$

estimate $2 \cdot 3 = 6$

exact

$$1\frac{2}{3} \cdot 2\frac{7}{10} = \frac{5}{3} \cdot \frac{27}{10} = \frac{\cancel{5}^{1}}{\cancel{3}_{1}} \cdot \frac{\cancel{27}^{9}}{\cancel{10}_{2}}$$

$$= \frac{1 \cdot 9}{1 \cdot 2} = \frac{9}{2} = 4\frac{1}{2}$$

7. $10 \cdot 7\frac{1}{4}$

estimate $10 \cdot 7 = 70$

exact

$$10 \cdot 7\frac{1}{4} = \frac{10}{1} \cdot \frac{29}{4} = \frac{\cancel{10}^{5}}{1} \cdot \frac{29}{\cancel{4}_{2}} = \frac{5 \cdot 29}{1 \cdot 2}$$

$$= \frac{145}{2} = 72\frac{1}{2}$$

11. $3 \cdot 1\frac{1}{2} \cdot 2\frac{2}{3}$

estimate $3 \cdot 2 \cdot 3 = 18$

exact

$$3 \cdot 1\frac{1}{2} \cdot 2\frac{2}{3} = \frac{\cancel{3}^{1}}{1} \cdot \frac{3}{\cancel{2}_{1}} \cdot \frac{\cancel{8}^{4}}{\cancel{3}_{1}} = 12$$

15. $2\frac{1}{2} \div 3$

estimate $3 \div 3 = 1$

exact

$$2\frac{1}{2} \div 3 = \frac{5}{2} \div \frac{3}{1} = \frac{5}{2} \cdot \frac{1}{3} = \frac{5}{6}$$

19. $\frac{1}{2} \div 2\frac{1}{4}$

estimate $1 \div 2 = \frac{1}{2}$

exact

$$\frac{1}{2} \div 2\frac{1}{4} = \frac{1}{2} \div \frac{9}{4} = \frac{1}{\cancel{2}_{1}} \cdot \frac{\cancel{4}^{2}}{9} = \frac{1 \cdot 2}{1 \cdot 9} = \frac{2}{9}$$

23. $5\frac{2}{3} \div 6$

estimate $6 \div 6 = 1$

exact

$$5\frac{2}{3} \div 6 = \frac{17}{3} \div \frac{6}{1} = \frac{17}{3} \cdot \frac{1}{6} = \frac{17}{18}$$

27. Divide the amount of baseboard available by the amount needed for each home.

estimate $1314 \div 110 \approx 12$ homes

exact

$$1314 \div 109\frac{1}{2} = \frac{1314}{1} \div \frac{219}{2}$$

$$= \frac{\cancel{1314}^{6}}{1} \cdot \frac{2}{\cancel{219}_{1}} = 12$$

12 homes can be fitted with the baseboard.

31. The answer should include:

Step 1 Change mixed numbers to improper fractions.

Step 2 Multiply the fractions.

Step 3 Write the answer in lowest terms changing to mixed or whole numbers where possible.

35. Divide the length of the tube by the length of each spacer.

estimate $10 \div 1 = 10$ spacers

exact

$$9\frac{3}{4} \div \frac{3}{4} = \frac{39}{4} \div \frac{3}{4} = \frac{\cancel{39}^{13}}{\cancel{4}_{1}} \cdot \frac{\cancel{4}^{1}}{\cancel{3}_{1}} = 13$$

13 spacers can be cut from the tube.

39. Divide the amount paid for the stock by the price per share.

estimate $5025 \div 8 \approx 628$ shares
exact

$$5025 \div 8\tfrac{3}{8} = \frac{\cancel{5025}^{75}}{1} \cdot \frac{8}{\cancel{67}_1}$$
$$= 600$$

She bought 600 shares.

43. $\dfrac{35}{50} = \dfrac{35 \div 5}{50 \div 5} = \dfrac{7}{10}$

Chapter 2 Review Exercises

1. $\dfrac{3}{4}$ There are 4 parts, and 3 are shaded.

2. $\dfrac{5}{8}$ There are 8 parts, and 5 are shaded.

3. $\dfrac{1}{4}$ There are 4 parts, and 1 is shaded.

4. Proper fractions have numerator (top) smaller than denominator (bottom).

They are: $\dfrac{1}{4}, \dfrac{5}{8}, \dfrac{2}{3}$.

Improper fractions have numerator (top) larger than denominator (bottom).

They are: $\dfrac{3}{2}, \dfrac{4}{4}$.

5. Proper fractions: $\dfrac{15}{16}, \dfrac{1}{8}$

Improper fractions: $\dfrac{6}{5}, \dfrac{16}{13}, \dfrac{5}{3}$

6. $4\tfrac{3}{8}$ $4 \cdot 8 = 32$
$32 + 3 = 35$
$4\tfrac{3}{8} = \dfrac{35}{8}$

7. $10\tfrac{4}{5}$ $10 \cdot 5 = 50$
$50 + 4 = 54$
$10\tfrac{4}{5} = \dfrac{54}{5}$

8. $\dfrac{21}{4}$

$\begin{array}{r} 5 \\ 4\overline{)21} \\ \underline{20} \\ 1 \end{array}$ ← whole number

← remainder

$\dfrac{21}{4} = 5\tfrac{1}{4}$

9. $\dfrac{63}{5}$

$\begin{array}{r} 12 \\ 5\overline{)63} \\ \underline{5} \\ 13 \\ \underline{10} \\ 3 \end{array}$ ← whole number

← remainder

$\dfrac{63}{5} = 12\tfrac{3}{5}$

10. Factorizations of 8:

$1 \cdot 8 = 8 \quad 2 \cdot 4 = 8$

The factors are 1, 2, 4, and 8.

11. Factorizations of 18:

$1 \cdot 18 = 18 \qquad 2 \cdot 9 = 18$
$3 \cdot 6 = 18$

The factors are 1, 2, 3, 6, 9, and 18.

12. Factorizations of 55:

$1 \cdot 55 = 55 \quad 5 \cdot 11 = 55$

The factors of 55 are 1, 5, 11, and 55.

13. Factorizations of 90:

$1 \cdot 90 = 90 \qquad 2 \cdot 45 = 90$
$3 \cdot 30 = 90 \qquad 5 \cdot 18 = 90$
$6 \cdot 15 = 90 \qquad 9 \cdot 10 = 9$

The factors of 90 are 1, 2, 3, 5, 6, 9, 10, 15, 18, 30, 45, and 90.

14.

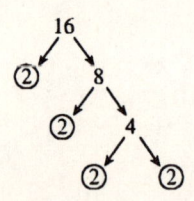

$16 = 2 \cdot 2 \cdot 2 \cdot 2 = 2^4$

15.

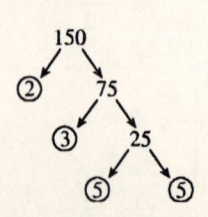

$150 = 2 \cdot 3 \cdot 5 \cdot 5 = 2 \cdot 3 \cdot 5^2$

Chapter 2 Review Exercises

16.

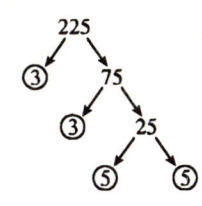

$$225 = 3 \cdot 3 \cdot 5 \cdot 5 = 3^2 \cdot 5^2$$

17. $5^2 = 5 \cdot 5 = 25$

18. $3^2 \cdot 2^3 = 3 \cdot 3 \cdot 2 \cdot 2 \cdot 2 = 9 \cdot 8 = 72$

19. $8^2 \cdot 3^3 = 8 \cdot 8 \cdot 3 \cdot 3 \cdot 3 = 64 \cdot 27 = 1728$

20. $4^3 \cdot 2^5 = 4 \cdot 4 \cdot 4 \cdot 2 \cdot 2 \cdot 2 \cdot 2 \cdot 2 = 64 \cdot 32 = 2048$

21. $\dfrac{12}{16} = \dfrac{12 \div 4}{16 \div 4} = \dfrac{3}{4}$

22. $\dfrac{35}{40} = \dfrac{35 \div 5}{40 \div 5} = \dfrac{7}{8}$

23. $\dfrac{75}{80} = \dfrac{75 \div 5}{80 \div 5} = \dfrac{15}{16}$

24. $\dfrac{25}{60} = \dfrac{5 \cdot \cancel{5}}{2 \cdot 2 \cdot 3 \cdot \cancel{5}} = \dfrac{5}{12}$

25. $\dfrac{384}{96} = \dfrac{\cancel{2} \cdot \cancel{2} \cdot \cancel{2} \cdot \cancel{2} \cdot 2 \cdot 2 \cdot \cancel{3}}{\cancel{2} \cdot \cancel{2} \cdot \cancel{2} \cdot \cancel{2} \cdot \cancel{2} \cdot \cancel{3}} = \dfrac{4}{1} = 4$

26. $\dfrac{4}{5}$ and $\dfrac{72}{90}$
$\quad 5 \cdot 72 = 360$
$\quad 4 \cdot 90 = 360$

The cross products are equal, so the fractions are equivalent.

27. $\dfrac{3}{4}$ and $\dfrac{42}{58}$
$\quad 4 \cdot 42 = 168$
$\quad 3 \cdot 58 = 174$

The cross products are not equal, so the fractions are not equivalent.

28. $\dfrac{2}{3} \cdot \dfrac{3}{4} = \dfrac{\cancel{2}}{\cancel{3}} \cdot \dfrac{\cancel{3}}{\cancel{4}} = \dfrac{1 \cdot 1}{1 \cdot 2} = \dfrac{1}{2}$

29. $\dfrac{4}{5} \cdot \dfrac{5}{12} = \dfrac{\cancel{4}}{\cancel{5}} \cdot \dfrac{\cancel{5}}{\cancel{12}} = \dfrac{1 \cdot 1}{1 \cdot 3} = \dfrac{1}{3}$

30. $\dfrac{70}{175} \cdot \dfrac{5}{14} = \dfrac{\cancel{70}}{\cancel{175}} \cdot \dfrac{\cancel{5}}{\cancel{14}} = \dfrac{1 \cdot 1}{7 \cdot 1} = \dfrac{1}{7}$

31. $\dfrac{44}{63} \cdot \dfrac{3}{11} = \dfrac{\cancel{44}}{\cancel{63}} \cdot \dfrac{\cancel{3}}{\cancel{11}} = \dfrac{4 \cdot 1}{21 \cdot 1} = \dfrac{4}{21}$

32. $\dfrac{5}{16} \cdot 48 = \dfrac{5}{\cancel{16}} \cdot \dfrac{\cancel{48}}{1} = \dfrac{5 \cdot 3}{1 \cdot 1} = \dfrac{15}{1} = 15$

33. $\dfrac{5}{8} \cdot 1000 = \dfrac{5}{\cancel{8}} \cdot \dfrac{\cancel{1000}}{1} = \dfrac{5 \cdot 125}{1 \cdot 1} = \dfrac{625}{1} = 625$

34. $\dfrac{1}{4} \div \dfrac{1}{2} = \dfrac{1}{\cancel{4}} \cdot \dfrac{\cancel{2}}{1} = \dfrac{1}{2}$

35. $\dfrac{5}{6} \div \dfrac{1}{2} = \dfrac{5}{\cancel{6}} \cdot \dfrac{\cancel{2}}{1} = \dfrac{5}{3} = 1\dfrac{2}{3}$

36. $\dfrac{\frac{15}{18}}{\frac{10}{30}} = \dfrac{15}{18} \div \dfrac{10}{30} = \dfrac{\cancel{15}}{\cancel{18}} \cdot \dfrac{\cancel{30}}{\cancel{10}} = \dfrac{5 \cdot \cancel{3}}{\cancel{6} \cdot 1} = \dfrac{5 \cdot 1}{2 \cdot 1}$
$\quad = \dfrac{5}{2} = 2\dfrac{1}{2}$

37. $\dfrac{\frac{3}{10}}{\frac{6}{40}} = \dfrac{3}{10} \div \dfrac{6}{40} = \dfrac{\cancel{3}}{\cancel{10}} \cdot \dfrac{\cancel{40}}{\cancel{6}} = \dfrac{1 \cdot 4}{1 \cdot 2} = \dfrac{4}{2} = 2$

38. $5 \div \dfrac{5}{8} = \dfrac{\cancel{5}}{1} \cdot \dfrac{8}{\cancel{5}} = 8$

39. $18 \div \dfrac{3}{4} = \dfrac{\cancel{18}}{1} \cdot \dfrac{4}{\cancel{3}} = 24$

40. $\dfrac{7}{8} \div 2 = \dfrac{7}{8} \cdot \dfrac{1}{2} = \dfrac{7}{16}$

41. $\dfrac{2}{3} \div 5 = \dfrac{2}{3} \div \dfrac{5}{1} = \dfrac{2}{3} \cdot \dfrac{1}{5} = \dfrac{2 \cdot 1}{3 \cdot 5} = \dfrac{2}{15}$

42. $\dfrac{\frac{12}{13}}{3} = \dfrac{12}{13} \div 3 = \dfrac{12}{13} \div \dfrac{3}{1} = \dfrac{\cancel{12}}{13} \cdot \dfrac{1}{\cancel{3}} = \dfrac{4 \cdot 1}{13 \cdot 1} = \dfrac{4}{13}$

43. To find the area, multiply the length and the width.

$$\dfrac{1}{2} \cdot \dfrac{15}{16} = \dfrac{1 \cdot 15}{2 \cdot 16} = \dfrac{15}{32} \text{ square yard}$$

44. To find the area, multiply the length and the width.

$$\dfrac{\cancel{2}}{3} \cdot \dfrac{7}{\cancel{8}} = \dfrac{1 \cdot 7}{3 \cdot 4} = \dfrac{7}{12} \text{ square inch}$$

45. Multiply the length and the width.

$$15 \cdot \frac{2}{3} = \frac{\cancel{15}^{5}}{1} \cdot \frac{2}{\cancel{3}_{1}} = \frac{5 \cdot 2}{1 \cdot 1}$$

$$= \frac{10}{1} = 10 \text{ square feet}$$

46. Multiply the length and the width.

$$48 \cdot \frac{3}{4} = \frac{\cancel{48}^{12}}{1} \cdot \frac{3}{\cancel{4}_{1}} = 36 \text{ square yards}$$

47. $2\frac{3}{8} \times 1\frac{1}{2}$

estimate $2 \cdot 2 = 4$
exact

$$2\frac{3}{8} \times 1\frac{1}{2} = \frac{19}{8} \times \frac{3}{2} = \frac{57}{16} = 3\frac{9}{16}$$

48. $2\frac{1}{4} \cdot 7\frac{1}{8} \cdot 1\frac{1}{3}$

estimate $2 \cdot 7 \cdot 1 = 14$
exact

$$2\frac{1}{4} \cdot 7\frac{1}{8} \cdot 1\frac{1}{3} = \frac{\cancel{9}^{3}}{4} \cdot \frac{57}{\cancel{8}_{2}} \cdot \frac{\cancel{4}^{1}}{\cancel{3}_{1}} = \frac{171}{8} = 21\frac{3}{8}$$

49. $15\frac{1}{2} \div 3$

estimate $16 \div 3 = 5\frac{1}{3}$
exact

$$15\frac{1}{2} \div 3 = \frac{31}{2} \cdot \frac{1}{3} = \frac{31}{6} = 5\frac{1}{6}$$

50. $3\frac{1}{8} \div 5\frac{5}{7}$

estimate $3 \div 6 = \frac{1}{2}$
exact

$$3\frac{1}{8} \div 5\frac{5}{7} = \frac{25}{8} \div \frac{40}{7} = \frac{\cancel{25}^{5}}{8} \cdot \frac{7}{\cancel{40}_{8}} = \frac{35}{64}$$

51. Divide the size of the bags by the weight of the sunflower seeds.

$$225 \div \frac{3}{4} = \frac{\cancel{225}^{75}}{1} \cdot \frac{4}{\cancel{3}_{1}} = 300$$

300 bags can be filled.

52. $\frac{2}{3}$ of the estate is to be divided into 5 parts.

$$\frac{2}{3} \div 5 = \frac{2}{3} \div \frac{5}{1} = \frac{2}{3} \cdot \frac{1}{5} = \frac{2 \cdot 1}{3 \cdot 5} = \frac{2}{15}$$

Each child will receive $\frac{2}{15}$ of the estate.

53. Divide the total yardage by the amount needed for each pull cord.

estimate $158 \div 4 \approx 40$ pull cords
exact

$$157\frac{1}{2} \div 4\frac{3}{8} = \frac{315}{2} \div \frac{35}{8}$$

$$= \frac{\cancel{315}^{9}}{\cancel{2}_{1}} \cdot \frac{\cancel{8}^{4}}{\cancel{35}_{1}} = 36$$

36 pull cords can be made.

54. Total wages equal the number of hours worked times the wages per hour.

estimate $9 \cdot 38 = \$342$
exact

$$38 \cdot 8\frac{1}{2} = \frac{\cancel{38}^{19}}{1} \cdot \frac{17}{\cancel{2}_{1}} = 323$$

Neta earned $323.

55. Ebony sold $\frac{1}{2}$ of 100 pounds.

$$\frac{1}{2} \cdot 100 = \frac{1}{\cancel{2}_{1}} \cdot \frac{\cancel{100}^{50}}{1} = \frac{1 \cdot 50}{1 \cdot 1}$$

$$= \frac{50}{1} = 50 \text{ pounds}$$

So, $100 - 50 = 50$ pounds remains. She gave $\frac{2}{5}$ of 50 to her parents.

$$\frac{2}{5} \cdot 50 = \frac{2}{\cancel{5}_{1}} \cdot \frac{\cancel{50}^{10}}{1} = \frac{2 \cdot 10}{1 \cdot 1}$$

$$= \frac{20}{1} = 20 \text{ pounds}$$

Ebony has 30 $(50 - 20)$ pounds left.

56. Mary paid $\frac{3}{8}$ of $1200 for room and board.

$$1200 \cdot \frac{3}{8} = \frac{\cancel{1200}^{150}}{1} \cdot \frac{3}{\cancel{8}_{1}} = 450$$

$450 was spent on room and board.

$$\$1200 - \$450 = \$750$$

Chapter 2 Review Exercises

She paid $\frac{1}{2}$ of $750 for school fees.

$$\frac{1}{2} \cdot 750 = \frac{1}{\cancel{2}} \cdot \frac{\overset{375}{\cancel{750}}}{1} = 375$$

$750 - $375 = $375 is left.

57. $\frac{5}{8}$ must be divided by 4.

$$\frac{5}{8} \div 4 = \frac{5}{8} \div \frac{4}{1} = \frac{5}{8} \cdot \frac{1}{4} = \frac{5 \cdot 1}{8 \cdot 4} = \frac{5}{32}$$

Each parish will receive $\frac{5}{32}$ of the budget.

58. $\frac{2}{3}$ of the profits must be divided evenly between 8 managers.

$$\frac{2}{3} \div 8 = \frac{2}{3} \div \frac{8}{1} = \frac{\cancel{2}}{3} \cdot \frac{1}{\underset{4}{\cancel{8}}} = \frac{1}{12}$$

Each manager recieves $\frac{1}{12}$ of the total.

59. $\frac{2}{3} \cdot \frac{1}{2} = \frac{\overset{1}{\cancel{2}} \cdot 1}{3 \cdot \underset{1}{\cancel{2}}} = \frac{1}{3}$

60. $\frac{1}{4} \cdot \frac{2}{3} = \frac{1 \cdot \overset{1}{\cancel{2}}}{\underset{2}{\cancel{4}} \cdot 3} = \frac{1}{6}$

61. $10\frac{1}{4} \cdot 2\frac{1}{2} = \frac{41}{4} \cdot \frac{5}{2} = \frac{205}{8} = 25\frac{5}{8}$

62. $12\frac{1}{2} \cdot 2\frac{1}{4} = \frac{25}{2} \cdot \frac{9}{4} = \frac{225}{8} = 28\frac{1}{8}$

63. $\frac{\frac{7}{8}}{6} = \frac{7}{8} \div \frac{6}{1} = \frac{7}{8} \cdot \frac{1}{6} = \frac{7}{48}$

64. $\frac{\frac{5}{8}}{4} = \frac{5}{8} \div \frac{4}{1} = \frac{5}{8} \cdot \frac{1}{4} = \frac{5}{32}$

65. $\frac{15}{31} \cdot 62 = \frac{15}{\underset{1}{\cancel{31}}} \cdot \frac{\overset{2}{\cancel{62}}}{1} = \frac{15 \cdot 2}{1 \cdot 1} = \frac{30}{1} = 30$

66. $3\frac{1}{4} \div 1\frac{1}{2} = \frac{13}{4} \div \frac{3}{2} = \frac{13}{\underset{2}{\cancel{4}}} \cdot \frac{\overset{1}{\cancel{2}}}{3} = \frac{13 \cdot 1}{2 \cdot 3} = \frac{13}{6} = 2\frac{1}{6}$

67. $\frac{8}{5}$

$$\begin{array}{r} 1 \leftarrow \text{whole number} \\ 5\overline{)8} \\ \underline{5} \\ 3 \leftarrow \text{remainder} \end{array}$$

$\frac{8}{5} = 1\frac{3}{5}$

68. $\frac{137}{3}$

$$\begin{array}{r} 45 \leftarrow \text{whole number} \\ 3\overline{)137} \\ \underline{12} \\ 17 \\ \underline{15} \\ 2 \leftarrow \text{remainder} \end{array}$$

$\frac{137}{3} = 45\frac{2}{3}$

69. $5\frac{2}{3}$ $\quad 5 \cdot 3 = 15$
$\qquad 15 + 2 = 17$

$5\frac{2}{3} = \frac{17}{3}$

70. $38\frac{3}{8}$ $\quad 38 \cdot 8 = 304$
$\qquad 304 + 3 = 307$

$38\frac{3}{8} = \frac{307}{8}$

71. $\frac{8}{12} = \frac{\overset{1}{\cancel{2}} \cdot \overset{1}{\cancel{2}} \cdot 2}{\underset{1}{\cancel{2}} \cdot \underset{1}{\cancel{2}} \cdot 3} = \frac{1 \cdot 1 \cdot 2}{1 \cdot 1 \cdot 3} = \frac{2}{3}$

72. $\frac{108}{210} = \frac{\overset{1}{\cancel{2}} \cdot 2 \cdot \overset{1}{\cancel{3}} \cdot 3 \cdot 3}{\underset{1}{\cancel{2}} \cdot \underset{1}{\cancel{3}} \cdot 5 \cdot 7} = \frac{1 \cdot 2 \cdot 1 \cdot 3 \cdot 3}{1 \cdot 1 \cdot 5 \cdot 7} = \frac{18}{35}$

73. $\frac{36}{48} = \frac{36 \div 12}{48 \div 12} = \frac{3}{4}$

74. $\frac{28}{84} = \frac{28 \div 28}{84 \div 28} = \frac{1}{3}$

75. $\frac{44}{110} = \frac{44 \div 22}{110 \div 22} = \frac{2}{5}$

76. $\frac{87}{261} = \frac{87 \div 87}{261 \div 87} = \frac{1}{3}$

77. Multiply the area by the amount needed for each square yard.

estimate $4 \cdot 44 = 176$ ounces
exact

$$43\frac{5}{9} \cdot 3\frac{1}{2} = \frac{\overset{196}{\cancel{392}}}{9} \cdot \frac{7}{\underset{1}{\cancel{2}}} = \frac{196 \cdot 7}{9 \cdot 1} = \frac{1372}{9}$$

$$\begin{array}{r} 152 \leftarrow \text{whole number} \\ 9\overline{)1372} \\ \underline{9} \\ 47 \\ \underline{45} \\ 22 \\ \underline{18} \\ 4 \leftarrow \text{remainder} \end{array}$$

$152\frac{4}{9}$ ounces of glue are needed.

78. Multiply the number of in-ground tanks by the number of quarts needed for each in-ground tank.

estimate $7 \cdot 26 = 182$ quarts
exact
$$25\frac{1}{2} \cdot 7\frac{1}{4} = \frac{51}{2} \cdot \frac{29}{4} = \frac{1479}{8} = 184\frac{7}{8}$$

$184\frac{7}{8}$ quarts are needed.

79. To find the area multiply the length and the width.

$$\frac{2}{3} \cdot \frac{3}{4} = \frac{\overset{1}{\cancel{2}}}{\cancel{3}} \cdot \frac{\overset{1}{\cancel{3}}}{\cancel{4}} = \frac{1 \cdot 1}{1 \cdot 2} = \frac{1}{2} \text{ square inch}$$

80. Multiply the length and the width to find the area.

$$\frac{1}{2} \cdot \frac{7}{8} = \frac{1 \cdot 7}{2 \cdot 8} = \frac{7}{16}$$

The area is $\frac{7}{16}$ square meter.

Chapter 2 Test

1. $\frac{3}{8}$ *There are 8 parts and 3 are shaded.*

2. $\frac{5}{6}$ *There are 6 parts and 5 are shaded.*

3. Proper fractions have the numerator (top) smaller than the denominator (bottom).

$$\frac{3}{4}, \frac{7}{8}, \frac{1}{6}, \frac{2}{9}$$

4. $4\frac{3}{8}$ $\quad 4 \cdot 8 = 32$
$\qquad\qquad 32 + 3 = 35$

$4\frac{3}{8} = \frac{35}{8}$

5. $\frac{125}{6}$
$\quad\quad 6)\overline{125} \;\; 20$
$\qquad\quad \underline{12}$
$\qquad\quad\;\; 5$
$\qquad\quad\;\; \underline{0}$
$\qquad\quad\;\; 5$

$\frac{125}{6} = 20\frac{5}{6}$

6. Factorizations of 18:

$\quad 1 \cdot 18 = 18 \qquad 2 \cdot 9 = 18$
$\quad 3 \cdot 6 = 18$

The factors of 18 are 1, 2, 3, 6, 9, and 18.

7.

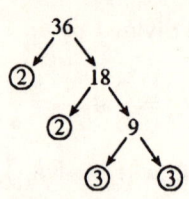

```
        36
       /  \
      2   18
         /  \
        2    9
            / \
           3   3
```

$36 = 2 \cdot 2 \cdot 3 \cdot 3 = 2^2 \cdot 3^2$

8.

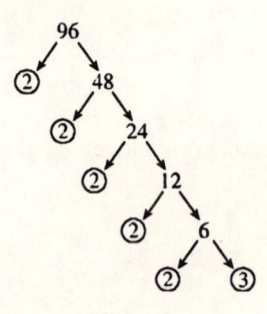

```
        96
       /  \
      2   48
         /  \
        2   24
           /  \
          2   12
             /  \
            2    6
               /  \
              2    3
```

$96 = 2 \cdot 2 \cdot 2 \cdot 2 \cdot 2 \cdot 3 = 2^5 \cdot 3$

9.

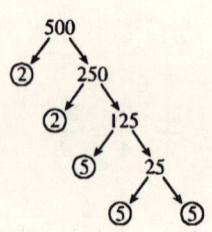

```
       500
       / \
      2  250
         / \
        2  125
           / \
          5  25
             / \
            5   5
```

$500 = 2 \cdot 2 \cdot 5 \cdot 5 \cdot 5 = 2^2 \cdot 5^3$

10. $\frac{15}{18} = \frac{15 \div 3}{18 \div 3} = \frac{5}{6}$

11. $\frac{56}{84} = \frac{\overset{1}{\cancel{2}} \cdot \overset{1}{\cancel{2}} \cdot 2 \cdot \overset{1}{\cancel{7}}}{\underset{1}{\cancel{2}} \cdot \underset{1}{\cancel{2}} \cdot 3 \cdot \underset{1}{\cancel{7}}} = \frac{1 \cdot 1 \cdot 2 \cdot 1}{1 \cdot 1 \cdot 3 \cdot 1} = \frac{2}{3}$

12. Write the prime factorization of both numerator and denominator. Use cancellation to divide numerator and denominator by any common factors. Multiply the remaining factors in numerator and denominator.

$$\frac{56}{84} = \frac{\overset{1}{\cancel{2}} \cdot \overset{1}{\cancel{2}} \cdot 2 \cdot \overset{1}{\cancel{7}}}{\underset{1}{\cancel{2}} \cdot \underset{1}{\cancel{2}} \cdot 3 \cdot \underset{1}{\cancel{7}}} = \frac{2}{3}$$

Cumulative Review Exercises (Chapters 1-2)

13. Multiply fractions by multiplying the numerators and multiplying the denominators. Divide the two fractions by inverting the second fraction (divisor) and multiplying.

14. $\dfrac{5}{8} \cdot \dfrac{4}{5} = \dfrac{\cancel{5}^1 \cdot \cancel{4}^1}{\cancel{8}_2 \cdot \cancel{5}_1} = \dfrac{1}{2}$

15. $24 \cdot \dfrac{3}{4} = \dfrac{\cancel{24}^6}{1} \cdot \dfrac{3}{\cancel{4}_1} = \dfrac{18}{1} = 18$

16. Multiply the length and the width.

    $\dfrac{3}{4} \cdot \dfrac{1}{2} = \dfrac{3}{8}$ square meter

17. Multiply the total number of students by the fraction of students who work.

    $8448 \cdot \dfrac{7}{8} = \dfrac{\cancel{8448}^{1056}}{1} \cdot \dfrac{7}{\cancel{8}_1} = 7392$

    The number of students who work is 7392.

18. $\dfrac{5}{8} \div \dfrac{3}{4} = \dfrac{5}{\cancel{8}_2} \cdot \dfrac{\cancel{4}^1}{3} = \dfrac{5}{6}$

19. $\dfrac{7}{\frac{4}{9}} = 7 \div \dfrac{4}{9} = \dfrac{7}{1} \div \dfrac{4}{9} = \dfrac{7}{1} \cdot \dfrac{9}{4} = \dfrac{7 \cdot 9}{1 \cdot 4} = \dfrac{63}{4} = 15\dfrac{3}{4}$

20. Divide to find how many vehicles can be filled with 60 tanks of fluid.

    $60 \div \dfrac{3}{5} = \dfrac{\cancel{60}^{20}}{1} \cdot \dfrac{5}{\cancel{3}_1} = \dfrac{20 \cdot 5}{1 \cdot 1} = 100$

    100 vehicles can be filled.

21. $5\dfrac{1}{4} \cdot 3\dfrac{3}{8}$

    estimate $5 \cdot 3 = 15$
    exact

    $5\dfrac{1}{4} \cdot 3\dfrac{3}{8} = \dfrac{21}{4} \cdot \dfrac{27}{8} = \dfrac{21 \cdot 27}{4 \cdot 8}$

    $= \dfrac{567}{32} = 17\dfrac{23}{32}$

22. $1\dfrac{5}{6} \cdot 4\dfrac{1}{3}$

    estimate $2 \cdot 4 = 8$
    exact

    $1\dfrac{5}{6} \cdot 4\dfrac{1}{3} = \dfrac{11}{6} \cdot \dfrac{13}{3} = \dfrac{11 \cdot 13}{6 \cdot 3}$

    $= \dfrac{143}{18} = 7\dfrac{17}{18}$

23. $4\dfrac{4}{5} \div 1\dfrac{1}{8}$

    estimate $5 \div 1 = 5$
    exact

    $4\dfrac{4}{5} \div 1\dfrac{1}{8} = \dfrac{24}{5} \div \dfrac{9}{8} = \dfrac{\cancel{24}^8}{5} \cdot \dfrac{8}{\cancel{9}_3}$

    $= \dfrac{8 \cdot 8}{5 \cdot 3} = \dfrac{64}{15} = 4\dfrac{4}{15}$

24. $\dfrac{8\frac{1}{2}}{1\frac{2}{3}}$

    estimate $9 \div 2 = 4\dfrac{1}{2}$
    exact

    $\dfrac{8\frac{1}{2}}{1\frac{2}{3}} = 8\dfrac{1}{2} \div 1\dfrac{2}{3}$

    $= \dfrac{17}{2} \div \dfrac{5}{3}$

    $= \dfrac{17}{2} \cdot \dfrac{3}{5} = \dfrac{17 \cdot 3}{2 \cdot 5}$

    $= \dfrac{51}{10} = 5\dfrac{1}{10}$

25. If $2\dfrac{1}{2}$ grams can be synthesized per day, multiply to find the amount for $12\dfrac{1}{4}$ days.

    estimate $3 \cdot 12 = 36$
    exact

    $2\dfrac{1}{2} \cdot 12\dfrac{1}{4} = \dfrac{5}{2} \cdot \dfrac{49}{4} = \dfrac{5 \cdot 49}{2 \cdot 4} = \dfrac{245}{8} = 30\dfrac{5}{8}$

    $30\dfrac{5}{8}$ grams can be synthesized.

Cumulative Review Exercises (Chapters 1-2)

1. 7̲ 18
   hundreds: 7
   tens: 1

2. 6̲, 7 4̲ 8, 215
   millions: 6
   ten thousands: 4

3. $\overset{1}{}27$
   43
   85
   + 11

   166

4. $\overset{111}{}82,121$
   5 468
   316
   + 61,294

   149,199

5. $\begin{array}{r} \overset{5\ 12}{2{,}\cancel{6}\cancel{2}8} \\ -\ 10\ 56 \\ \hline 15\ 72 \end{array}$

6. $\begin{array}{r} \overset{7\ 11\ 8\ 1510}{4{,}\cancel{8}\cancel{1}\cancel{9}{,}\cancel{6}\cancel{0}4} \\ -\ 1{,}5\ 9\ 7{,}7\ 8\ 3 \\ \hline 3{,}2\ 2\ 1{,}8\ 2\ 1 \end{array}$

7. $\begin{array}{r} \overset{4}{96} \\ \times\ \ 8 \\ \hline 768 \end{array}$

8. $6 \cdot 3 \cdot 5$
$(6 \cdot 3) \cdot 5 = 18 \cdot 5 = 90$
or
$6 \cdot (3 \cdot 5) = 6 \cdot 15 = 90$

9. $\begin{array}{r} 3784 \\ \times\ 573 \end{array}$ $3784 \cdot 573 = 2{,}168{,}232$

10. $\begin{array}{r} 629 \\ \times\ 700 \end{array}$ $\begin{array}{r} \overset{2\ 6}{629} \\ \times\ \ \ 7 \\ \hline 4403 \end{array}$

$\begin{array}{r} 629 \\ \times\ 700 \\ \hline 440{,}300 \end{array}$ *Attach 2 zeros*

11. $\dfrac{54}{6}$ $\begin{array}{r} 9 \\ 6\overline{)54} \end{array}$
$\dfrac{54}{6} = 9$

12. $\begin{array}{r} 7\ 581 \\ 18\overline{)136{,}458} \\ \underline{126\phantom{{,}000}} \\ 10\ 4 \\ \underline{9\ 0} \\ 1\ 45 \\ \underline{1\ 44} \\ 18 \\ \underline{18} \\ 0 \end{array}$ Check: $\begin{array}{r} 7581 \\ \times\ \ \ 18 \\ \hline 60\ 648 \\ 75\ 81 \\ \hline 136{,}458 \end{array}$

13. $16{,}942 \div 4$

$\begin{array}{r} 4\ 235\ \ \text{R2} \\ 4\overline{)16{,}942} \\ \underline{16\phantom{{,}000}} \\ 0\ 9 \\ \underline{8} \\ 14 \\ \underline{12} \\ 22 \\ \underline{20} \\ 2 \end{array}$ Check: $\begin{array}{r} 4235 \\ \times\ \ \ \ 4 \\ \hline 16{,}940 \\ +\ \ \ \ 2 \\ \hline 16{,}942 \end{array}$

14. $\begin{array}{r} 22\ \ \text{R26} \\ 492\overline{)10{,}850} \\ \underline{9\ 84} \\ 1\ 010 \\ \underline{984} \\ 26 \end{array}$ Check: $\begin{array}{r} 492 \\ \times\ \ \ 22 \\ \hline 984 \\ 9\ 84 \\ \hline 10{,}824 \\ +\ \ \ 26 \\ \hline 10{,}850 \end{array}$

15. 8626 to the nearest ten: ≈ 8630

    86<u>2</u>6   Next digit is 5 or more.
             Tens place changes $(2 + 1 = 3)$.
             All digits to the right of the underlined place change to 0.

8626 to the nearest hundred: ≈ 8600

    8<u>6</u>26   Next digit is 4 or less.
             Hundreds place does not changes. All digits to the right of the underlined place change to 0.

8626 to the nearest thousand: ≈ 9000

    <u>8</u>626   Next digit is 5 or more.
             Thousands place changes $(8 + 1 = 9)$. All digits to the right of the underlined place change to 0.

16. 85,462 to the nearest ten: $\approx 85{,}460$

    85,4<u>6</u>2   Next digit is 4 or less.
               Tens place does not change.
               All digits to the right of the underlined place change to 0.

85,462 to the nearest hundred: $\approx 85{,}500$

    85,<u>4</u>62   Next digit is 5 or more.
               Hundreds place changes $(4 + 1 = 5)$.
               All digits to the right of the underlined place change to 0.

85,462 to the nearest thousand: $\approx 85{,}000$

    8<u>5</u>,462   Next digit is 4 or less.
               Thousands place does not change
               All digits to the right of the underlined place change to 0.

17. $5^2 - 9 \cdot 2$ *Exponent*
    $25 - 9 \cdot 2$ *Multiply*
    $25 - 18 = 7$ *Subtract*

18. $\sqrt{36} - 2 \cdot 3 + 5$ *Square root*
    $6 - 2 \cdot 3 + 5$ *Multiply*
    $6 - 6 + 5$ *Subtract*
    $0 + 5 = 5$ *Add*

Cumulative Review Exercises (Chapters 1-2)

19. Multiply to find the cost of each order; then add to find the total.

$$\begin{array}{r} \$35 \\ \times\ 6 \\ \hline \$210 \end{array} \qquad \begin{array}{r} \$45 \\ \times\ 9 \\ \hline \$405 \end{array} \qquad \begin{array}{r} \$210 \\ +\ 405 \\ \hline \$615 \end{array}$$

The total cost is $615.

20. Subtract to find the difference between the 2 models.

$$\begin{array}{r} \$150 \\ -\ 20 \\ \hline \$130 \end{array}$$

Jenn paid $130 more than Scott.

21. Find the number of hairs lost in 2 years and subtract to find the hairs remaining.

$$\begin{array}{r} 365 \\ \times\ 100 \\ \hline 36,500 \end{array} \qquad \begin{array}{r} 36,500 \\ \times\ \ \ \ 2 \\ \hline 73,000 \end{array} \qquad \begin{array}{r} 120,000 \\ -\ 73,000 \\ \hline 47,000 \end{array}$$

47,000 hairs remain.

22. Divide the total cost by the number of families.

$$\begin{array}{r} 175 \\ 18\overline{)\$3150} \\ \underline{18} \\ 135 \\ \underline{126} \\ 90 \\ \underline{90} \\ 0 \end{array}$$

The cost for each family is $175.

23. Multiply the length and width to find the area.

$$\frac{3}{4} \cdot \frac{7}{12} = \frac{\cancel{3}^{1}}{4} \cdot \frac{7}{\cancel{12}_{4}} = \frac{1 \cdot 7}{4 \cdot 4} = \frac{7}{16}$$

The area of the lamp base is $\frac{7}{16}$ square foot.

24. Multiply the cost per minute by the number of minutes the hair dryer is used.

$$30 \text{ minutes} = \frac{1}{2} \text{ hour}$$

$$\frac{1}{5}\cancel{c} \cdot 30 = \frac{1}{\cancel{5}} \cdot \frac{30}{1} = 6\cancel{c}$$

The cost of operating the hair dryer for $\frac{1}{2}$ hour is 6¢.

25. $\frac{3}{4}$ is *proper* because the numerator (3) is smaller than the denominator (4).

26. $\frac{9}{9}$ is *improper* because the numerator (9) is larger or the same as the denominator (9).

27. $\frac{7}{16}$ is *proper* because the numerator (7) is smaller than the denominator (16).

28. $2\frac{1}{2}$ $\quad 2 \cdot 2 = 4$
$\qquad\qquad 4 + 1 = 5$

$$2\frac{1}{2} = \frac{5}{2}$$

29. $7\frac{1}{3}$ $\quad 7 \cdot 3 = 21$
$\qquad\qquad 21 + 1 = 22$

$$7\frac{1}{3} = \frac{22}{3}$$

30. $\frac{12}{7}$ $\qquad \begin{array}{r} 1 \leftarrow \text{whole number} \\ 7\overline{)12} \\ \underline{7} \\ 5 \leftarrow \text{remainder} \end{array}$

$$\frac{12}{7} = 1\frac{5}{7}$$

31. $\frac{103}{8}$ $\qquad \begin{array}{r} 12 \leftarrow \text{whole number} \\ 8\overline{)103} \\ \underline{8} \\ 23 \\ \underline{16} \\ 7 \leftarrow \text{remainder} \end{array}$

$$\frac{103}{8} = 12\frac{7}{8}$$

32.

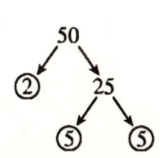

$$50 = 2 \cdot 5 \cdot 5 = 2 \cdot 5^2$$

33.

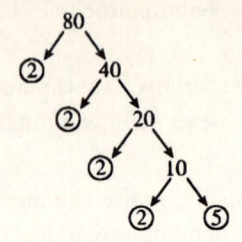

$80 = 2 \cdot 2 \cdot 2 \cdot 2 \cdot 5 = 2^4 \cdot 5$

34.

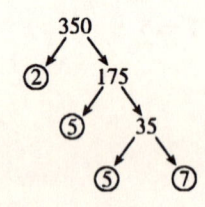

$350 = 2 \cdot 5 \cdot 5 \cdot 7 = 2 \cdot 5^2 \cdot 7$

35. $2^2 \cdot 3^2 = 2 \cdot 2 \cdot 3 \cdot 3 = 4 \cdot 9 = 36$

36. $3^3 \cdot 5^2 = 3 \cdot 3 \cdot 3 \cdot 5 \cdot 5 = 27 \cdot 25 = 675$

37. $2^3 \cdot 4^2 \cdot 5 = 2 \cdot 2 \cdot 2 \cdot 4 \cdot 4 \cdot 5 = 8 \cdot 16 \cdot 5 = 128 \cdot 5 = 640$

38. $\dfrac{35}{40} = \dfrac{35 \div 5}{40 \div 5} = \dfrac{7}{8}$

39. $\dfrac{16}{24} = \dfrac{16 \div 8}{24 \div 8} = \dfrac{2}{3}$

40. $\dfrac{30}{54} = \dfrac{30 \div 6}{54 \div 6} = \dfrac{5}{9}$

41. $\dfrac{3}{4} \cdot \dfrac{1}{3} = \dfrac{\cancel{3}^{1} \cdot 1}{4 \cdot \cancel{3}_{1}} = \dfrac{1}{4}$

42. $30 \cdot \dfrac{2}{3} \cdot \dfrac{3}{5} = \dfrac{\cancel{30}^{6} \cdot 2 \cdot \cancel{3}^{1}}{\cancel{3}_{1} \cdot \cancel{5}_{1}} = 12$

43. $7\tfrac{1}{2} \cdot 3\tfrac{1}{3} = \dfrac{\cancel{15}^{5}}{\cancel{2}_{1}} \cdot \dfrac{\cancel{10}^{5}}{\cancel{3}_{1}} = \dfrac{25}{1} = 25$

44. $\dfrac{3}{8} \div \dfrac{2}{3} = \dfrac{3}{8} \cdot \dfrac{3}{2} = \dfrac{9}{16}$

45. $\dfrac{3}{8} \div 1\tfrac{1}{4} = \dfrac{3}{8} \div \dfrac{5}{4} = \dfrac{3}{\cancel{8}_{2}} \cdot \dfrac{\cancel{4}^{1}}{5} = \dfrac{3}{10}$

46. $3 \div 1\tfrac{1}{4} = \dfrac{3}{1} \div \dfrac{5}{4} = \dfrac{3}{1} \cdot \dfrac{4}{5} = \dfrac{12}{5} = 2\tfrac{2}{5}$

Chapter 3

ADDING AND SUBTRACTING FRACTIONS

3.1 Adding and Subtracting Like Fractions

3.1 Margin Exercises

1. (a) $\frac{3}{4}, \frac{1}{4}$

    The denominators are the same. $\frac{3}{4}$ and $\frac{1}{4}$ are *like* fractions.

    (b) $\frac{2}{3}, \frac{2}{5}$

    The denominators are different. $\frac{2}{3}$ are $\frac{2}{5}$ are *unlike* fractions.

    (c) $\frac{11}{12}, \frac{9}{12}$

    The denominators are the same. $\frac{11}{12}$ and $\frac{9}{12}$ are *like* fractions.

    (d) $\frac{7}{3}, \frac{7}{4}$

    The denominators are different. $\frac{7}{3}$ and $\frac{7}{4}$ are *unlike* fractions.

2. (a) $\frac{4}{8} + \frac{1}{8} = \frac{4+1}{8} = \frac{5}{8}$

    (b) $\frac{5}{9} + \frac{2}{9}$

    Add numerators. The denominator stays the same.

    $$\frac{5+2}{9} = \frac{7}{9}$$

    (c) $\frac{1}{8} + \frac{3}{8} = \frac{1+3}{8} = \frac{4}{8} = \frac{1}{2}$ Lowest terms

    (d) $\frac{3}{10} + \frac{1}{10} + \frac{4}{10} = \frac{3+1+4}{10} = \frac{8}{10} = \frac{4}{5}$

3. (a) $\frac{11}{15} - \frac{4}{15} = \frac{11-4}{15} = \frac{7}{15}$

    (b) $\frac{8}{9} - \frac{5}{9}$

    $\frac{8-5}{9} = \frac{3}{9}$ Subtract numerators Same denominator

    $= \frac{1}{3}$ Lowest terms

    (c) $\frac{27}{8} - \frac{14}{8} = \frac{27-14}{8} = \frac{13}{8} = 1\frac{5}{8}$

    (d) $\frac{103}{108} - \frac{48}{108}$

    $\frac{103}{108} - \frac{48}{108} = \frac{103-48}{108} = \frac{55}{108}$

3.1 Section Exercises

3. $\frac{7}{10} + \frac{2}{10} = \frac{7+2}{10} = \frac{9}{10}$

7. $\frac{14}{12} + \frac{1}{12}$

    $\frac{14}{12} + \frac{1}{12} = \frac{15}{12} = 1\frac{3}{12} = 1\frac{1}{4}$

11. $\frac{6}{20} + \frac{4}{20} + \frac{3}{20} = \frac{6+4+3}{20} = \frac{13}{20}$

15. $\frac{3}{8} + \frac{7}{8} + \frac{2}{8} = \frac{3+7+2}{8} = \frac{12}{8} = 1\frac{4}{8} = 1\frac{1}{2}$

19. $\frac{4}{5} - \frac{1}{5} = \frac{4-1}{5} = \frac{3}{5}$

23. $\frac{9}{10} - \frac{3}{10} = \frac{9-3}{10} = \frac{6 \div 2}{10 \div 2} = \frac{3}{5}$

27. $\frac{27}{40} - \frac{19}{40}$

    $\frac{27}{40} - \frac{19}{40} = \frac{27-19}{40} = \frac{8 \div 8}{40 \div 8} = \frac{1}{5}$

31. $\dfrac{87}{144} - \dfrac{71}{144} = \dfrac{87-71}{144} = \dfrac{16 \div 16}{144 \div 16} = \dfrac{1}{9}$

35. Three steps to add like fractions are:

    (1) Add the numerators of the fractions to find the numerator of the sum (the answer.)
    (2) Use the denominator of the fractions as the denominator of the sum.
    (3) Write the answer in lowest terms.

39. $\dfrac{11}{16} - \dfrac{5}{16} = \dfrac{11-5}{16} = \dfrac{6}{16} = \dfrac{6 \div 2}{16 \div 2} = \dfrac{3}{8}$

    He must inspect an additional $\dfrac{3}{8}$ mile.

43. $10 = 2 \cdot 5$

47. $75 = 3 \cdot 5 \cdot 5$

3.2 Least Common Multiples

3.2 Margin Exercises

1. (a) The multiples of 8 are:

    $8, 16, 24, 32, 40, 48, \ldots$.

    (b) The multiples of 10 are:

    $10, 20, 30, 40, 50, \ldots$.

    (c) Look at the answers for (a) and (b). 40 is the only number found in both lists so it is the least common multiple.

2. (a) 4 and 6

    The multiples of 6 are

    $6, 12, 18, 24, 30, 36 \ldots$.

    The first multiple of 6 that is divisible by 4 is 12. The least common multiple of numbers 4 and 6 is 12.

    (b) 3 and 7

    The multiples of 7 are

    $7, 14, 21, 28, 35, 42 \ldots$.

    The first multiple of 7 that is divisible by 3 is 21. The least common multiple of numbers 3 and 7 is 21.

    (c) 6 and 8

    The multiples of 8 are

    $8, 16, 24, 32, 40, 48, \ldots$.

    The first multiple of 8 that is divisible by 6 is 24. The least common multiple of numbers 6 and 8 is 24.

    (d) 5 and 9

    The multiples of 9 are

    $9, 18, 27, 36, 45, 54, \ldots$.

    The first multiple of 9 that is divisible by 5 is 45. The least common multiple of numbers 5 and 9 is 45.

3. (a) $36 = 2 \cdot 2 \cdot 3 \cdot 3$
    $54 = 2 \cdot 3 \cdot 3 \cdot 3$

    (b)

prime	2	3
36 =	2 · 2 ·	3 · 3
54 =	2 ·	3 · 3 · 3

    (c) The largest product in the 2 column is $2 \cdot 2$. The largest product in the 3 column is $3 \cdot 3 \cdot 3$.

    (d) The least common multiple is $2 \cdot 2 \cdot 3 \cdot 3 \cdot 3 = 4 \cdot 27 = 108$.

4. (a) $\dfrac{2}{3}$ and $\dfrac{1}{10}$

prime	2	3	5
3 =		3	
10 =	2 ·		5

    The least common multiple is $3 \cdot 2 \cdot 5 = 30$.

    (b) $\dfrac{3}{10}$ and $\dfrac{6}{5}$

prime	2	5
8 =	2 · 2 · 2	
5 =		5

    The least common multiple is $2 \cdot 2 \cdot 2 \cdot 5 = 40$.

    (c) $\dfrac{5}{6}$ and $\dfrac{1}{14}$

prime	2	3	7
6 =	2 ·	3	
14 =	2 ·		7

    The least common multiple is $2 \cdot 3 \cdot 7 = 42$.

Section 3.2   Least Common Multiples

(d) $\frac{5}{18}$ and $\frac{7}{24}$

prime	2	3
18 =	2 ·	3 · 3
24 =	2 · 2 · 2 ·	3

The least common multiple is $2 \cdot 2 \cdot 2 \cdot 3 \cdot 3 = 72$.

5. (a) 12, 15

prime	2	3	5
12 =	2 · 2 ·	3	
15 =		3 ·	5

The least common multiple is $2 \cdot 2 \cdot 3 \cdot 5 = 60$.

(b) 8, 9, 12

prime	2	3
8 =	2 · 2 · 2	
9 =		3 · 3
12 =	2 · 2 ·	3

The least common multiple is $2 \cdot 2 \cdot 2 \cdot 3 \cdot 3 = 72$.

(c) 18, 20, 30

prime	2	3	5
18 =	2 ·	3 · 3	
20 =	2 · 2 ·		5
30 =	2 ·	3 ·	5

The least common multiple is $2 \cdot 2 \cdot 3 \cdot 3 \cdot 5 = 180$.

(d) 15, 20, 30, 40

prime	2	3	5
15 =		3	5
20 =	2 · 2 ·		5
30 =	2 ·	3	5
40 =	2 · 2 · 2 ·		5

The least common multiple is $2 \cdot 2 \cdot 2 \cdot 3 \cdot 5 = 120$.

6. (a)
```
2 | 6    15
3 | 3    15
5 | 1     5
  | 1     1
```

The least common multiple is the product of the numbers on the left side:

$$2 \cdot 3 \cdot 5 = 30.$$

(b)
```
2 | 20   36
2 | 10   18
3 |  5    9
3 |  5    3
5 |  5    1
  |  1    1
```

The least common multiple is the product of the numbers on the left side:

$$2 \cdot 2 \cdot 3 \cdot 3 \cdot 5 = 180.$$

7. (a) 9 and 24

```
2 | 9   24
2 | 9   12
2 | 9    6
3 | 9    3
3 | 3    1
  | 1    1
```

The least common multiple is:

$$2 \cdot 2 \cdot 2 \cdot 3 \cdot 3 = 72.$$

(b) 25 and 30

```
2 | 25   30
3 | 25   15
5 | 25    5
5 |  5    1
  |  1    1
```

The least common multiple is:

$$2 \cdot 3 \cdot 5 \cdot 5 = 150.$$

(c) 4, 8, and 12

```
2 | 4    8   12
2 | 2    4    6
2 | 1    2    3
3 | 1    1    3
  | 1    1    1
```

The least common multiple is

$$2 \cdot 2 \cdot 2 \cdot 3 = 24.$$

(d) 25, 20, and 35

```
2 | 25   20   35
2 | 25   10   35
5 | 25    5   35
5 |  5    1    7
7 |  1    1    7
  |  1    1    1
```

The least common multiple is :

$$2 \cdot 2 \cdot 5 \cdot 5 \cdot 7 = 700.$$

8. (a) $\dfrac{1}{3} = \dfrac{?}{12}$ $\quad 12 \div 3 = 4$

$\dfrac{1}{3} = \dfrac{1 \cdot 4}{3 \cdot 4} = \dfrac{4}{12}$

(b) $\dfrac{7}{9} = \dfrac{?}{27}$ $\quad 27 \div 9 = 3$

$\dfrac{7}{9} = \dfrac{7 \cdot 3}{9 \cdot 3} = \dfrac{21}{27}$

(c) $\dfrac{4}{5} = \dfrac{?}{50}$ $\quad 50 \div 5 = 10$

$\dfrac{4}{5} = \dfrac{4 \cdot 10}{5 \cdot 10} = \dfrac{40}{50}$

(d) $\dfrac{6}{11} = \dfrac{?}{55}$ $\quad 55 \div 11 = 5$

$\dfrac{6}{11} = \dfrac{6 \cdot 5}{11 \cdot 5} = \dfrac{30}{55}$

3.2 Section Exercises

3. 4 and 6

Multiples of 6:

$6, \underline{12}, 18, 24, 30, \ldots$

12 is the first number divisible by 4. $(12 \div 4 = 3)$
The least common multiple of 4 and 6 is 12.

7. 2 and 7

Multiples of 7:

$7, \underline{14}, 21, 28, 35, 42, \ldots$

14 is the first number divisible by 2. $(14 \div 2 = 7)$
The least common multiple of 2 and 7 is 14.

11. 20 and 50

Multiples of 50:

$50, \underline{100}, 150, 200, 250, 300, \ldots$

100 is the first number divisible by 20.
$(100 \div 20 = 5)$
The least common multiple of 20 and 50 is 100.

15. 18, 24

2	18	24
2	9	12
2	9	6
3	9	3
3	3	1
	1	1

The least common multiple is

$2 \cdot 2 \cdot 2 \cdot 3 \cdot 3$ is 72.

19. 6, 8, 10, 12

prime	2	3	5
6 =	2 ·	3	
8 =	$\underline{2 \cdot 2 \cdot 2}$		
10 =	2 ·		$\underline{5}$
12 =	2 · 2 ·	$\underline{3}$	

The least common multiple is

$2 \cdot 2 \cdot 2 \cdot 3 \cdot 5 = 120.$

23. 15, 20, 30, 40

2	15	20	30	40
2	15	10	15	20
2	15	5	15	10
3	15	5	15	5
5	5	5	5	5
	1	1	1	1

The least common multiple is

$2 \cdot 2 \cdot 2 \cdot 3 \cdot 5 = 120.$

27. $\dfrac{3}{4} = \dfrac{}{24}$ $\quad 24 \div 4 = 6$

$\dfrac{3}{4} = \dfrac{3 \cdot 6}{4 \cdot 6} = \dfrac{18}{24}$

31. $\dfrac{1}{2} = \dfrac{}{4}$ $\quad 4 \div 2 = 2$

$\dfrac{1}{2} = \dfrac{1 \cdot 2}{2 \cdot 2} = \dfrac{2}{4}$

35. $\dfrac{7}{8} = \dfrac{}{32}$ $\quad 32 \div 8 = 4$

$\dfrac{7}{8} = \dfrac{7 \cdot 4}{8 \cdot 4} = \dfrac{28}{32}$

39. $\dfrac{9}{8} = \dfrac{}{40}$ $\quad 40 \div 8 = 5$

$\dfrac{9}{8} = \dfrac{9 \cdot 5}{8 \cdot 5} = \dfrac{45}{40}$

43. $\dfrac{8}{3} = \dfrac{}{51}$ $\quad 51 \div 3 = 17$

$\dfrac{8 \cdot 17}{3 \cdot 17} = \dfrac{136}{51}$

47. $\dfrac{3}{16} = \dfrac{}{144}$ $\quad 144 \div 16 = 9$

$\dfrac{3}{16} = \dfrac{3 \cdot 9}{16 \cdot 9} = \dfrac{27}{144}$

Section 3.3 Adding and Subtracting Unlike Fractions 61

51. $\dfrac{17}{800}, \dfrac{23}{3600}$

2	800	3600
2	400	1800
2	200	900
2	100	450
2	50	225
3	25	225
3	25	75
5	25	25
5	5	5
	1	1

The least common multiple is

$$2 \cdot 2 \cdot 2 \cdot 2 \cdot 2 \cdot 3 \cdot 3 \cdot 5 \cdot 5 = 7200.$$

55. $\dfrac{8}{5}$ $\quad 1 \leftarrow$ whole number
$\phantom{55.\ \dfrac{8}{5}\ \ }5\overline{)8}$
$\phantom{55.\ \dfrac{8}{5}\ \ \ \ }\underline{5}$
$\phantom{55.\ \dfrac{8}{5}\ \ \ \ }3 \leftarrow$ remainder

$\dfrac{8}{5} = 1\dfrac{3}{5}$

59. $\dfrac{27}{7}$ $\quad 3 \leftarrow$ whole number
$\phantom{59.\ \dfrac{27}{7}\ \ }7\overline{)27}$
$\phantom{59.\ \dfrac{27}{7}\ \ \ \ }\underline{21}$
$\phantom{59.\ \dfrac{27}{7}\ \ \ \ }6 \leftarrow$ remainder

$\dfrac{27}{7} = 3\dfrac{6}{7}$

3.3 Adding and Subtracting Unlike Fractions

3.3 Margin Exercises

1. (a) Step 1 $\dfrac{1}{2} + \dfrac{1}{4}$

   $\dfrac{1}{2} = \dfrac{1 \cdot 2}{2 \cdot 2} = \dfrac{2}{4}$ LCD is 4

   Step 2

   $\dfrac{1}{2} + \dfrac{1}{4} = \dfrac{2}{4} + \dfrac{1}{4}$
   $\phantom{\dfrac{1}{2} + \dfrac{1}{4}} = \dfrac{2+1}{4} = \dfrac{3}{4}$

   (b) Step 1 $\dfrac{1}{8} + \dfrac{3}{4}$

   $\dfrac{3}{4} = \dfrac{3 \cdot 2}{4 \cdot 2} = \dfrac{6}{8}$ LCD is 8

   Step 2

   $\dfrac{1}{8} + \dfrac{3}{4} = \dfrac{1}{8} + \dfrac{6}{8}$
   $\phantom{\dfrac{1}{8} + \dfrac{3}{4}} = \dfrac{1+6}{8} = \dfrac{7}{8}$

   (c) Step 1 $\dfrac{3}{10} + \dfrac{2}{5}$

   $\dfrac{2}{5} = \dfrac{2 \cdot 2}{5 \cdot 2} = \dfrac{4}{10}$ LCD is 10

   Step 2

   $\dfrac{3}{10} + \dfrac{2}{5} = \dfrac{3}{10} + \dfrac{4}{10}$
   $\phantom{\dfrac{3}{10} + \dfrac{2}{5}} = \dfrac{3+4}{10}$
   $\phantom{\dfrac{3}{10} + \dfrac{2}{5}} = \dfrac{7}{10}$

   (d) Step 1 $\dfrac{1}{12} + \dfrac{5}{6}$

   $\dfrac{5}{6} = \dfrac{5 \cdot 2}{6 \cdot 2} = \dfrac{10}{12}$ LCD is 12

   Step 2

   $\dfrac{1}{12} + \dfrac{5}{6} = \dfrac{1}{12} + \dfrac{10}{12} = \dfrac{1+10}{12} = \dfrac{11}{12}$

2. (a) $\dfrac{1}{5} + \dfrac{3}{10}$

   Step 1 $\dfrac{1}{5} + \dfrac{3}{10} = \dfrac{2}{10} + \dfrac{3}{10}$

   Step 2 $\dfrac{2}{10} + \dfrac{3}{10} = \dfrac{5}{10}$

   Step 3 $\dfrac{5}{10} = \dfrac{1}{2}$

   (b) $\dfrac{1}{3} + \dfrac{1}{12}$

   Step 1 $\dfrac{1}{3} + \dfrac{1}{12} = \dfrac{4}{12} + \dfrac{1}{12}$

   Step 2 $\dfrac{4}{12} + \dfrac{1}{12} = \dfrac{5}{12}$

   (c) $\dfrac{1}{10} + \dfrac{1}{3} + \dfrac{1}{6}$

   Step 1 $\dfrac{1}{10} + \dfrac{1}{3} + \dfrac{1}{6} = \dfrac{3}{30} + \dfrac{10}{30} + \dfrac{5}{30}$

   Step 2 $\dfrac{3}{30} + \dfrac{10}{30} + \dfrac{5}{30} = \dfrac{18}{30}$

   Step 3 $\dfrac{18}{30} = \dfrac{3}{5}$

3. (a) $\begin{aligned}&\frac{1}{8}=\frac{1}{8}\\+&\frac{3}{4}=\frac{6}{8}\\&\overline{\frac{7}{8}}\end{aligned}$

(b) $\begin{aligned}&\frac{2}{3}=\frac{6}{9}\\+&\frac{2}{9}=\frac{2}{9}\\&\overline{\frac{8}{9}}\end{aligned}$

4. (a) $\frac{1}{2}-\frac{3}{8}$

Step 1 $\frac{1}{2}-\frac{3}{8}=\frac{4}{8}-\frac{3}{8}$

Step 2 $\frac{4}{8}-\frac{3}{8}=\frac{1}{8}$

(b) $\frac{7}{8}-\frac{5}{6}$

Step 1 $\frac{7}{8}-\frac{5}{6}=\frac{21}{24}-\frac{20}{24}$

Step 2 $\frac{21}{24}-\frac{20}{24}=\frac{1}{24}$

(c) $\begin{aligned}&\frac{17}{18}=\frac{17\cdot 3}{18\cdot 3}=\frac{51}{54}\\-&\frac{20}{27}=\frac{20\cdot 2}{27\cdot 2}=\frac{40}{54}\\&\overline{\frac{11}{54}}\end{aligned}$

3.3 Section Exercises

3. $\frac{1}{14}+\frac{3}{7}=\frac{1}{14}+\frac{6}{14}=\frac{1+6}{14}=\frac{7}{14}=\frac{1}{2}$

7. $\frac{3}{5}+\frac{3}{8}=\frac{24}{40}+\frac{15}{40}=\frac{24+15}{40}=\frac{39}{40}$

11. $\frac{1}{3}+\frac{3}{5}$ *LCD is* 15

$=\frac{5}{15}+\frac{9}{15}=\frac{5+9}{15}$

$=\frac{14}{15}$

15. $\frac{3}{10}+\frac{2}{5}+\frac{3}{20}$ *LCD is* 20

$=\frac{6}{20}+\frac{8}{20}+\frac{3}{20}$

$=\frac{6+8+3}{20}=\frac{17}{20}$

19. $\begin{aligned}&\frac{1}{3}=\frac{1\cdot 4}{3\cdot 4}=\frac{4}{12}\\+&\frac{1}{4}=\frac{1\cdot 3}{4\cdot 3}=\frac{3}{12}\\&\overline{\frac{7}{12}}\end{aligned}$

23. $\frac{3}{4}-\frac{1}{8}=\frac{6}{8}-\frac{1}{8}=\frac{6-1}{8}=\frac{5}{8}$

27. $\frac{5}{12}-\frac{1}{4}$

$=\frac{5}{12}-\frac{3}{12}$ *LCD is* 12

$=\frac{5-3}{12}=\frac{2}{12}$

$=\frac{1}{6}$ Lowest terms

31. $\frac{8}{9}-\frac{7}{15}=\frac{40}{45}-\frac{21}{45}=\frac{40-21}{45}=\frac{19}{45}$

35. $\begin{aligned}&\frac{5}{12}=\frac{5\cdot 4}{12\cdot 4}=\frac{20}{48}\\-&\frac{1}{16}=\frac{1\cdot 3}{16\cdot 3}=\frac{3}{48}\\&\overline{\frac{17}{48}}\end{aligned}$

39. The indicator word *remainder* tells you to subtract.

$\begin{aligned}&\frac{3}{4}=\frac{9}{12}\\-&\frac{1}{6}=\frac{2}{12}\\&\overline{\frac{7}{12}}\end{aligned}$

$\frac{7}{12}$ acre is buildable.

43. First add to find the total loss.

$\frac{1}{6}+\frac{1}{3}=\frac{1}{6}+\frac{2}{6}=\frac{1+2}{6}=\frac{3}{6}=\frac{1}{2}$

Then subtract to find the amount remaining.

$\frac{7}{8}-\frac{1}{2}=\frac{7}{8}-\frac{4}{8}=\frac{7-4}{8}=\frac{3}{8}$

$\frac{3}{8}$ gallon remains.

47. Add the time spent in class and in study.

$\frac{1}{12}+\frac{1}{6}=\frac{1}{12}+\frac{2}{12}=\frac{1+2}{12}=\frac{3}{12}=\frac{1}{4}$

$\frac{1}{4}$ of the student's day was spent in class and study.

Section 3.4 Adding and Subtracting Mixed Numbers

51. First add the lengths of the three unknown sides.

$$\frac{1}{4} + \frac{1}{6} + \frac{3}{8} = \frac{6}{24} + \frac{4}{24} + \frac{9}{24}$$
$$= \frac{6+4+9}{24} = \frac{19}{24}$$

Then subtract this sum from the total length of the fencing to find the length of the fourth side.

$$\frac{7}{8} - \frac{19}{24} = \frac{21}{24} - \frac{19}{24}$$
$$\frac{21-19}{24} = \frac{2}{24} = \frac{1}{12}$$

The fourth side is $\frac{1}{12}$ mile.

55. $5 \cdot 2\frac{7}{10} = \frac{5}{1} \cdot \frac{27}{10} = \frac{5 \cdot 27}{10} = \frac{135}{10} = 13\frac{5}{10} = 13\frac{1}{2}$

3.4 Adding and Subtracting Mixed Numbers

3.4 Margin Exercises

1. (a) $\frac{5}{2}$ 2 ← whole number
2)5
4
1 ← remainder

$\frac{5}{2} = 2\frac{1}{2}$

(b) $\frac{14}{3}$ 4 ← whole number
3)14
12
2 ← remainder

$\frac{14}{3} = 4\frac{2}{3}$

(c) $6\frac{3}{4}$ $4 \cdot 6 = 24$
$24 + 3 = 27$

$6\frac{3}{4} = \frac{27}{4}$

(d) $4\frac{5}{8}$ $8 \cdot 4 = 32$
$32 + 5 = 37$

$4\frac{5}{8} = \frac{37}{8}$

2. (a) estimate   exact

$\begin{array}{r} 5 \\ +\ 3 \\ \hline 8 \end{array}$ $\begin{array}{r} 4\frac{5}{8} = 4\frac{15}{24} \\ +\ 3\frac{1}{4} = 3\frac{6}{24} \\ \hline 7\frac{21}{24} = 7\frac{7}{8} \end{array}$

(b)

$25\frac{3}{5} + 12\frac{3}{10} = 25\frac{6}{10} + 12\frac{3}{10}$
$= 37\frac{9}{10}$ exact
$26 + 12 = 38$ estimate

(c) estimate   exact

$\begin{array}{r} 5 \\ -\ 3 \\ \hline 2 \end{array}$ $\begin{array}{r} 5\frac{4}{9} = 5\frac{4}{9} \\ -3\frac{1}{3} = 3\frac{3}{9} \\ \hline 2\frac{1}{9} \end{array}$

3. (a) estimate   exact

$\begin{array}{r} 10 \\ +\ 8 \\ \hline 18 \end{array}$ $\begin{array}{r} 9\frac{3}{4} = 9\frac{6}{8} \\ +\ 7\frac{1}{2} = 7\frac{4}{8} \\ \hline 16\frac{10}{8} \end{array}$

$16\frac{10}{8} = 16 + \frac{10}{8} = 16 + 1\frac{1}{4} = 17\frac{1}{4}$

(b) estimate   exact

$\begin{array}{r} 19 \\ +\ 17 \\ \hline 36 \end{array}$ $\begin{array}{r} 18\frac{2}{3} = 18\frac{10}{15} \\ +\ 16\frac{3}{5} = 16\frac{9}{15} \\ \hline 34\frac{19}{15} \end{array}$

$34 + \frac{19}{15} = 34 + 1\frac{4}{15} = 35\frac{4}{15}$

4. (a) estimate   exact

$\begin{array}{r} 4 \\ -\ 2 \\ \hline 2 \end{array}$ $\begin{array}{r} 4\frac{1}{3} = 4\frac{2}{6} \\ -\ 1\frac{5}{6} = 1\frac{5}{6} \end{array}$

$4\frac{2}{6} + 4 + \frac{2}{6} = 3 + \frac{6}{6} + \frac{2}{6} = 3\frac{8}{6}$

$\begin{array}{r} 3\frac{8}{6} \\ -\ 1\frac{5}{6} \\ \hline 2\frac{3}{6} = 2\frac{1}{2} \end{array}$

(b) estimate   exact

$\begin{array}{r} 3 \\ -\ 2 \\ \hline 1 \end{array}$ $\begin{array}{r} 2\frac{5}{8} = 2\frac{10}{16} \\ -\ 1\frac{15}{16} = 1\frac{15}{16} \end{array}$

$2\frac{10}{16} = 2 + \frac{10}{16} = 1 + 1 + \frac{10}{16}$
$= 1 + \frac{16}{16} + \frac{10}{16} = 1\frac{26}{16}$

$$1\tfrac{26}{16}$$
$$-\,1\tfrac{15}{16}$$
$$\tfrac{11}{16}$$

(c) estimate exact

$$25 \qquad 25\tfrac{1}{6} = 25\tfrac{5}{30}$$
$$-\,19 \qquad -\,18\tfrac{11}{15} = 18\tfrac{22}{30}$$
$$6$$

$$25\tfrac{5}{30} = 25 + \tfrac{5}{30} = 24 + 1 + \tfrac{5}{30}$$
$$= 24 + \tfrac{30}{30} + \tfrac{5}{30} = 24\tfrac{35}{30}$$

$$24\tfrac{35}{30}$$
$$-\,18\tfrac{22}{30}$$
$$6\tfrac{13}{30}$$

5. (a) $1\tfrac{3}{4} = \tfrac{7}{4} = \tfrac{14}{8}$
   $+\,3\tfrac{1}{8} = \tfrac{25}{8} = \tfrac{25}{8}$
   $\tfrac{39}{8} = 4\tfrac{7}{8}$

(b) $6\tfrac{1}{2} = \tfrac{13}{2} = \tfrac{65}{10}$
   $+\,2\tfrac{3}{5} = \tfrac{13}{5} = \tfrac{26}{10}$
   $\tfrac{91}{10} = 9\tfrac{1}{10}$

(c) $7\tfrac{2}{3} = \tfrac{23}{3} = \tfrac{92}{12}$
   $-\,5\tfrac{1}{4} = \tfrac{21}{4} = \tfrac{63}{12}$
   $\tfrac{29}{12} = 2\tfrac{5}{12}$

(d) $8\tfrac{1}{2} = \tfrac{17}{2} = \tfrac{51}{6}$
   $-\,3\tfrac{1}{6} = \tfrac{19}{6} = \tfrac{19}{6}$
   $\tfrac{32}{6} = 5\tfrac{2}{6} = 5\tfrac{1}{3}$

3.4 Section Exercises

3. estimate exact

$$10 \qquad 10\tfrac{1}{6} = 10\tfrac{1}{6}$$
$$+\,5 \qquad +\,5\tfrac{1}{3} = 5\tfrac{2}{6}$$
$$15 \qquad 15\tfrac{3}{6} = 15\tfrac{1}{2}$$

7. estimate exact

$$25 \qquad 24\tfrac{5}{6}$$
$$+\,19 \qquad +\,18\tfrac{5}{6}$$
$$44 \qquad 42\tfrac{10}{6}$$

$$42\tfrac{10}{6} = 42 + 1\tfrac{4}{6}$$
$$= 43\tfrac{2}{3}$$

11. estimate exact

$$23 \qquad 22\tfrac{3}{4} = 22\tfrac{21}{28}$$
$$+\,15 \qquad +\,15\tfrac{3}{7} = 15\tfrac{12}{28}$$
$$38 \qquad 37\tfrac{33}{28}$$

$$37\tfrac{33}{28} = 37 + 1\tfrac{5}{28}$$
$$= 38\tfrac{5}{28}$$

15. estimate exact

$$33 \qquad 32\tfrac{3}{4} = 32\tfrac{18}{24}$$
$$6 \qquad 6\tfrac{1}{3} = 6\tfrac{8}{24}$$
$$+\,15 \qquad +\,14\tfrac{5}{8} = 14\tfrac{15}{24}$$
$$54 \qquad 52\tfrac{41}{24}$$

$$52\tfrac{41}{24} = 52 + 1\tfrac{17}{24} = 53\tfrac{7}{24}$$

19. estimate exact

$$11 \qquad 11\tfrac{9}{20} = 11\tfrac{9}{20} = 10\tfrac{29}{20}$$
$$-\,5 \qquad -\,4\tfrac{3}{5} = 4\tfrac{12}{20} = 4\tfrac{12}{20}$$
$$6 \qquad \qquad\qquad\qquad\qquad\quad 6\tfrac{17}{20}$$

23. estimate exact

$$35 \qquad 35$$
$$-\,17 \qquad -\,17\tfrac{3}{8}$$
$$18$$

Borrow: $35 = 34 + \tfrac{8}{8} = 34\tfrac{8}{8}$

$$35 \quad = \quad 34\tfrac{8}{8}$$
$$-\,17\tfrac{3}{8} = -17\tfrac{3}{8}$$
$$17\tfrac{5}{8}$$

27. estimate estimate

$$26 \qquad 26\tfrac{5}{18} = 26\tfrac{20}{72}$$
$$-\,12 \qquad -\,12\tfrac{11}{24} = 12\tfrac{33}{72}$$
$$14$$

Section 3.4 Adding and Subtracting Mixed Numbers

Borrow:
$$26\tfrac{20}{72} = 25 + 1 + \tfrac{20}{72}$$
$$= 25 + \tfrac{72}{72} + \tfrac{20}{72}$$
$$= 25\tfrac{92}{72}$$

$$26\tfrac{5}{18} = 25\tfrac{92}{72}$$
$$-\,12\tfrac{11}{24} = -12\tfrac{33}{72}$$
$$\overline{\phantom{-12\tfrac{11}{24}} 13\tfrac{59}{72}}$$

31. $2\tfrac{2}{3} = \tfrac{8}{3} = \tfrac{32}{12}$
    $+\,1\tfrac{1}{6} = \tfrac{7}{6} = \tfrac{14}{12}$
    $\overline{\phantom{+\,1\tfrac{1}{6}} \tfrac{46}{12} = 3\tfrac{10}{12} = 3\tfrac{5}{6}}$

35. $1\tfrac{3}{8} = \tfrac{11}{8} = \tfrac{11}{8}$
    $+\,6\tfrac{3}{4} = \tfrac{27}{4} = \tfrac{54}{8}$
    $\overline{\phantom{+\,6\tfrac{3}{4}} \tfrac{65}{8} = 8\tfrac{1}{8}}$

39. $5\tfrac{5}{8} = \tfrac{45}{8} = \tfrac{45}{8}$
    $-\,2\tfrac{3}{4} = \tfrac{11}{4} = \tfrac{22}{8}$
    $\overline{\phantom{-\,2\tfrac{3}{4}} \tfrac{23}{8} = 2\tfrac{7}{8}}$

43. Find the least common denominator. Change the fraction parts so that they have the same denominator. Add the fraction parts. Add the whole number parts. Write the answer as a mixed number.

47. Add the lengths of the two pieces of trim.

    estimate: $13 + 9 = 22$ feet
    exact:
    $$12\tfrac{1}{2} = 12\tfrac{3}{6}$$
    $$+\,8\tfrac{2}{3} = 8\tfrac{4}{6}$$
    $$\overline{\phantom{+\,8\tfrac{2}{3}} 20\tfrac{7}{6} = 20 + \tfrac{6}{6} + \tfrac{1}{6}}$$
    $$= 21\tfrac{1}{6} \text{ feet}$$

    He has $21\tfrac{1}{6}$ feet of trim.

51. Add the lengths of the four sides.
    estimate:
    $$35 + 24 + 35 + 24 = 118 \text{ inches}$$

exact:
$$34\tfrac{1}{2} + 23\tfrac{3}{4} + 34\tfrac{1}{2} + 23\tfrac{3}{4}$$
$$= 34\tfrac{2}{4} + 23\tfrac{3}{4} + 34\tfrac{2}{4} + 23\tfrac{3}{4}$$
$$= 114\tfrac{10}{4} = 116\tfrac{1}{2} \text{ inches}$$

The craftsperson needs $116\tfrac{1}{2}$ inches of lead stripping.

55. Add the lengths of the three sides and subtract this amount from the total length to find the length of the fourth side.

estimate:
$$527 - 108 - 151 - 139 = 129 \text{ feet}$$

exact:
$$107\tfrac{2}{3} = 107\tfrac{16}{24}$$
$$150\tfrac{3}{4} = 150\tfrac{18}{24}$$
$$+\,138\tfrac{5}{8} = 138\tfrac{15}{24}$$
$$\overline{\phantom{+\,138\tfrac{5}{8}} 395\tfrac{49}{24}}$$

$$395 + \tfrac{24}{24} + \tfrac{24}{24} + \tfrac{1}{24} = 397\tfrac{1}{24}$$

$$527\tfrac{1}{24}$$
$$-\,397\tfrac{1}{24}$$
$$\overline{\phantom{-\,397\tfrac{1}{24}} 130 \text{feet}}$$

The length of the fourth side is 130 feet.

59. First add the two given portions of the line.

$$2\tfrac{3}{8}$$
$$+\,2\tfrac{3}{8}$$
$$\overline{\phantom{+\,2\tfrac{3}{8}} 4\tfrac{6}{8} \text{inches}}$$

Then subtract to find the length of the unknown portion of the line.

$$9\tfrac{7}{16} = 9\tfrac{7}{16} = 8\tfrac{23}{16}$$
$$-\,4\tfrac{6}{8} = 4\tfrac{12}{16} = 4\tfrac{12}{16}$$
$$\overline{\phantom{-\,4\tfrac{6}{8}} 4\tfrac{11}{16} \text{inches}}$$

The length of the section is $4\tfrac{11}{16}$ inches.

63. $6^2 + 3 - 9$ *Exponent*
     $36 + 3 - 9$ *Add*
     $39 - 9 = 30$ *Subtract*

67. $3^2 \cdot (5 - 2)$ *Parentheses*
     $3^2 \cdot 3$ *Exponent*
     $9 \cdot 3 = 27$ *Multiply*

3.5 Order Relations and the Order of Operations

3.5 Margin Exercises

1. (a)–(d) See the number line in the margin exercise answers.

2. (a) 2 is to the left of $\frac{9}{4}$ on the number line, so 2 is less than $\frac{9}{4}$.
$$2 < \frac{9}{4}$$

(b) $\frac{11}{4}$ is to the right of $\frac{4}{3}$ on the number line, so $\frac{11}{4}$ is greater than $\frac{4}{3}$.
$$\frac{11}{4} > \frac{4}{3}$$

(c) 0 is to the left of 2 on the number line, so 0 is less than 2.
$$0 < 2$$

(d) $\frac{11}{4}$ is to the right of $\frac{5}{3}$ on the number line, so $\frac{11}{4}$ is greater than $\frac{5}{3}$.
$$\frac{11}{4} > \frac{5}{3}$$

3. (a) $\frac{3}{8} \text{---} \frac{7}{12}$

$\frac{3}{8} = \frac{9}{24}, \frac{7}{12} = \frac{14}{24}$ LCD is 24

$\frac{9}{24} < \frac{14}{24}$, so $\frac{3}{8} < \frac{7}{12}$.

(b) $\frac{11}{18} \text{---} \frac{5}{9}$

$\frac{5}{9} = \frac{10}{18}$

$\frac{11}{18} > \frac{10}{18}$, so $\frac{11}{18} > \frac{5}{9}$.

(c) $\frac{17}{24} \text{---} \frac{5}{6}$

$\frac{5}{6} = \frac{20}{24}$

$\frac{17}{24} < \frac{20}{24}$, so $\frac{17}{24} < \frac{5}{6}$.

(d) $\frac{13}{15} \text{---} \frac{8}{9}$

$\frac{13}{15} = \frac{39}{45}, \frac{8}{9} = \frac{40}{45}$

$\frac{39}{45} < \frac{40}{45}$, so $\frac{13}{15} < \frac{8}{9}$

4. (a) $\left(\frac{1}{2}\right)^2 = \frac{1}{2} \cdot \frac{1}{2} = \frac{1 \cdot 2}{2 \cdot 2} = \frac{1}{4}$

(b) $\left(\frac{7}{8}\right)^2 = \frac{7}{8} \cdot \frac{7}{8} = \frac{7 \cdot 7}{8 \cdot 8} = \frac{49}{64}$

(c) $\left(\frac{2}{3}\right)^2 \cdot \left(\frac{1}{2}\right)^3 = \left(\frac{2}{3} \cdot \frac{2}{3}\right) \cdot \left(\frac{1}{2} \cdot \frac{1}{2} \cdot \frac{1}{2}\right)$

$= \frac{\cancel{2} \cdot \cancel{2} \cdot 1 \cdot 1 \cdot 1}{3 \cdot 3 \cdot \cancel{2} \cdot \cancel{2} \cdot 2}$

$= \frac{1}{18}$

(d) $\left(\frac{1}{4}\right)^2 \cdot \left(\frac{8}{3}\right)^2 = \left(\frac{1}{4} \cdot \frac{1}{4}\right) \cdot \left(\frac{8}{3} \cdot \frac{8}{3}\right)$

$= \frac{1 \cdot 1 \cdot \cancel{8} \cdot \cancel{8}}{\cancel{4} \cdot \cancel{4} \cdot 3 \cdot 3}$

$= \frac{4}{9}$

5. (a) $\frac{2}{3} - \frac{5}{9} \cdot \frac{3}{4} = \frac{2}{3} - \frac{5}{\cancel{9}} \cdot \frac{\cancel{3}}{4}$

$= \frac{2}{3} - \frac{5}{3} \cdot \frac{1}{4}$

$= \frac{2}{3} - \frac{5}{12}$

$= \frac{8}{12} - \frac{5}{12}$

$= \frac{3}{12} = \frac{1}{4}$

(b) $\frac{3}{5} \cdot \left(\frac{3}{4} - \frac{1}{3}\right) = \frac{3}{5} \cdot \left(\frac{9}{12} - \frac{4}{12}\right)$

$= \frac{\cancel{3}}{\cancel{5}} \cdot \frac{\cancel{5}}{\cancel{12}} = \frac{1}{4}$

(c) $\frac{3}{4} \cdot \frac{2}{3} - \left(\frac{1}{2}\right)^2 = \frac{\cancel{3}}{\cancel{4}} \cdot \frac{\cancel{2}}{\cancel{3}} - \frac{1}{2} \cdot \frac{1}{2}$

$= \frac{1}{2} - \frac{1}{4}$

$= \frac{2}{4} - \frac{1}{4} = \frac{1}{4}$

Section 3.5 Order Relations and the Order of Operations

(d) $\dfrac{\left(\frac{5}{6}\right)^2}{\frac{4}{3}} = \dfrac{\frac{5}{6} \cdot \frac{5}{6}}{\frac{4}{3}}$

$= \dfrac{\frac{25}{36}}{\frac{4}{3}}$

$= \dfrac{25}{36} \div \dfrac{4}{3}$

$= \dfrac{25}{\cancel{36}_{12}} \cdot \dfrac{\cancel{3}^1}{4} = \dfrac{25}{48}$

3.5 Section Exercises

For Exercises 3–11, see the number line graph in the answer section of the textbook.

3. $\dfrac{3}{2}$ 7. $2\frac{1}{6}$ 11. $3\frac{1}{4}$

15. $\dfrac{5}{6} \mathrel{\rule{1em}{0.4pt}} \dfrac{11}{12}$

$\dfrac{5}{6} = \dfrac{10}{12}$ LCD is 12

$\dfrac{10}{12} < \dfrac{11}{12}$, so $\dfrac{5}{6} < \dfrac{11}{12}$.

19. $\dfrac{7}{12} \mathrel{\rule{1em}{0.4pt}} \dfrac{11}{18}$

$\dfrac{7}{12} = \dfrac{21}{36}, \dfrac{11}{18} = \dfrac{22}{36}$ LCD is 36

$\dfrac{21}{36} < \dfrac{22}{36}$, so $\dfrac{7}{12} < \dfrac{11}{18}$.

23. $\dfrac{37}{50} \mathrel{\rule{1em}{0.4pt}} \dfrac{13}{20}$

$\dfrac{37}{50} = \dfrac{74}{100}, \dfrac{13}{20} = \dfrac{65}{100}$

$\dfrac{74}{100} > \dfrac{65}{100}$, so $\dfrac{37}{50} > \dfrac{13}{20}$.

27. $\left(\dfrac{5}{7}\right)^2 = \dfrac{5}{7} \cdot \dfrac{5}{7} = \dfrac{25}{49}$

31. $\left(\dfrac{5}{6}\right)^3 = \dfrac{5}{6} \cdot \dfrac{5}{6} \cdot \dfrac{5}{6} = \dfrac{125}{216}$

35. $\left(\dfrac{1}{2}\right)^5 = \dfrac{1}{2} \cdot \dfrac{1}{2} \cdot \dfrac{1}{2} \cdot \dfrac{1}{2} \cdot \dfrac{1}{2} = \dfrac{1}{32}$

39. $4 + 2 - 2^2$ *Exponent*
    $4 + 2 - 4$ *Add*
    $6 - 4 = 2$ *Subtract*

43. $\left(\dfrac{1}{2}\right)^2 \cdot 4$ *Exponent*

$\dfrac{1}{2} \cdot \dfrac{1}{2} \cdot 4$ *Multiply from left to right*

$\dfrac{1}{4} \cdot \dfrac{4}{1} = 1$

47. $\left(\dfrac{3}{4}\right)^2 \cdot \left(\dfrac{2}{3}\right)^2$ *Exponents*

$= \dfrac{\cancel{3}^1}{\cancel{4}_2} \cdot \dfrac{\cancel{3}^1}{\cancel{4}_2} \cdot \dfrac{\cancel{2}^1}{\cancel{3}_1} \cdot \dfrac{\cancel{2}^1}{\cancel{3}_1} = \dfrac{1}{4}$ *Multiply*

51. $\dfrac{4}{3} \cdot \dfrac{3}{8} + \dfrac{3}{4} \cdot \dfrac{1}{4}$

$= \dfrac{\cancel{4}^1}{\cancel{3}_1} \cdot \dfrac{\cancel{3}^1}{\cancel{8}_2} + \dfrac{3}{4} \cdot \dfrac{1}{4}$ *Multiply*

$= \dfrac{1}{2} + \dfrac{3}{16}$

$= \dfrac{8}{16} + \dfrac{3}{16} = \dfrac{11}{16}$ *Add*

55. $\left(\dfrac{1}{3} + \dfrac{1}{6}\right) \cdot \dfrac{1}{2}$

$= \left(\dfrac{4}{12} + \dfrac{2}{12}\right) \cdot \dfrac{1}{2}$ *Parentheses*

$= \dfrac{\cancel{6}^3}{12} \cdot \dfrac{1}{\cancel{2}_1} = \dfrac{3}{12} = \dfrac{1}{4}$ *Multiply*

59. $\left(\dfrac{3}{5} - \dfrac{1}{10}\right) \div \dfrac{5}{2}$

$= \left(\dfrac{6}{10} - \dfrac{1}{10}\right) \div \dfrac{5}{2}$ *Parentheses*

$= \dfrac{5}{10} \div \dfrac{5}{2}$ *Invert*

$= \dfrac{\cancel{5}^1}{\cancel{10}_5} \cdot \dfrac{\cancel{2}^1}{\cancel{5}_1} = \dfrac{1}{5}$ *Multiply*

63. $\left(\dfrac{3}{4}\right)^2 - \left(\dfrac{3}{4} - \dfrac{1}{8}\right) \div \dfrac{7}{4}$

$= \left(\dfrac{3}{4}\right)^2 - \left(\dfrac{6}{8} - \dfrac{1}{8}\right) \div \dfrac{7}{4}$ *Parentheses*

$= \left(\dfrac{3}{4}\right)^2 - \dfrac{5}{8} \div \dfrac{7}{4}$ *Exponent*

$= \dfrac{3}{4} \cdot \dfrac{3}{4} - \dfrac{5}{8} \div \dfrac{7}{4}$ *Multiply*

$= \dfrac{9}{16} - \dfrac{5}{8} \div \dfrac{7}{4}$ *Invert*

$$= \frac{9}{16} - \frac{\cancel{5}}{\cancel{8}_2} \cdot \frac{\cancel{4}^1}{7} \qquad \textit{Multiply}$$

$$= \frac{9}{16} - \frac{5}{14}$$

$$= \frac{63}{112} - \frac{40}{112} = \frac{23}{112} \qquad \textit{Subtract}$$

67. $\left(\frac{3}{4}\right)^2 \cdot \left(\frac{2}{3} - \frac{5}{9}\right) - \frac{1}{4} \cdot \frac{1}{8}$

$$= \left(\frac{3}{4}\right)^2 \cdot \left(\frac{6}{9} - \frac{5}{9}\right) - \frac{1}{4} \cdot \frac{1}{8} \qquad \textit{Parentheses}$$

$$= \left(\frac{3}{4}\right)^2 \cdot \frac{1}{9} - \frac{1}{4} \cdot \frac{1}{8} \qquad \textit{Exponent}$$

$$= \frac{\cancel{3}^1}{4} \cdot \frac{\cancel{3}^1}{4} \cdot \frac{1}{\cancel{9}_1} - \frac{1}{4} \cdot \frac{1}{8} \qquad \textit{Multiply}$$

$$= \frac{1}{16} - \frac{1}{32}$$

$$= \frac{2}{32} - \frac{1}{32} = \frac{1}{32} \qquad \textit{Subtract}$$

71. 4,071,280 is four million, seventy-one thousand, two hundred eighty.

Chapter 3 Review Exercises

1. $\frac{2}{8} + \frac{5}{8} = \frac{2+5}{8} = \frac{7}{8}$

2. $\frac{1}{5} + \frac{2}{5} = \frac{1+2}{5} = \frac{3}{5}$

3. $\frac{1}{8} + \frac{3}{8} + \frac{2}{8} = \frac{1+3+2}{8} = \frac{6}{8} = \frac{3}{4}$

4. $\frac{7}{12} - \frac{2}{12} = \frac{7-2}{12} = \frac{5}{12}$

5. $\frac{3}{10} - \frac{1}{10} = \frac{3-1}{10} = \frac{2}{10} = \frac{1}{5}$

6. $\frac{5}{16} - \frac{1}{16} = \frac{4}{16} = \frac{1}{4}$

7. $\frac{36}{62} - \frac{10}{62} = \frac{36-10}{62} = \frac{26}{62} = \frac{13}{31}$

8. $\frac{79}{108} - \frac{47}{108} = \frac{79-47}{108} = \frac{32}{108} = \frac{8}{27}$

9. Add to find what fraction of the lumber he milled in 2 days.

$$\frac{3}{16} + \frac{5}{16} = \frac{8}{16} = \frac{1}{2}$$

He milled $\frac{1}{2}$ of the lumber.

10. Subtract the fraction of her workout in the afternoon from her workout in the morning.

$$\frac{7}{10} - \frac{1}{10} = \frac{7-1}{10} = \frac{6}{10} = \frac{3}{5}$$

She has $\frac{3}{5}$ less of a workout in the afternoon.

11. 4, 3

Multiples of 4:

$$4, 8, \underline{12}, 16, 20, 24, \ldots$$

12 is the first number divisible by 3. $(12 \div 3 = 4)$
The least common multiple of 4 and 3 is 12.

12. 8, 5

Multiples of 8:

$$8, 16, 24, 32, \underline{40}, 48, \ldots$$

40 is the first number divisible by 5. $(40 \div 5 = 8)$
The least common multiple of 8 and 5 is 40.

13.
2	10	12	20
2	5	6	10
3	5	3	5
5	5	1	5
	1	1	1

LCM $= 2 \cdot 2 \cdot 3 \cdot 5 = 60$

14.
2	9	20	15
2	9	10	15
3	9	5	15
3	3	5	5
5	1	5	5
	1	1	1

LCM $= 2 \cdot 2 \cdot 3 \cdot 3 \cdot 5 = 180$

15.
2	6	8	5	15
2	3	4	5	15
2	3	2	5	15
3	3	1	5	15
5	1	1	5	5
	1	1	1	1

LCM $= 2 \cdot 2 \cdot 2 \cdot 3 \cdot 5 = 120$

16.
2	24	5	16
2	12	5	8
2	6	5	4
2	3	5	2
3	3	5	1
5	1	5	1
	1	1	1

LCM $= 2 \cdot 2 \cdot 2 \cdot 2 \cdot 3 \cdot 5 = 240$

Chapter 3 Review Exercises

17. $\dfrac{3}{4} = \dfrac{}{16}$ $16 \div 4 = 4$

$\dfrac{3}{4} = \dfrac{3 \cdot 4}{4 \cdot 4} = \dfrac{12}{16}$

18. $\dfrac{2}{3} = \dfrac{}{15}$ $15 \div 3 = 5$

$\dfrac{2}{3} = \dfrac{2 \cdot 5}{3 \cdot 5} = \dfrac{10}{15}$

19. $\dfrac{2}{5} = \dfrac{}{25}$ $25 \div 5 = 5$

$\dfrac{2}{5} = \dfrac{2 \cdot 5}{5 \cdot 5} = \dfrac{10}{25}$

20. $\dfrac{5}{9} = \dfrac{}{81}$ $81 \div 9 = 9$

$\dfrac{5}{9} = \dfrac{5 \cdot 9}{9 \cdot 9} = \dfrac{45}{81}$

21. $\dfrac{7}{16} = \dfrac{}{144}$ $144 \div 16 = 9$

$\dfrac{7}{16} = \dfrac{7 \cdot 9}{16 \cdot 9} = \dfrac{63}{144}$

22. $\dfrac{3}{22} = \dfrac{}{88}$ $88 \div 22 = 4$

$\dfrac{3}{22} = \dfrac{3 \cdot 4}{22 \cdot 4} = \dfrac{12}{88}$

23. $\dfrac{1}{4} + \dfrac{1}{3} = \dfrac{3}{12} + \dfrac{4}{12} = \dfrac{3+4}{12} = \dfrac{7}{12}$

24. $\dfrac{1}{5} + \dfrac{3}{10} + \dfrac{3}{8} = \dfrac{8}{40} + \dfrac{12}{40} + \dfrac{15}{40}$

$= \dfrac{8 + 12 + 15}{40}$

$= \dfrac{35}{40} = \dfrac{7}{8}$

25. $\dfrac{9}{16} = \dfrac{27}{48}$

$+ \dfrac{1}{12} = \dfrac{4}{48}$

$\dfrac{31}{48}$

26. $\dfrac{4}{5} - \dfrac{1}{4} = \dfrac{16}{20} - \dfrac{5}{20} = \dfrac{16-5}{20} = \dfrac{11}{20}$

27. $\dfrac{3}{4} = \dfrac{9}{12}$

$- \dfrac{1}{3} = \dfrac{4}{12}$

$\dfrac{5}{12}$

28. $\dfrac{11}{12} = \dfrac{33}{36}$

$- \dfrac{4}{9} = \dfrac{16}{36}$

$\dfrac{17}{36}$

29. To find the total cubic yards of gravel on the truck add the fractional amounts.

$\dfrac{1}{4} + \dfrac{1}{3} + \dfrac{3}{8} = \dfrac{1 \cdot 6}{4 \cdot 6} + \dfrac{1 \cdot 8}{3 \cdot 8} + \dfrac{3 \cdot 3}{8 \cdot 3}$

$= \dfrac{6}{24} + \dfrac{8}{24} + \dfrac{9}{24}$

$= \dfrac{6 + 8 + 9}{24} = \dfrac{23}{24}$

The truck contains $\dfrac{23}{24}$ cubic yard of gravel.

30. Add the fractional amounts that have already been raised.

$\dfrac{2}{5} = \dfrac{24}{60}$

$\dfrac{1}{3} = \dfrac{20}{60}$

$+ \dfrac{1}{4} = \dfrac{15}{60}$

$\dfrac{59}{60}$

They have raised $\dfrac{59}{60}$ of the amount needed.

31. estimate   exact

$\quad\quad 26 \quad\quad\quad 25\tfrac{3}{4} = 25\tfrac{6}{8}$

$\quad + 16 \quad\quad + 16\tfrac{3}{8} = 16\tfrac{3}{8}$

$\quad\quad 42 \quad\quad\quad\quad\quad\quad\quad 41\tfrac{9}{8}$

$41\tfrac{9}{8} = 41 + 1\tfrac{1}{8} = 42\tfrac{1}{8}$

32. estimate   exact

$\quad\quad 78 \quad\quad\quad 78\tfrac{3}{7}$

$\quad + 18 \quad\quad + 17\tfrac{6}{7}$

$\quad\quad 96 \quad\quad\quad 95\tfrac{9}{7} = 95 + 1\tfrac{2}{7} = 96\tfrac{2}{7}$

33. estimate   exact

$\quad\quad 13 \quad\quad\quad 12\tfrac{3}{5} = 12\tfrac{48}{80}$

$\quad\quad\; 9 \quad\quad\quad\;\; 8\tfrac{5}{8} = 8\tfrac{50}{80}$

$\quad + 10 \quad\quad + 10\tfrac{5}{16} = 10\tfrac{25}{80}$

$\quad\quad 32 \quad\quad\quad\quad\quad\quad\quad 30\tfrac{123}{80}$

$30\tfrac{123}{80} + 1\tfrac{43}{80} = 31\tfrac{43}{80}$

34.

estimate	exact
18	$18\frac{1}{3} = 18\frac{4}{12} = 17\frac{16}{12}$
$-\ 13$	$-\ 12\frac{3}{4} = 12\frac{9}{12} = 12\frac{9}{12}$
5	$5\frac{7}{12}$

35.

estimate	exact
74	$73\frac{1}{2} = 73\frac{3}{6} = 72\frac{9}{6}$
$-\ 56$	$-\ 55\frac{2}{3} = 55\frac{4}{6} = 55\frac{4}{6}$
18	$17\frac{5}{6}$

36.

estimate	exact
215	$215\frac{7}{16}$
$-\ 136$	$-\ 136$
79	$79\frac{7}{16}$

37.
$3\frac{1}{4} = \frac{13}{4} = \frac{13}{4}$
$+\ 2\frac{1}{2} = \frac{5}{2} = \frac{10}{4}$
$\frac{23}{4} = 5\frac{3}{4}$

38.
$2\frac{1}{3} = \frac{7}{3} = \frac{28}{12}$
$+\ 3\frac{3}{4} = \frac{15}{4} = \frac{45}{12}$
$\frac{73}{12} = 6\frac{1}{12}$

39.
$3\frac{3}{5} = \frac{18}{5} = \frac{54}{15}$
$+\ 2\frac{2}{3} = \frac{8}{3} = \frac{40}{15}$
$\frac{94}{15} = 6\frac{4}{15}$

40.
$4\frac{1}{4} = \frac{17}{4} = \frac{51}{12}$
$-\ 1\frac{5}{12} = \frac{17}{12} = \frac{17}{12}$
$\frac{34}{12} = 2\frac{5}{6}$

41.
$8\frac{1}{3} = \frac{25}{3} = \frac{50}{6}$
$-\ 2\frac{5}{6} = \frac{17}{6} = \frac{17}{6}$
$\frac{33}{6} = 5\frac{1}{2}$

42.
$5\frac{5}{12} = \frac{65}{12} = \frac{130}{24}$
$-\ 2\frac{5}{8} = \frac{21}{8} = \frac{63}{24}$
$\frac{67}{24} = 2\frac{19}{24}$

43. Add to find the total gallons used. Then subtract the gallons used from the total gallons to find the amount remaining.

estimate: $15 - 6 - 7 = 2$ gallons

exact:

$5\frac{1}{2} = 5\frac{2}{4}$
$+\ 6\frac{3}{4} = 6\frac{3}{4}$
$11\frac{5}{4} = 11 + 1\frac{1}{4} = 12\frac{1}{4}$

$14\frac{2}{3} = 14\frac{8}{12}$
$-\ 12\frac{1}{4} = 12\frac{3}{12}$
$2\frac{5}{12}$

The lab has $2\frac{5}{12}$ gallons remaining.

44. Add the tons collected on Saturday and the tons collected on Sunday.

estimate: $15 + 19 = 34$ tons

exact:

$14\frac{3}{4} + 18\frac{2}{3} = 14\frac{9}{12} + 18\frac{8}{12}$
$= 32\frac{17}{12} = 33\frac{5}{12}$

The ecology club collected $33\frac{5}{12}$ tons of cardboard.

45. To find their total weight add.

estimate: $6 + 5 + 5 = 16$ pounds

exact:

$5\frac{3}{4} = 5\frac{18}{24}$
$4\frac{7}{8} = 4\frac{21}{24}$
$+\ 5\frac{1}{3} = 5\frac{8}{24}$
$14\frac{47}{24} = 14 + 1\frac{23}{24} = 15\frac{23}{24}$

The triplet's total weight at birth was $15\frac{23}{24}$ pounds.

46. To find the total amount of land that she already has, add the two parcels.
To find how much more land that she needs, subtract the total amount she has from the total amount she needs.

estimate: $9 - 2 - 3 = 4$ acres

Chapter 3 Review Exercises

exact:

$$1\tfrac{11}{16} = 1\tfrac{11}{16}$$
$$+\ 2\tfrac{3}{4} = 2\tfrac{12}{16}$$
$$\overline{\phantom{+\ 2\tfrac{3}{4}} \ 3\tfrac{23}{16}} = 3 + 1\tfrac{7}{16} = 4\tfrac{7}{16}$$

$$8\tfrac{1}{2} = 8\tfrac{8}{16}$$
$$-\ 4\tfrac{7}{16} = 4\tfrac{7}{16}$$
$$\overline{\phantom{-\ 4\tfrac{7}{16}} \ 4\tfrac{1}{16}}$$

She needs $4\tfrac{1}{16}$ acres of land.

For Exercises 47-50, see the number line graphs in the answer section of the textbook.

47. $\dfrac{3}{8}$

48. $\dfrac{7}{4}$

49. $\dfrac{8}{3}$

50. $2\tfrac{1}{5}$

51. $\dfrac{3}{4}$ — $\dfrac{7}{8}$

$\dfrac{3}{4} = \dfrac{6}{8}$

$\dfrac{6}{8} < \dfrac{7}{8}$, so $\dfrac{3}{4} < \dfrac{7}{8}$.

52. $\dfrac{5}{8}$ — $\dfrac{2}{3}$

$\dfrac{5}{8} = \dfrac{15}{24}$, $\dfrac{2}{3} = \dfrac{16}{24}$

$\dfrac{15}{24} < \dfrac{16}{24}$, so $\dfrac{5}{8} < \dfrac{2}{3}$.

53. $\dfrac{2}{3}$ — $\dfrac{8}{15}$

$\dfrac{2}{3} = \dfrac{10}{15}$

$\dfrac{10}{15} > \dfrac{8}{15}$, so $\dfrac{2}{3} > \dfrac{8}{15}$.

54. $\dfrac{7}{10}$ — $\dfrac{8}{15}$

$\dfrac{7}{10} = \dfrac{21}{30}$, $\dfrac{8}{15} = \dfrac{16}{30}$

$\dfrac{21}{30} > \dfrac{16}{30}$, so $\dfrac{7}{10} > \dfrac{8}{15}$.

55. $\dfrac{5}{12}$ — $\dfrac{8}{18}$

$\dfrac{5}{12} = \dfrac{15}{36}$, $\dfrac{8}{18} = \dfrac{16}{36}$

$\dfrac{15}{36} < \dfrac{16}{36}$, so $\dfrac{5}{12} < \dfrac{8}{18}$.

56. $\dfrac{7}{20}$ — $\dfrac{8}{25}$

$\dfrac{7}{20} = \dfrac{35}{100}$, $\dfrac{8}{25} = \dfrac{32}{100}$

$\dfrac{35}{100} > \dfrac{32}{100}$, so $\dfrac{7}{20} > \dfrac{8}{25}$.

57. $\dfrac{19}{36}$ — $\dfrac{29}{54}$

$\dfrac{19}{36} = \dfrac{57}{108}$, $\dfrac{29}{54} = \dfrac{58}{108}$

$\dfrac{57}{108} < \dfrac{58}{108}$, so $\dfrac{19}{36} < \dfrac{29}{54}$.

58. $\dfrac{19}{132}$ — $\dfrac{7}{55}$

$\dfrac{19}{132} = \dfrac{95}{660}$, $\dfrac{7}{55} = \dfrac{84}{660}$

$\dfrac{95}{660} > \dfrac{84}{660}$, so $\dfrac{19}{132} > \dfrac{7}{55}$.

59. $\left(\dfrac{1}{3}\right)^2 = \dfrac{1}{3} \cdot \dfrac{1}{3} = \dfrac{1}{9}$

60. $\left(\dfrac{3}{4}\right)^2 = \dfrac{3}{4} \cdot \dfrac{3}{4} = \dfrac{9}{16}$

61. $\left(\dfrac{3}{5}\right)^3 = \dfrac{3}{5} \cdot \dfrac{3}{5} \cdot \dfrac{3}{5} = \dfrac{27}{125}$

62. $\left(\dfrac{3}{8}\right)^4 = \dfrac{3}{8} \cdot \dfrac{3}{8} \cdot \dfrac{3}{8} \cdot \dfrac{3}{8} = \dfrac{81}{4096}$

63. $\quad 5 \cdot \left(\dfrac{1}{4}\right)^2 \quad\quad$ *Exponent*

$= 5 \cdot \dfrac{1}{4} \cdot \dfrac{1}{4} \quad$ *Multiply*

$= \dfrac{5}{16}$

64. $\quad \left(\dfrac{3}{4}\right)^2 \cdot 20 \quad\quad$ *Exponent*

$= \dfrac{3}{4} \cdot \dfrac{3}{\cancel{4}} \cdot \dfrac{\cancel{20}^{\,5}}{1} \quad$ *Multiply*

$= \dfrac{45}{4} = 11\tfrac{1}{4}$

65. $\left(\dfrac{3}{4}\right)^2 \cdot \left(\dfrac{8}{9}\right)^2$ *Exponents*

$= \dfrac{3}{4} \cdot \dfrac{3}{4} \cdot \dfrac{8}{9} \cdot \dfrac{8}{9}$

$= \dfrac{\cancel{3}^1}{\cancel{4}_1} \cdot \dfrac{\cancel{3}^1}{\cancel{4}_1} \cdot \dfrac{\cancel{8}^2}{\cancel{9}_3} \cdot \dfrac{\cancel{8}^2}{\cancel{9}_3}$ *Multiply*

$= \dfrac{4}{9}$

66. $\dfrac{3}{5} \div \left(\dfrac{1}{10} + \dfrac{1}{5}\right)$

$= \dfrac{3}{5} \div \left(\dfrac{1}{10} + \dfrac{2}{10}\right)$ *Parentheses*

$= \dfrac{3}{5} \div \dfrac{3}{10}$ *Invert*

$= \dfrac{\cancel{3}^1}{\cancel{5}_1} \cdot \dfrac{\cancel{10}^2}{\cancel{3}_1} = 2$ *Multiply*

67. $\left(\dfrac{1}{2}\right)^2 \cdot \left(\dfrac{1}{4} + \dfrac{1}{2}\right)$ *Exponent*

$= \dfrac{1}{2} \cdot \dfrac{1}{2} \cdot \left(\dfrac{1}{4} + \dfrac{1}{2}\right)$ *Parentheses*

$= \dfrac{1}{2} \cdot \dfrac{1}{2} \cdot \dfrac{3}{4} = \dfrac{3}{16}$ *Multiply*

68. $\left(\dfrac{1}{4}\right)^3 + \left(\dfrac{5}{8} + \dfrac{3}{4}\right)$ *Parentheses*

$= \left(\dfrac{1}{4}\right)^3 + \dfrac{11}{8}$ *Exponent*

$= \dfrac{1}{4} \cdot \dfrac{1}{4} \cdot \dfrac{1}{4} + \dfrac{11}{8}$ *Multiply*

$= \dfrac{1}{64} + \dfrac{11}{8}$

$= \dfrac{1}{64} + \dfrac{88}{64} = 1\dfrac{25}{64}$ *Add*

69. $\dfrac{7}{8} - \dfrac{3}{8} = \dfrac{7-3}{8} = \dfrac{4}{8} = \dfrac{1}{2}$

70. $\dfrac{2}{3} - \dfrac{1}{4} = \dfrac{8}{12} - \dfrac{3}{12} = \dfrac{8-3}{12} = \dfrac{5}{12}$

71. $\dfrac{75}{86} - \dfrac{4}{43} = \dfrac{75-8}{86} = \dfrac{67}{86}$

72. $\dfrac{1}{4} + \dfrac{1}{8} + \dfrac{5}{16} = \dfrac{4}{16} + \dfrac{2}{16} + \dfrac{5}{16}$

$= \dfrac{4+2+5}{16} = \dfrac{11}{16}$

73. $\begin{aligned}5\tfrac{2}{3} &= 5\tfrac{4}{6}\\ -2\tfrac{1}{2} &= 2\tfrac{3}{6}\\ \hline &3\tfrac{1}{6}\end{aligned}$

74. $\begin{aligned}9\tfrac{1}{2} &= \tfrac{19}{2} = \tfrac{38}{4}\\ +16\tfrac{3}{4} &= \tfrac{67}{4} = \tfrac{67}{4}\\ \hline &\tfrac{105}{4} = 26\tfrac{1}{4}\end{aligned}$

75. $\begin{aligned}7 &= 6\tfrac{8}{8}\\ -1\tfrac{5}{8} &= 1\tfrac{5}{8}\\ \hline &5\tfrac{3}{8}\end{aligned}$

76. $\begin{aligned}2\tfrac{3}{5} &= 2\tfrac{48}{80}\\ 8\tfrac{5}{8} &= 8\tfrac{50}{80}\\ +\tfrac{5}{16} &= \tfrac{25}{80}\\ \hline 10\tfrac{123}{80} &= 10 + 1\tfrac{43}{80} = 11\tfrac{43}{80}\end{aligned}$

77. $\begin{aligned}92\tfrac{5}{16}\\ -27\phantom{\tfrac{5}{16}}\\ \hline 65\tfrac{5}{16}\end{aligned}$

78. $\dfrac{7}{22} + \dfrac{3}{22} + \dfrac{3}{11} = \dfrac{7}{22} + \dfrac{3}{22} + \dfrac{6}{22}$

$= \dfrac{7+3+6}{22} = \dfrac{16}{22} = \dfrac{8}{11}$

79. $\left(\dfrac{1}{4}\right)^2 \cdot \left(\dfrac{2}{5}\right)^3$ *Exponent*

$= \dfrac{1}{\cancel{4}_2} \cdot \dfrac{1}{\cancel{4}_2} \cdot \dfrac{\cancel{2}^1}{5} \cdot \dfrac{\cancel{2}^1}{5} \cdot \dfrac{\cancel{2}^1}{5}$ *Multiply*

$= \dfrac{1}{250}$

80. $\dfrac{1}{4} \div \left(\dfrac{1}{3} + \dfrac{1}{6}\right)$

$= \dfrac{1}{4} \div \left(\dfrac{2}{6} + \dfrac{1}{6}\right)$ *Parentheses*

$= \dfrac{1}{4} \div \dfrac{3}{6}$ *Invert*

$= \dfrac{1}{4} \cdot \dfrac{6}{3} = \dfrac{6}{12} = \dfrac{1}{2}$ *Multiply*

81. $\left(\dfrac{2}{3}\right)^2 \cdot \left(\dfrac{1}{3} + \dfrac{1}{6}\right)$ *Parentheses*

$= \left(\dfrac{2}{3}\right)^2 \cdot \dfrac{1}{2}$ *Exponent*

$= \dfrac{\cancel{4}^2}{9} \cdot \dfrac{1}{\cancel{2}_1} = \dfrac{2}{9}$ *Multiply*

Chapter 3 Test

82. $\left(\dfrac{2}{3}\right)^3 + \left(\dfrac{2}{3} - \dfrac{5}{9}\right)$ *Parentheses*

$= \left(\dfrac{2}{3}\right)^3 + \dfrac{1}{9}$ *Exponent*

$= \dfrac{2}{3} \cdot \dfrac{2}{3} \cdot \dfrac{2}{3} + \dfrac{1}{9}$ *Multiply*

$= \dfrac{8}{27} + \dfrac{1}{9} = \dfrac{11}{27}$ *Add*

83. $\dfrac{7}{8} \text{—} \dfrac{13}{16}$ *LCD is* 16

$\dfrac{14}{16} > \dfrac{13}{16}$, so $\dfrac{7}{8} > \dfrac{13}{16}$.

84. $\dfrac{7}{10} \text{—} \dfrac{13}{20}$ *LCD is* 20

$\dfrac{14}{20} > \dfrac{13}{20}$, so $\dfrac{7}{10} > \dfrac{13}{20}$.

85. $\dfrac{19}{40} \text{—} \dfrac{29}{60}$ *LCD is* 120

$\dfrac{57}{120} < \dfrac{58}{120}$, so $\dfrac{19}{40} < \dfrac{29}{60}$.

86. $\dfrac{5}{8} \text{—} \dfrac{17}{30}$ *LCD is* 120

$\dfrac{75}{120} > \dfrac{68}{120}$, so $\dfrac{5}{8} > \dfrac{17}{30}$.

87.
2	18	24
2	9	12
2	9	6
3	9	3
3	3	1
	1	1

The least common multiple is $2 \cdot 2 \cdot 2 \cdot 3 \cdot 3 = 72$.

88.
2	10	15	20	25
2	5	15	10	25
3	5	15	5	25
5	5	5	5	25
5	1	1	1	5
	1	1	1	1

The least common multiple is $2 \cdot 2 \cdot 3 \cdot 5 \cdot 5 = 300$.

89.
2	8	9	12	18
2	4	9	6	9
2	2	9	3	9
3	1	9	3	9
3	1	3	1	3
	1	1	1	1

The least common multiple is $2 \cdot 2 \cdot 2 \cdot 3 \cdot 3 = 72$.

90. $\dfrac{3}{8} = \dfrac{}{48}$ $48 \div 8 = 6$

$\dfrac{3}{8} = \dfrac{3 \cdot 6}{8 \cdot 6} = \dfrac{18}{48}$

91. $\dfrac{9}{12} = \dfrac{}{144}$ $144 \div 12 = 12$

$\dfrac{9}{12} = \dfrac{9 \cdot 12}{12 \cdot 12} = \dfrac{108}{144}$

92. $\dfrac{3}{7} = \dfrac{}{420}$ $420 \div 7 = 60$

$\dfrac{3}{7} = \dfrac{3 \cdot 60}{7 \cdot 60} = \dfrac{180}{420}$

93. Add to find the number of feet needed to carpet the two rooms. Then subtract to find the number of feet remaining on the roll.

estimate : $93 - 14 - 22 = 57$ feet

exact :

$\begin{aligned} 13\tfrac{1}{2} &= 13\tfrac{4}{8} \\ + \; 22\tfrac{3}{8} &= 22\tfrac{3}{8} \\ \hline &\; 35\tfrac{7}{8} \end{aligned}$

$\begin{aligned} 92\tfrac{3}{4} &= 92\tfrac{6}{8} = 91\tfrac{14}{8} \\ - \; 35\tfrac{7}{8} &= 35\tfrac{7}{8} = 35\tfrac{7}{8} \\ \hline &\phantom{92\tfrac{6}{8} =}\; 56\tfrac{7}{8} \end{aligned}$

After carpeting two rooms, $56\tfrac{7}{8}$ feet of carpet remain.

94. Add the liters of bloodwine and ale that were sold. Subtract this total from the amount of liters that Quark had in stock.

estimate : $10 - 2 - 5 = 3$ liters

exact :

$\begin{aligned} 2\tfrac{3}{8} &= 2\tfrac{3}{8} \\ + \; 4\tfrac{1}{2} &= 4\tfrac{4}{8} \\ \hline &\; 6\tfrac{7}{8} \end{aligned}$

$\begin{aligned} 10 &= 9\tfrac{8}{8} \\ - \; 6\tfrac{7}{8} &= 6\tfrac{7}{8} \\ \hline &\; 3\tfrac{1}{8} \end{aligned}$

Quark should have $3\tfrac{1}{8}$ liters in stock.

Chapter 3 Test

1. $\dfrac{3}{8} + \dfrac{1}{8} = \dfrac{3+1}{8} = \dfrac{4}{8} = \dfrac{1}{2}$

2. $\dfrac{5}{10} + \dfrac{1}{10} = \dfrac{5+1}{10} = \dfrac{6}{10} = \dfrac{3}{5}$

3. $\dfrac{5}{8} - \dfrac{1}{8} = \dfrac{5-1}{8} = \dfrac{4}{8} = \dfrac{1}{2}$

4. $\dfrac{7}{12} - \dfrac{5}{12} = \dfrac{7-5}{12} = \dfrac{2}{12} = \dfrac{1}{6}$

5.
2	3	4	6
2	3	2	3
3	3	1	3
	1	1	1

The least common multiple is $2 \cdot 2 \cdot 3 = 12$.

6.
3	7	15	3	5
5	7	5	1	5
7	7	1	1	1
	1	1	1	1

The least common multiple is $3 \cdot 5 \cdot 7 = 105$.

7.
2	6	9	27	36
2	3	9	27	18
3	3	9	27	9
3	1	3	9	3
3	1	1	3	1
	1	1	1	1

The least common multiple is $2 \cdot 2 \cdot 3 \cdot 3 \cdot 3 = 108$.

8. $\dfrac{2}{3} + \dfrac{1}{4} = \dfrac{8}{12} + \dfrac{3}{12} = \dfrac{8+3}{12} = \dfrac{11}{12}$

9. $\dfrac{2}{9} + \dfrac{5}{12} = \dfrac{8}{36} + \dfrac{15}{36} = \dfrac{8+15}{36} = \dfrac{23}{36}$

10. $\dfrac{7}{8} - \dfrac{2}{3} = \dfrac{21}{24} - \dfrac{16}{24} = \dfrac{21-16}{24} = \dfrac{5}{24}$

11. $\dfrac{3}{8} - \dfrac{1}{5} = \dfrac{15}{40} - \dfrac{8}{40} = \dfrac{15-8}{40} = \dfrac{7}{40}$

12. $5\dfrac{1}{6} + 6\dfrac{2}{3}$

    estimate : $5 + 7 = 12$

    exact : $5\dfrac{1}{6} + 6\dfrac{2}{3} = 5\dfrac{1}{6} + 6\dfrac{4}{6} = 11\dfrac{5}{6}$

13. $16\dfrac{2}{5} - 11\dfrac{2}{3}$

    estimate : $16 - 12 = 4$

    exact :
    $16\dfrac{2}{5} = 16\dfrac{6}{15} = 15\dfrac{21}{15}$
    $-\ 11\dfrac{2}{3} = 11\dfrac{10}{15} = 11\dfrac{10}{15}$
    $\phantom{-\ 11\dfrac{2}{3} = 11\dfrac{10}{15} = \ }4\dfrac{11}{15}$

14. $18\dfrac{3}{4} + 9\dfrac{2}{5} + 12\dfrac{1}{3}$

    estimate: $19 + 9 + 12 = 40$

    exact :

    $18\dfrac{3}{4} \qquad 18\dfrac{45}{60}$
    $9\dfrac{2}{5} \qquad\ \ 9\dfrac{24}{60}$
    $+\ 12\dfrac{1}{3} \ = 12\dfrac{20}{60}$
    $\phantom{+\ 12\dfrac{1}{3} \ = }\ 39\dfrac{89}{60} = 39 + 1\dfrac{29}{60} = 40\dfrac{29}{60}$

15. $24 - 18\dfrac{3}{8}$

    estimate: $24 - 18 = 6$

    exact: $24\ \ = 23\dfrac{8}{8}$
    $\ -\ 18\dfrac{3}{8} = 18\dfrac{3}{8}$
    $\phantom{-\ 18\dfrac{3}{8} = \ }5\dfrac{5}{8}$

16. Probably addition and subtraction of fractions is more difficult because you have to find the least common denominator and then change the fractions to the same denominator.

17. Round mixed numbers to the nearest whole number. Then add, subtract, multiply, or divide to estimate the answer. The estimate may vary from the exact answer but it lets you know if your answer is reasonable.

18. Add the number of hours that Ann-Marie trained each day.

    estimate : $5 + 7 + 3 + 5 + 7 = 27$ hours

    exact :

    $4\dfrac{5}{6}\ \ = 4\dfrac{10}{12}$
    $6\dfrac{2}{3}\ \ = 6\dfrac{8}{12}$
    $3\dfrac{1}{4}\ \ = 3\dfrac{3}{12}$
    $5\dfrac{1}{3}\ \ = 5\dfrac{4}{12}$
    $+\ 7\dfrac{1}{6}\ \ = 7\dfrac{2}{12}$
    $\phantom{+\ 7\dfrac{1}{6}\ \ = }25\dfrac{27}{12} = 27\dfrac{3}{12} = 27\dfrac{1}{4}$

    Ann-Marie trained $27\dfrac{1}{4}$ hours.

19. Add the number of gallons of paint that were used. Then, subtract the number of gallons that were used from the amount the contractor had when he arrived, to find the number of gallons remaining.

    estimate : $148 - 69 - 37 - 6 = 36$ gallons

    exact :

    $68\dfrac{1}{2}\ \ = \ \ 68\dfrac{4}{8}$
    $37\dfrac{3}{8}\ \ = \ \ 37\dfrac{3}{8}$
    $+\ \ 5\dfrac{3}{4}\ \ = \ \ \ \ 5\dfrac{6}{8}$
    $\phantom{+\ \ 5\dfrac{3}{4}\ \ = \ }110\dfrac{13}{8} = 110 + 1\dfrac{5}{8} = 111\dfrac{5}{8}$

Cumulative Review Exercises (Chapters 1-3)

$$147\tfrac{1}{2} = 147\tfrac{4}{8} = 146\tfrac{12}{8}$$
$$-\ 111\tfrac{5}{8} = 111\tfrac{5}{8} = 111\tfrac{5}{8}$$
$$\overline{\phantom{-\ 111\tfrac{5}{8} = 111\tfrac{5}{8} = }35\tfrac{7}{8}}$$

$35\tfrac{7}{8}$ gallons of paint remain.

20. $\dfrac{2}{3} \text{---} \dfrac{13}{20}$

$\dfrac{2}{3} = \dfrac{40}{60},\ \dfrac{13}{20} = \dfrac{39}{60}$

$\dfrac{40}{60} > \dfrac{39}{60}$, so $\dfrac{2}{3} > \dfrac{13}{20}$.

21. $\dfrac{19}{24} \text{---} \dfrac{17}{36}$

$\dfrac{19}{24} = \dfrac{57}{72},\ \dfrac{17}{36} = \dfrac{34}{72}$

$\dfrac{57}{72} > \dfrac{34}{72}$, so $\dfrac{19}{24} > \dfrac{17}{36}$.

22. $\left(\dfrac{1}{2}\right)^3 \cdot 24$ *Exponent*

$= \dfrac{1}{\cancel{2}} \cdot \dfrac{1}{\cancel{2}} \cdot \dfrac{1}{\cancel{2}} \cdot \dfrac{\cancel{24}}{1}$ *Multiply*

$= 3$

23. $\left(\dfrac{3}{4}\right)^2 - \left(\dfrac{7}{8} \cdot \dfrac{1}{3}\right)$ *Parentheses*

$= \left(\dfrac{3}{4}\right)^2 - \dfrac{7}{24}$ *Exponent*

$= \dfrac{3}{4} \cdot \dfrac{3}{4} - \dfrac{7}{24}$ *Multiply*

$= \dfrac{9}{16} - \dfrac{7}{24}$

$= \dfrac{27}{48} - \dfrac{14}{48} = \dfrac{13}{48}$ *Subtract*

24. $\left(\dfrac{5}{6} - \dfrac{5}{12}\right) \cdot 3$

$= \left(\dfrac{10}{12} - \dfrac{5}{12}\right) \cdot 3$ *Parentheses*

$= \dfrac{5}{12} \cdot 3 = \dfrac{5}{\cancel{12}} \cdot \dfrac{\cancel{3}}{1}$ *Multiply*

$= \dfrac{5}{4} = 1\tfrac{1}{4}$

25. $\dfrac{2}{3} + \dfrac{5}{\cancel{8}} \cdot \dfrac{\cancel{4}}{3}$ *Multiply*

$= \dfrac{2}{3} + \dfrac{5}{6}$

$= \dfrac{4}{6} + \dfrac{5}{6}$

$= \dfrac{4+5}{6} = \dfrac{9}{6} = 1\tfrac{1}{2}$

Cumulative Review Exercises (Chapters 1-3)

1. 58<u>3</u>

   3 in the ones place
   5 in the hundreds place

2. 2,78<u>5</u>,476

   5 in the thousands place
   2 in the millions place

3. 1746 to the nearest ten: ≈ 1750

   17<u>4</u>6   Next digit is 5 or more.

   Tens places changes $(4+1=5)$. All digits to the right of the underlined place change to 0.

   1746 to the nearest hundred: ≈ 1700

   1<u>7</u>46   Next digit is 4 or less.

   Hundreds place does not change. All digits to the right of the underlined place change to 0.

   1746 to the nearest thousand: ≈ 2000

   <u>1</u>746   Next digit is 5 or more.

   Thousands place changes $(1+1=2)$. All digits to the right of the underlined place change to 0.

4. 59,803 rounded to the nearest ten: $\approx 59,800$

   59,8<u>0</u>3   Next digit is 4 or less.

   Tens place does not change. All digits to the right of the underlined place change to 0.

   59,803 rounded to the nearest hundred: $\approx 59,800$

   59,<u>8</u>03   Next digit is 4 or less.

   Hundreds place does not change. All digits to the right of the underlined place change to 0.

   59,803 rounded to the nearest thousand: $\approx 60,000$

   5<u>9</u>,803   Next digit is 5 or more.

Thousands place does not change. All digits to the right of the underlined place change to 0.

5. estimate   exact

      10,000   9 834
         300   279
      50,000   51,506
      50,000   51,702
    ─────   ─────
    110,300   113,321

6. estimate   exact

      20,000   24,276
    − 10,000   − 9 887
    ─────   ─────
      10,000   14,389

7. estimate   exact

        2000   2375
    ×   400   ×   370
    ─────   ─────
    800,000   166 250
                   712 5
                  878,750

8. estimate   exact

         2 500   3 211
    40)100,000   35)112,385
                    105
                      7 3
                      7 0
                        38
                        35
                        35
                        35
                         0

9.   3   10.   375,899
      9   521,742
      4   + 357,968
    + 8   ─────────
    ──   1,255,609
    24

11. 1479   12. 3,896,502
    − 1187   − 1,094,807
    ────   ─────────
      292   2,801,695

13. $5 \times 9 \times 3$
    $(5 \times 9) \times 3 = 45 \times 3 = 135$
    or
    $5 \times (9 \times 3) = 5 \times 27 = 135$

14. $7 \times 2 \times 8$
    $(7 \times 2) \times 8 = 14 \times 8 = 112$
    or
    $7 \times (2 \times 8) = 7 \times 16 = 112$

15. $9 \times 4 \times 6$
    $(9 \times 4) \times 6 = 36 \times 6 = 216$
    or
    $9 \times (4 \times 6) = 9 \times 24 = 216$

16. $\overset{5}{6}8$ 18.   450
    ×   7   × 60
    ───   ─────
    476   27,000

17.   962
    × 384   19.   1 5 8
    ─────   9)14^{5}27^2
    369,408

20. $13,467 \div 5$

        2 6 9 3 R2
    5)13,^{3}4^{4}6^{1}7

21.   32 R166
    506)16,358
        15 18
         1 178
         1 012
           166

22. To find the perimeter add the measurements of the 4 sides.

    estimate : $20 + 9 + 5 + 20 + 9 + 5 = 68$ feet

    exact :
    $$18 + 9 + 5 + 18 + 9 + 5$$
    $$= 64$$

    The perimeter of this parking space is 64 feet.

23. To find the area of the parking space multiply the length and the width.

    estimate : $20 \cdot 10 = 200$ square feet

    exact :

       18
    × 14
    ───
       72
       18
    ───
      252

    The area of the parking space is 252 square feet.

Cumulative Review Exercises (Chapters 1-3)

24. Divide to find out how many cans of oil can be filled with the oil in the tank.

    estimate : $20{,}000 \div 30 \approx 667$ cans

    exact : $20{,}160 \div 32 = 630$

    The tank can fill 630 cans.

25. Multiply the revolutions in one minute and the number of minutes.

    estimate : $2000 \times 50 = 100{,}000$ revolutions.

    exact :

    $50 \cdot 1800 = 90{,}000$ revolutions will be made in 50 minutes.

26. Multiply the length and the width to find the area.

    estimate : $2 \cdot 3 = 6$ square yards

    exact :

    $$1\tfrac{3}{4} \cdot 2\tfrac{2}{3} = \frac{7}{\underset{1}{\cancel{4}}} \cdot \frac{\overset{2}{\cancel{8}}}{3} = \frac{14}{3} = 4\tfrac{2}{3}$$

    The area of the game table is $4\tfrac{2}{3}$ square yards.

27. Multiply the length and the width to find the area.

    estimate : $4 \cdot 5 = 20$ square miles

    exact :

    $$3\tfrac{1}{2} \cdot 5\tfrac{3}{8} = \frac{7}{2} \cdot \frac{43}{8} = \frac{301}{16} = 18\tfrac{13}{16}$$

    There are $18\tfrac{13}{16}$ square miles in the wildlife refuge.

28. Multiply to find the number of cords he could deliver by the number of loads.

    estimate : $5 \cdot 4 = 20$ cords

    exact :

    $$5\tfrac{1}{4} \cdot 3\tfrac{1}{2} = \frac{21}{4} \cdot \frac{7}{2} = \frac{147}{8}$$
    $$= 18\tfrac{3}{8}$$

    He could deliver $18\tfrac{3}{8}$ cords.

29. Subtract the height of the flagpole from the height of the building.

    estimate : $1537 - 83 = 1454$ feet

    exact :

    $$\begin{array}{r} 1536\tfrac{7}{8} = 1536\tfrac{7}{8} \\ -82\tfrac{1}{2} = 82\tfrac{4}{8} \\ \hline 1454\tfrac{3}{8} \end{array}$$

    The height of the building itself is $1454\tfrac{3}{8}$ feet.

30.

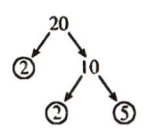

    $20 = 2 \cdot 2 \cdot 5 = 2^2 \cdot 5$

31.

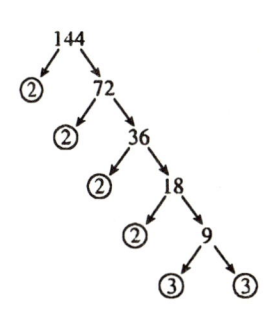

    $144 = 2 \cdot 2 \cdot 2 \cdot 2 \cdot 3 \cdot 3 = 2^4 \cdot 3^2$

32.

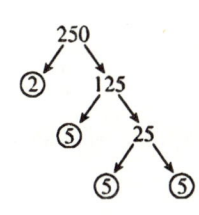

    $250 = 2 \cdot 5 \cdot 5 \cdot 5 = 2 \cdot 5^3$

33. $4^2 \cdot 2^3 = 4 \cdot 4 \cdot 2 \cdot 2 \cdot 2 = 16 \cdot 8 = 128$

34. $2^4 \cdot 3^2 = 2 \cdot 2 \cdot 2 \cdot 2 \cdot 3 \cdot 3 = 16 \cdot 9 = 144$

35. $4^2 \cdot 3^3 = 4 \cdot 4 \cdot 3 \cdot 3 \cdot 3 = 16 \cdot 27 = 432$

36. $\sqrt{25} = \sqrt{5 \cdot 5} = 5$

37. $\sqrt{49} = \sqrt{7 \cdot 7} = 7$

38. $\sqrt{144} = \sqrt{12 \cdot 12} = 12$

39. $\begin{array}{ll} 6^2 - 3 \cdot 7 & \textit{Exponent} \\ 36 - 21 = 15 & \textit{Subtract} \end{array}$

40. $\begin{array}{ll} \sqrt{25} + 5 \cdot 9 - 6 & \textit{Square root} \\ 5 + 5 \cdot 9 - 6 & \textit{Multiply} \\ 5 + 45 - 6 & \textit{Add} \\ 50 - 6 = 44 & \textit{Subtract} \end{array}$

41. $\left(\dfrac{3}{8} - \dfrac{1}{3}\right) \cdot \dfrac{1}{2}$

    $= \left(\dfrac{9}{24} - \dfrac{8}{24}\right) \cdot \dfrac{1}{2} \quad \textit{Parentheses}$

    $= \dfrac{1}{24} \cdot \dfrac{1}{2} = \dfrac{1}{48} \quad \textit{Multiply}$

42. $\dfrac{3}{4} \div \left(\dfrac{1}{3} + \dfrac{1}{2}\right)$

   $= \dfrac{3}{4} \div \left(\dfrac{2}{6} + \dfrac{3}{6}\right)$ *Parentheses*

   $= \dfrac{3}{4} \div \dfrac{5}{6}$ *Invert*

   $= \dfrac{3}{\cancel{4}_2} \cdot \dfrac{\cancel{6}^3}{5} = \dfrac{9}{10}$ *Multiply*

43. $\dfrac{2}{3} + \left(\dfrac{7}{8}\right)^2 - \dfrac{1}{4}$ *Exponent*

   $= \dfrac{2}{3} + \dfrac{49}{64} - \dfrac{1}{4}$

   $= \dfrac{128}{192} + \dfrac{147}{192} - \dfrac{1}{4}$ *Add*

   $= \dfrac{275}{192} - \dfrac{1}{4}$

   $= \dfrac{275}{192} - \dfrac{48}{192}$ *Subtract*

   $= \dfrac{227}{192} = 1\dfrac{35}{192}$

44. $\dfrac{2}{3}$ proper

   The numerator is smaller than the denominator.

45. $\dfrac{5}{5}$ improper

   The numerator is equal to the denominator.

46. $\dfrac{8}{7}$ improper

   The numerator is larger than the denominator.

47. $\dfrac{35}{50} = \dfrac{35 \div 5}{50 \div 5} = \dfrac{7}{10}$

48. $\dfrac{38}{50} = \dfrac{38 \div 2}{50 \div 2} = \dfrac{19}{25}$

49. $\dfrac{105}{300} = \dfrac{105 \div 15}{300 \div 15} = \dfrac{7}{20}$

50. $\dfrac{2}{3} \times \dfrac{3}{4} = \dfrac{\cancel{2}^1}{\cancel{3}_1} \times \dfrac{\cancel{3}^1}{\cancel{4}_2} = \dfrac{1}{2}$

51. $\dfrac{9}{11} \cdot \dfrac{5}{18} = \dfrac{\cancel{9}^1}{11} \cdot \dfrac{5}{\cancel{18}_2} = \dfrac{1 \cdot 5}{11 \cdot 2} = \dfrac{5}{22}$

52. $42 \times \dfrac{7}{8} = \dfrac{\cancel{42}^{21}}{1} \times \dfrac{7}{\cancel{8}_4} = \dfrac{147}{4} = 36\dfrac{3}{4}$

53. $\dfrac{4}{5} \div \dfrac{2}{3} = \dfrac{\cancel{4}^2}{5} \cdot \dfrac{3}{\cancel{2}_1} = \dfrac{6}{5} = 1\dfrac{1}{5}$

54. $\dfrac{25}{40} \div \dfrac{10}{35} = \dfrac{\cancel{25}^5}{\cancel{40}_8} \cdot \dfrac{35}{\cancel{10}_2} = \dfrac{35}{16} = 2\dfrac{3}{16}$

55. $9 \div \dfrac{2}{3} = \dfrac{9}{1} \cdot \dfrac{3}{2} = \dfrac{27}{2} = 13\dfrac{1}{2}$

56. $\dfrac{5}{8} + \dfrac{1}{3} = \dfrac{15}{24} + \dfrac{8}{24} = \dfrac{15 + 8}{24} = \dfrac{23}{24}$

57. $\dfrac{5}{16} + \dfrac{1}{4} + \dfrac{3}{8} = \dfrac{5}{16} + \dfrac{4}{16} + \dfrac{6}{16} = \dfrac{5 + 4 + 6}{16} = \dfrac{15}{16}$

58. $\dfrac{11}{18} - \dfrac{5}{12} = \dfrac{22}{36} - \dfrac{15}{36} = \dfrac{7}{36}$

59. *estimate* *exact*

$$\begin{array}{r} 2 \\ +\ 4 \\ \hline 6 \end{array} \qquad \begin{array}{r} 2\tfrac{1}{4} = 2\tfrac{2}{8} \\ +\ 3\tfrac{5}{8} = 3\tfrac{5}{8} \\ \hline 5\tfrac{7}{8} \end{array}$$

60. *estimate* *exact*

$$\begin{array}{r} 22 \\ +\ 4 \\ \hline 26 \end{array} \qquad \begin{array}{r} 21\tfrac{7}{8} = 21\tfrac{21}{24} \\ +\ 4\tfrac{5}{12} = 4\tfrac{10}{24} \\ \hline 25\tfrac{31}{24} \end{array}$$

$25\dfrac{31}{24} = 25 + 1\dfrac{7}{24} = 26\dfrac{7}{24}$

61. *estimate* *exact*

$$\begin{array}{r} 5 \\ -\ 2 \\ \hline 3 \end{array} \qquad \begin{array}{r} 5\phantom{\tfrac{3}{8}} = 4\tfrac{8}{8} \\ -\ 2\tfrac{3}{8} = 2\tfrac{3}{8} \\ \hline 2\tfrac{5}{8} \end{array}$$

62.
2	12	18
2	6	9
3	3	9
3	1	3
	1	1

The least common multiple is $2 \cdot 2 \cdot 3 \cdot 3 = 36$.

63.
2	15	20	50
2	15	10	25
3	15	5	25
5	5	5	25
5	1	1	5
	1	1	1

The least common multiple is $2 \cdot 2 \cdot 3 \cdot 5 \cdot 5 = 300$.

Cumulative Review Exercises (Chapters 1-3)

64.

2	12	16	18
2	6	8	9
2	3	4	9
2	3	2	9
3	3	1	9
3	1	1	3
	1	1	1

The least common multiple is $2 \cdot 2 \cdot 2 \cdot 2 \cdot 3 \cdot 3 = 144$.

65. $\dfrac{7}{8} = \dfrac{}{40}$

$\dfrac{7}{8} = \dfrac{7 \cdot 5}{8 \cdot 5} = \dfrac{35}{40}$

66. $\dfrac{7}{12} = \dfrac{}{132}$

$\dfrac{7}{12} = \dfrac{7 \cdot 11}{12 \cdot 11} = \dfrac{77}{132}$

67. $\dfrac{9}{15} = \dfrac{}{135}$

$\dfrac{9}{15} = \dfrac{9 \cdot 9}{15 \cdot 9} = \dfrac{81}{135}$

68. $\dfrac{5}{7} = \dfrac{}{84}$

$\dfrac{5}{7} = \dfrac{5 \cdot 12}{7 \cdot 12} = \dfrac{60}{84}$

For Exercises 69-72, see the number line graphs in the answer section of the textbook.

69. $\dfrac{3}{4}$ **70.** $\dfrac{1}{9}$ **71.** $\dfrac{5}{3}$ **72.** $\dfrac{10}{3}$

73. $\dfrac{7}{10} \text{—} \dfrac{37}{50}$

$\dfrac{7}{10} = \dfrac{35}{50}$

$\dfrac{35}{50} < \dfrac{37}{50}$, so $\dfrac{7}{10} < \dfrac{37}{50}$.

74. $\dfrac{19}{25} \text{—} \dfrac{23}{30}$

$\dfrac{19}{25} = \dfrac{114}{150}, \dfrac{23}{30} = \dfrac{115}{150}$

$\dfrac{114}{150} < \dfrac{115}{150}$, so $\dfrac{19}{25} < \dfrac{23}{30}$.

75. $\dfrac{7}{12} \text{—} \dfrac{11}{18}$

$\dfrac{7}{12} = \dfrac{21}{36}, \dfrac{11}{18} = \dfrac{22}{36}$

$\dfrac{21}{36} < \dfrac{22}{36}$, so $\dfrac{7}{12} < \dfrac{11}{18}$.

Chapter 4

DECIMALS

4.1 Reading and Writing Decimals

4.1 Margin Exercises

1. **(a)** The figure has 10 equal parts; 1 part is shaded.

    $\frac{1}{10}$; 0.1 one tenth

   (b) The figure has 10 equal parts; 3 parts are shaded.

    $\frac{3}{10}$; 0.3; three tenths

   (c) The figure has 10 equal parts; 9 parts are shaded.

    $\frac{9}{10}$; 0.9; nine tenths

2. **(a)** $\frac{3}{10}$; 0.3; three tenths

   (b) $\frac{41}{100}$; 0.41; forty-one hundredths

3. **(a)** $0.7 = \frac{7}{10}$

   (b) $0.9 = \frac{9}{10}$

   (c) $0.03 = \frac{3}{100}$

   (d) $0.69 = \frac{69}{100}$

   (e) $0.047 = \frac{47}{1000}$

   (f) $0.351 = \frac{351}{1000}$

4. **(a)** 971.54
   hundreds: 9
   tens: 7
   ones: 1
   tenths: 5
   hundredths: 4

   (b) 0.4
   ones: 0
   tenths: 4

   (c) 5.60
   ones: 5
   tenths: 6
   hundredths: 0

   (d) 0.0835
   ones: 0
   tenths: 0
   hundredths: 8
   thousandths: 3
   ten-thousandths: 5

5. **(a)** 0.3 is three tenths.

   (b) 0.46 is forty-six hundredths.

   (c) 0.09 is nine hundredths.

   (d) 0.409 is four hundred nine thousandths.

   (e) 0.0003 is three ten-thousandths.

   (f) 0.0703 is seven hundred three ten-thousandths.

   (g) 0.088 is eighty-eight thousandths.

6. **(a)** 3.8 is three and eight tenths.

   (b) 15.1 is fifteen and one tenth.

   (c) 0.72 is seventy-two hundredths.

   (d) 64.309 is sixty-four and three hundred nine thousandths.

7. **(a)** $0.7 = \frac{7}{10}$

   (b) $9.89 = 9\frac{89}{100}$

   (c) $0.101 = \frac{101}{1000}$

   (d) $0.007 = \frac{7}{1000}$

   (e) $1.3717 = 1\frac{3717}{10,000}$

8. **(a)** $0.2 = \frac{2}{10} = \frac{2 \div 2}{10 \div 2} = \frac{1}{5}$

   (b) $12.6 = 12\frac{6}{10} = 12\frac{6 \div 2}{10 \div 2} = 12\frac{3}{5}$

   (c) $0.85 = \frac{85}{100} = \frac{85 \div 5}{100 \div 5} = \frac{17}{20}$

   (d) $3.05 = 3\frac{5}{100} = 3\frac{5 \div 5}{100 \div 5} = 3\frac{1}{20}$

   (e) $0.225 = \frac{225}{1000} = \frac{225 \div 25}{1000 \div 25} = \frac{9}{40}$

   (f) $420.0802 = 420\frac{802}{10,000} = 420\frac{802 \div 2}{10,000 \div 2} = 420\frac{401}{5000}$

4.1 Section Exercises

3. 0.2518
hundredths: 5
thousandths: 1
ten-thousandths: 8

7. 314.658
tens: 1
tenths: 6
hundreds: 3

11. 6285.7125
thousands: 6
thousandths: 2
hundredths: 1

15. 3 thousandths, 4 hundredths, 6 ones, 2 ten-thousandths, 5 tenths
$$6.5432$$

19. $0.7 = \dfrac{7}{10}$

23. $0.35 = \dfrac{35}{100} = \dfrac{35 \div 5}{100 \div 5} = \dfrac{7}{20}$

27. $10.17 = 10\dfrac{17}{100}$

31. $0.205 = \dfrac{205}{1000} = \dfrac{205 \div 5}{1000 \div 5} = \dfrac{41}{200}$

35. $0.686 = \dfrac{686}{1000} = \dfrac{686 \div 2}{1000 \div 2} = \dfrac{343}{500}$

39. 0.78 is seventy-eight hundredths.

43. 12.04 is twelve and four hundredths.

47. six and seven tenths
$$6\dfrac{7}{10} = 6.7$$

51. four hundred twenty and eight thousandths
$$420\dfrac{8}{1000} = 420.008$$

55. seventy-five and thirty thousandths
$$75\dfrac{30}{1000} = 75.030$$

59. Six tenths is 0.6, so the correct part is 3-C.

63. The size of part number 4-E is 1.602 centimeters which in words is one and six hundred two thousandths centimeters.

67. 0.72436955 is seventy-two million four hundred thirty-six thousand nine hundred fifty-five hundred-millionths.

71. 8235 to the nearest ten: ≈ 8240

$$82\underline{3}5$$

Next digit is 5 or more.
Tens place changes (3 + 1 = 4). All digits to the right of the underlined place change to 0.

8235 to the nearest hundred: ≈ 8200

$$8\underline{2}35$$

Next digit is 4 or less.
Hundreds place does not change. All digits to the right of the underlined place change to 0.

8235 to the nearest thousand: ≈ 8000

$$\underline{8}235$$

Next digit is 4 or less.
Thousands place does not change. All digits to the right of the underlined place change to 0.

4.2 Rounding Decimals

4.2 Margin Exercises

1. To the nearest thousandth:

(a) 0.334|92
Draw a cut-off line.
The first digit cut is 9 which is 5 or more. Round up the thousandth place.

$$\begin{array}{r} 0.334 \\ +\ 0.001 \\ \hline 0.335 \end{array}$$

Answer: ≈ 0.335

(b) 8.008|51
Draw a cut-off line.
The first digit cut is 5 which is 5 or more. Round up the thousandths place.

$$\begin{array}{r} 8.008 \\ +\ 0.001 \\ \hline 8.009 \end{array}$$

Answer: ≈ 8.009

(c) 265.420|68
Draw a cut-off line.
The first digit cut is 5 or more. Round up the thousandths place.

$$\begin{array}{r} 265.420 \\ +0.001 \\ \hline 265.421 \end{array}$$

Answer: ≈ 265.421

(d) 10.701|80
Draw a cut-off line.
The first digit cut is 5 or more. Round up the thousandths place.

$$\begin{array}{r} 10.701 \\ +0.001 \\ \hline 10.702 \end{array}$$

Answer: ≈ 10.702

2. (a) 0.8988 to the nearest hundredth

0.89|88

Draw a cut-off line.
The first digit cut is 5 or more. Round up the hundredth place.

$$\begin{array}{r} 0.89 \\ +0.01 \\ \hline 0.09 \end{array}$$

Answer: ≈ 0.90

(b) 5.8903 to the nearest hundredth

5.89|03

Draw a cut-off line.
The first digit cut is less than 5. The part you keep stays the same.

Answer: ≈ 5.89

(c) 11.0299 to the nearest thousandth

11.029|9

Draw a cut-off line.
The first digit cut is 5 or more. Round up the thousandth place.

$$\begin{array}{r} 11.029 \\ +0.001 \\ \hline 11.030 \end{array}$$

Answer: ≈ 11.030

(d) 0.545 to the nearest tenth

0.5|45

Draw a cut-off line.
The first digit cut is less than 5. The part you keep stays the same.

Answer: ≈ 0.5

3. Round to the nearest cent

(a) $14.59|5
Draw a cut-off line.
The first digit cut is 5 or more. Round up the hundredth place.

$$\begin{array}{r} \$14.59 \\ +0.01 \\ \hline \$14.60 \end{array}$$

Answer: ≈ $14.60

(b) $578.06|63
Draw a cut-off line.
The first digit cut is 5 or more so round up.

$$\begin{array}{r} \$578.06 \\ +0.01 \\ \hline \$578.07 \end{array}$$

Answer: ≈ $578.07

(c) $0.84|9
Draw a cut-off line.
The first digit cut is 5 or more so round up.

$$\begin{array}{r} \$0.84 \\ +0.01 \\ \hline \$0.85 \end{array}$$

Answer: ≈ $0.85

(d) $0.05|48
Draw a cut-off line.
The first digit cut is less than 5. The part you keep stays the same.

Answer: ≈ $0.05

4. Round to the nearest dollar.

(a) $29.|10
First digit cut is less than 5 so the part you keep stays the same.
Answer: ≈ $29

Section 4.2 Rounding Decimals

(b) $136.|49$

First digit cut is less than 5 so the part you keep stays the same.
Answer: ≈ $136

(c) $990.|91$

First digit cut is 5 or more so round up by adding $1.

$$\begin{array}{r} \$990 \\ +\ \ \ 1 \\ \hline \$991 \end{array}$$

Answer: ≈ $991

(d) $5949.|88$

First digit cut is 5 or more so round up by adding $1.

$$\begin{array}{r} \$5949 \\ +\ \ \ \ 1 \\ \hline \$5950 \end{array}$$

Answer: ≈ $5950

(e) $49.|60$

First digit cut is 5 or more so round up by adding $1.

$$\begin{array}{r} \$49 \\ +\ 1 \\ \hline \$50 \end{array}$$

Answer: ≈ $50

(f) $0.|55$

First digit cut is 5 or more so round up by adding $1.

$$\begin{array}{r} \$0 \\ +\ 1 \\ \hline \$1 \end{array}$$

Answer: ≈ $1

(g) $1.|08$

First digit cut is less than 5 so the part you keep stays the same.
Answer: ≈ $1

4.2 Section Exercises

3. 0.95647 to the nearest thousandth

$$0.956|47$$

Draw cut-off line after the thousandth place. First digit cut is less than 5 so the part you keep stays the same.
Answer: ≈ 0.956

7. 3.66062 to the nearest thousandth

$$3.660|62$$

Draw cut-off line after the thousandth place. First digit cut is 5 or more. Round up the thousandth place.

$$\begin{array}{r} 3.660 \\ +\ 0.001 \\ \hline 3.661 \end{array}$$

Answer: ≈ 3.661

11. 0.09804 to the nearest ten-thousandth

$$0.0980|4$$

Draw cut-off line after the ten-thousandth place. First digit cut is less than 5 so the part you keep stays the same.
Answer: ≈ 0.0980

15. 9.0906 to the nearest hundredth

$$9.09|06$$

Draw cut-off line after the hundredth place. First digit cut is less than 5 so the part you keep stays the same.
Answer: ≈ 9.09

19. Round $0.81666 to the nearest cent.

$$\$0.81|666$$

Draw cut-off line.
First digit cut is 5 or more so round up.

$$\begin{array}{r} \$0.81 \\ +\ 0.01 \\ \hline \$0.82 \end{array}$$

Nardos pays $0.82.

23. Round $0.4983 to the nearest cent.

$$\$0.49|83$$

Draw cut-off line.
First digit cut is 5 or more so round up.

$$\begin{array}{r} \$0.49 \\ +\ 0.01 \\ \hline \$0.50 \end{array}$$

Nardos pays $0.50.

27. Round $310.08 to the nearest dollar.

$$\$310.|08$$

Draw cut-off line.
First digit cut is less than 5 so the part you keep stays the same.
Union dues: ≈ $310

31. If you round $0.499 to the nearest dollar, it will round to $0 (zero dollars) because $0.499 is closer to $0 than $1.

35. $499.98 to the nearest dollar

$$\$499.|98$$

Draw cut-off line.
First digit cut is 5 or more so round up.

$$\begin{array}{r}\$499\\+1\\\hline\$500\end{array}$$

Answer: ≈ $500

39. $999.73 to the nearest dollar

$$\$999.|73$$

Draw cut-off line.
First digit cut is 5 or more so round up.

$$\begin{array}{r}\$999\\+1\\\hline\$1000\end{array}$$

Answer: ≈ $1000

43. $\underline{80,000} + \underline{100} + \underline{800} = \underline{80,900}$ *estimate*
$81,976 + 98 + 785 = \underline{82,859}$ *exact*

4.3 Adding Decimals

4.3 Margin Exercises

1. (a) 2.86 + 7.09

$$\begin{array}{r}2.86\\+7.09\\\hline 9.95\end{array}\quad \textit{Line up decimal points}$$

(b) 13.761 + 8.325

$$\begin{array}{r}13.761\\+8.325\\\hline 22.086\end{array}\quad \textit{Line up decimal points}$$

(c) 0.319 + 56.007 + 8.252

$$\begin{array}{r}0.319\\56.007\\+8.252\\\hline 64.578\end{array}\quad \textit{Line up decimal points}$$

(d) 39.4 + 0.4 + 177.2

$$\begin{array}{r}39.4\\0.4\\+177.2\\\hline 217.0\end{array}\quad \textit{Line up decimal points}$$

2. (a) 6.54 + 9.8

$$\begin{array}{r}6.54\\+9.80\\\hline 16.34\end{array}\quad \begin{array}{l}\textit{Line up decimal points}\\ \textit{Write in 0}\end{array}$$

(b) 0.831 + 222.2 + 10

$$\begin{array}{r}0.831\\222.200\\+10.000\\\hline 233.031\end{array}\quad \begin{array}{l}\textit{Line up decimal points}\\ \textit{Write in 0's}\end{array}$$

(c) 8.64 + 39.115 + 3.0076

$$\begin{array}{r}8.6400\\39.1150\\+3.0076\\\hline 50.7626\end{array}\quad \begin{array}{l}\textit{Line up decimal points}\\ \textit{Write in 0's}\end{array}$$

(d) 5 + 429.823 + 0.76

$$\begin{array}{r}5.000\\429.823\\+0.760\\\hline 435.583\end{array}\quad \begin{array}{l}\textit{Line up decimal points}\\ \textit{Write in 0's}\end{array}$$

3. (a) 2.83 + 5.009 + 76.1

estimate	*exact*
3	2.830
5	5.009
+ 80	+ 76.100
88	83.939

(b) 398.81 + 47.658 + 4158.7

estimate	*exact*
400	398.810
50	47.658
+ 4000	+ 4158.700
4450	4605.168

Section 4.4 Subtracting Decimals

(c) 3217.6 + 5.4 + 37.288

estimate	exact
3000	3217.600
5	5.400
+ 40	+ 37.288
3045	3260.288

4.3 Section Exercises

3.   8224.008
     0.995
  + 96.409
     8321.412

7.   0.38
     7.00   *Line up decimal points*
  + 4.60   *Write in 0's*
    11.98

11. 27.65 + 18.714 + 9.749 + 3.21

  27.650   *Line up decimal points*
  18.714   *Write in 0's*
   9.749
  + 3.210
   59.323

15. 6 should be written 6.00. The sum should be 0.72 + 6.00 + 39.50 = 46.22.

19.
estimate	exact
400	392.700
1	0.865
+ 20	+ 21.080
421	414.645

23.
estimate	exact
400	382.504
600	591.089
+ 600	+ 612.715
1600	1586.308

27.
estimate	exact
5	4.50
6	6.25
+ 4	+ 3.74
15 days	14.49

He worked 14.49 days.

31.
estimate	exact
8000	7942.1
200	154.8
+ 200	+ 154.8
8400 miles	8251.7

The odometer should read 8251.7 miles.

35. Add the hours for each day.
estimate :

$$5 + 6 + 5 + 10 + 5 = 31 \text{ hours}$$

exact :

$$4.5 + 6.2 + 5 + 9.5 + 4.8 = 30$$

Yiangos worked 30 hours.

39. $0.3000 = \dfrac{3000 \div 1000}{10{,}000 \div 1000} = \dfrac{3}{10} = 0.3$

43. First, find the second score.

   9.649
 + 0.188
   9.837

Add this sum to the first score.

   9.837
 + 9.649
  19.486

Dominique's total score for two events was 19.486.

47.
estimate	exact
300	301
− 100	− 104
200	197

4.4 Subtracting Decimals

4.4 Margin Exercises

1. (a) Subtract 22.7 from 72.9.

72.9	Check:	50.2
− 22.7		+ 22.7
50.2		72.9

(b) Subtract 6.425 from 11.813

    11.813   *Line up decimal points*
   − 6.425
     5.388   Check: 6.425
                            + 5.388
                               11.813

(c) 20.15 − 19.67

   20.15   Check: 19.67
− 19.67   + 0.48
    0.48   20.15

2. (a) Subtract 18.651 from 25.3

   25.300   *Write two 0's*
− 18.651
    6.649   Check: 18.651
                           + 6.649
                             25.300

(b) 5.816 − 4.98

   5.816
− 4.980   *Write one 0*
   0.836   Check: 4.980
                           + 0.836
                            5.816

(c) 40 less 3.66

  40.00   Check: 36.34
− 3.66   + 3.66
 36.34   40.00

(d) 1 − 0.325

  1.000   Check: 0.325
− 0.325   + 0.675
  0.675   1.000

3. (a) 11.365 from 38

estimate   *exact*

   40   38.000
− 10   − 11.365
   30   26.635

(b) 214.603 − 53.4

estimate   *exact*

  200   214.603
− 50   − 53.400
  150   161.203

(c) $19.28 less $1.53

estimate   *exact*

  $20 $19.28
−   2   − 1.53
  $18 $17.75

(d) difference between 12.837 meters and 46.091 meters

estimate   *exact*

  50   46.091
− 10   − 12.837
  40   33.254 meters

4.4 Section Exercises

3. 58.413   Check: 25.847
   − 25.847   + 32.566
    32.566   58.414

7. 21.000   *Write decimal point*
  − 0.896   *and three 0's*
   20.104

            Check: 0.896
                    + 20.104
                      21.000

11. 90.5 − 0.8

  90.5   Check: 89.7
− 0.8   + 0.8
 89.7   90.5

15. 6 − 5.09

  6.00   Check: 5.09
− 5.09   + 0.91
  0.91   6.00

19. 15.32 should be on top. The correct answer is 7.87.

23. 8.6 less 3.751

estimate   *exact*

  9   8.600
− 4   − 3.751
  5   4.849

Section 4.5 Multiplying Decimals   87

27.   *estimate*   *exact*

$$\begin{array}{r} 400 \\ -9 \\ \hline 391 \end{array} \qquad \begin{array}{r} {}^{714\ 1\ \cancel{10}\cancel{10}}\\ 3\cancel{8}\cancel{4}\cancel{2}\cancel{00} \\ -9.006 \\ \hline 375.194 \text{ liters} \end{array}$$

31. $6.5 - 0.007$

6.493   0.6493   64.93

$$\begin{array}{r} 7 \\ -\ 0 \\ \hline 5 \end{array} \leftarrow \text{rounds to} \quad \begin{array}{r} 6.500 \\ -\ 0.007 \end{array}$$

The most reasonable answer is 6.493.

35. $6004.003 - 52.7172$

59.512858   595.12858   5951.2858

$$\begin{array}{r} 6000 \\ -\ 50 \\ \hline 5950 \end{array} \leftarrow \begin{array}{l} \text{rounds to} \\ \text{rounds to} \end{array} \begin{array}{r} 6004.003 \\ -\ 52.7172 \end{array}$$

The most reasonable answer is 5951.2858.

39. Subtract the price of the groceries from the money given to the cashier.

estimate   *exact*

$$\begin{array}{r} \$20 \\ -\ 9 \\ \hline \$11 \end{array} \qquad \begin{array}{r} \$20.00 \\ -\ 9.12 \\ \hline \$10.88 \end{array}$$

Steven got $10.88 in change.

43. Add all the monthly expenses.

$$\begin{array}{r} {}^{443\ 2}\\ \$515.00 \\ 190.78 \\ 105.00 \\ 19.95 \\ 42.10 \\ 27.36 \\ 95.81 \\ 57.75 \\ +\ 52.00 \\ \hline \$1105.75 \end{array}$$

Maria's total expenses for the month were $1105.75.

47. Subtract the car expenses from the rent.

$$\begin{array}{rl} \$190.78 & \text{car payment} \\ +\ 105.00 & \text{car repairs, gas} \\ \hline \$295.78 & \text{car expenses} \end{array}$$

$$\begin{array}{rl} \$515.00 & \text{rent} \\ -\ 295.78 & \text{car expenses} \\ \hline \$219.22 & \end{array}$$

Maria spent $219.22 more on rent than on car expenses.

51. Add to find the number of gallons in a full tank.

estimate   *exact*

$$\begin{array}{r} 20 \\ +\ 1 \\ \hline 21 \end{array} \qquad \begin{array}{r} 16.6 \\ +\ 1.4 \\ \hline 18.0 \end{array}$$

Subtract to find how much gas was in the tank before it was filled.

$$\begin{array}{r} 21 \\ -\ 9 \\ \hline 12 \text{ gallons} \end{array} \qquad \begin{array}{r} 18.000 \\ -\ 8.628 \\ \hline 9.372 \end{array}$$

There were 9.372 gallons in the tank.

55. Add the known lengths and subtract the sum from the total length.

$$\begin{array}{r} 3.569 \\ +\ 3.569 \\ \hline 7.138 \end{array} \qquad \begin{array}{r} {}^{410}\\ 9.9\cancel{5}\cancel{0} \\ -\ 7.138 \\ \hline 2.812 \end{array}$$

$k = 2.812$ inches.

59. $\underbrace{4000}\ \times\ \underbrace{200}\ =\ 800{,}000$ *estimate*

$\overbrace{3789}\ \times\ \overbrace{205}\ =\ 776{,}745$ *exact*

4.5   Multiplying Decimals

4.5   Margin Exercises

1. (a) $\begin{array}{r} 2.6 \\ \times\ 0.4 \\ \hline 1.04 \end{array} \begin{array}{l} \leftarrow 1 \text{ decimal place} \\ \leftarrow 1 \text{ decimal place} \\ \leftarrow 2 \text{ decimal places} \end{array}$

(b) $\begin{array}{r} 45.2 \\ \times\ 0.25 \\ \hline 2\ 260 \\ 9\ 04 \\ \hline 11.300 \end{array} \begin{array}{l} \leftarrow 1 \text{ decimal place} \\ \leftarrow 2 \text{ decimal places} \\ \\ \\ \leftarrow 3 \text{ decimal places} \end{array}$

(c) $\begin{array}{r} 0.104 \\ \times\ 7 \\ \hline 0.728 \end{array} \begin{array}{l} \leftarrow 3 \text{ decimal places} \\ \leftarrow 0 \text{ decimal places} \\ \leftarrow 3 \text{ decimal places} \end{array}$

(d)   3.18   ← 2 *decimal places*
   × 2.23   ← 2 *decimal places*
   954
   636
   6 36
   7.0914 ← 4 *decimal places*

(e)   611
   × 3.7   ← 1 *decimal place*
   427 7
   1833
   2260.7 ← 1 *decimal place*

2. (a) 0.04×0.09

   0.04   ← 2 *decimal places*
   × 0.09 ← 2 *decimal places*
   0.0036 ← 4 *decimal places*
   Count 4 places. Write in decimal point and 0's.

(b) $0.2 \cdot 0.008$

   0.008   ← 3 *decimal places*
   × 0.2   ← 1 *decimal place*
   0.0016 ← 4 *decimal places*
   Count 4 places. Write in decimal point and 0's.

(c) $(0.063)(0.04)$

   0.063   ← 3 *decimal places*
   × 0.04   ← 2 *decimal places*
   0.00252 ← 5 *decimal places*
   Count 5 places. Write in decimal point and 0's.

(d) $0.0081 \cdot 0.003$

   0.0081   ← 4 *decimal places*
   × .003   ← 3 *decimal places*
   0.0000243 ← 7 *decimal places*
   Count 7 places. Write in decimal point and 0's.

(e) $(0.11)(0.0005)$

   0.11   ← 2 *decimal places*
   × 0.0005 ← 4 *decimal places*
   0.000055 ← 6 *decimal places*
   Count 6 places. Write in decimal point and 0's.

3. (a) $(11.62)(4.01)$

estimate	*exact*
10	11.62 ← 2 *decimal places*
× 4	× 4.01 ← 2 *decimal places*
40	1162
	46 480
	46.5962 ← 4 *decimal places*

(b) $(5.986)(33)$

estimate	*exact*
6	5.986 ← 3 *decimal places*
× 30	× 33
180	17 958
	179 58
	197.538 ← 3 *decimal places*

(c) $8.31 \cdot 4.2$

estimate	*exact*
8	8.31 ← 2 *decimal places*
× 4	× 4.2 ← 1 *decimal place*
32	1 662
	33 24
	34.902 ← 3 *decimal places*

(d) $58.6 \cdot 17.4$

estimate	*exact*
60	58.6 ← 1 *decimal place*
× 20	× 17.4 ← 1 *decimal place*
1200	23 44
	410 2
	586
	1019.64 ← 2 *decimal places*

4.5 Section Exercises

3.   21.5   ← 1 *decimal place*
   × 7.4   ← 1 *decimal place*
   8 60
   150 5
   159.10 ← 2 *decimal places*

7. $51.88   ← 2 *decimal places*
   ×   665
   $34,500.20 ← 2 *decimal places*

Section 4.5   Multiplying Decimals

11. (7.2)(0.06)

72	7.2	← 1 decimal place
× 6	× 0.06	← 2 decimal places
432	0.432	← 3 decimal places

15. 0.0072 × 0.6

72	0.0072	← 4 decimal places
× 6	0.6	← 1 decimal place
432	0.00432	← 5 decimal places

Write 0's to get 5 decimal places.

19. 0.003 · 0.002

0.003	← 3 decimal places
× 0.002	← 3 decimal places
0.000006	← 6 decimal places

Count 6 places. Write in decimal point and 0's.

23.   estimate   exact

40	39.6	← 1 decimal place
× 5	× 4.8	← 1 decimal place
200	31 68	
	158 4	
	190.08	← 2 decimal places

27.   estimate   exact

7	6.53	← 2 decimal places
× 5	× 4.6	← 1 decimal place
35	3 918	
	26 12	
	30.038	← 3 decimal places

31. An $18.90 car payment is *unreasonable*. A reasonable answer would be $189.00.

35. A gallon of milk for $319 is *unreasonable*. A reasonable answer would be $3.19.

39. Multiply her pay per hour times the hours she worked.

$11.73	← 2 decimal places
× 50.5	← 1 decimal place
5 865	
586 50	
$592.365	← 3 decimal places
592.36|5	5 *or more, add* 0.01

LaTasha made ≈ $592.37.

43. Multiply the number of gallons that she pumped into her pickup truck by the price per gallon.

18.65
× $1.45
9325
7 460
18 65
27.0425

Round 27.0425 to the nearest cent.

Michelle paid ≈ $27.04 for the gas.

47. Multiply the monthly cost for cable times 12 months.

$28.96
× 12
57 92
289 6
$347.52

The cost for a year is $347.52.

51. Find the cost of the 4 long sleeve, solid color shirts.

$18.95
× 4
$75.80

Then find the cost of the 2 short-sleeve striped shirts.

$16.75
× 2
$33.50

Add these two amounts and the $2 per shirt charge for the extra-large size.

$2	$75.80
× 6	33.50
$12	+ 12.00
	$121.30

The total cost is $121.30.

55. First find the cost for 4 days.

$29.95 × 4 = $119.80

Then find the cost for mileage.

926 × $0.29 = $268.54

Add the two amounts.

$$268.54 + 119.80 = 388.34$$

The cost of her rental is $388.34.

59.

estimate

```
   200
5)1000
```

exact

```
   190 R4
5)954
   5
   45
   45
    4
    0
    4
```

4.6 Dividing Decimals

4.6 Margin Exercises

1. (a)
```
    23.4
4)93.6
   8
   13
   12
    1 6
    1 6
      0
```
Check:
```
  23.4
×    4
  93.6
```

(b)
```
    1.134
6)6.804
   6
   0 8
     6
     20
     18
      24
      24
       0
```
Check:
```
  1.134
×     6
  6.804
```

(c)
```
     25.3
11)278.3
   22
   58
   55
    3 3
    3 3
      0
```
Check:
```
   25.3
×    11
   25 3
  253
  278.3
```

(d) $0.51835 \div 5$
```
   0.10367
5)0.51835
   5
   1
   0
   18
   15
   33
   30
   35
   35
    0
```
Check:
```
  0.10367
×       5
  0.51835
```

(e) $213.45 \div 15$
```
     14.23
15)213.45
   15
   63
   60
    3 4
    3 0
     45
     45
      0
```
Check:
```
   14.23
×     15
   71 15
  142 3
  213.45
```

2. (a)
```
    1.28
5)6.40   ← Write one 0
   5
   1 4
   1 0
     40
     40
      0
```
Check:
```
   1.28
×     5
   6.40
```

(b) $30.87 \div 14$
```
     2.205
14)30.870
   28
   2 8
   2 8
     07
      0
     70
     70
      0
```
Check:
```
   2.205
×     14
   8 820
  22 05
  30.870
```

Section 4.6 Dividing Decimals

(c) $\dfrac{259.5}{30}$

```
       8.65
30)259.50   ← Write one 0
   240
    19 5
    18 0
     1 50
     1 50
        0
```
Check:
```
    8.65
  ×  30
  259.50
```

(d) $0.3 \div 8$

```
      0.0375
8)0.3000   ← Write three 0's
  0
  30
  24
   60
   56
    40
    40
     0
```
Check:
```
  0.0375
×      8
  0.3000
```

3. (a) $13\overline{)267.01}$

$267.01 \div 13 = 20.539231$
There are no repeating digits visible on the calculator.
$20.539|231$ rounds to ≈ 20.539.

Check: $20.539 \cdot 13 = 267.007$

(b) $6\overline{)20.5}$

$20.5 \div 6 = 3.416666$
There is a repeating decimal: $3.41\bar{6}$.
$3.416|666$ rounds to ≈ 3.417.

Check: $3.417 \cdot 6 = 20.502$

(c) $\dfrac{10.22}{9} = 10.22 \div 9 = 1.135555$

There is a repeating decimal: $1.13\bar{5}$.
$1.135|555$ rounds to ≈ 1.136.

Check: $1.136 \cdot 9 = 10.224$

(d) $16.15 \div 3 = 5.383333$

There is a repeating decimal: $5.38\bar{3}$.
$5.383|333$ rounds to ≈ 5.383.

Check: $5.383 \cdot 3 = 16.149$

(e) $116.3 \div 7 = 16.614286$

The answer has a repeating decimal that starts repeating in the eighth decimal place as $16.6\overline{142857}$. $16.614|286$ rounds to ≈ 16.614.

Check: $16.614 \cdot 7 = 116.298$

4. (a)
```
         5.2
0.2ˆ)1.0ˆ4
    1 0
     0 4
       4
       0
```

(b)
```
          30 .12
0.06ˆ)1.80ˆ72
      1 8
        00
         0
         0 7
           6
           12
           12
            0
```

(c)
```
           6 400
0.005ˆ)32.000ˆ
       30
        2 0
        2 0
          00
           0
           00
            0
            0
```

(d) $8.1 \div 0.025$

```
          324
0.025ˆ)8.100ˆ
       7 5
         60
         50
         100
         100
           0
```

91

(e) $\dfrac{7}{1.3}$

$$\begin{array}{r} 5.384 \approx 5.38 \\ 1.3_\wedge\overline{)70_\wedge000} \\ \underline{65} \\ 5\ 0 \\ \underline{3\ 9} \\ 1\ 10 \\ \underline{1\ 04} \\ 60 \\ \underline{52} \\ 8 \end{array}$$

(f) $5.3091 \div 6.2$

$$\begin{array}{r} 0.856 \approx 0.86 \\ 6.2_\wedge\overline{)5.3_\wedge091} \\ \underline{4\ 9\ 6} \\ 3\ 49 \\ \underline{3\ 10} \\ 391 \\ \underline{372} \\ 19 \end{array}$$

5. (a) $42.75 \div 3.8 = 1.125$

estimate: $40 \div 4 = 10$

The answer is not reasonable.

$$\begin{array}{r} 1\ 1.25 \\ 3.8_\wedge\overline{)42.7_\wedge50} \\ \underline{38} \\ 4\ 7 \\ \underline{3\ 8} \\ 9\ 5 \\ \underline{7\ 6} \\ 1\ 90 \\ \underline{1\ 90} \\ 0 \end{array}$$

The answer should be 11.25.

(b) $807.1 \div 1.76 = 458.580$

estimate: $800 \div 2 = 400$

The answer is reasonable.

(c) $48.63 \div 52 = 93.519$

estimate: $50 \div 50 = 1$

The answer is not reasonable.

$$\begin{array}{r} 0.9351 \approx 0.935 \\ 52\overline{)48.6300} \\ \underline{46\ 8} \\ 1\ 83 \\ \underline{1\ 56} \\ 270 \\ \underline{260} \\ 100 \\ \underline{52} \\ 48 \end{array}$$

The answer should be 0.935.

(d) $9.0584 \div 2.68 = 0.338$

estimate: $9 \div 3 = 3$

The answer is not reasonable.

$$\begin{array}{r} 3.38 \\ 2.68_\wedge\overline{)9.05_\wedge84} \\ \underline{8\ 04} \\ 1\ 01\ 8 \\ \underline{80\ 4} \\ 21\ 44 \\ \underline{21\ 44} \\ 0 \end{array}$$

The answer should be 3.38.

6. (a) $4.6 - 0.79 + 1.5^2$ *Exponent*
$4.6 - 0.79 + 2.25$ *Subtract*
$3.81 + 2.25 = 6.06$ *Add*

(b) $3.64 \div 1.3 \cdot 3.6$ *Divide*
$2.8 \cdot 3.6 = 10.08$ *Multiply*

(c) $0.08 + 0.6 \cdot (3 - 2.99)$ *Parentheses*
$0.08 + 0.6 \cdot 0.01$ *Multiply*
$0.08 + 0.006 = 0.086$ *Add*

(d) $10.85 - 2.3 \cdot 5.2 \div 3.2$ *Multiply*
$10.85 - 11.96 \div 3.2$ *Divide*
$10.85 - 3.7375 = 7.1125$ *Subtract*

4.6 Section Exercises

3. $\dfrac{4.23}{9}$

$$\begin{array}{r} 0.47 \\ 9\overline{)4.23} \quad \textit{Line up decimal points} \\ \underline{3\ 6} \\ 63 \\ \underline{63} \\ 0 \end{array}$$

Section 4.6 Dividing Decimals

7.
$$\begin{array}{r} 3\ 6. \\ 1.5_\wedge\overline{)54.0_\wedge} \\ \underline{45} \\ 9\ 0 \\ \underline{9\ 0} \\ 0 \end{array}$$
Move decimal point in divisor and dividend 1 place

11. $0.018\overline{)108}$ $108 \div 18 = 6$

$108 \div 0.018 = 108{,}000 \div 18 = 6000$

15. $\dfrac{3.1}{0.006}$

$$\begin{array}{r} 516.666 \\ 0.006_\wedge\overline{)3.100_\wedge 000} \\ \underline{3\ 0} \\ 10 \\ \underline{6} \\ 40 \\ \underline{36} \\ 4\ 0 \\ \underline{3\ 6} \\ 40 \\ \underline{36} \\ 40 \\ \underline{36} \\ 4 \end{array}$$

Line up decimal points

Move decimal point in divisor and dividend 3 places

Write three 0's

516.666 rounds to ≈ 516.67.

19. $0.034\overline{)342.81}$

$342.81 \div 0.034 \approx 10{,}082.67$

23. $37.8 \div 8 = 47.25$

estimate: $40 \div 8 = 5$
47.25 is unreasonable.

$$\begin{array}{r} 4.725 \\ 8\overline{)37.800} \\ \underline{32} \\ 5\ 8 \\ \underline{5\ 6} \\ 20 \\ \underline{16} \\ 40 \\ \underline{40} \\ 0 \end{array}$$

The correct answer is 4.725.

27. $307.02 \div 5.1 = 6.2$

estimate: $300 \div 5 = 60$
6.2 is unreasonable.

$$\begin{array}{r} 6\ 0.2 \\ 5.1_\wedge\overline{)307.0_\wedge 2} \\ \underline{306} \\ 1\ 0 \\ \underline{0} \\ 1\ 0\ 2 \\ \underline{1\ 0\ 2} \\ 0 \end{array}$$

The correct answer is 60.2.

31. Divide the cost by the number of pairs of tights.

$$\begin{array}{r} 3.996 \\ 6\overline{)23.980} \\ \underline{18} \\ 5\ 9 \\ \underline{5\ 4} \\ 5\ 8 \\ \underline{5\ 4} \\ 40 \\ \underline{36} \\ 4 \end{array}$$

$3.996 rounds to $\approx \$4.00$.
One pair costs $\approx \$4.00$.

35. Divide the total cost by the number of bricks to find the cost per brick.

$$\begin{array}{r} 0.30 \\ 619\overline{)185.70} \\ \underline{185\ 7} \\ 00 \\ \underline{0} \\ 0 \end{array}$$

One brick costs $0.30.

39. Divide the miles driven by the gallons of gas in the full tank.

$346.2 \div 16.35 = 21.17$ or ≈ 21.2

=She got ≈ 21.2 miles per gallon.

43. Subtract the distance of the third place jump from the second place jump.

$$\begin{array}{r} 8.29 \\ -\ 8.24 \\ \hline 0.05 \end{array}$$

The second place jump was 0.05 meter longer.

47. $7.2 - 5.2 + 3.5^2$ *Exponent*
$7.2 - 5.2 + 12.25$ *Subtract*
$2 + 12.25 = 14.25$ *Add*

51. $8.68 - 4.6 \cdot 10.4 \div 6.4$ *Multiply*
$8.68 - 47.84 \div 6.4$ *Divide*
$8.68 - 7.475 = 1.205$ *Subtract*

55. Multiply the price per can by the number of cans.

$$\begin{array}{r} \$0.57 \\ \times \quad 6 \\ \hline \$3.42 \end{array}$$

Subtract to find total savings.

$$\begin{array}{r} \$3.42 \\ -\ 3.25 \\ \hline \$0.17 \end{array}$$

There are six cans so divide by 6 to find the savings per can.

$$\begin{array}{r} \$0.028 \\ 6\overline{)\$0.170} \\ \underline{12} \\ 50 \\ \underline{48} \\ 2 \end{array}$$ $\$0.028$ rounds to $\approx \$0.03$.

You will save $\approx \$0.03$ per can.

59. $\dfrac{7}{12} - \dfrac{3}{4}$

$\dfrac{3}{4} = \dfrac{9}{12}$

$\dfrac{7}{12} < \dfrac{9}{12}$, so $\dfrac{7}{12} < \dfrac{3}{4}$.

63. $\dfrac{13}{24} - \dfrac{23}{36}$

$\dfrac{13}{24} = \dfrac{39}{72}$, $\dfrac{23}{36} = \dfrac{46}{72}$

$\dfrac{39}{72} < \dfrac{46}{72}$, so $\dfrac{13}{24} < \dfrac{23}{36}$.

4.7 Writing Fractions as Decimals

4.7 Margin Exercises

1. (a) $\dfrac{1}{9}$ is written $9\overline{)1}$.

(b) $\dfrac{2}{3}$ is written $3\overline{)2}$.

(c) $\dfrac{5}{4}$ is written $4\overline{)5}$.

(d) $\dfrac{3}{10}$ is written $10\overline{)3}$.

(e) $\dfrac{21}{16}$ is written $16\overline{)21}$.

(f) $\dfrac{1}{50}$ is written $50\overline{)1}$.

2. (a) $\dfrac{1}{4}$

$$\begin{array}{r} 0.25 \\ 4\overline{)1.00} \\ \underline{8} \\ 20 \\ \underline{20} \\ 0 \end{array}$$

$\dfrac{1}{4} = 0.25$

(b) $2\dfrac{1}{2} = \dfrac{5}{2}$

$$\begin{array}{r} 2.5 \\ 2\overline{)5.0} \\ \underline{4} \\ 1\ 0 \\ \underline{1\ 0} \\ 0 \end{array}$$

$2\dfrac{1}{2} = 2.5$

(c) $\dfrac{5}{8}$

$$\begin{array}{r} 0.625 \\ 8\overline{)5.000} \\ \underline{4\ 8} \\ 20 \\ \underline{16} \\ 40 \\ \underline{40} \\ 0 \end{array}$$

$\dfrac{5}{8} = 0.625$

(d) $4\dfrac{3}{5}$

$$\begin{array}{r} 0.6 \\ 5\overline{)3.0} \\ \underline{3\ 0} \\ 0 \end{array}$$

$4 + 0.6 = 4.6$
$4\dfrac{3}{5} = 4.6$

Section 4.7 Writing Fractions as Decimals

(e) $\frac{7}{8}$

```
    0.875
8)7.000
    6 4
      60
      56
      40
      40
       0
```

$\frac{7}{8} = 0.875$

3. (a) $\frac{1}{3}$

```
   0.3333
3)1.0000
   9
   10
    9
   10
    9
   10
    9
    1
```

Rounded to the nearest thousandth,

$\frac{1}{3} \approx 0.333.$

(b) $2\frac{7}{9} = \frac{25}{9}$

```
    2.7777
9)25.0000
   18
    7 0
    6 3
      70
      63
      70
      63
      70
      63
       7
```

Rounded to the nearest thousandth,

$2\frac{7}{9} \approx 2.778.$

(c) $\frac{10}{11}$

```
    0.9090
11)10.0000
    9 9
      10
       0
     100
      99
      10
       0
      10
```

Rounded to the nearest thousandth,

$\frac{10}{11} \approx 0.909.$

(d) $\frac{3}{7}$

```
    0.4285
7)3.0000
   2 8
     20
     14
     60
     56
     40
     35
      5
```

Rounded to the nearest thousandth,

$\frac{3}{7} \approx 0.429.$

(e) $3\frac{5}{6} = \frac{23}{6}$

```
    3.8333
6)23.0000
   18
    5 0
    4 8
     20
     18
     20
     18
     20
     18
     20
     18
      0
```

Rounded to the nearest thousandth,

$3\frac{5}{6} \approx 3.833.$

4. (a) $0.4375 < 0.5$

(b) $0.75 > 0.6875$

(c) $0.625 > 0.0625$

(d) $\frac{2}{8} = \frac{1}{4} = 0.250$

$0.250 < 0.375$, so $\frac{2}{8} < 0.375$

(e) $0.8\bar{3} = \frac{5}{6}$

(f) $\frac{1}{2} < 0.\bar{5}$

(g) $0.\bar{1} < 0.1\bar{6}$

(h) $\dfrac{8}{9} = 0.\bar{8}$

(i) $\dfrac{4}{6} = \dfrac{2}{3} = 0.\bar{6}$

$0.\bar{7} > 0.\bar{6}$, so $0.\bar{7} > \dfrac{4}{6}$

(j) $\dfrac{1}{4} = 0.25$

5. (a) 0.7   0.703   0.7029
       ↓   ↓   ↓
       0.700   0.7030   0.7029

From smallest to largest:

0.700, 0.7029, 0.7030.

or

0.7, 0.7029, 0.703

(b) 6.39   6.309   6.4   6.401
     ↓   ↓   ↓   ↓
     6.390   6.309   6.400   6.401

From smallest to largest:

6.309, 6.390, 6.400, 6.401

or

6.309, 6.39, 6.4, 6.401

(c) 1.085 $1\frac{3}{4}$ 0.9
     ↓   ↓   ↓
     1.085   1.750   0.900

From smallest to largest:

0.900, 1.085, 1.750

or

$0.9, 1.085, 1\frac{3}{4}$

(d) $\dfrac{1}{4}, \dfrac{2}{5}, \dfrac{3}{7}, 0.428$

To compare, change fractions to decimals.

$\dfrac{1}{4} = 0.25 \qquad \dfrac{2}{5} = 0.4$

$\dfrac{3}{7} \approx 0.429$

From smallest to largest:

0.25, 0.4, 0.428, 0.429

or

$\dfrac{1}{4}, \dfrac{2}{5}, 0.428, \dfrac{3}{7}$

4.7 Section Exercises

3. $\dfrac{3}{4} = 0.75$

```
      0.75
   4)3.00
     2 8
       20
       20
        0
```

7. $\dfrac{9}{10} = 0.9$

```
      0.9
   10)9.0
      9 0
        0
```

11. $\dfrac{7}{8} = 0.875$

```
       0.875
    8)7.000
      6 4
        60
        56
         40
         40
          0
```

15. $14\dfrac{7}{10} = 14.7$

19. $\dfrac{1}{3} = 1 \div 3 = 0.3333333 \approx 0.333$

23. $1\dfrac{8}{9} = \dfrac{17}{9} \approx 1.8888889 \approx 1.889$

27. Just add the whole number part to 0.375. So

$1\dfrac{3}{8} = 1.375; \ 3\dfrac{3}{8} = 3.375; \ 295\dfrac{3}{8} = 295.375.$

31. $0.625 = \dfrac{625}{1000} = \dfrac{625 \div 125}{1000 \div 125} = \dfrac{5}{8}$

35. $\dfrac{7}{20} = 0.35$

```
       0.35
    20)7.00
       6 0
         1 00
         1 00
             0
```

39. $0.15 = \dfrac{15}{100} = \dfrac{15 \div 5}{100 \div 5} = \dfrac{3}{20}$

43. $0.09 = \dfrac{9}{100}$

Chapter 4 Review Exercises

47. Compare the two lengths.

average length → 20.80 *larger*
Charlene's baby → 20.08 *shorter*

$$\begin{array}{r} 20.80 \\ -\ 20.08 \\ \hline 0.72 \end{array}$$

Her baby is 20.08 inches long which is 0.72 inch *shorter* than the average length.

51. Compare the two amounts.

$3\frac{3}{4}$ → 3.75 *less*
3.8 → 3.80 *more*

$$\begin{array}{r} 3.80 \\ -\ 3.75 \\ \hline 0.05 \end{array}$$

3.8 inches is 0.05 inch *more* than Ginny hoped for.

55. 5.8, 5.79, 5.0079, 5.804

5.8 = 5.8000
5.79 = 5.7900
5.0079 = 5.0079
5.804 = 5.8040

From smallest to largest:

5.0079, 5.79, 5.8, 5.804

59. 5.8751, 4.876, 2.8902, 3.88

5.8751 = 5.8751
4.876 = 4.8876
2.8902 = 2.8902
3.88 = 3.8800

From smallest to largest:

2.8902, 3.88, 4.876, 5.8751

63. $\frac{3}{8}, \frac{2}{5}, 0.37, 0.4001$

$\frac{3}{8}$ = 0.3750
$\frac{2}{5}$ = 0.4000
0.37 = 0.3700
0.4001 = 0.4001

From smallest to largest:

0.37, $\frac{3}{8}$, $\frac{2}{5}$, 0.4001

67. $\frac{1}{4} = 0.25$

0.25 rounded the nearest tenth is ≈ 0.3.

Length (c) is ≈ 0.3 inch.

71. $\frac{6}{11}, \frac{5}{9}, \frac{4}{7}, 0.571$

$\frac{6}{11} \approx 0.5455$ $\quad \frac{5}{9} \approx 0.5556$

$\frac{4}{7} \approx 0.5714$ $\quad 0.5710$

From smallest to largest:

$\frac{6}{11}, \frac{5}{9}, 0.571, \frac{4}{7}$

75. $\frac{3}{16}, \frac{1}{6}, \frac{1}{5}, 0.188$

$\frac{3}{16} = 0.1875$ $\quad \frac{1}{6} \approx 0.1667$

$\frac{1}{5} = 0.2000$ $\quad 0.1880$

From smallest to largest;

$\frac{1}{6}, \frac{3}{16}, 0.188, \frac{1}{5}$

79. $\frac{60}{80} = \frac{60 \div 20}{80 \div 20} = \frac{3}{4}$

Chapter 4 Review Exercises

1. 243.059
   tenths: 0
   hundredths: 5

2. 0.6817
   ones: 0
   tenths: 6

3. $5824.39
   hundreds: 8
   hundredths: 9

4. 896.503
   tenths: 5
   tens: 9

5. 20.73861
   tenths: 7
   ten-thousandths: 6

6. $0.5 = \frac{5}{10} = \frac{1}{2}$

7. $0.75 = \frac{75}{100} = \frac{75 \div 25}{100 \div 25} = \frac{3}{4}$

8. $4.05 = 4\frac{5}{100} = 4\frac{5 \div 5}{100 \div 5} = 4\frac{1}{20}$

9. $0.875 = \frac{875}{1000} = \frac{875 \div 125}{1000 \div 125} = \frac{7}{8}$

10. $0.027 = \frac{27}{1000}$

11. $27.8 = 27\frac{8}{10} = 27\frac{4}{5}$

12. 0.8 is eight tenths.

13. 400.29 is four hundred and twenty-nine hundredths.

14. 12.007 is twelve and seven thousandths.

15. 0.0306 is three hundred six ten-thousandths.

16. eight and three tenths

    $8\frac{3}{10} = 8.3$

17. two hundred five thousandths

    $\frac{205}{1000} = 0.205$

18. seventy and sixty-six ten-thousandths

    $70\frac{66}{10,000} = 70.0066$

19. thirty hundredths

    $\frac{30}{100} = 0.30$

20. 275.635 to the nearest tenth: ≈ 275.6

    275.6|35

    Draw cut-off line. First digit cut is less than 5 so the part you keep stays the same.

21. 72.789 to the nearest hundredth: ≈ 72.79

    72.78|9

    Draw cut-off line. First digit cut is 5 or more so round up.

22. 0.1604 to the nearest thousandth: ≈ 0.160

    0.160|4

    Draw cut-off line. First digit cut is less than 5 so the part you keep stays the same.

23. 0.0905 to the nearest thousandth: ≈ 0.091

    0.090|5

    Draw cut-off line. First digit cut is 5 or more so round up.

24. 0.98 to the nearest tenth: ≈ 1.0

    0.9|8

    Draw cut-off line. First digit cut is 5 or more so round up ($9 + 1 = 10$).

25. $15.8333 to the nearest cent: $\approx \$15.83$

    $15.83|33

    Draw cut-off line. First digit cut is less than 5 so the part you keep stays the same.

26. $0.698 to the nearest cent: $\approx \$0.70$

    $0.69|8

    Draw cut-off line. First digit cut is 5 or more so round up.

27. $17,625.7906 to the nearest cent: $\approx \$17,625.79$

    $17,625.79|06

    Draw cut-off line. First digit cut is less than 5 so the part you keep stays the same.

28. $350.48 to the nearest dollar: $\approx \$350$

    $350.|48

    Draw cut-off line. First digit cut is less than 5 so the part you keep stays the same.

29. $129.50 to the nearest dollar: $\approx \$130$

    $129.|50

    Draw cut-off line. First digit cut is 5 or more so round up.

30. $99.61 to the nearest dollar: $\approx \$100$

    $99.|61

    Draw cut-off line. First digit cut is 5 or more so round up.

Chapter 4 Review Exercises

31. $29.37 to the nearest dollar: ≈ $29

$29.|37

Draw cut-off line. First digit cut is less than 5 so the part you keep stays the same.

32.
estimate	exact
6	5.81
400	423.96
+ 20	+ 15.09
426	444.86

33.
estimate	exact
80	75.6
1	1.29
100	122.045
1	0.88
+ 30	+ 33.7
212	233.515

34.
estimate	exact
300	308.5 (borrowed: 2 $\cancel{10}$ $\cancel{7}$ 15)
− 20	− 17.8
280	290.7

35.
estimate	exact
9	9.2000 (borrowed: 8 $\cancel{11}$ $\cancel{9}$ $\cancel{10}$ 10)
− 8	− 7.9316
1	1.2684

36.
estimate	exact
13	12.50 (borrowed: $\cancel{11}$ $\cancel{14}$ $\cancel{5}$ 10)
− 10	− 9.75
3 hours	2.75

Tim will work 2.75 hours.

37. Add the amounts of the two checks.

estimate	exact
$200	$215.53
+ 40	+ 44.47
$240	$260.00

The total amount of the two checks was $260.00.

38. First total the money that Joey spent.

estimate	exact
$2	$1.59
5	5.33
+ 20	+ 18.94
$27	$25.86

Then subtract to find the change.

estimate	exact
$30	$30.00
− 27	− 25.86
$ 3	$ 4.14

Joey's change was $4.14.

39. Add the kilometers that she raced each day.

estimate	exact
2	2.30
4	4.00
+ 5	+ 5.25
11 kilometers	11.55

Roseanne raced 11.55 kilometers.

40.
estimate	exact
6	6.138
× 4	× 3.7
24	4 2966
	18 414
	22.7106

41.
estimate	exact
40	42.9
× 3	× 3.3
120	12 87
	128 7
	141.57

42. (5.6)(0.002)

5.6
× 0.002
0.0112

43. (0.071)(0.005)

0.071
× 0.005
0.000355

99

44. $706.2 \div 12 = 58.85$

estimate : $700 \div 10 = 70$

58.85 is reasonable.

45. $26.6 \div 2.8 = 0.95$

estimate : $30 \div 3 = 10$

0.95 is not reasonable.

```
          9.5
2.8ₐ)26.6ₐ0     Move decimal point 1
     25 2       place in divisor and
      1 4 0    dividend; write one 0
      1 4 0
          0
```

The correct answer is 9.5.

46.
```
     14.4666    Write three 0' in
3)43.4000       the dividend
  3
  13
  12
   1 4
   1 2
     20
     18
      20
      18
       20
       18
        0
```

14.4666 rounds to ≈ 14.467.

47. $\dfrac{72}{0.06}$

$72 \div 0.06 \;=\; 7200 \div 6$
$ \;=\; 1200$

48. $0.00048 \div 0.0012$

$0.00048 \div 0.0012 \;=\; 4.8 \div 12$
$ \;=\; 0.4$

```
     0.4
12)4.8
   4 8
     0
```

49. Multiply the hourly wage times the hours worked.

```
    $9.59
  ×  36.5
   4 795
  57 54
 287 7
$350.035
```

Round to the nearest dollar.

$350.|035

Draw cut-off line. First digit cut is less then five so part you keep stays the same.
Adrienne's total earnings were $\approx$ $350.

50. Divide the cost of the book by the number of tickets in the book.

```
        1.9908
12)$23.8900
   12
   11 8
   10 8
    1 09
    1 08
      100
       96
        4
```

Round to the nearest cent.

$1.99|08

Draw a cut-off line. First digit cut is less than 5 so part you keep stays the same.

Each ticket costs $\approx$ $1.99.

51. Divide the amount of the investment by the price per share.

```
           1 33.3
3.75ₐ)500.00ₐ0
      375
      125 0
      112 5
       12 50
       11 25
        1 25 0
        1 12 5
          12 5
```

Round 133.|3 to the nearest whole share. Draw cut-off line. First digit cut is less than 5 so part you keep stays the same.
Kenneth could buy $\approx$ 133 shares.

Chapter 4 Review Exercises

52. Multiply the price per pound by the amount to be purchased.

$$\begin{array}{r} \$0.89 \\ \times \quad 3.5 \\ \hline 445 \\ 2\;67 \\ \hline \$3.115 \end{array}$$

$3.115 rounds to $3.12.
Ms. Lee will pay ≈ $3.12.

53. $3.5^2 + 8.7 \cdot 1.95$ *Exponent*
$12.25 + 8.7 \cdot 1.95$ *Multiply*
$12.25 + 16.965 = 29.215$ *Add*

54. $11 - 3.06 \div (3.95 - 0.35)$ *Parentheses*
$11 - 3.06 \div 3.6$ *Divide*
$11 - 0.85 = 10.15$ *Subtract*

55. $3\frac{4}{5} = \frac{19}{5} = 3.8$

$$\begin{array}{r} 3.8 \\ 5\overline{)19.0} \\ \underline{15} \\ 4\,0 \\ \underline{4\,0} \\ 0 \end{array}$$

56. $\frac{16}{25} = 0.64$

$$\begin{array}{r} 0.64 \\ 25\overline{)16.00} \\ \underline{15\,0} \\ 1\,00 \\ \underline{1\,00} \\ 0 \end{array}$$

57. $1\frac{7}{8} = \frac{15}{8} = 1.875$

$$\begin{array}{r} 1.875 \\ 8\overline{)15.000} \\ \underline{8} \\ 70 \\ \underline{64} \\ 60 \\ \underline{56} \\ 40 \\ \underline{40} \\ 0 \end{array}$$

58. $\frac{1}{9}$

$$\begin{array}{r} 0.1111 \\ 9\overline{)1.0000} \\ \underline{9} \\ 10 \\ \underline{9} \\ 10 \\ \underline{9} \\ 10 \\ \underline{9} \\ 1 \end{array}$$

0.1111 rounds to 0.111.
$\frac{1}{9} \approx 0.111$

59. 3.68, 3.806, 3.6008

$$3.6008 = 3.6008$$
$$3.806 = 3.8060$$
$$3.68 = 3.6800$$

From smallest to largest:

3.6008, 3.68, 3.806

60. 0.215, 0.22, 0.209, 0.2102

$$0.215 = 0.2150$$
$$0.22 = 0.2200$$
$$0.209 = 0.2090$$
$$0.2102 = 0.2102$$

From smallest to largest:

0.209, 0.2102, 0.215, 0.22

61. 0.17, $\frac{3}{20}$, $\frac{1}{8}$, 0.159

$$0.17 = 0.170$$
$$\frac{3}{20} = 0.150$$
$$\frac{1}{8} = 0.125$$

From smallest to largest:

$\frac{1}{8}, \frac{3}{20}, 0.159, 0.17$

62.
$$\begin{array}{r} 89.190 \\ 0.075 \\ 310.600 \\ +\quad 5.000 \\ \hline 404.865 \end{array}$$

63.
```
    72.8    1 decimal place
  ×  3.5    1 decimal place
   36 40
  218 4
  254.80    2 decimal places
```

64. $1648.3 \div 0.46 = 3583.2609$

3583.2609 rounds to ≈ 3583.261.

65.
```
   2 9 9 9 9
   3̸0̸.0̸0̸0̸0̸
 −  0.9102
   29.0898
```

66. $(4.38)(0.007)$
```
     4.38    2 decimal places
  × 0.007    3 decimal places
   0.03066   5 decimal places
```

67.
```
              9.4
  0.005⌃)0.047⌃0    Move decimal point 3
         45         places in divisor and
         2 0        dividend
         2 0
           0
```

68.
```
     72.105
      8.200
  +  95.370
    175.675
```

69.
```
       9.04
    9)81.36
      81
       0 3
         0
         36
         36
          0
```

70.
$(5.6 - 1.22) + 4.8 \cdot 3.15$ *Parentheses*
$4.38 + 4.8 \cdot 3.15$ *Multiply*
$4.38 + 15.12 = 19.50$ *Add*

71.
```
    0.455   ← 3 decimal places
  ×   18
    3 640
    4 55
    8.190   ← 3 decimal places
```

72.
```
      0.58   ← 2 decimal places
  ×   1.6    ← 1 decimal place
      348
      58
     0.928   ← 3 decimal places
```

73. $0.218\overline{)7.63}$

$7.63 \div 0.218 = 35$

74.
```
        0 10
      2 1̸.0̸ 59
  −   2 0.8 00
        0.2 59
```

75. $18.3 - 3^2 \div 0.5$ *Exponent*
$18.3 - 9 \div 0.5$ *Divide*
$18.3 - 18 = 0.3$ *Subtract*

76. Men's socks are 3 pairs for $8.99. Divide the price by 3 to find the cost of one pair.

```
      2.996
    3)8.990
      6
      2 9
      2 7
        29
        27
         20
         18
          2
```

$2.996 rounds to $3.00.
One pair of men's socks cost $\approx$ $3.00.

77. Children's socks cost 6 pairs for $5.00. Find the cost for one pair.

```
      0.833
    6)5.000
      4 8
        20
        18
         20
         18
          2
```

$0.833 rounds to $0.83.

Chapter 4 Test

Subtract to find how much more men's socks cost.

$$\begin{array}{r} \$3.00 \\ -0.83 \\ \hline \$2.17 \end{array}$$

Men's socks cost ≈ $2.17 more.

78. A dozen pair of socks is 4 · 3 = 12 pair of socks. So multiply 4 times $8.99.

$$\begin{array}{r} \$8.99 \\ \times 4 \\ \hline \$35.96 \end{array}$$

The cost for a dozen pair of men's socks is $35.96.

79. Five pairs of teen jeans cost $19.95 times 5.

$$\begin{array}{r} \$19.95 \\ \times 5 \\ \hline \$99.75 \end{array}$$

Four pairs of women's jeans cost $24.99 times 4.

$$\begin{array}{r} \$24.99 \\ \times 4 \\ \hline \$99.96 \end{array}$$

Add the two sums.

$$\begin{array}{r} \$99.75 \\ +99.96 \\ \hline \$199.71 \end{array}$$

Akiko would pay $199.71.

80. The highest regular price for athletic shoes is $149.50. The cheapest sale price is $71. Subtract to find the difference.

$$\begin{array}{r} \$149.50 \\ -71.00 \\ \hline \$78.50 \end{array}$$

The difference in price is $78.50.

Chapter 4 Test

1. $18.4 = 18\frac{4}{10} = 18\frac{2}{5}$

2. $0.075 = \frac{75}{1000} = \frac{75 \div 25}{1000 \div 25} = \frac{3}{40}$

3. 60.007 is sixty and seven thousandths.

4. 0.0208 is two hundred eight ten-thousandths.

5. 725.6089 to the nearest tenth: ≈ 725.6

725.6|089

Draw a cut-off line. First digit cut is less than five so part you keep stays the same.

6. 0.62951 to the nearest thousandth: ≈ 0.630

0.629|51

Draw a cut-off line. First digit cut is 5 or more so round up.

7. $1.4945 to the nearest cent: ≈ $1.49

$1.49|45

Draw a cut-off line. First digit cut is less than 5 so part you keep stays the same.

8. $7859.51 to the nearest dollar: ≈ $7860

$7859|.51

Draw a cut-off line. First digit cut is 5 or more so round up.

9.
estimate	exact
8	7.6000
80	82.0128
+ 40	+ 39.5900
128	129.2028

10.
estimate	exact
80	79.100
− 4	− 3.602
76	75.498

11.
estimate	exact
6	5.79
× 1	× 1.2
6	1 158
	5 79
	6.948

12.
```
 estimate          exact
     4             4.175
  5)20         4.8̬)20.0̬400
                   19 2
                    8 4
                    4 8
                    3 60
                    3 36
                      240
                      240
                        0
```

13.
```
     53.100
      4.631
    782.000
   +  0.031
    839.762
```

14.
```
      6⁹⁄0 ¹⁰⁄0 ¹⁰⁄0 ¹⁰
      6 7̸0̸,0̸0̸0̸
    -     0.9 9 6
      6 6 9.0 0 4
```

15. $(0.0069)(0.007)$

```
     0.0069      ← 4 decimal places
   ×  0.007      ← 3 decimal places
   0.0000483     ← 7 decimal places
```

16.
```
            4 80.
   0.15̬)72.00̬       Move decimal point 2
         60        places in dividend and
         12 0      divisor; write 2 0's
         12 0
           00
            0
            0
```

17. $2\frac{5}{8} = \frac{21}{8}$

```
        2.625
     8)21.000
        16
         5 0
         4 8
           20
           16
            40
            40
             0
```

$2\frac{5}{8} = 2.625$

18. $0.44,\ 0.451,\ \frac{9}{20},\ 0.4506$

Change to ten-thousandths, if necessary and compare.

$$0.44 = 0.4400$$
$$0.451 = 0.4510$$
$$\frac{9}{20} = 0.4500$$
$$0.4506 = 0.4506$$

From smallest to largest:

$$0.44,\ \frac{9}{20},\ 0.4506,\ 0.451$$

19.
$$6.3^2 - 5.9 + 3.4 \cdot 0.5 \quad \textit{Exponent}$$
$$39.69 - 5.9 + 3.4 \cdot 0.5 \quad \textit{Multiply}$$
$$39.69 - 5.9 + 1.7 \quad \textit{Subtract}$$
$$33.79 + 1.7 = 35.49 \quad \textit{Add}$$

20. To find the balance add the interest and the deposit to the balance and then subtract the bank charge.

```
    $71.15        $462.87
      0.95      -   16.00
  + 390.77        $446.87
    $462.87
```

The new balance is $446.87.

21. Compare the two times.

    Angela: 3.500 minutes   *more time*
    Davida: 3.059 minutes   *less time*

```
      3.500
    - 3.059
      0.441
```

Davida won by 0.441 minute.

22. Multiply the price per pound by the amount purchased.

```
      $2.89
    ×  1.85
       1445
      2 312
      2 89
     $5.3465
```

Round $5.3465 to the nearest cent.

$$\$5.34|65$$

Draw cut-off line. First digit cut is 5 or more so round up.

Mr. Yamamoto paid ≈$5.35 for the cheese.

Cumulative Review Exercises (Chapters 1-4)

23. Subtract the two temperatures.

$$\begin{array}{r} \overset{9}{\cancel{1}}\overset{11}{\cancel{0}}\overset{17}{\cancel{2}}\overset{}{\cancel{7}} \\ -\ \ 9\ 9.9 \\ \hline 2.8 \end{array}$$

The temperature dropped 2.8 degrees.

24. Divide to find the cost per meter.

$$\begin{array}{r} 4.55 \\ 3.4_\wedge)\overline{\$15.4_\wedge 70} \\ \underline{13\ 6} \\ 1\ 8\ 7 \\ \underline{1\ 7\ 0} \\ 1\ 70 \\ \underline{1\ 70} \\ 0 \end{array}$$ *Move decimal 1 place in divisor and dividend; write one 0*

The fabric costs $4.55 per meter.

25. Answer varies.

Cumulative Review Exercises (Chapters 1-4)

1. 1<u>9</u>,076,<u>5</u>42
   hundreds: 5
   millions: 9
   ones: 2

2. <u>8</u>3.0<u>75</u>4
   tenths: 0
   thousandths: 5
   tens: 8

3. 499,501 to the nearest thousand: ≈ 500,000

   49<u>9</u>,501

   Next digit is 5 or more. Thousands place changes (9 + 1 = 10). All digits to the right of the underlined place are changed to zero.

4. 602.4937 to the nearest hundredth: ≈ 602.49

   602.49|37

   Draw cut-off line. First digit cut is less than 5 so part you keep stays the same.

5. $709.60 to the nearest dollar: ≈ $710

   $709.|60

   Draw cut-off line. First digit cut is 5 or more so round up.

6. $0.0528 to the nearest cent: ≈ $0.05

   $0.05|28

   Draw cut-off line. First digit cut is less than 5 so part you keep stays the same.

7. | estimate | exact |
   |---|---|
   | 4 000 | 3 672 |
   | 600 | 589 |
   | + 9 000 | + 9 078 |
   | 13,600 | 13,339 |

8. | estimate | exact |
   |---|---|
   | 4 | 4.060 |
   | 20 | 15.700 |
   | + 1 | + 0.923 |
   | 25 | 20.683 |

9. | estimate | exact |
   |---|---|
   | 5000 | $\overset{4\ 10\ 0\ 18}{\cancel{5}\cancel{0}\cancel{1}\cancel{8}}$ |
   | − 2000 | − 1809 |
   | 3000 | 3 2 0 9 |

10. | estimate | exact |
    |---|---|
    | 50 | $\overset{411\ 5\ \overset{9}{\cancel{10}}10}{\cancel{5}\cancel{1}\cancel{6}\cancel{0}\cancel{0}}$ |
    | − 7 | − 7.0 9 4 |
    | 43 | 4 4 .5 0 6 |

11. | estimate | exact |
    |---|---|
    | 3000 | 3317 |
    | × 200 | × 166 |
    | 600,000 | 19 902 |
    | | 199 02 |
    | | 331 7 |
    | | 550,622 |

12. | estimate | exact |
    |---|---|
    | 7 | 6.82 |
    | × 7 | × 7.3 |
    | 49 | 2 046 |
    | | 47 74 |
    | | 49.786 |

13.
```
 estimate            exact
   2 000              2 690
50)100,000        46)123,740
                     92
                     31 7
                     27 6
                      4 14
                      4 14
                        00
                         0
                         0
```

14.
```
estimate           exact
    5                4.5
 8)40           8.4∧)37.8∧0
                    33 6
                     4 2 0
                     4 2 0
                         0
```

15. *estimate*: $2 \cdot 4 = 8$

exact

$$1\frac{9}{10} \cdot 3\frac{3}{4} = \frac{19}{\cancel{10}_2} \cdot \frac{\cancel{15}^3}{4} = \frac{57}{8} = 7\frac{1}{8}$$

16. *estimate*: $2 \div 1 = 2$

exact

$$2\frac{1}{3} \div \frac{5}{6} = \frac{7}{3} \div \frac{5}{6} = \frac{7}{\cancel{3}_1} \cdot \frac{\cancel{6}^2}{5}$$
$$= \frac{14}{5} = 2\frac{4}{5}$$

17. *estimate*: $2 + 2 = 4$

exact

$$1\frac{4}{5} + 1\frac{2}{3} = \frac{9}{5} + \frac{5}{3} = \frac{27}{15} + \frac{25}{15}$$
$$= \frac{52}{15} = 3\frac{7}{15}$$

18. *estimate*: $5 - 2 = 3$

exact

$$4\frac{1}{2} - 1\frac{7}{8} = \frac{9}{2} - \frac{15}{8} = \frac{36}{8} - \frac{15}{8} = \frac{21}{8} = 2\frac{5}{8}$$

19. $10 - 0.329$

```
   9  9 9
  ⁄1⁄0.⁄0⁄0⁄010
 − 0 . 3 2 9
   9 . 6 7 1
```

20. $2\frac{3}{5} \cdot \frac{5}{9} = \frac{13}{5} \cdot \frac{5}{9} = \frac{13}{\cancel{5}} \cdot \frac{\cancel{5}^1}{9} = \frac{13}{9} = 1\frac{4}{9}$

21.
```
       9
   72,417
 +    799
   73,225
```

22. $11\frac{1}{5} \div 8 = \frac{56}{5} \div \frac{8}{1} = \frac{\cancel{56}^7}{5} \cdot \frac{1}{\cancel{8}_1} = \frac{7}{5} = 1\frac{2}{5}$

23. $5006 - 92$

```
   4 10 10
   ⁄5 ⁄0 ⁄0 6
 −      9 2
   4 9 1 4
```

24.
```
     0.700
    85.000
 +   7.903
    93.603
```

25.
```
      404  R3
  7)2831
    28
    03
     0
     31
     28
      3
```

26.
$$\frac{5}{6} = \frac{20}{24}$$
$$+ \frac{7}{8} = \frac{21}{24}$$
$$\overline{\frac{41}{24} = 1\frac{17}{24}}$$

27.
```
       332
   ×   704
     1 328
   232 40
   233,728
```

Cumulative Review Exercises (Chapters 1-4) 107

28. $\quad$ 0.006 $\leftarrow$ 3 decimal places
$\quad\times$ 5.44 $\leftarrow$ 2 decimal places
$\quad\quad$ 24
$\quad\quad$ 24
$\quad\quad$ 30
$\quad\overline{0.03264}$ $\leftarrow$ 5 decimal places

29. $\quad$ 3.2
$\quad\times$ 2.5
$\quad$ 1 60
$\quad$ 6 4
$\quad$ 8.00

30. $\quad 0.56_\wedge \overline{)25.20_\wedge}$ quotient 45
$\quad$ 22 4
$\quad\quad$ 2 80
$\quad\quad$ 2 80
$\quad\quad\quad$ 0

31. $\dfrac{2}{3} \div 5\dfrac{1}{6} = \dfrac{2}{3} \div \dfrac{31}{6} = \dfrac{2}{\cancel{3}} \cdot \dfrac{\cancel{6}^2}{31} = \dfrac{4}{31}$

32. $\quad 5\dfrac{1}{4} = 5\dfrac{3}{12} = 4\dfrac{15}{12}$
$\quad -4\dfrac{7}{12} = 4\dfrac{7}{12} = 4\dfrac{7}{12}$
$\quad\quad\quad\quad\quad\quad\quad \dfrac{8}{12} = \dfrac{2}{3}$

33. $\quad 9.3_\wedge \overline{)4.7_\wedge 000}$ quotient 0.505
$\quad$ 4 6 5
$\quad\quad$ 500
$\quad\quad$ 465
$\quad\quad\quad$ 35

Round 0.505 to the nearest hundredth: ≈ 0.51

$\quad\quad$ 0.50|5

Draw cut-off line. First digit cut is 5 or more so round up.

34. $10 - 4 \div 2 \cdot 3$ $\quad$ Divide
$\quad 10 - 2 \cdot 3$ $\quad$ Multiply
$\quad 10 - 6 = 4$ $\quad$ Subtract

35. $\sqrt{36} + 3 \cdot 8 - 4^2$ $\quad$ Exponent
$\quad \sqrt{36} + 3 \cdot 8 - 16$ $\quad$ Square root
$\quad 6 + 3 \cdot 8 - 16$ $\quad$ Multiply
$\quad 6 + 24 - 16$ $\quad$ Add
$\quad 30 - 16 = 14$ $\quad$ Subtract

36. $\dfrac{2}{3} \cdot \left(\dfrac{7}{8} - \dfrac{1}{2}\right)$
$\quad \dfrac{2}{3} \cdot \left(\dfrac{7}{8} - \dfrac{4}{8}\right)$ $\quad$ Parentheses
$\quad \dfrac{\cancel{2}^1}{\cancel{3}_1} \cdot \dfrac{\cancel{3}^1}{\cancel{8}_4} = \dfrac{1}{4}$ $\quad$ Multiply

37. $0.9^2 + 10.6 \div 0.53$ $\quad$ Exponent
$\quad 0.81 + 10.6 \div 0.53$ $\quad$ Divide
$\quad 0.81 + 20 = 20.81$ $\quad$ Add

38. $4^3 \cdot 3^2 = 4 \cdot 4 \cdot 4 \cdot 3 \cdot 3 = 64 \cdot 9 = 576$

39. $\sqrt{196} = \sqrt{14 \cdot 14} = 14$

40.

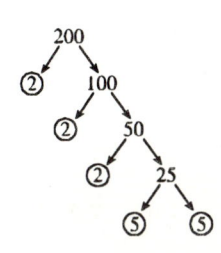

$\quad\quad$ 200
$\quad$ 2 — 100
$\quad\quad$ 2 — 50
$\quad\quad\quad$ 2 — 25
$\quad\quad\quad\quad$ 5 — 5

$200 = 2 \cdot 2 \cdot 2 \cdot 5 \cdot 5 = 2^3 \cdot 5^2$

41. 40.035 is forty and thirty-five thousandths.

42. Three hundred six ten-thousandths is 0.0306.

43. $0.125 = \dfrac{125}{1000} = \dfrac{125 \div 125}{1000 \div 125} = \dfrac{1}{8}$

44. $3.08 = 3\dfrac{8}{100} = 3\dfrac{8 \div 4}{100 \div 4} = 3\dfrac{2}{25}$

45. $2\dfrac{3}{5} = \dfrac{13}{5} = 2.6 \quad\quad 5\overline{)13.0}$ quotient 2.6
$\quad\quad\quad\quad\quad\quad\quad\quad\quad$ 10
$\quad\quad\quad\quad\quad\quad\quad\quad\quad$ 3 0
$\quad\quad\quad\quad\quad\quad\quad\quad\quad$ 3 0
$\quad\quad\quad\quad\quad\quad\quad\quad\quad\quad$ 0

46. $\dfrac{7}{11}$ $\quad\quad$ $11\overline{)7.000}$ quotient 0.6363
$\quad\quad\quad\quad$ 6 6
$\quad\quad\quad\quad\quad$ 40
$\quad\quad\quad\quad\quad$ 33
$\quad\quad\quad\quad\quad\quad$ 70
$\quad\quad\quad\quad\quad\quad$ 66
$\quad\quad\quad\quad\quad\quad\quad$ 40
$\quad\quad\quad\quad\quad\quad\quad$ 33
$\quad\quad\quad\quad\quad\quad\quad\quad$ 7

0.6363 rounded to the nearest thousandth is 0.636.

$\frac{7}{11} \approx 0.636$

47. $\frac{5}{8}$ — $\frac{4}{9}$

$\frac{5}{8} = \frac{45}{72}, \frac{4}{9} = \frac{32}{72}$

$\frac{45}{72} > \frac{32}{72}$, so $\frac{5}{8} > \frac{4}{9}$.

48. 7.005, 7.5005, 7.5, 7.505

$$7.005 = 7.0050$$
$$7.5005 = 7.5005$$
$$7.5 = 7.5000$$
$$7.505 = 7.5050$$

From smallest to largest:

7.005, 7.5, 7.5005, 7.505

49. $\frac{7}{8}$, 0.8, $\frac{21}{25}$, 0.8015

$$\frac{7}{8} = 0.8750$$
$$0.8 = 0.8000$$
$$\frac{21}{25} = 0.8400$$
$$0.8015$$

From smallest to largest:

0.8, 0.8015, $\frac{21}{25}$, $\frac{7}{8}$

50. Compare the distances.

67.950 *longer*   67.950
67.905 *shorter* − 67.905
                    0.045

The figure would be too short by 0.045 meter.

51. Find $\frac{7}{8}$ of 96.

$\frac{7}{8} \cdot 96 = \frac{7}{8} \cdot \frac{\overset{12}{\cancel{96}}}{1} = \frac{7 \cdot 12}{1} = 84$

84 children would be expected to be right-handed.

52. First find how much money Lameck spent.

estimate $20 − $8 − $1 = $11

$7.96
+ 0.87
$8.83

This is less than ten dollars, so he only needs to use one $10 bill.

$10.00
− 8.83
$ 1.17

He has $10 + $1.17 = $11.17 left.

53. Subtract the two measurements.

estimate   50 − 47 = 3 inches

exact   50 = $49\frac{8}{8}$
            −$46\frac{5}{8}$ = $46\frac{5}{8}$
                              $3\frac{3}{8}$

She has grown $3\frac{3}{8}$ inches.

54. Multiply the hourly wage by the hours worked.

estimate $9 × 17 = $153

exact $8.73
            × 16.5
            4 365
           52 38
           87 3
          $144.045

$144.054 rounded to the nearest cent is $144.05.
Sharon earned ≈ $144.05.

55. Find the number of students in each classroom. Then add the two sums.

estimate

(8 × 20) + (10 × 30) = 160 + 300
                     = 460 students

exact

    22   26   176
  × 8   × 12   + 312
   176   52   488
              26
             312

There are 488 students attending the school.

Cumulative Review Exercises (Chapters 1-4)

56. Add the two purchases.
    estimate $2 + 4 = 6$ yards
    exact
    $$2\tfrac{1}{3} = 2\tfrac{8}{24}$$
    $$+\ 3\tfrac{7}{8} = 3\tfrac{21}{24}$$
    $$5\tfrac{29}{24} = 5 + 1 + \tfrac{5}{24}$$
    $$= 6\tfrac{5}{24}$$

    Toshihiro bought $6\tfrac{5}{24}$ yards of fabric.

57. Add the two deposits to the amount Kimberly had in her account. Then subtract the amount for the check that she wrote and the overdraft charge.
    estimate
    $$\$30 + \$200 - \$40 - \$20 = \$170$$

    exact

	\$29.44	*Balance on hand*
$+$	220.06	*Deposit*
	\$249.50	
$-$	40.00	*Check*
	\$209.50	
$-$	18.00	*Overdraft*
	\$191.50	*New balance*

    The new balance in her account is \$191.50.

58. Divide the price of the grapes by the number of pounds of grapes that Paulette bought.

    estimate $\$3 \div 3 = \$1$ per pound

    exact $\$2.56 \div 2.7$

    ```
                0.948
    2.7 )$2.5 600    Move decimal point
         2 4 3       one place in divisor
           1 30      and dividend
           1 08
             220
             216
               4
    ```

    \$0.948 rounds to $\approx$ \$0.95.
    The cost of the grapes is $\approx$ \$0.95 per pound.

59. Divide the amount of the grant by the number of students.
    estimate $\$80,000 \div 100 = \$800$

exact

```
            728.9
107 )$78,000.0
      74 9
       3 10
       2 14
         960
         856
         104 0
          96 3
           7 7
```

728.9 rounds to $\approx$ 729.
Each student could be given $\approx$ \$729.

Chapter 5

RATIOS AND PROPORTION

5.1 Ratios

5.1 Margin Exercises

1. (a) $7 spent on fresh fruit to $5 spent on milk

$$\frac{7}{5}$$

(b) $5 spent on milk to $14 spent on meat

$$\frac{5}{14}$$

(c) $14 spent on meat to $5 spent on milk

$$\frac{14}{5}$$

2. (a) 9 hours to 12 hours

$$\frac{9}{12} = \frac{9 \div 3}{12 \div 3} = \frac{3}{4}$$

(b) 100 meters to 50 meters

$$\frac{100}{50} = \frac{100 \div 50}{50 \div 50} = \frac{2}{1}$$

(c) width to length or 24 feet to 48 feet

$$\frac{24}{48} = \frac{24 \div 24}{48 \div 48} = \frac{1}{2}$$

3. (a) The increase in price is

$$\$4.25 - \$3.75 = \$0.50.$$

The ratio of increase in price to original price is

$$\frac{0.50}{3.75}.$$

Rewrite as two whole numbers.

$$\frac{0.50}{3.75} = \frac{0.50 \cdot 100}{3.75 \cdot 100} = \frac{50}{375}$$

Write in lowest terms.

$$\frac{50 \div 25}{375 \div 25} = \frac{2}{15}$$

(b) The decrease in hours is

$$4.5 \text{ hours} - 3 \text{ hours} = 1.5 \text{ hours}.$$

The ratio of decrease in hours to the original hours is

$$\frac{1.5}{4.5}.$$

Rewrite as two whole numbers.

$$\frac{1.5 \cdot 10}{4.5 \cdot 10} = \frac{15}{45}$$

Write in lowest terms.

$$\frac{15 \div 15}{45 \div 15} = \frac{1}{3}$$

4. (a) $3\frac{1}{2}$ to 4

$$\frac{3\frac{1}{2}}{4} = \frac{\frac{7}{2}}{\frac{4}{1}} = \frac{7}{2} \div \frac{4}{1} = \frac{7}{2} \cdot \frac{1}{4} = \frac{7}{8}$$

(b) $5\frac{5}{8}$ pounds to $3\frac{3}{4}$ pounds

$$\frac{5\frac{5}{8}}{3\frac{3}{4}} = \frac{\frac{45}{8}}{\frac{15}{4}} = \frac{45}{8} \div \frac{15}{4} = \frac{\overset{3}{\cancel{45}}}{\underset{2}{\cancel{8}}} \cdot \frac{\overset{1}{\cancel{4}}}{\underset{1}{\cancel{15}}} = \frac{3}{2}$$

(c) $3\frac{1}{2}$ inches to $\frac{7}{8}$ inch

$$\frac{3\frac{1}{2}}{\frac{7}{8}} = \frac{\frac{7}{2}}{\frac{7}{8}} = \frac{7}{2} \div \frac{7}{8} = \frac{\overset{1}{\cancel{7}}}{\underset{1}{\cancel{2}}} \cdot \frac{\overset{4}{\cancel{8}}}{\underset{1}{\cancel{7}}} = \frac{4}{1}$$

5. (a) 9 inches to 6 feet

$$6 \text{ feet} = 6 \cdot 12 \text{ inches}$$
$$= 72 \text{ inches}$$

$$\frac{9 \text{ inches}}{72 \text{ inches}} = \frac{9}{72} = \frac{9 \div 9}{72 \div 9} = \frac{1}{8}$$

(b) 2 days to 8 hours

2 days = $2 \cdot 24$ hours = 48 hours

$$\frac{48 \text{ hours}}{8 \text{ hours}} = \frac{48}{8} = \frac{48 \div 8}{8 \div 8} = \frac{6}{1}$$

(c) 7 yards to 14 feet

7 yards = $7 \cdot 3$ feet = 21 feet

$$\frac{21 \text{ feet}}{14 \text{ feet}} = \frac{21}{14} = \frac{21 \div 7}{14 \div 7} = \frac{3}{2}$$

Section 5.1 Ratios

(d) 3 quarts to 3 gallons
3 gallons = 3 · 4 = 12 quarts

$$\frac{3 \text{ quarts}}{12 \text{ quarts}} = \frac{3}{12} = \frac{3 \div 3}{12 \div 3} = \frac{1}{4}$$

(e) 25 minutes to 2 hours

2 hours = 2 · 60 minutes
= 120 minutes

$$\frac{25 \text{ minutes}}{120 \text{ minutes}} = \frac{25}{120} = \frac{25 \div 5}{120 \div 5} = \frac{5}{24}$$

(f) 4 pounds to 12 ounces

4 pounds = 4 · 16 ounces
= 64 ounces

$$\frac{64 \text{ ounces}}{12 \text{ ounces}} = \frac{64}{12} = \frac{64 \div 4}{12 \div 4} = \frac{16}{3}$$

5.1 Section Exercises

3. $100 to $50

$$\frac{\$100}{\$50} = \frac{100}{50} = \frac{100 \div 50}{50 \div 50} = \frac{2}{1}$$

7. 80 miles to 50 miles

$$\frac{80 \text{ miles}}{50 \text{ miles}} = \frac{80}{50} = \frac{80 \div 10}{50 \div 10} = \frac{8}{5}$$

11. $4.50 to $3.50

$$\frac{\$4.50}{\$3.50} = \frac{4.50}{3.50} = \frac{4.50 \cdot 10}{3.50 \cdot 10} = \frac{45}{35} = \frac{45 \div 5}{35 \div 5} = \frac{9}{7}$$

15. $1\frac{1}{4}$ to $1\frac{1}{2}$

$$\frac{1\frac{1}{4}}{1\frac{1}{2}} = \frac{\frac{5}{4}}{\frac{3}{2}} = \frac{5}{4} \div \frac{3}{2} = \frac{5}{\cancel{4}_2} \cdot \frac{\cancel{2}^1}{3} = \frac{5}{6}$$

19. 5 minutes to 1 hour
1 hour = 60 minutes

$$\frac{5 \text{ minutes}}{60 \text{ minutes}} = \frac{5}{60} = \frac{5 \div 5}{60 \div 5} = \frac{1}{12}$$

23. 5 gallons to 5 quarts
5 gallons = 5 · 4 quarts = 20 quarts

$$\frac{20 \text{ quarts}}{5 \text{ quarts}} = \frac{20}{5} = \frac{20 \div 5}{5 \div 5} = \frac{4}{1}$$

27. 20 men to 16 women

$$\frac{20}{16} = \frac{20 \div 4}{16 \div 4} = \frac{5}{4}$$

The ratio of men to women is $\frac{5}{4}$.

31. 22 million piano players
to 2 million violin players

$$\frac{22}{2} = \frac{22 \div 2}{2 \div 2} = \frac{11}{1}$$

The ratio of piano players to violin players is $\frac{11}{1}$.

35. A ratio of 3 to 1 means your income is 3 times your friend's income.

39. rent to total income

$$\frac{\$750}{\$2000} = \frac{750}{2000} = \frac{750 \div 250}{2000 \div 250} = \frac{3}{8}$$

The ratio of rent to total income is $\frac{3}{8}$.

43. $\dfrac{\text{longest side}}{\text{shortest side}} = \dfrac{1.8 \text{ meters}}{0.3 \text{ meter}} = \dfrac{1.8}{0.3}$

$$= \frac{1.8 \cdot 10}{0.3 \cdot 10} = \frac{18}{3} = \frac{18 \div 3}{3 \div 3} = \frac{6}{1}$$

The ratio of the longest side to the shortest side is $\frac{6}{1}$.

47. The increase in price is

$9.90 − $6.60 = $3.30.

$$\frac{\$3.30}{\$6.60} = \frac{3.30}{6.60} = \frac{3.30 \cdot 10}{6.60 \cdot 10} = \frac{33}{66}$$

$$\frac{33 \div 33}{66 \div 33} = \frac{1}{2}$$

The ratio of the increase in price to the original price is $\frac{1}{2}$.

51. Answer varies. Some possibilities are:

$$\frac{4}{5} = \frac{8}{10} = \frac{12}{15} = \frac{16}{20} = \frac{20}{25} = \frac{24}{30} = \frac{28}{35}.$$

55.
```
      1.025
   4)4.100
     4
     0 1
       0
       10   ← Write a 0 in the dividend
        8
        20  ← Write a 0 in the dividend
        20
         0
```

5.2 Rates

5.2 Margin Exercises

1. **(a)** $6 for 30 packages

$$\frac{\$6}{30 \text{ packages}} = \frac{\$6 \div 6}{30 \text{ packages} \div 6} = \frac{\$1}{5 \text{ packages}}$$

(b) 500 miles in 10 hours

$$\frac{500 \text{ miles}}{10 \text{ hours}} = \frac{500 \text{ miles} \div 10}{10 \text{ hours} \div 10} = \frac{50 \text{ miles}}{1 \text{ hour}}$$

(c) 4 teachers for 90 students

$$\frac{4 \text{ teachers}}{90 \text{ students}} = \frac{4 \text{ teachers} \div 2}{90 \text{ students} \div 2} = \frac{2 \text{ teachers}}{45 \text{ students}}$$

(d) 1270 bushels on 30 acres

$$\frac{1270 \text{ bushels}}{30 \text{ acres}} = \frac{1270 \text{ bushels} \div 10}{30 \text{ acres} \div 10} = \frac{127 \text{ bushels}}{3 \text{ acres}}$$

2. **(a)** $4.35 for 3 pounds

$$\frac{\$4.35}{3 \text{ pounds}} = \frac{\$4.35 \div 3}{3 \text{ pounds} \div 3} = \frac{\$1.45}{1 \text{ pound}}$$

The unit rate is $1.45/pound.

(b) 304 miles on 9.5 gallons of gas

$$\frac{304 \text{ miles}}{9.5 \text{ gallons}} = \frac{304 \text{ miles} \div 9.5}{9.5 \text{ gallons} \div 9.5} = \frac{32 \text{ miles}}{1 \text{ gallon}}$$

The unit rate is 32 miles/gallon.

(c) $850 in 5 days

$$\frac{\$850}{5 \text{ days}} = \frac{\$850 \div 5}{5 \text{ days} \div 5} = \frac{\$170}{1 \text{ day}}$$

The unit rate is $170/day.

(d) 24-pound turkey for 15 people

$$\frac{24 \text{ pounds}}{15 \text{ people}} = \frac{24 \text{ pounds} \div 15}{15 \text{ people} \div 15} = \frac{1.6 \text{ pounds}}{1 \text{ person}}$$

The unit rate is 1.6 pounds/person.

3. **(a)**

size	costs per unit
2 quarts	$\frac{\$3.25}{2 \text{ quarts}} = \$1.625$
3 quarts	$\frac{\$4.95}{3 \text{ quarts}} = \$1.65$
4 quarts	$\frac{\$6.48}{4 \text{ quarts}} = \$1.62$

The lowest cost per quart is $1.62, so the best buy is 4 quarts for $6.48.

(b)

size	cost per unit
6 cans	$\frac{\$1.99}{6 \text{ cans}} \approx \$0.332$
12 cans	$\frac{\$3.49}{12 \text{ cans}} \approx \$0.291$
24 cans	$\frac{\$7}{24 \text{ cans}} \approx \$0.292$

The lowest price per can is $\approx\$0.291$, so the best buy is 12 cans for $3.49.

4. **(a)** One battery that lasts twice as long (like getting two) is the better buy. The cost per unit is

$$\frac{\$1.19}{2 \text{ batteries}} \approx \$0.595.$$

The cost of the four-pack is

$$\frac{\$2.79}{4 \text{ batteries}} = \$0.6975 \approx \$0.698 \text{ per battery.}$$

5.2 Section Exercises

3. 15 feet in 35 seconds

$$\frac{15 \text{ feet} \div 5}{35 \text{ seconds} \div 5} = \frac{3 \text{ feet}}{7 \text{ seconds}}$$

Section 5.3   Proportions

7. 25 letters in 5 minutes

$$\frac{25 \text{ letters} \div 5}{5 \text{ minutes} \div 5} = \frac{5 \text{ letters}}{1 \text{ minute}}$$

11. 72 miles on 4 gallons

$$\frac{72 \text{ miles} \div 4}{4 \text{ gallons} \div 4} = \frac{18 \text{ miles}}{1 \text{ gallon}}$$

15. 50 eggs from 10 chickens

$$10\overline{)50} \quad 5$$

The unit rate is 5 eggs per chicken or 5 eggs/chicken.

19. $413.20 for 4 days

$$4\overline{)413.20} \quad 103.30$$

The unit rate is $103.30 per day.

23. Miles traveled:

$$28,396.7 - 28,058.1 = 338.6$$

Miles per gallon:

$$\frac{338.6 \text{ miles}}{16.2 \text{ gallons}} = 338.6 \div 16.2$$
$$\approx 20.901235$$
$$\approx 20.9$$

27.

size	cost per unit
15 ounces	$\frac{\$2.60}{15 \text{ ounces}} \approx \$0.173$
17 ounces	$\frac{\$2.89}{17 \text{ ounces}} = \$0.17$
21 ounces	$\frac{\$3.79}{21 \text{ ounces}} \approx \$0.180$

The best buy is 17 ounces for $2.89.

31. You might choose Brand B because you like more chicken. The cost per chicken chunk may actually be the same or less than Brand A.

35. 7 hours to $85.82

$$\frac{\$85.82 \div 7}{7 \text{ hours} \div 7} = \frac{\$12.26}{1 \text{ hour}}$$

His rate is $12.26 per hour.

39. seconds per meter

$$\frac{20 \text{ seconds} \div 20}{200 \text{ meters} \div 20} = \frac{1}{10} \text{ or } 0.1 \text{ second/meter}$$

meters per second

$$\frac{200 \text{ meters} \div 20}{20 \text{ seconds} \div 20} = \frac{10 \text{ meters}}{1 \text{ second}}$$

43. One battery for $1.79 is the better buy which is like getting 3 batteries for

$$\$1.79 \div 3 \approx \$0.597 \text{ per battery.}$$

An eight-pack of AAA batteries for $4.99 is

$$\frac{\$4.99}{8} \approx \$0.624 \text{ per battery.}$$

47. $4 \cdot 2\frac{3}{4} = \frac{\cancel{4}^1}{1} \cdot \frac{11}{\cancel{4}_1} = \frac{1 \cdot 11}{1 \cdot 1} = 11$

51. $1\frac{1}{6} \cdot 3 = \frac{7}{\cancel{6}_2} \cdot \frac{\cancel{3}^1}{1} = \frac{7 \cdot 1}{2 \cdot 1} = 3\frac{1}{2}$

5.3 Proportions

5.3 Margin Exercises

1. (a) $7 is to 3 cans as $28 is to 12 cans

$$\frac{\$7}{3 \text{ cans}} = \frac{\$28}{12 \text{ cans}}$$

(b) 9 meters is to 16 meters as 18 meters is to 32 meters

$$\frac{9}{16} = \frac{18}{32} \quad \textit{Common units cancel}$$

(c) 5 is to 7 as 35 is to 49

$$\frac{5}{7} = \frac{35}{49}$$

(d) 10 is 30 as 60 is 180

$$\frac{10}{30} = \frac{60}{180}$$

113

2. (a) $\dfrac{6}{12} = \dfrac{15}{30}$

$$\dfrac{6 \div 6}{12 \div 6} = \dfrac{1}{2} \text{ and } \dfrac{15 \div 15}{30 \div 15} = \dfrac{1}{2}$$

Both ratios are equivalent to $\frac{1}{2}$, so the proportion is true.

(b) $\dfrac{20}{24} = \dfrac{3}{4}$

$$\dfrac{20}{24} = \dfrac{20 \div 4}{24 \div 4} = \dfrac{5}{6} \text{ and } \dfrac{3}{4}$$

Because $\frac{5}{6}$ is not equivalent to $\frac{3}{4}$, the proportion is false.

(c) $\dfrac{25}{40} = \dfrac{30}{48}$

$$\dfrac{25 \div 5}{40 \div 5} = \dfrac{5}{8} \text{ and } \dfrac{30 \div 6}{48 \div 6} = \dfrac{5}{8}$$

Both ratios are equivalent to $\frac{5}{8}$, so the proportion is true.

(d) $\dfrac{35}{45} = \dfrac{12}{18}$

$$\dfrac{35 \div 5}{45 \div 5} = \dfrac{7}{9} \text{ and } \dfrac{12 \div 6}{18 \div 6} = \dfrac{2}{3}$$

Because $\frac{7}{9}$ is not equivalent to $\frac{2}{3}$, the proportion is false.

(e) $\dfrac{21}{45} = \dfrac{56}{120}$

$$\dfrac{21 \div 3}{45 \div 3} = \dfrac{7}{15} \text{ and } \dfrac{56 \div 8}{120 \div 8} = \dfrac{7}{15}$$

Both ratios are equivalent to $\frac{7}{15}$, so the proportion is true.

3. (a) $\dfrac{5}{9} = \dfrac{10}{18}$

$$\begin{aligned} 5 \cdot 18 &= 90 \leftarrow \textit{Cross products} \\ 9 \cdot 10 &= 90 \leftarrow \textit{are equal} \end{aligned}$$

True

(b) $\dfrac{32}{15} = \dfrac{16}{8}$

$$\begin{aligned} 32 \cdot 8 &= 256 \leftarrow \textit{Cross products} \\ 15 \cdot 16 &= 240 \leftarrow \textit{are unequal} \end{aligned}$$

False

(c) $\dfrac{10}{17} = \dfrac{20}{34}$

$$\begin{aligned} 10 \cdot 34 &= 340 \leftarrow \textit{Cross products} \\ 17 \cdot 20 &= 340 \leftarrow \textit{are equal} \end{aligned}$$

True

(d) $\dfrac{2.4}{6} = \dfrac{5}{12}$

$$\begin{aligned} 2.4 \cdot 12 &= 28.8 \leftarrow \textit{Cross products} \\ 6 \cdot 5 &= 30 \leftarrow \textit{are unequal} \end{aligned}$$

False

(e) $\dfrac{3}{4.25} = \dfrac{24}{34}$

$$\begin{aligned} 3 \cdot 34 &= 102 \leftarrow \textit{Cross products} \\ 4.25 \cdot 24 &= 102 \leftarrow \textit{are unequal} \end{aligned}$$

True

(f) $\dfrac{1\frac{1}{6}}{2\frac{1}{3}} = \dfrac{4}{8}$

$$\begin{aligned} 1\tfrac{1}{6} \cdot 8 &= \dfrac{7}{\cancel{6}_3} \cdot \dfrac{\cancel{8}^4}{1} = \dfrac{28}{3} \\ 2\tfrac{1}{3} \cdot 4 &= \dfrac{7}{3} \cdot \dfrac{4}{1} = \dfrac{28}{3} \end{aligned}$$

The cross products are equal.
True

5.3 Section Exercises

3. 200 adults is to 450 children as 4 adults is to 9 children

$$\dfrac{200 \text{ adults}}{450 \text{ children}} = \dfrac{4 \text{ adults}}{9 \text{ children}}$$

7. 2.2 hours is to 3.3 hours as 3.2 hours to to 4.8 hours

$$\dfrac{2.2}{3.3} = \dfrac{3.2}{4.8} \quad \textit{Common units cancel}$$

11. $\dfrac{6}{10} = \dfrac{3}{5}$

$$\dfrac{6 \div 2}{10 \div 2} = \dfrac{3}{5} \text{ and } \dfrac{3}{5}$$

Both ratios are equivalent to $\frac{3}{5}$, so the proportion is true.

Section 5.4 Solving Proportions

15. $\dfrac{150}{200} = \dfrac{200}{300}$

$\dfrac{150 \div 50}{200 \div 50} = \dfrac{3}{4}$ and $\dfrac{200 \div 100}{300 \div 100} = \dfrac{2}{3}$

Because $\dfrac{3}{4}$ is not equivalent to $\dfrac{2}{3}$, the proportion is false.

19. $\dfrac{32}{18} = \dfrac{48}{27}$

$\dfrac{32 \div 2}{18 \div 2} = \dfrac{16}{9}$ and $\dfrac{48 \div 3}{27 \div 3} = \dfrac{16}{9}$

Both ratios are equivalent to $\dfrac{16}{9}$, so the proportion is true.

23. $\dfrac{2}{9} = \dfrac{6}{27}$

$2 \cdot 27 = 54 \leftarrow$ Cross products
$9 \cdot 6 = 54 \leftarrow$ are equal

True

27. $\dfrac{110}{18} = \dfrac{160}{27}$

$110 \cdot 27 = 2970 \leftarrow$ Cross products
$18 \cdot 160 = 2880 \leftarrow$ are unequal

False

31. $\dfrac{18}{16} = \dfrac{2.8}{2.5}$

$18 \cdot 2.5 = 45 \leftarrow$ Cross products
$16 \cdot 2.8 = 44.8 \leftarrow$ are unequal

False

35. $\dfrac{2\frac{5}{8}}{3\frac{1}{4}} = \dfrac{21}{26}$

$2\frac{5}{8} \cdot 26 = \dfrac{21}{\cancel{8}_4} \cdot \dfrac{\cancel{26}^{13}}{1} = \dfrac{273}{4}$ ←

$3\frac{1}{4} \cdot 21 = \dfrac{13}{4} \cdot \dfrac{21}{1} = \dfrac{273}{4}$ ←

The cross products are equal.
True

39. $\dfrac{\frac{2}{3}}{2} = \dfrac{2.7}{8}$

$\dfrac{2}{3} \cdot 8 = \dfrac{2}{3} \cdot \dfrac{8}{1} = \dfrac{16}{3} = 5.3$

$2 \cdot 2.7 = 5.4$

The cross products are unequal.
False

43. $\dfrac{60}{48} = \dfrac{60 \div 12}{48 \div 12} = \dfrac{5}{4} = 1\frac{1}{4}$

47. $\dfrac{65}{10} = \dfrac{65 \div 5}{10 \div 5} = \dfrac{13}{2} = 6\frac{1}{2}$

5.4 Solving Proportions

5.4 Margin Exercises

1. (a) $\dfrac{1}{2} = \dfrac{x}{12}$

$2 \cdot x = 1 \cdot 12$ Cross products are equivalent

$\dfrac{\cancel{2}^1 \cdot x}{\cancel{2}_1} = \dfrac{1 \cdot \cancel{12}^6}{\cancel{2}_1}$

$x = 6$

(b) $\dfrac{6}{10} = \dfrac{15}{x}$

$6 \cdot x = 10 \cdot 15$ Cross products are equivalent

$\dfrac{\cancel{6}^1 \cdot x}{\cancel{6}_1} = \dfrac{\cancel{150}^{25}}{\cancel{6}_1}$

$x = 25$

(c) $\dfrac{28}{x} = \dfrac{21}{9}$

$x \cdot 21 = 28 \cdot 9$

$\dfrac{x \cdot \cancel{21}^1}{\cancel{21}_1} = \dfrac{252}{21}$

$x = 12$

(d) $\dfrac{x}{8} = \dfrac{3}{5}$

$x \cdot 5 = 8 \cdot 3$ Cross products are equivalent

$\dfrac{x \cdot \cancel{5}^1}{\cancel{5}_1} = \dfrac{24}{5}$

$x = \dfrac{24}{5}$

$x = 4.8$

(e) $\dfrac{14}{11} = \dfrac{x}{3}$

$11 \cdot x = 14 \cdot 3$ *Cross products are equivalent*

$11 \cdot x = 42$

$\dfrac{\cancel{11}^1 \cdot x}{\cancel{11}_1} = \dfrac{42}{11}$

$x = \dfrac{42}{11}$

$x \approx 3.82$ *(rounded to the nearest hundredth)*

2. (a) $\dfrac{3\frac{1}{4}}{2} = \dfrac{x}{8}$

$2 \cdot x = 3\frac{1}{4} \cdot 8$ *Cross products are equivalent*

$2 \cdot x = \dfrac{13}{\cancel{4}_1} \cdot \dfrac{\cancel{8}^2}{1}$

$\dfrac{\cancel{2}^1 \cdot x}{\cancel{2}_1} = \dfrac{\cancel{26}^{13}}{\cancel{2}_1}$

$x = 13$

Check your answer by finding the cross products.

$2 \cdot 13 = 26$

$3\frac{1}{4} \cdot 8 = \dfrac{13}{\cancel{4}_1} \cdot \dfrac{\cancel{8}^2}{1} = 26$

The cross products are equal, so 13 is the correct solution.

(b) $\dfrac{x}{3} = \dfrac{1\frac{2}{3}}{5}$

$5 \cdot x = 3 \cdot 1\frac{2}{3}$ *Cross products are equivalent*

$5 \cdot x = \cancel{3}^1 \cdot \dfrac{5}{\cancel{3}_1}$

$\dfrac{\cancel{5}^1 \cdot x}{\cancel{5}_1} = \dfrac{1 \cdot \cancel{5}^1}{\cancel{5}_1}$

$x = 1$

Check your answer by finding the cross products.

$5 \cdot 1 = 5$

$3 \cdot 1\frac{2}{3} = \dfrac{\cancel{3}^1}{1} \cdot \dfrac{5}{\cancel{3}_1} = 5$

The cross products are equal, so 1 is the correct solution.

(c) $\dfrac{0.06}{x} = \dfrac{0.3}{0.4}$

$0.3 \cdot x = 0.06 \cdot 0.4$ *Cross products are equivalent*

$\dfrac{\cancel{0.3}^1 \cdot x}{\cancel{0.3}_1} = \dfrac{\cancel{0.024}^{0.08}}{\cancel{0.3}_1}$

$x = 0.08$

Check your answer by finding the cross products.

$0.3 \cdot 0.08 = 0.024$
$0.06 \cdot 0.4 = 0.024$

The cross products are equal, so 0.08 is the correct solution.

(d) $\dfrac{2.2}{5} = \dfrac{13}{x}$

$2.2 \cdot x = 5 \cdot 13$ *Cross products are equivalent*

$\dfrac{2.2}{2.2} \cdot x = \dfrac{65}{2.2}$

$x = \dfrac{65}{2.2}$

$x \approx 29.545455$

$x \approx 29.55$ *(rounded to nearest hundredth)*

Check your answer by finding the cross products.

$2.2 \cdot 29.55 = 65.01$
$5 \cdot 13 = 65$

Because 29.55 was rounded, the cross products are not equal, but they are close enough to see that ≈ 29.55 is the correct solution.

(e) $\dfrac{x}{6} = \dfrac{0.5}{1.2}$

$1.2 \cdot x = 6 \cdot 0.5$ *Cross products are equivalent*

$\dfrac{\cancel{1.2}^1 \cdot x}{\cancel{1.2}_1} = \dfrac{3}{1.2}$

$x = 2.5$

Check your answer by finding the cross products.

$2.5 \cdot 1.2 = 3$
$6 \cdot 0.5 = 3$

The cross products are equal, so 3 is the correct solution.

Section 5.4 Solving Proportions

(f) $\quad \dfrac{0}{2} = \dfrac{x}{7.092}$

$2 \cdot x = 0 \cdot 7.092 \quad$ *Cross products are equivalent*

$\dfrac{\cancel{2}^{1} \cdot x}{\cancel{2}_{1}} = \dfrac{0}{2}$

$x = 0$

Check your answer by finding the cross products.

$2 \cdot 0 \;=\; 0$
$7.092 \cdot 0 \;=\; 0$

The cross products are equal, so 0 is the correct solution.

5.4 Section Exercises

3. $\quad \dfrac{15}{10} = \dfrac{3}{x}$

$15 \cdot x = 10 \cdot 3 \quad$ *Cross products are equivalent*

$\dfrac{\cancel{15}^{1} \cdot x}{\cancel{15}_{1}} = \dfrac{30}{15} \quad$ *Divide both sides by 1.5*

$x = 2$

Check your answer by finding the cross products.

$15 \cdot 2 \;=\; 30$
$3 \cdot 10 \;=\; 30$

The cross products are equal, so 2 is the correct solution.

7. $\quad \dfrac{42}{x} = \dfrac{18}{39}$

$x \cdot 18 = 42 \cdot 39 \quad$ *Cross products are equivalent*

$\dfrac{x \cdot \cancel{18}^{1}}{\cancel{18}_{1}} = \dfrac{\cancel{42}^{7} \cdot \cancel{39}^{13}}{\cancel{18}_{6\,1}}$

$x = 91$

Check:

$18 \cdot 91 \;=\; 1638$
$42 \cdot 39 \;=\; 1638$

The cross products are equal, so 91 is the correct solution.

11. $\quad \dfrac{8}{x} = \dfrac{24}{30}$

$\dfrac{8}{x} = \dfrac{4}{5} \quad$ *Write $\tfrac{24}{30}$ in lowest terms*

$40 = 4 \cdot x \quad$ *Cross products are equivalent*

$\dfrac{\cancel{40}^{10}}{\cancel{4}_{1}} = \dfrac{\cancel{4}^{1} \cdot x}{\cancel{4}_{1}} \quad$ *Divide both sides by 4*

$10 = x$

Check:

$24 \cdot 10 \;=\; 240$
$8 \cdot 30 \;=\; 240$

The cross products are equal, so 10 is the correct solution.

15. $\quad \dfrac{0.7}{9.8} = \dfrac{3.6}{x}$

$0.7 \cdot x = 9.8 \cdot 3.6 \quad$ *Cross products are equivalent*

$\dfrac{\cancel{0.7}^{1} \cdot x}{\cancel{0.7}_{1}} = \dfrac{\cancel{35.28}^{50.4}}{\cancel{0.7}_{1}} \quad$ *Divide both sides by 0.7*

$x = 50.4$

Check:

$0.7 \cdot 50.4 \;=\; 35.28$
$3.6 \cdot 9.8 \;=\; 35.28$

The cross products are equal, so 50.4 is the correct solution.

19. $\quad \dfrac{10}{4} = \dfrac{5}{3}$

$\dfrac{6.67}{4} = \dfrac{5}{3} \quad$ or $\quad \dfrac{10}{6} = \dfrac{5}{3}$

or $\quad \dfrac{10}{4} = \dfrac{7.5}{3} \quad$ or $\quad \dfrac{10}{4} = \dfrac{5}{2}$

23. $\quad \dfrac{2\tfrac{1}{3}}{1\tfrac{1}{2}} = \dfrac{x}{2\tfrac{1}{4}}$

$1\tfrac{1}{2} \cdot x = 2\tfrac{1}{3} \cdot 2\tfrac{1}{4} \quad$ *Cross products are equivalent*

$\dfrac{3}{2} \cdot x = \dfrac{7}{\cancel{3}_{1}} \cdot \dfrac{\cancel{9}^{3}}{4}$

$$\frac{3}{2} \cdot x = \frac{21}{4}$$

$$\frac{\frac{3}{2} \cdot x}{\frac{3}{2}} = \frac{\frac{21}{4}}{\frac{3}{2}} \quad \textit{Divide both sides by } \frac{3}{3}$$

$$x = \frac{21}{4} \div \frac{3}{2}$$

$$x = \frac{\cancel{21}^{7}}{\cancel{4}_{2}} \cdot \frac{\cancel{2}^{1}}{\cancel{3}_{1}} = \frac{7}{2}$$

$$x = 3\frac{1}{2}$$

27. $\dfrac{x}{\frac{3}{50}} = \dfrac{0.15}{1\frac{4}{5}}$

Change to decimals.

$$\frac{x}{0.06} = \frac{0.15}{1.8}$$

$$x \cdot 1.8 = 0.15 \cdot 0.06$$

$$\frac{x \cdot 1.8}{1.8} = \frac{0.009}{1.8}$$

$$x = 0.005$$

Change to fractions.

$$\frac{x}{\frac{3}{50}} = \frac{\frac{3}{20}}{1\frac{4}{5}}$$

$$1\frac{4}{5} \cdot x = \frac{3}{50} \cdot \frac{3}{20}$$

$$\frac{1\frac{4}{5} \cdot x}{1\frac{4}{5}} = \frac{\frac{9}{1000}}{1\frac{4}{5}}$$

$$x = \frac{9}{1000} \div 1\frac{4}{5}$$

$$= \frac{\cancel{9}^{1}}{\cancel{1000}_{200}} \cdot \frac{\cancel{5}^{1}}{\cancel{9}_{1}}$$

$$= \frac{1}{200}$$

31. 170 miles on 6.8 gallons
330 miles on 13.2 gallons

$$\frac{170 \text{ miles}}{6.8 \text{ gallons}} = \frac{330 \text{ miles}}{13.2 \text{ gallons}}$$

$$170 \cdot 13.2 = 2244 \quad \textit{Cross products are equivalent}$$

$$6.8 \cdot 330 = 2244$$

True

5.5 Applications of Proportions

5.5 Margin Exercises

1. (a) $\dfrac{2 \text{ pounds}}{50 \text{ square feet}} = \dfrac{x \text{ pounds}}{225 \text{ square feet}}$

$$50 \cdot x = 2 \cdot 225 \quad \textit{Cross products are equivalent}$$

$$50 \cdot x = 450$$

$$\frac{50 \cdot x}{50} = \frac{450}{50} \quad \textit{Divide both sides by } 50$$

$$x = 9$$

9 pounds of fertilizer are needed for 225 square feet.

(b) $\dfrac{1 \text{ inch}}{75 \text{ miles}} = \dfrac{4.75 \text{ inches}}{x \text{ miles}}$

$$1 \cdot x = 75 \cdot 4.75 \quad \textit{Cross products are equivalent}$$

$$x = 356.25 \text{ or } x \approx 356 \text{ miles}$$

The lake's actual length is ≈ 356 miles.

(c) $\dfrac{30 \text{ milliters}}{100 \text{ pounds}} = \dfrac{x \text{ milliliters}}{34 \text{ pounds}}$

$$100 \cdot x = 30 \cdot 34 \quad \textit{Cross products are equivalent}$$

$$\frac{100 \cdot x}{100} = \frac{1020}{100} \quad \textit{Divide both sides by } 100$$

$$x = 10.2 \text{ or } \approx 10 \text{ milliliters}$$

A 34-pound child should be given ≈ 10 milliliters of cough syrup.

2. (a) $\dfrac{2 \text{ people}}{3 \text{ people}} = \dfrac{x}{150 \text{ people}}$

$$3 \cdot x = 2 \cdot 150 \quad \textit{Cross products are equivalent}$$

$$\frac{3 \cdot x}{3} = \frac{300}{3} \quad \textit{Divide both sides by } 100$$

$$x = 100$$

In a group of 150, 100 people want to lose weight. This is a reasonable answer.

Section 5.5 Applications of Proportions

Incorrect setup

$$\frac{3 \text{ people}}{2 \text{ people}} = \frac{x}{150 \text{ people}}$$

$$2 \cdot x = 3 \cdot 150$$
$$\frac{2 \cdot x}{2} = \frac{450}{2}$$
$$x = 225$$

The incorrect setup gives 225 people and there are only 150 people in the group.

(b) $\dfrac{3 \text{ students}}{5 \text{ students}} = \dfrac{x}{4500 \text{ students}}$
(that receive financial aid) (that receive financial aid)

$5 \cdot x = 3 \cdot 4500$ *Cross products are equivalent*

$\dfrac{5 \cdot x}{5} = \dfrac{13{,}500}{5}$ *Divide both sides by 5*

$x = 2700$

At Central Community College 2700 students receive financial aid.
This is a reasonable answer.

Incorrect setup

$$\frac{5 \text{ students}}{3 \text{ students}} = \frac{x}{4500 \text{ students}}$$

$$3 \cdot x = 5 \cdot 4500$$
$$\frac{3 \cdot x}{3} = \frac{22{,}500}{3}$$
$$x = 7500$$

The incorrect setup gives 7500 students and there are only 4500 students at the college.

(c) *dentists who recommend sugarless gum*
↓   ↓
$\dfrac{9}{10} = \dfrac{x}{60}$
↑   ↑
dentists in our city

$10 \cdot x = 9 \cdot 60$ *Cross products are equivalent*

$\dfrac{10 \cdot x}{10} = \dfrac{540}{10}$

$x = 54$

If the advertisement is true, 54 dentists would recommend sugarless gum.
This is a reasonable answer.

Incorrect setup

$$\frac{10}{9} = \frac{x}{60}$$

$$9 \cdot x = 10 \cdot 60$$
$$\frac{9 \cdot x}{9} = \frac{600}{9}$$
$$x \approx 66.67 \text{ or } 67$$

The incorrect setup gives 67 dentists and there are only 60 dentists in the city.

5.5 Section Exercises

3. $\dfrac{60 \text{ newspapers}}{\$27} = \dfrac{16 \text{ newspapers}}{x}$

$60 \cdot x = 27 \cdot 16$ *Cross products are equivalent*

$\dfrac{60 \cdot x}{60} = \dfrac{432}{60}$ *Divide both sides by 60*

$x = 7.2$

The cost of 16 newspapers is $7.20.

7. $\dfrac{\$255.75}{5 \text{ days}} = \dfrac{x}{3 \text{ days}}$

$5 \cdot x = 255.75 \cdot 3$ *Cross products are equivalent*

$\dfrac{5 \cdot x}{5} = \dfrac{767.25}{5}$ *Divide both sides by 5*

$x = 153.45$

In 3 days Tom makes $153.45.

11. First find the length of the dining room.

$$\frac{3.5 \text{ inches}}{x} = \frac{1 \text{ inch}}{4 \text{ feet}}$$

$$x = 4 \cdot 3.5$$
$$= 14$$

Then find the width.

$4.5 - 2.5 \text{ inches} = 2 \text{ inches}$

$\dfrac{2 \text{ inches}}{x} = \dfrac{1 \text{ inch}}{4 \text{ feet}}$

$x = 2 \cdot 4$
$= 8$

The length of the dining room is 14 feet and the width is 8 feet.

15. $\dfrac{7}{10} = \dfrac{x}{950}$

$10 \cdot x = 7 \cdot 950$

$\dfrac{10 \cdot x}{10} = \dfrac{6650}{10}$

$x = 665$

665 students will probably need a refresher course. This is a reasonable answer.

Incorrect setup

$\dfrac{7}{10} = \dfrac{950}{x}$

$7 \cdot x = 10 \cdot 950$

$\dfrac{7 \cdot x}{7} = \dfrac{9500}{7}$

$x \approx 1357$

The incorrect setup gives ≈ 1357 students and there are only 950 students in the group.

19. $\dfrac{\$1}{\$20} = \dfrac{x}{\$110}$

$20 \cdot x = 110$ *Cross products are equivalent*

$\dfrac{20 \cdot x}{20} = \dfrac{110}{20}$ *Divide both sides by 20*

$x = 5.5$

The tax is $5.50 on a $110 item.

23. $\dfrac{65 \text{ miles}}{3 \text{ hours}} = \dfrac{100 \text{ miles}}{x}$

$65 \cdot x = 3 \cdot 100$ *Cross products are equivalent*

$\dfrac{65 \cdot x}{65} = \dfrac{300}{65}$ *Divide both sides by 65*

$x \approx 4.615$

It will take ≈ 4.6 hours to travel 100 miles.

27. $\dfrac{1.05 \text{ meters}}{1.68 \text{ meters}} = \dfrac{6.58 \text{ meters}}{x}$

$1.05 \cdot x = 6.58 \cdot 1.68$ *Cross products are equivalent*

$\dfrac{1.05 \cdot x}{1.05} \approx \dfrac{11.0544}{1.05}$ *Divide both sides by 1.5*

$x \approx 10.53$

The height of the tree is ≈ 10.53 meters.

31. $\dfrac{3\frac{1}{2} \text{ cups}}{12 \text{ servings}} = \dfrac{x}{15 \text{ servings}}$

$12 \cdot x = 3\frac{1}{2} \cdot 15$ *Cross products are equivalent*

$\dfrac{12 \cdot x}{12} = \dfrac{52\frac{1}{2}}{12}$ *Divide both sides by 12*

$x = 4\frac{3}{8}$

For 15 servings you need $4\frac{3}{8}$ cups of water.

35. First find the number of coffee drinkers.

$\dfrac{4}{5} = \dfrac{x}{38,000}$ *Cross products are equivalent*

$5 \cdot x = 4 \cdot 38,000$

$\dfrac{5 \cdot x}{5} = \dfrac{152,000}{5}$ *Divide both sides by 5*

$x = 30,400$

The survey showed that 30,400 students drink coffee.

Now find the number of coffee drinkers that use cream.

$\dfrac{1}{8} = \dfrac{x}{30,400}$ *Cross products are equivalent*

$8 \cdot x = 30,400$

$\dfrac{8 \cdot x}{8} = \dfrac{30,400}{8}$ *Divide both sides by 8*

$x = 3800$

According to the survey 3800 students use cream.

39. $2.87 \times 1000 = 2870$

Move the decimal point three places to the right.

Chapter 5 Review Exercises

1. 3 oranges to 11 oranges

$\dfrac{3 \text{ oranges}}{11 \text{ oranges}} = \dfrac{3}{11}$

2. 19 miles to 7 miles

$\dfrac{19 \text{ miles}}{7 \text{ miles}} = \dfrac{19}{7}$

3. 9 doughnuts to 6 doughnuts

$\dfrac{9 \text{ doughnuts}}{6 \text{ doughnuts}} = \dfrac{9}{6} = \dfrac{9 \div 3}{6 \div 3} = \dfrac{3}{2}$

4. 90 feet to 50 feet

$\dfrac{90 \text{ feet}}{50 \text{ feet}} = \dfrac{90}{50} = \dfrac{90 \div 10}{50 \div 10} = \dfrac{9}{5}$

Chapter 5 Review Exercises

5. $\dfrac{\$2.50}{\$1.25} = \dfrac{2.50}{1.25} = \dfrac{2.50 \div 1.25}{1.25 \div 1.25} = \dfrac{2}{1}$

6. $0.30 to $0.45
$$\dfrac{\$0.30}{\$0.45} = \dfrac{0.30}{0.45} = \dfrac{0.30 \div 15}{0.45 \div 15} = \dfrac{2}{3}$$

7. $1\tfrac{2}{3}$ cups to $\tfrac{2}{3}$ cup

$$\dfrac{1\tfrac{2}{3} \text{ cups}}{\tfrac{2}{3} \text{ cup}} = \dfrac{1\tfrac{2}{3}}{\tfrac{2}{3}} = \dfrac{5}{3} \div \dfrac{2}{3}$$

$$= \dfrac{5}{\cancel{3}} \cdot \dfrac{\cancel{3}}{2} = \dfrac{5}{2}$$

8. $2\tfrac{3}{4}$ miles to $16\tfrac{1}{2}$ miles

$$\dfrac{2\tfrac{3}{4} \text{ miles}}{16\tfrac{1}{2} \text{ miles}} = \dfrac{2\tfrac{3}{4}}{16\tfrac{1}{2}} = \dfrac{\tfrac{11}{4}}{\tfrac{33}{2}} = \dfrac{11}{4} \div \dfrac{33}{2}$$

$$= \dfrac{\cancel{11}}{\cancel{4}} \cdot \dfrac{\cancel{2}}{\cancel{33}} = \dfrac{1}{6}$$

9. 5 hours to 100 minutes
5 hours $= 5 \cdot 60$ minutes $= 300$ minutes
$$\dfrac{300 \text{ minutes}}{100 \text{ minutes}} = \dfrac{300}{100} = \dfrac{300 \div 100}{100 \div 100} = \dfrac{3}{1}$$

10. 9 inches to 2 feet
2 feet = 24 inches
$$\dfrac{9 \text{ inches}}{24 \text{ inches}} = \dfrac{9}{24} = \dfrac{9 \div 3}{24 \div 3} = \dfrac{3}{8}$$

11. 1 ton to 1500 pounds
1 ton = 2000 pounds
$$\dfrac{2000 \text{ pounds}}{1500 \text{ pounds}} = \dfrac{2000}{1500} = \dfrac{2000 \div 500}{1500 \div 500} = \dfrac{4}{3}$$

12. 8 hours to 3 days
3 days $= 3 \cdot 24$ hours $= 72$ hours
$$\dfrac{8 \text{ hours}}{72 \text{ hours}} = \dfrac{8}{72} = \dfrac{8 \div 8}{72 \div 8} = \dfrac{1}{9}$$

13. $500 to $350
$$\dfrac{\$500}{\$350} = \dfrac{500 \div 50}{350 \div 50} = \dfrac{10}{7}$$

The ratio of her sales to his is $\tfrac{10}{7}$.

14. $\dfrac{35 \text{ miles per gallon}}{25 \text{ miles per gallon}} = \dfrac{35}{25} = \dfrac{35 \div 5}{25 \div 5} = \dfrac{7}{5}$

The ratio of the new car's mileage to the old car's mileage is $\tfrac{7}{5}$.

15. $\dfrac{60 \text{ students}}{72 \text{ students}} = \dfrac{60}{72} = \dfrac{60 \div 12}{72 \div 12} = \dfrac{5}{6}$

The ratio of the math students to the English students is $\tfrac{5}{6}$.

16. $\dfrac{5 \text{ basketball players}}{9 \text{ baseball players}} = \dfrac{5}{9}$

The ratio of the basketball players to the baseball players is $\tfrac{5}{9}$.

17. $88 for 8 dozen
$$\dfrac{\$88 \div 8}{8 \text{ dozen} \div 8} = \dfrac{\$11}{1 \text{ dozen}}$$

18. 96 children in 40 families
$$\dfrac{96 \text{ children} \div 8}{40 \text{ familes} \div 8} = \dfrac{12 \text{ children}}{5 \text{ families}}$$

19. Both compare two things. In a ratio the common units cancel, but in rate the units are different and must be written.
Examples are:

$$\text{ratio} \quad \dfrac{5 \; \cancel{\text{feet}}}{10 \; \cancel{\text{feet}}} = \dfrac{1}{2}$$

$$\text{rate} \quad \dfrac{55 \text{ miles}}{1 \text{ hour}}$$

20. A unit rate has 1 in the denominator. Examples are: 55 miles in 1 hour, $440 in 1 week, or 30 miles on 1 gallon of gas. We usually write them using "per" or a slash mark: 55 miles per hour, etc.

21. 4 pages in 20 minutes

$$\dfrac{4 \text{ pages} \div 20}{20 \text{ minutes} \div 20} = \dfrac{0.2 \text{ page}}{1 \text{ minute}}$$

$$= 0.2 \text{ page/minute}$$

or $\dfrac{4 \text{ pages} \div 4}{20 \text{ minutes} \div 4} = \dfrac{1 \text{ page}}{5 \text{ minute}}$

$$\dfrac{20 \text{ minutes} \div 4}{4 \text{ pages} \div 4} = \dfrac{5 \text{ minutes}}{1 \text{ page}}$$

$$= 5 \text{ minutes/page}$$

22. $24 in 3 hours

$$\dfrac{\$24 \div 3}{3 \text{ hours} \div 3} = \dfrac{\$8}{1 \text{ hour}} = \$8/\text{hour}$$

or $\dfrac{3 \text{ hours} \div 3}{\$24 \div 3} = \dfrac{1 \text{ hour}}{\$8}$

$$= \dfrac{1}{8} \text{ hour/dollar}$$

or 0.125 hour/dollar

23.

size	cost per unit
13 ounces	$\frac{\$2.29}{13 \text{ ounces}} \approx \$0.176$
8 ounces	$\frac{\$1.45}{8 \text{ ounces}} \approx \$0.181$
3 ounces	$\frac{\$0.95}{3 \text{ ounces}} \approx \$0.317$

The best buy is 13 ounces for $2.29.

24. 50 pounds for $19.95 − $1.00(coupon) = $18.95

$$\frac{\$18.95}{50 \text{ pounds}} = \$0.379$$

25 pounds for $10.40 − $1.00(coupon) = $9.40.

$$\frac{\$9.40}{25 \text{ pounds}} = \$0.376$$

8 pounds for $3.40

$$\frac{\$3.40}{8 \text{ pounds}} = \$0.425$$

The best buy is 25 pounds for $10.40 with the $1 coupon.

25. 5 is to 10 as 20 is to 40.

$$\frac{5}{10} = \frac{20}{40}$$

26. 7 is to 2 as 35 is to 10.

$$\frac{7}{2} = \frac{35}{10}$$

27. $1\frac{1}{2}$ is to 6 as $2\frac{1}{4}$ is to 9.

$$\frac{1\frac{1}{2}}{6} = \frac{2\frac{1}{4}}{9}$$

28. $\frac{6}{10} = \frac{9}{15}$

$\frac{6}{10} = \frac{3}{5}, \frac{9}{15} = \frac{3}{5}$ Equivalent

True

29. $\frac{16}{48} = \frac{9}{36}$

$16 \cdot 36 = 576 \leftarrow Cross\ products$
$48 \cdot 9 = 432 \leftarrow are\ unequal$

False

30. $\frac{47}{10} = \frac{98}{20}$

$47 \cdot 20 = 940 \leftarrow Cross\ products$
$10 \cdot 98 = 980 \leftarrow are\ unequal$

False

31. $\frac{64}{36} = \frac{96}{54}$

$\frac{64}{36} = \frac{16}{9}, \frac{96}{54} = \frac{16}{9}$ Equivalent

True

32. $\frac{1.5}{2.4} = \frac{2}{3.2}$

$1.5 \cdot 3.2 = 4.8 \leftarrow Cross\ products$
$2.4 \cdot 2 = 4.8 \leftarrow are\ equal$

True

33. $\frac{3\frac{1}{2}}{2\frac{1}{3}} = \frac{6}{4}$

$3\frac{1}{2} \cdot 4 = \frac{7}{\cancel{2}} \cdot \frac{\cancel{4}^2}{1} = 14 \leftarrow$

$2\frac{1}{3} \cdot 6 = \frac{7}{\cancel{3}} \cdot \frac{\cancel{6}^2}{1} = 14 \leftarrow$

The cross products are equal.
True

34. $\frac{4}{42} = \frac{150}{x}$

$\frac{2}{21} = \frac{150}{x}$ Write $\frac{4}{42}$ in lowest terms

$2 \cdot x = 21 \cdot 150$ Cross products are equivalent

$\frac{2 \cdot x}{2} = \frac{3150}{2}$ Divide both sides by 2

$x = 1575$

35. $\frac{16}{x} = \frac{12}{15}$

$\frac{16}{x} = \frac{4}{5}$ Write $\frac{12}{15}$ in lowest terms

$4 \cdot x = 5 \cdot 16$ Cross products are equivalent

$\frac{4 \cdot x}{4} = \frac{80}{4}$ Divide both sides by 4

$x = 20$

Chapter 5 Review Exercises

36. $\dfrac{100}{14} = \dfrac{x}{56}$

$14 \cdot x = 100 \cdot 56$ *Cross products are equivalent*

$\dfrac{14 \cdot x}{14} = \dfrac{5600}{14}$ *Divide both sides by 7*

$x = 400$

37. $\dfrac{5}{8} = \dfrac{x}{20}$

$8 \cdot x = 5 \cdot 20$ *Cross products are equivalent*

$\dfrac{8 \cdot x}{8} = \dfrac{100}{8}$ *Divide both sides by 8*

$x = 12.5$

38. $\dfrac{x}{24} = \dfrac{11}{18}$

$18 \cdot x = 24 \cdot 11$ *Cross products are equivalent*

$\dfrac{18 \cdot x}{18} = \dfrac{264}{18}$

$x \approx 14.67$

39. $\dfrac{7}{x} = \dfrac{18}{21}$

$\dfrac{7}{x} = \dfrac{6}{7}$ *Write $\tfrac{18}{21}$ in lowest terms*

$6 \cdot x = 7 \cdot 7$

$\dfrac{6 \cdot x}{6} = \dfrac{49}{6}$

$x \approx 8.17$

40. $\dfrac{x}{3.6} = \dfrac{9.8}{0.7}$

$0.7 \cdot x = 9.8 \cdot 3.6$

$\dfrac{0.7 \cdot x}{0.7} = \dfrac{35.28}{0.7}$

$x = 50.4$

41. $\dfrac{13.5}{1.7} = \dfrac{4.5}{x}$

$13.5 \cdot x = 1.7 \cdot 4.5$

$x = \dfrac{7.65}{13.5}$

$= 7.65 \div 13.5 \approx 0.5666667$

$x \approx 0.57$

42. $\dfrac{0.82}{1.89} = \dfrac{x}{5.7}$

$1.89 \cdot x = 0.82 \cdot 5.7$

$x = \dfrac{4.674}{1.89}$

$= 4.674 \div 1.89 \approx 2.4730159$

$x \approx 2.47$

43. $\dfrac{3 \text{ cats}}{5 \text{ dogs}} = \dfrac{x}{45 \text{ dogs}}$

$5 \cdot x = 3 \cdot 45$

$\dfrac{5 \cdot x}{5} = \dfrac{135}{5}$

$x = 27$

There are 27 cats.

44. $\dfrac{8 \text{ hits}}{28 \text{ at bats}} = \dfrac{x}{161 \text{ at bats}}$

$28 \cdot x = 8 \cdot 161$

$\dfrac{28 \cdot x}{28} = \dfrac{1288}{28}$

$x = 46$

She will get 46 hits.

45. $\dfrac{3.5 \text{ pounds}}{\$13.79} = \dfrac{5.6 \text{ pounds}}{x}$

$3.5 \cdot x = 13.79 \cdot 5.6$

$\dfrac{3.5 \cdot x}{3.5} = \dfrac{77.224}{3.5}$

$x \approx 22.06$

The cost for 5.6 pounds of steak is $\approx \$22.06$.

46.
$\begin{array}{c} \text{Students} \\ \text{expected to} \\ \text{vote} \\ \downarrow \\ \dfrac{4}{10} = \dfrac{x}{8247} \\ \uparrow \\ \text{students} \end{array}$

$10 \cdot x = 4 \cdot 8247$

$10 \cdot x = 32{,}988$

$x \approx 3299$

They should expect ≈ 3299 students to vote.

47. $\dfrac{1 \text{ inch}}{16 \text{ feet}} = \dfrac{4.25 \text{ inches}}{x}$

$1 \cdot x = 4.25 \cdot 16$

$x = 68$

The length of the box car is 68 feet.

48. $\dfrac{3.5 \text{ milligrams}}{50 \text{ pounds}} = \dfrac{x}{210 \text{ pounds}}$

$50 \cdot x = 3.5 \cdot 210$

$\dfrac{50 \cdot x}{50} = \dfrac{735}{50}$

$x = 14.7$

Each patient who weighs 210 pounds should be given 14.7 milligrams.

49. $\dfrac{\$91}{14 \text{ hours}} = \dfrac{\$520}{x}$

$91 \cdot x = 520 \cdot 14$

$\dfrac{91 \cdot x}{91} = \dfrac{7280}{91}$

$x = 80$

Damien must work 80 hours.

50. 2 dozen necklaces $= 2 \cdot 12 = 24$ necklaces

$\dfrac{24 \text{ necklaces}}{16\frac{1}{2} \text{ hours}} = \dfrac{40 \text{ necklaces}}{x}$

$24 \cdot x = 16\frac{1}{2} \cdot 40$

$24 \cdot x = \dfrac{33}{2} \cdot \dfrac{40}{1}$

$\dfrac{24 \cdot x}{24} = \dfrac{660}{24}$

$x = 27\frac{1}{2}$

It will take Marvette $27\frac{1}{2}$ or 27.5 hours to make 40 necklaces.

51. $\dfrac{x}{45} = \dfrac{70}{30}$

$30 \cdot x = 70 \cdot 45$

$\dfrac{30 \cdot x}{30} = \dfrac{3150}{30}$

$x = 105$

52. $\dfrac{x}{52} = \dfrac{0}{20}$

$20 \cdot x = 52 \cdot 0$

$\dfrac{20 \cdot x}{20} = \dfrac{0}{20}$

$x = 0$

53. $\dfrac{64}{10} = \dfrac{x}{20}$

$10 \cdot x = 20 \cdot 64$

$\dfrac{10 \cdot x}{10} = \dfrac{1280}{10}$

$x = 128$

54. $\dfrac{15}{x} = \dfrac{65}{100}$

$65 \cdot x = 15 \cdot 100$

$\dfrac{65 \cdot x}{65} = \dfrac{1500}{65}$

$x \approx 23.08$

55. $\dfrac{7.8}{3.9} = \dfrac{13}{x}$

$\dfrac{2}{1} = \dfrac{13}{x}$ *Write $\dfrac{7.8}{3.9}$ in lowest terms*

$\dfrac{2 \cdot x}{2} = \dfrac{13}{2}$

$x = 6.5$

56. $\dfrac{34.1}{x} = \dfrac{0.77}{2.65}$

$x = \dfrac{34.1 \cdot 2.65}{0.77}$

$= 90.365 \div 0.77$

≈ 117.35714

$x \approx 117.36$

57. $\dfrac{55}{18} = \dfrac{80}{27}$

$55 \cdot 27 = 1485$ ← *Cross products*
$18 \cdot 80 = 1440$ ← *are unequal*

False

58. $\dfrac{5.6}{0.6} = \dfrac{18}{1.94}$

$5.6 \cdot 1.94 = 10.864$ ← *Cross products*
$0.6 \cdot 18 = 10.8$ ← *are unequal*

False

59. $\dfrac{\frac{1}{5}}{2} = \dfrac{1\frac{1}{6}}{11\frac{2}{3}}$

$\dfrac{1}{5} \cdot 11\tfrac{2}{3} = \dfrac{1}{\cancel{5}} \cdot \dfrac{\cancel{35}^{7}}{3} = \dfrac{7}{3} = 2\tfrac{1}{3}$

$$2 \cdot 1\tfrac{1}{6} = \frac{\cancel{2}^{1}}{1} \cdot \frac{7}{\cancel{6}_{3}} = \frac{7}{3} = 2\tfrac{1}{3}$$

Cross products are equal

True

60. 4 dollars to 10 quarters

4 dollars = $4 \cdot 4 = 16$ quarters

$$\frac{16 \text{ quarters} \div 2}{10 \text{ quarters} \div 2} = \frac{8}{5}$$

61. $4\tfrac{1}{8}$ inches to 10 inches

$$\frac{4\tfrac{1}{8} \text{ inches}}{10 \text{ inches}} = \frac{\tfrac{33}{8}}{10} = \frac{33}{8} \div 10$$
$$= \frac{33}{8} \cdot \frac{1}{10} = \frac{33}{80}$$

62. 10 yards to 8 feet

10 yards = $10 \cdot 3 = 30$ feet

$$\frac{30 \text{ feet}}{8 \text{ feet}} = \frac{30 \div 2}{8 \div 2} = \frac{15}{4}$$

63. $3.60 to $0.90

$$\frac{\$3.60}{\$0.90} = \frac{3.60 \div 0.90}{0.90 \div 0.90} = \frac{4}{1}$$

64. 12 eggs to 15 eggs

$$\frac{12 \text{ eggs}}{15 \text{ eggs}} = \frac{12 \div 3}{15 \div 3} = \frac{4}{5}$$

65. 37 meters to 7 meters

$$\frac{37 \text{ meters}}{7 \text{ meters}} = \frac{37}{7}$$

66. 3 pints to 4 quarts

4 quarts = $4 \cdot 2 = 8$ pints

$$\frac{3 \text{ pints}}{8 \text{ pints}} = \frac{3}{8}$$

67. 15 minutes to 3 hours

3 hours = $3 \cdot 60 = 180$ minutes

$$\frac{15 \text{ minutes}}{180 \text{ minutes}} = \frac{15 \div 15}{180 \div 15} = \frac{1}{12}$$

68. $4\tfrac{1}{2}$ miles to $1\tfrac{3}{10}$ miles

$$\frac{4\tfrac{1}{2} \text{ miles}}{1\tfrac{3}{10} \text{ miles}} = \frac{4\tfrac{1}{2}}{1\tfrac{3}{10}} = 4\tfrac{1}{2} \div 1\tfrac{3}{10}$$
$$= \frac{9}{2} \div \frac{13}{10} = \frac{9}{\cancel{2}_{1}} \cdot \frac{\cancel{10}^{5}}{13}$$
$$= \frac{45}{13}$$

69.

fans who buy
something to drink
↓ ↓
$$\frac{7}{8} = \frac{x}{28{,}500}$$
↑ ↑
fans who attend
the game

$$8 \cdot x = 7 \cdot 28{,}500$$
$$\frac{8 \cdot x}{8} = \frac{199{,}500}{8}$$
$$x \approx 24{,}937.5$$

or 24,900 *(rounded to the nearest hundred)*

At today's game ≈ 24,900 fans can be expected to buy a beverage.

70. $$\frac{\$400 \text{ spent on car insurance}}{\$150 \text{ spent on repairs}} = \frac{400 \div 50}{150 \div 50} = \frac{8}{3}$$

The ratio of the amount spent on insurance to the amount spent on repairs is $\tfrac{8}{3}$.

71. 25 feet for $0.78

$$\frac{\$0.78}{25 \text{ feet}} \approx \$0.031 \text{ per foot}$$

75 feet for $1.99 - $0.50 (coupon) = $1.49

$$\frac{\$1.49}{75 \text{ feet}} \approx \$0.020 \text{ per foot}$$

100 feet for $2.59 - $0.50 (coupon) = $2.09

$$\frac{\$2.09}{100 \text{ feet}} \approx \$0.021 \text{ per foot}$$

The best buy is 75 feet for $1.99 with a 50¢ coupon.

72. $$\frac{1 \text{ inch}}{6 \text{ feet}} = \frac{2.75 \text{ inches}}{x}$$
$$1 \cdot x = 6 \cdot 2.75$$
$$x = 16.5$$

The actual length of the patio when it is built will be 16.5 feet.

73. $$\frac{1\tfrac{1}{2} \text{ teaspoons}}{24 \text{ pounds}} = \frac{x}{8 \text{ pounds}}$$
$$24 \cdot x = 1\tfrac{1}{2} \cdot 8$$
$$24 \cdot x = \frac{3}{2} \cdot \frac{8}{1}$$
$$\frac{24 \cdot x}{24} = \frac{12}{24}$$
$$x = \frac{1}{2} \quad \text{or} \quad 0.5$$

The infant should be given $\tfrac{1}{2}$ or 0.5 teaspoon.

74. $$\frac{251 \text{ points}}{169 \text{ minutes}} = \frac{x}{14 \text{ minutes}}$$
$$169 \cdot x = 251 \cdot 14$$
$$x = \frac{251 \cdot 14}{169}$$
$$= 3514 \div 169$$
$$x = 20.792899$$

Charles should score ≈ 21 points.

75. Set up the proportion to compare teaspoons to pounds on both sides.

$$\frac{1.5 \text{ tsp}}{24 \text{ pounds}} = \frac{x \text{ tsp}}{8 \text{ pounds}}$$

Show that the cross products are equal.

$$24 \cdot x = 1.5 \cdot 8$$

Divide both sides by 24.

$$\frac{\cancel{24} \cdot x}{\cancel{24}} = \frac{12}{24}$$

$$x = \frac{1}{2} \text{ tsp or 0.5 tsp}$$

76. $$\frac{0.8 \text{ gallons}}{3 \text{ hours}} = \frac{2 \text{ gallons}}{x}$$
$$0.8 \cdot x = 3 \cdot 2$$
$$\frac{0.8 \cdot x}{0.8} = \frac{6}{0.8}$$
$$x = 7.5 \text{ or } 7\frac{1}{2}$$

The lawn mower should run 7.5 or $7\frac{1}{2}$ hours on a full tank.

Chapter 5 Test

1. 16 fish to 20 fish
$$\frac{16 \text{ fish}}{20 \text{ fish}} = \frac{16 \div 4}{20 \div 4} = \frac{4}{5}$$

2. 300 miles on 15 gallons
$$\frac{300 \text{ miles} \div 15}{15 \text{ gallons} \div 15} = \frac{20 \text{ miles}}{1 \text{ gallon}}$$

3. $15 for 75 minutes
$$\frac{\$15 \div 15}{75 \text{ minutes} \div 15} = \frac{\$1}{5 \text{ minutes}}$$

4. $$\frac{1200 \text{ seats}}{320 \text{ seats}} = \frac{1200 \div 80}{320 \div 80} = \frac{15}{4}$$

5. 3 quarts to 60 gallons

60 gallons = 60 · 4 quarts = 240 quarts
$$\frac{3 \text{ quarts} \div 3}{240 \text{ quarts} \div 3} = \frac{1}{80}$$

6. 3 hours to 40 minutes

3 hours = 3 · 60 minutes = 180 minutes
$$\frac{180 \text{ minutes}}{40 \text{ minutes}} = \frac{180 \div 20}{40 \div 20} = \frac{9}{2}$$

7. 28 ounces of Brand X for $3.89 − $0.75 (coupon) = $3.14

$$\frac{\$3.14}{28 \text{ ounces}} \approx \$0.112 \text{ per ounce}$$

18 ounces of Brand Y for $1.89 − $0.25 (coupon) = $1.64

$$\frac{\$1.64}{18 \text{ ounces}} \approx \$0.091 \text{ per ounce}$$

13 ounces of Brand Z for $1.29.

$$\frac{\$1.29}{13 \text{ ounces}} \approx \$0.099 \text{ per ounce}$$

The best buy is 18 ounces of Brand Y for $1.89 with a 25¢ coupon.

8. You earned less this year.
An example is:

last year → $\frac{\$15{,}000}{\$10{,}000} = \frac{3}{2}$.
this year →

9. $$\frac{6}{14} = \frac{18}{45}$$
$$6 \cdot 45 = 270$$
$$14 \cdot 18 = 252$$

The cross products are not equal, so the proportion is false.

10. $$\frac{8.4}{2.8} = \frac{2.1}{0.7}$$
$$\frac{3}{1} = \frac{3}{1} \quad \textit{Write in lowest terms}$$

The proportion is true.

11. $$\frac{5}{9} = \frac{x}{45}$$
$$9 \cdot x = 5 \cdot 45$$
$$\frac{9 \cdot x}{9} = \frac{225}{9}$$
$$x = 25$$

Cumulative Review Exercises (Chapters 1-5)

12. $\dfrac{3}{1} = \dfrac{8}{x}$

$3 \cdot x = 8 \cdot 1$

$\dfrac{3 \cdot x}{3} = \dfrac{8}{3}$

$x \approx 2.67$

13. $\dfrac{x}{20} = \dfrac{6.5}{0.4}$

$0.4 \cdot x = 6.5 \cdot 20$

$\dfrac{0.4 \cdot x}{0.4} = \dfrac{130}{0.4}$

$x = 325$

14. $\dfrac{2\frac{1}{3}}{x} = \dfrac{\frac{8}{9}}{4}$

$\dfrac{8}{9} \cdot x = 2\frac{1}{3} \cdot 4$

$\dfrac{\frac{8}{9} \cdot x}{\frac{8}{9}} = \dfrac{9\frac{1}{3}}{\frac{8}{9}}$

$x = 9\frac{1}{3} \div \dfrac{8}{9} = \dfrac{\cancel{28}^{7}}{\cancel{3}_{1}} \cdot \dfrac{\cancel{9}^{3}}{\cancel{8}_{2}}$

$= \dfrac{21}{2} = 10\frac{1}{2}$

15. $\dfrac{240 \text{ words}}{5 \text{ minutes}} = \dfrac{x}{12 \text{ minutes}}$

$5 \cdot x = 240 \cdot 12$

$\dfrac{5 \cdot x}{5} = \dfrac{2880}{5}$

$x = 576$

Pedro can type 576 words in 12 minutes.

16. $\dfrac{75 \text{ miles}}{4 \text{ hours}} = \dfrac{120 \text{ miles}}{x}$

$75 \cdot x = 4 \cdot 120$

$\dfrac{75 \cdot x}{75} = \dfrac{480}{75}$

$x = 6.4$

It will take 6.4 hours to travel 120 miles.

17. $\dfrac{2 \text{ people}}{15 \text{ people}} = \dfrac{x}{650 \text{ students}}$

$15 \cdot x = 2 \cdot 650$

$\dfrac{15 \cdot x}{15} = \dfrac{1300}{15}$

$x = 86.67 \text{ or } \approx 87$

You could expect ≈ 87 students to be left-handed.

18. No, 4875 cannot be correct because there are only 650 students in the whole school.

19. $\dfrac{8.2 \text{ grams}}{50 \text{ pounds}} = \dfrac{x}{145 \text{ pounds}}$

$50 \cdot x = 8.2 \cdot 145$

$\dfrac{50 \cdot x}{50} = \dfrac{1189}{50}$

$x = 23.78 \text{ or } \approx 23.8$

A 145-pound person should be given ≈ 23.8 grams.

20. $\dfrac{1 \text{ inch}}{8 \text{ feet}} = \dfrac{7.5 \text{ inches}}{x}$

$1 \cdot x = 7.5 \cdot 8$

$x = 60$

The actual height of the building is 60 feet.

Cumulative Review Exercises (Chapters 1-5)

1. 21<u>6</u>,47<u>5</u>,0<u>3</u>8
   thousands: 5
   tens: 3
   million: 6

2. 34<u>0</u>.69<u>15</u>
   hundredths: 9
   ones: 0
   ten-thousandths: 5

3. 9903 to the nearest hundred: ≈ 9900

    9<u>9</u>03

   Next digit is less than 5. Hundreds place does not change. All digits to the right of the underlined place change to 0.

4. 617.0519 to the nearest tenth: ≈ 617.1

    617.0|519

   Draw cut-off line. First digit cut is 5 or more so round up.

5. $99.81 to the nearest dollar: $\approx \$100$

    $99.|81

   Draw cut-off line. First digit cut is 5 or more so round up.

6. $3.0555 to the nearest cent: ≈ $3.06

$$\$3.05|55$$

Draw cut-off line. First digit cut is 5 or more so round up.

7. *estimate*   *exact*

$$\begin{array}{r} 30 \\ 5000 \\ +\ 400 \\ \hline 5430 \end{array} \qquad \begin{array}{r} 28 \\ 5206 \\ +\ 351 \\ \hline 5585 \end{array}$$

8. *estimate*   *exact*

$$\begin{array}{r} 60 \\ -\ 6 \\ \hline 54 \end{array} \qquad \begin{array}{r} 63.100 \\ -\ 5.692 \\ \hline 57.408 \end{array}$$

9. *estimate*   *exact*

$$\begin{array}{r} 5000 \\ \times\ \ 800 \\ \hline 4{,}000{,}000 \end{array} \qquad \begin{array}{r} 4716 \\ \times\ \ \ 804 \\ \hline 18\ 864 \\ 3\ 772\ 80\ \ \\ \hline 3{,}791{,}664 \end{array}$$

10. *estimate*   *exact*

$$\begin{array}{r} 1 \\ \times\ 18 \\ \hline 18 \end{array} \qquad \begin{array}{r} 0.982 \\ \times\ \ 17.8 \\ \hline 7856 \\ 6\ 874\ \ \\ 9\ 82\ \ \ \ \\ \hline 17.4796 \end{array}$$

11. *estimate*   *exact*

$$\begin{array}{r} 1\ 000 \\ 50\overline{)50{,}000} \end{array} \qquad \begin{array}{r} 907 \\ 53\overline{)48{,}071} \\ \underline{47\ 7}\ \ \ \\ 37\ \ \ \\ \underline{\ \ 0}\ \ \ \\ 371 \\ \underline{371} \\ 0 \end{array}$$

12. *estimate*   *exact*

$$\begin{array}{r} 400 \\ 5\overline{)2000} \end{array} \qquad \begin{array}{r} 36\ 4 \\ 4.5_\wedge\overline{)1638.0_\wedge} \\ \underline{135}\ \ \ \ \ \\ 288\ \ \ \\ \underline{270}\ \ \ \\ 18\ 0 \\ \underline{18\ 0} \\ 0 \end{array}$$

13. *estimate* $2 \cdot 4 = 8$
 exact

$$1\tfrac{5}{6} \times 3\tfrac{3}{5} = \frac{11}{\cancel{6}_1} \cdot \frac{\cancel{18}^3}{5} = \frac{33}{5} = 6\tfrac{3}{5}$$

14. *estimate* $5 \div 1 = 5$
 exact

$$5\tfrac{1}{4} \div \tfrac{7}{8} = 5\tfrac{1}{4} \cdot \tfrac{8}{7} = \frac{\cancel{21}^3}{\cancel{4}_1} \cdot \frac{\cancel{8}^2}{\cancel{7}_1} = 6$$

15. *estimate* $3 - 2 = 1$
 exact

$$2\tfrac{4}{5} - 1\tfrac{5}{6} = \frac{14}{5} - \frac{11}{6} = \frac{84}{30} - \frac{55}{30} = \frac{29}{30}$$

16. *estimate* $3 + 11 = 14$
 exact

$$\begin{aligned} 2\tfrac{9}{10} + 10\tfrac{1}{2} &= 2\tfrac{9}{10} + 10\tfrac{5}{10} \\ &= 12\tfrac{14}{10} = 13\tfrac{4}{10} = 13\tfrac{2}{5} \end{aligned}$$

17. $988 + 373{,}422 + 6$

$$\begin{array}{r} 988 \\ 373{,}422 \\ +\ \ \ \ \ \ 6 \\ \hline 374{,}416 \end{array}$$

18. $30 - 0.66$

$$\begin{array}{r} \overset{2\ 9}{\cancel{3}}\overset{\overset{9}{10}}{\cancel{0}}.\overset{10}{\cancel{0}}\cancel{0} \\ -\ \ 0.6\ 6 \\ \hline 2\ 9.\ 3\ 4 \end{array}$$

19.
$$\begin{array}{r} 610\ \ \text{R}27 \\ 33\overline{)20{,}157} \\ \underline{19\ 8}\ \ \ \ \ \\ 35\ \ \ \\ \underline{33}\ \ \ \\ 27 \\ \underline{\ \ 0} \\ 27 \end{array}$$

Cumulative Review Exercises (Chapters 1-5)

20. $(1.9)(0.004)$

$$\begin{array}{r} 1.9 \\ \times\ 0.004 \\ \hline 0.0076 \end{array} \begin{array}{l} \leftarrow\ 1\ decimal\ place \\ \leftarrow\ 3\ decimal\ places \\ \hline 4\ decimal\ places \end{array}$$

21. $3020 - 708$

$$\begin{array}{r} \overset{2\ 10\ 1\ 10}{\cancel{3}\cancel{0}\cancel{2}\cancel{0}} \\ -\ 7\ 0\ 8 \\ \hline 2\ 3\ 1\ 2 \end{array}$$

22. $0.401 + 62.98 + 5$

$$\begin{array}{r} 0.401 \\ 62.980 \\ 5.00 \\ \hline 68.381 \end{array} \quad Write\ in\ 0's$$

23. $1.39 \div 0.025$

$$\begin{array}{r} 55.6 \\ 0.025_\wedge)\overline{1.390_\wedge 0} \\ \underline{1\ 25} \\ 140 \\ \underline{125} \\ 15\ 0 \\ \underline{15\ 0} \\ 0 \end{array}$$

Move decimal point in divisor and dividend

Write 0 in the dividend

24. $(6392)(5609)$
$= 6392 \cdot 5609$
$= 35,852,728$

25. $36 + 18 \div 6$ *Divide*
$36 + 3 = 39$ *Add*

26. $8 \div 4 + (10 - 3^2) \cdot 4^2$ *Exponents*
$8 \div 4 + (10 - 9) \cdot 16$ *Parentheses*
$8 \div 4 + 1 \cdot 16$ *Divide*
$2 + 1 \cdot 16$ *Multiply*
$2 + 16 = 18$ *Add*

27. $88 \div \sqrt{121} \cdot 2^3$ *Exponent*
$88 \div \sqrt{121} \cdot 8$ *Square root*
$88 \div 11 \cdot 8$ *Divide*
$8 \cdot 8 = 64$ *Multiply*

28. $(16.2 - 5.85) - 2.35 \cdot 4$ *Parentheses*
$10.35 - 2.35 \cdot 4$ *Multiply*
$10.35 - 9.4 = 0.95$ *Subtract*

29. 0.0105 is one hundred five ten-thousandths.

30. Sixty and seventy-one thousandths is 60.071.

31. $\dfrac{5}{16} \approx 0.313$

$$\begin{array}{r} 0.3125 \\ 16)\overline{5.0000} \\ \underline{4\ 8} \\ 20 \\ \underline{16} \\ 40 \\ \underline{32} \\ 80 \\ \underline{80} \\ 0 \end{array}$$

32. $4\dfrac{7}{9} = \dfrac{43}{9} \approx 4.778$

$$\begin{array}{r} 4.7777 \\ 9)\overline{43.0000} \\ \underline{36} \\ 7\ 0 \\ \underline{6\ 3} \\ 70 \\ \underline{63} \\ 70 \\ \underline{63} \\ 70 \\ \underline{63} \\ 7 \end{array}$$

33. 0.0711, 0.7, 0.707, 0.07

$$\begin{array}{rcl} 0.0711 & = & 0.0711 \\ 0.7 & = & 0.7000 \\ 0.707 & = & 0.7070 \\ 0.07 & = & 0.0700 \end{array}$$

From smallest to largest:

0.07, 0.0711, 0.7, 0.707

34. $\dfrac{3}{8}, \dfrac{7}{20}, 0.305, \dfrac{1}{3}$

$$\begin{array}{rcl} \dfrac{3}{8} & = & 0.375 \\ \dfrac{7}{20} & = & 0.350 \\ & & 0.305 \\ \dfrac{1}{3} & = & 0.333 \end{array}$$

From smallest to largest:

$0.305, \dfrac{1}{3}, \dfrac{7}{20}, \dfrac{3}{8}$

35. 20 cars to 5 cars

$$\frac{20 \text{ cars}}{5 \text{ cars}} = \frac{20 \div 5}{5 \div 5} = \frac{4}{1}$$

36. $39 for 6 hours

$$\frac{\$39 \div 3}{6 \text{ hours} \div 3} = \frac{\$13}{2 \text{ hours}}$$

37. 20 minutes to 4 hours

4 hours to $4 \cdot 60 = 240$ minutes

$$\frac{20 \text{ minutes}}{240 \text{ minutes}} = \frac{20 \div 20}{240 \div 20} = \frac{1}{12}$$

38. 8 inches to 2 feet
$2 \cdot 12 = 24$ inches

$$\frac{8 \text{ inches}}{24 \text{ inches}} = \frac{8 \div 8}{24 \div 8} = \frac{1}{3}$$

39. 55 years to 25 years

$$\frac{55 \text{ years}}{25 \text{ years}} = \frac{55 \div 5}{25 \div 5} = \frac{11}{5}$$

40. 20 servings for $1.59

$$\frac{\$1.59}{20 \text{ servings}} \approx \$0.0795 \text{ per serving}$$

36 servings for $3.24 − $0.50 (coupon) = $2.74

$$\frac{\$2.74}{36 \text{ servings}} \approx \$0.0761 \text{ per serving}$$

48 servings for $4.99 − $0.50 (coupon) = $4.49

$$\frac{\$4.49}{48 \text{ servings}} \approx \$0.0935 \text{ per serving}$$

The best buy is 36 servings for $3.24 with a 50¢ coupon.

41. $\dfrac{9}{12} = \dfrac{x}{28}$

$12 \cdot x = 9 \cdot 28$ *Cross products are equivalent*

$\dfrac{12 \cdot x}{12} = \dfrac{252}{12}$ *Divide both sides by 12*

$x = 21$

42. $\dfrac{7}{12} = \dfrac{10}{x}$

$7 \cdot x = 10 \cdot 12$ *Cross products are equivalent*

$\dfrac{7 \cdot x}{7} = \dfrac{120}{7}$ *Divide both sides by 7*

$x \approx 17.14$

43. $\dfrac{x}{\frac{3}{4}} = \dfrac{2\frac{1}{2}}{\frac{1}{6}}$

$\dfrac{1}{6} \cdot x = 2\frac{1}{2} \cdot \dfrac{3}{4}$

$\dfrac{\frac{1}{6} \cdot x}{\frac{1}{6}} = \dfrac{\frac{15}{8}}{\frac{1}{6}}$

$x = \dfrac{15}{8} \div \dfrac{1}{6} = \dfrac{15}{\cancel{8}_4} \cdot \dfrac{\cancel{6}^3}{1} = \dfrac{45}{4} = 11\dfrac{1}{4}$

44. $\dfrac{6.7}{x} = \dfrac{62.8}{9.15}$

$62.8 \cdot x = 6.7 \cdot 9.15$

$x = \dfrac{6.7 \cdot 9.15}{62.8}$

$ = 61.305 \div 62.8$

$ \approx 0.9761943$

$ \approx 0.98$

45. Find the amount already collected.

$$\dfrac{5}{\cancel{6}_1} \cdot \dfrac{\cancel{1500}^{250}}{1} = 1250$$

$1500 - 1250 = 250$

They need to collect 250 pounds.

46. $\dfrac{10 \text{ centimeters}}{15 \text{ centimeters}} = \dfrac{x}{40 \text{ centimeters}}$

$15 \cdot x = 10 \cdot 40$

$\dfrac{15 \cdot x}{15} = \dfrac{400}{15}$

$x \approx 26.7$

The enlarged length of the photo is 26.7 centimeters.

47. Add the enrollment for each class.
estimate

$2000 + 2000 + 2000 + 2000 = 8000$ students

exact

freshmen	2400
sophmores	2150
juniors	2000
seniors	+ 1850
	8400

The total enrollment at the college is 8400 students.

48. Divide the amount budgeted for freshman orientation by the number of freshmen.

estimate
$$\$200,000 \div 2000 = \$100$$

exact
$$\$186,400 \div 2400 = \$77.666667$$
$$\approx \$78$$

49. $\dfrac{2400 \text{ students} \div 1200}{8400 \text{ students} \div 1200} = \dfrac{2}{7}$

50. Multiply the fee and the total enrollment.

estimate
$$\$4 \cdot 8000 = \$32,000$$

exact
$$\begin{array}{r} \$3.75 \\ \times 8400 \\ \hline 1\ 500\ 00 \\ 30\ 00 \\ \hline \$31,500.00 \end{array}$$

The total amount collected is $31,500.

51. Add the number of times Norma ran in the morning and in the afternoon. Multiply the sum by the distance around Dunning Pond.

estimate $4 + 3 = 7;\ 7 \cdot 1 = 7$ miles

exact
$$4 + 2\tfrac{1}{2} = 6\tfrac{1}{2}$$
$$1\tfrac{1}{10} \cdot 6\tfrac{1}{2} = \dfrac{11}{10} \cdot \dfrac{13}{2} = \dfrac{143}{20} = 7\tfrac{3}{20}$$

Norma ran $7\tfrac{3}{20}$ miles.

52. Divide the number of miles driven by the number of gallons of gas purchased.

estimate

900 miles ÷ 50 gallons = 18 miles per gallon

exact
$$\begin{array}{r} 1\ 8.00 \\ 49.8_\wedge\overline{)896.5_\wedge 00} \\ 498 \\ \hline 398\ 5 \\ 398\ 4 \\ \hline 1\ 0 \\ 0 \\ \hline 1\ 00 \\ 0 \\ \hline 1\ 00 \end{array}$$

Rodney's car got ≈18.0 miles per gallon on the vacation.

53. $\dfrac{5 \text{ residents}}{6 \text{ residents}} = \dfrac{x}{240 \text{ residents}}$

$$6 \cdot x = 5 \cdot 240$$
$$\dfrac{6 \cdot x}{6} = \dfrac{1200}{6}$$
$$x = 200$$

You would expect 200 residents to be bothered by noise.

54. plant   food
       ↓   ↓

$$\dfrac{\tfrac{1}{2} \text{ teaspoon}}{2 \text{ quarts water}} = \dfrac{x}{5 \text{ quarts water}}$$

$$2 \cdot x = \dfrac{1}{2} \cdot 5$$

$$\dfrac{2 \cdot x}{2} = \dfrac{\tfrac{5}{2}}{2}$$

$$x = \dfrac{5}{2} \div 2 = \dfrac{5}{2} \cdot \dfrac{1}{2}$$

$$= \dfrac{5}{4} = 1\tfrac{1}{4}$$

Use $1\tfrac{1}{4}$ teaspoons of plant food.

Chapter 6

PERCENT

6.1 Basics of Percent

6.1 Margin Exercises

1. **(a)** 63 out of 100 is $\left(\frac{63}{100}\right)$ or 63% of the people are unmarried.

   (b) The tax rate is $14 per $100
   $$\left(\frac{14}{100}\right) \text{ or } 14\%.$$

   (c) 36 out of 100 is $\left(\frac{36}{100}\right)$ or 36% of the students are attending school full time.

2. **(a)** $53\% = 53 \div 100 = 0.53$

   (b) $27\% = 27 \div 100 = 0.27$

   (c) $38.6\% = 38.6 \div 100 = 0.386$

   (d) $150\% = 150 \div 100 = 1.5$

3. **(a)** $88\% = 0.88$
   Drop the percent sign and move the decimal point two places to the left.

   (b) $4\% = 0.04$
   Drop the percent sign and move the decimal point two places to the left.

   (c) $21.6\% = 0.216$
   Drop the percent sign and move the decimal point two places to the left.

   (d) $0.8\% = 0.008$
   Drop the percent sign and move the decimal point two places to the left.

4. **(a)** $0.95 = 95\%$
   Move the decimal point two places to the right. (The decimal point is not written with whole number percents.) Attach percent sign.

   (b) $0.18 = 18\%$
   Move the decimal point two places to the right and attach percent sign.

   (c) $0.09 = 9\%$
   Move the decimal point two places to the right and attach percent sign.

   (d) $0.617 = 61.7\%$
   Move the decimal point two places to the right and attach percent sign.

   (e) $0.834 = 83.4\%$
   Move the decimal point two places to the right and attach percent sign.

   (f) $5.34 = 534\%$
   Move the decimal point two places to the right and attach percent sign.

   (g) $2.8 = 280\%$
   Move the decimal point two places to the right and attach percent sign.

   (h) $4 = 400\%$
   Two 0's are attached so the decimal point can be moved two places to the right. Attach percent sign.

5. **(a)** 100% of $3.95 is $\underline{\$3.95}$.

   (b) 100% of 3000 students is $\underline{3000 \text{ students}}$.

   (c) 100% of 7 pages is $\underline{7 \text{ pages}}$.

   (d) 100% of 305 miles is $\underline{305 \text{ miles}}$.

   (e) 100% of $10\frac{1}{2}$ hours is $\underline{10\frac{1}{2} \text{ hours}}$.

6. **(a)** 50% of $10 is *half* of the money.
   So, 50% of $10 is $\underline{\$5}$.

   (b) 50% of 36 cookies is *half* of the cookies.
   So, 50% of the 36 cookies is $\underline{18 \text{ cookies.}}$

   (c) 50% of 6000 women is *half* of the women.
   So, 50% of the 6000 women is $\underline{3000 \text{ women}}$.

   (d) 50% of 8 hours is *half* of 8 hours.
   So, 50% of 8 hours is $\underline{4 \text{ hours}}$.

   (e) 50% of $2.50 is *half* of the money.
   So, 50% of $2.50 is $\underline{\$1.25}$.

6.1 Section Exercises

3. $30\% = 0.30$ or 0.3
   Drop the percent sign and move the decimal point two places to the left.

132

Section 6.2 Percents and Fractions

7. $140\% = 1.40$ or 1.4
Drop the percent sign and move the decimal point two places to the left.

11. $100\% = 1.00$ or 1
Drop the percent sign and move the decimal point two place to the left.

15. $0.35\% = 0.0035$
Drop the percent sign. Attach two 0's so the decimal point can be moved two places to the left.

19. $0.62 = 62\%$
Move the decimal point two places to the right and attach percent sign. (The decimal point is not written with whole numbers.)

23. $0.125 = 12.5\%$
Move the decimal point two places to the right and attach percent sign.

27. $2 = 200\%$
Attach two 0's so the decimal point can be moved two places to the right. Attach percent sign.

31. $0.0312 = 3.12\%$
Move the decimal point two places to the right and attach percent sign.

35. $0.0017 = 0.17\%$
Move the decimal point two places to the right and attach percent sign.

39. Drop the percent sign and move the decimal point two places to the left.

8% sales tax rate $= 0.08$

43. Move the decimal point two places to the right and attach percent sign.

0.035 property tax rate $= 3.5\%$

47. Move the decimal point two places to the right and attach percent sign.

0.005 of the population $= 0.5\%$

51. 100% of $\$78$ is $\underline{\$78}$.

55. 50% of 180 miles is $\underline{90\text{ miles}}$.

59. 50% of 8200 college students is $\underline{4100\text{ students}}$.

63. Ninety-five parts of the one hundred parts are shaded.
$$\frac{95}{100} = 0.95 = 95\%$$
Five parts of the one hundred parts are unshaded.
$$\frac{5}{100} = 0.05 = 5\%$$

67. Three parts of the four parts are shaded.
$$\frac{3}{4} = \frac{75}{100} = 0.75 = 75\%$$
One part of the four parts is unshaded.
$$\frac{1}{4} = \frac{25}{100} = 0.25 = 25\%$$

71. $\dfrac{2}{5} = \dfrac{2 \cdot 2}{5 \cdot 2} = \dfrac{4}{10} = 0.4$

75. $\dfrac{7}{8} = 0.875$

$$\begin{array}{r}0.875\\8\overline{)7.000}\\\underline{6\ 4}\\60\\\underline{56}\\40\\\underline{40}\\0\end{array}$$

6.2 Percents and Fractions

6.2 Margin Exercises

1. (a) $50\% = \dfrac{50 \div 50}{100 \div 50} = \dfrac{1}{2}$

   (b) $22\% = \dfrac{22 \div 2}{100 \div 2} = \dfrac{11}{50}$

   (c) $68\% = \dfrac{68 \div 4}{100 \div 4} = \dfrac{17}{25}$

   (d) $61\% = \dfrac{61}{100}$

   (e) $120\% = \dfrac{120 \div 20}{100 \div 20} = \dfrac{6}{5} = 1\dfrac{1}{5}$

   (f) $210\% = \dfrac{210 \div 10}{100 \div 10} = \dfrac{21}{10} = 2\dfrac{1}{10}$

2. (a) $18.5\% = \dfrac{18.5}{100} = \dfrac{18.5 \cdot 10}{100 \cdot 10} = \dfrac{185 \div 5}{1000 \div 5} = \dfrac{37}{200}$

   (b) $87.5\% = \dfrac{87.5}{100} = \dfrac{87.5 \cdot 10}{100 \cdot 10} = \dfrac{875 \div 125}{1000 \div 125} = \dfrac{7}{8}$

(c) $6.5\% = \dfrac{6.5}{100} = \dfrac{6.5 \cdot 10}{100 \cdot 10} = \dfrac{65 \div 5}{1000 \div 5} = \dfrac{13}{200}$

(d) $66\tfrac{2}{3}\% = \dfrac{66\tfrac{2}{3}}{100} = \dfrac{\tfrac{200}{3}}{100} = \dfrac{200}{3} \div \dfrac{100}{1}$
$= \dfrac{200}{3} \cdot \dfrac{1}{100} = \dfrac{2}{3}$

(e) $12\tfrac{1}{3}\% = \dfrac{12\tfrac{1}{3}}{100} = \dfrac{\tfrac{37}{3}}{100} = \dfrac{37}{3} \div \dfrac{100}{1}$
$= \dfrac{37}{3} \cdot \dfrac{1}{100} = \dfrac{37}{300}$

(f) $62\tfrac{1}{2}\% = \dfrac{62\tfrac{1}{2}}{100} = \dfrac{\tfrac{125}{2}}{100} = \dfrac{125}{2} \div \dfrac{100}{1}$
$= \dfrac{125}{2} \cdot \dfrac{1}{100} = \dfrac{5}{8}$

3. (a) $\dfrac{3}{4} = \dfrac{p}{100}$
$4 \cdot p = 3 \cdot 100$ *Cross products are equivalent*
$\dfrac{4 \cdot p}{4} = \dfrac{300}{4}$
$p = 75$
$\dfrac{3}{4} = 75\%$

(b) $\dfrac{7}{25} = \dfrac{p}{100}$
$25 \cdot p = 7 \cdot 100$ *Cross products are equivalent*
$\dfrac{25 \cdot p}{25} = \dfrac{700}{25}$
$p = 28$
$\dfrac{7}{25} = 28\%$

(c) $\dfrac{9}{10} = \dfrac{p}{100}$
$10 \cdot p = 9 \cdot 100$ *Cross products are equivalent*
$\dfrac{10 \cdot p}{10} = \dfrac{900}{10}$
$p = 90$
$\dfrac{9}{10} = 90\%$

(d) $\dfrac{3}{8} = \dfrac{p}{100}$
$8 \cdot p = 3 \cdot 100$ *Cross products are equivalent*
$\dfrac{8 \cdot p}{8} = \dfrac{300}{8}$
$p = 37.5$
$\dfrac{3}{8} = 37.5\%$

(e) $\dfrac{1}{6} = \dfrac{p}{100}$
$6 \cdot p = 1 \cdot 100$ *Cross products are equivalent*
$\dfrac{6 \cdot p}{6} = \dfrac{100}{6}$
$p \approx 16.7$
$\dfrac{1}{6} \approx 16.7\%$ or exactly $16\tfrac{2}{3}\%$

(f) $\dfrac{2}{9} = \dfrac{p}{100}$
$9 \cdot p = 2 \cdot 100$ *Cross products are equivalent*
$\dfrac{9 \cdot p}{9} = \dfrac{200}{9}$
$p \approx 22.2$
$\dfrac{2}{9} \approx 22.2\%$ or exactly $22\tfrac{2}{9}\%$

4. (a) $\tfrac{1}{2}$ as a percent
$\tfrac{1}{2} = 50\%$

(b) $12\tfrac{1}{2}\%$ as a fraction
$12\tfrac{1}{2}\% = \tfrac{1}{8}$

(c) ≈ 0.667 as a fraction
$0.667 = \tfrac{2}{3}$

(d) 20% as a fraction
$20\% = \tfrac{1}{5}$

(e) $\tfrac{7}{8}$ as a percent
$\tfrac{7}{8} = 87\tfrac{1}{2}\%$ or 87.5%

(f) $\tfrac{1}{4}$ as a percent
$\tfrac{1}{4} = 25\%$

Section 6.2 Percents and Fractions

(g) $33\frac{1}{3}\%$ as a fraction

$33\frac{1}{3}\% = \frac{1}{3}$

(h) $\frac{4}{5}$ as a percent

$\frac{4}{5} = 80\%$

6.2 Section Exercises

3. $50\% = \frac{50 \div 50}{100 \div 50} = \frac{1}{2}$

7. $37.5\% = \frac{37.5 \cdot 10}{100 \cdot 10} = \frac{375}{1000} = \frac{375 \div 125}{1000 \div 125} = \frac{3}{8}$

11. $16\frac{2}{3}\% = \frac{16\frac{2}{3}}{100} = 16\frac{2}{3} \div 100 = \frac{50}{3} \cdot \frac{1}{100} = \frac{1}{6}$

15. $0.5\% = \frac{0.5 \cdot 10}{100 \cdot 10} = \frac{5 \div 5}{1000 \div 5} = \frac{1}{200}$

19. $250\% = \frac{250 \div 50}{100 \div 50} = \frac{5}{2} = 2\frac{1}{2}$

23. $\frac{3}{10} = \frac{p}{100}$

$10 \cdot p = 3 \cdot 100$ *Cross products are equivalent*

$\frac{10 \cdot p}{10} = \frac{300}{10}$

$p = 30$

$\frac{3}{10} = 30\%$

27. $\frac{37}{100} = 0.37 = 37\%$

31. $\frac{7}{8} = \frac{p}{100}$

$8 \cdot p = 7 \cdot 100$ *Cross products are equivalent*

$\frac{8 \cdot p}{8} = \frac{700}{8}$

$p = 87.5$

$\frac{7}{8} = 87.5\%$

35. $\frac{23}{50} = \frac{23 \cdot 2}{50 \cdot 2} = \frac{46}{100} = 0.46 = 46\%$

39. $\frac{5}{6} = \frac{p}{100}$

$6 \cdot p = 5 \cdot 100$

$\frac{6 \cdot p}{6} = \frac{500}{6}$

$p \approx 83.3$

$\frac{5}{6} \approx 83.3\%$

43. $\frac{1}{7} = \frac{p}{100}$

$7 \cdot p = 1 \cdot 100$

$\frac{7 \cdot p}{7} = \frac{100}{7}$

$p \approx 14.3$

$\approx 14.3\%$

47. $87.5\% = 0.875$ *decimal*

$= \frac{875 \div 125}{1000 \div 125} = \frac{7}{8}$ *fraction*

51. $\frac{1}{6} \approx 0.167$ *decimal*

$\frac{1}{6} \approx 16.7\%$ *percent*

$\begin{array}{r}0.1666\\6\overline{)1.0000}\\\underline{6}\\40\\\underline{36}\\40\\\underline{36}\\40\\\underline{36}\\4\end{array}$

55. $12.5\% = 0.125$ *decimal*

$= \frac{125 \div 125}{1000 \div 125} = \frac{1}{8}$ *fraction*

59. $\frac{1}{10} = 0.1$ *decimal*

$= 10\%$ *percent*

63. $\frac{1}{200} = \frac{1 \cdot 5}{200 \cdot 5} = \frac{5}{1000} = 0.005$ *decimal*

$= 0.5\%$ *percent*

67. $3\frac{1}{4} = \frac{13}{4}$

$\frac{13}{4} = \frac{p}{100}$

$4 \cdot p = 1300$

$\frac{4 \cdot p}{4} = \frac{1300}{4}$

$p = 325$

$3\frac{1}{4} = 325\%$ *percent*

$= 3.25$ *decimal*

71. 76 out of 100 questions

$$\frac{76}{100} = \frac{76 \div 4}{100 \div 4} = \frac{19}{25} \quad fraction$$

$$\frac{76}{100} = 0.76 \quad decimal$$

$$\frac{76}{100} = 76\% \quad percent$$

75. 9 out of 15 are single parents.

$$\frac{9}{15} = \frac{3}{5} \quad fraction$$

$$\frac{3}{5} = \frac{6}{10} = 0.6 \quad decimal$$

$$\frac{3}{5} = 0.60 = 60\% \quad percent$$

79. 342 out of 380 do not have a reaction.
380 − 342 = 38 do have a reaction.

$$\frac{38}{380} = \frac{1}{10} \quad fraction$$

$$\frac{1}{10} = 0.1 \quad decimal$$

$$0.1 = 10\% \quad percent$$

83. 1680 students out of 4200 drive their own car.

$$\frac{1680}{4200} = \frac{1680 \div 840}{4200 \div 840} = \frac{2}{5} \quad fraction$$

$$\frac{2}{5} = \frac{4}{10} = 0.4 \quad decimal$$

$$= 40\% \quad percent$$

87. $\quad \dfrac{4}{y} = \dfrac{12}{15}$

$y \cdot 12 = 4 \cdot 15 \quad$ *Cross products are equivalent*

$\dfrac{y \cdot 12}{12} = \dfrac{60}{12}$

$y = 5$

6.3 The Percent Proportion

6.3 Margin Exercises

1. (a) $\dfrac{3}{4} = \dfrac{75}{100} \qquad 4 \cdot 75 = 300$
$\phantom{\dfrac{3}{4} = \dfrac{75}{100}} \qquad 3 \cdot 100 = 300$

The cross products are equivalent, so the proportion is true.

(b) $\dfrac{3}{8} = \dfrac{75}{200} \qquad 8 \cdot 75 = 600$
$\phantom{\dfrac{3}{8} = \dfrac{75}{200}} \qquad 3 \cdot 200 = 600$

The cross products are equivalent, so the proportion is true.

(c) $\dfrac{4}{5} = \dfrac{108}{140} \qquad 4 \cdot 140 = 560$
$\phantom{\dfrac{4}{5} = \dfrac{108}{140}} \qquad 5 \cdot 108 = 540$

The cross products are not equivalent, so the proportion is false.

(d) $\dfrac{29}{83} = \dfrac{145}{415} \qquad 29 \cdot 415 = 12{,}035$
$\phantom{\dfrac{29}{83} = \dfrac{145}{415}} \qquad 83 \cdot 145 = 12{,}035$

The cross products are equivalent, so the proportion is true.

(e) $\dfrac{104}{37} = \dfrac{515}{185} \qquad 104 \cdot 185 = 19{,}240$
$\phantom{\dfrac{104}{37} = \dfrac{515}{185}} \qquad 37 \cdot 515 = 19{,}055$

The cross products are not equivalent, so the proportion is false.

2. (a) $\quad \dfrac{a}{b} = \dfrac{p}{100} \qquad a = 15,\ p = 20$

$\dfrac{15}{b} = \dfrac{20}{100}$

$20 \cdot b = 15 \cdot 100 \quad$ *Cross products are equivalent*

$\dfrac{20 \cdot b}{20} = \dfrac{1500}{20}$

$b = 75$

(b) $\quad \dfrac{a}{b} = \dfrac{p}{100} \qquad a = 50,\ b = 200$

$\dfrac{50}{200} = \dfrac{p}{100}$

$200 \cdot p = 50 \cdot 100$

$\dfrac{200 \cdot p}{200} = \dfrac{5000}{200}$

$p = 25$

The percent is 25%.

(c) $\quad \dfrac{a}{b} = \dfrac{p}{100} \qquad b = 175,\ p = 12$

$\dfrac{a}{175} = \dfrac{12}{100}$

$a \cdot 100 = 175 \cdot 12$

$\dfrac{a \cdot 100}{100} = \dfrac{2100}{100}$

$a = 21$

Section 6.3 The Percent Proportion

(d) $\dfrac{a}{b} = \dfrac{p}{100}$ $b = 5000, p = 27$

$\dfrac{a}{5000} = \dfrac{27}{100}$

$a \cdot 100 = 27 \cdot 5000$

$\dfrac{a \cdot 100}{100} = \dfrac{135{,}000}{100}$

$a = 1350$

(e) $\dfrac{a}{b} = \dfrac{p}{100}$ $a = 74, b = 185$

$\dfrac{74}{185} = \dfrac{p}{100}$

$185 \cdot p = 74 \cdot 100$

$\dfrac{185 \cdot p}{185} = \dfrac{7400}{185}$

$p = 40$

The percent is 40%.

6.3 Section Exercises

3. $\dfrac{a}{b} = \dfrac{p}{100}$ $a = 60, p = 50$

$\dfrac{60}{b} = \dfrac{50}{100}$

$b \cdot 50 = 60 \cdot 100$

$\dfrac{b \cdot 50}{50} = \dfrac{6000}{50}$

$b = 120$

7. $\dfrac{a}{b} = \dfrac{p}{100}$ $a = 25, p = 6$

$\dfrac{25}{b} = \dfrac{6}{100}$

$\dfrac{25}{b} = \dfrac{3}{50}$ *Lowest terms*

$3 \cdot b = 25 \cdot 50$

$3 \cdot b = 1250$

$\dfrac{3 \cdot b}{3} = \dfrac{1250}{3}$

$b \approx 416.7$

11. $\dfrac{a}{b} = \dfrac{p}{100}$ $a = 105, b = 35$

$\dfrac{105}{35} = \dfrac{p}{100}$

$\dfrac{3}{1} = \dfrac{p}{100}$ *Lowest terms*

$1 \cdot p = 3 \cdot 100$

$p = 300$

The percent is 300%.

15. $\dfrac{a}{b} = \dfrac{p}{100}$ $b = 52, p = 50$

$\dfrac{a}{52} = \dfrac{50}{100}$

$\dfrac{a}{52} = \dfrac{1}{2}$ *Lowest terms*

$2 \cdot a = 52 \cdot 1$

$\dfrac{2 \cdot a}{2} = \dfrac{52}{2}$

$a = 26$

19. $\dfrac{a}{b} = \dfrac{p}{100}$ $b = 47.2, p = 28$

$\dfrac{a}{47.2} = \dfrac{28}{100}$

$\dfrac{a}{47.2} = \dfrac{7}{25}$ *Lowest terms*

$25 \cdot a = 7 \cdot 47.2$

$\dfrac{25 \cdot a}{25} = \dfrac{330.4}{25}$

$a \approx 13.2$

23. $\dfrac{a}{b} = \dfrac{p}{100}$ $a = 89, p = 25$

$\dfrac{89}{b} = \dfrac{25}{100}$

$\dfrac{89}{b} = \dfrac{1}{4}$ *Lowest terms*

$1 \cdot b = 89 \cdot 4$

$b = 356$

27. $\dfrac{a}{b} = \dfrac{p}{100}$

$\dfrac{53.75}{2150} = \dfrac{p}{100}$

$2150 \cdot p = 100 \cdot 53.75$

$\dfrac{2150 \cdot p}{2150} = \dfrac{5375}{2150}$

$p = 2.5$

The percent is 2.5%.

31. $\dfrac{1}{2} = \dfrac{1 \cdot 50}{2 \cdot 50} = \dfrac{50}{100} = 0.50 = 50\%$

35. $\dfrac{7}{8} = 0.875 = 87.5\%$

6.4 Identifying the Parts in a Percent Problem

6.4 Margin Exercises

1. **(a)** Of the $2000, 15% will be spent on a washing machine.

    p is 15.

    (b) Of the 750 employees, 8% will retire.

    p is 8.

    (c) Find the sales tax by multiplying $590 and $6\frac{1}{2}$ percent.

    p is $6\frac{1}{2}$.

    (d) 105 is 3% of what number?

    p is 3.

    (e) What percent of the 110 rental cars will be sold today?
    The problem asks what percent.
    p is unknown.

2. **(a)** b is $2000.

    (b) b is 750.

    (c) b is $590.

    (d) b is what number (an unknown).

    (e) b is 110.

3. **(a)** Of the $2000, 15% will be spent on a $300 washing machine.

    a is $300.

    (b) Of the 750 employees, 8%, or 60 employees will retire.

    a is 60.

    (c) Find the sales tax of $38.35 by multiplying $590 and $6\frac{1}{2}$ percent.

    a is $38.35.

    (d) $105 is 3% of what number?

    a is $105.

    (e) 90% of the 110 rental cars will be rented today.

    a is unknown.

6.4 Section Exercises

3. 80% of $950 is $760.
     ↑   ↑   ↑
     a p b
     80   950   760

7. 9 is 36% what number of guests?
   ↑   ↑   ↑
   a p b
   9   36   unknown

11. What percent of $296 is $177.60?
    ↑   ↑   ↑
    p b a
    unknown   296   177.6

15. 0.68% of 487 is what number?
    ↑   ↑   ↑
    p b a
    0.68   487   unknown

19. What percent of 810 trees is 640 trees?
    ↑   ↑   ↑
    p b a
    unknown   810   640

23. 23% prefer fat-free dressing   610 is the total number of customers   the number of customers who prefer fat-free dressing
    ↑   ↑   ↑
    p b a
    23   610   unknown

27. 78% of the students   a survey of 650 students   the number of students who consider this a high priority
    ↑   ↑   ↑
    p b a
    78   650   unknown

31. 16.8% were late   total number of patients   504 patients were late
    ↑   ↑   ↑
    p b a
    16.8   unknown   504

Section 6.5 Using Proportions to Solve Percent Problems

35. $\dfrac{r}{36} = \dfrac{\frac{4}{3}}{12}$ *proportion*

$12 \cdot r = \dfrac{4}{3} \cdot \dfrac{36}{1}$

$\dfrac{12 \cdot r}{12} = \dfrac{48}{12}$

$r = 4$ *missing number*

6.5 Using Proportions to Solve Percent Problems

6.5 Margin Exercises

1. **(a)** p is 20; b is 1800; a is unknown.

$$\dfrac{a}{b} = \dfrac{p}{100}$$

$$\dfrac{a}{1800} = \dfrac{20}{100}$$

$$100 \cdot a = 20 \cdot 1800$$

$$\dfrac{100 \cdot a}{100} = \dfrac{36{,}000}{100}$$

$$a = 360$$

20% of 1800 calories is 360 calories.

(b) b is 2032; p is 25; a is unknown.

$$\dfrac{a}{b} = \dfrac{p}{100}$$

$$\dfrac{a}{2032} = \dfrac{25}{100}$$

$$100 \cdot a = 25 \cdot 2032$$

$$\dfrac{100 \cdot a}{100} = \dfrac{50{,}800}{100}$$

$$a = 508$$

25% of $2032 is $508.

(c) p is 9; b is 3250; a is unknown.

$$\dfrac{a}{b} = \dfrac{p}{100}$$

$$\dfrac{a}{3250} = \dfrac{9}{100}$$

$$100 \cdot a = 9 \cdot 3250$$

$$\dfrac{100 \cdot a}{100} = \dfrac{29{,}250}{100}$$

$$a = 292.5$$

9% of 3250 miles is 292.5 miles.

(d) p is 78; b is 610; a is unknown.

$$\dfrac{a}{b} = \dfrac{p}{100}$$

$$\dfrac{a}{610} = \dfrac{78}{100}$$

$$100 \cdot a = 78 \cdot 610$$

$$\dfrac{100 \cdot a}{100} = \dfrac{47{,}580}{100}$$

$$a = 475.8$$

78% of 610 meters is 475.8 meters.

2. **(a)** 45% of 6000 hogs
Write the percent as a decimal.

$$45\% = 0.45$$

Multiply 0.45 and 6000.

$$a = 0.45 \cdot 6000$$
$$a = 2700 \text{ hogs}$$

(b) 18% of 80 feet
Write the percent as a decimal.

$$18\% = 0.18$$

Multiply 0.18 and 80.

$$a = 0.18 \cdot 80$$
$$a = 14.4 \text{ feet}$$

(c) 125% of 78 acres
Write the percent as a decimal.

$$125\% = 1.25$$

Multiply 1.25 and 78.

$$a = 1.25 \cdot 78$$
$$a = 97.5 \text{ acres}$$

(d) 0.6% of $120
Write the percent as a decimal.

$$0.6\% = 0.006$$

Multiply 0.006 and 120.

$$a = 0.006 \cdot 120$$
$$a = \$0.72$$

3. (a) 35% of 1460 people

$$a = 0.35 \cdot 1460$$
$$a = 511$$

35% of 1460 people is 511 people.

(b) 28% of 9250 students

$$a = 0.28 \cdot 9250$$
$$a = 2590$$

28% of 9250 students is 2590 students.

4. (a) a is 75; p is 20; b is unknown.

$$\frac{a}{b} = \frac{p}{100}$$
$$\frac{75}{b} = \frac{20}{100}$$
$$\frac{75}{b} = \frac{1}{5} \quad \text{Lowest terms}$$
$$1 \cdot b = 5 \cdot 75$$
$$b = 375$$

75 bidders is 20% of 375 bidders.

(b) a is 30; p is 15; b is unknown.

$$\frac{a}{b} = \frac{p}{100}$$
$$\frac{30}{b} = \frac{15}{100}$$
$$15 \cdot b = 30 \cdot 100$$
$$\frac{15 \cdot b}{15} = \frac{3000}{15}$$
$$b = 200$$

30 lines is 15% of 200 lines.

(c) a is 774; p is 72; b is unknown.

$$\frac{a}{b} = \frac{p}{100}$$
$$\frac{774}{b} = \frac{72}{100}$$
$$72 \cdot b = 774 \cdot 100$$
$$\frac{72 \cdot b}{72} = \frac{77,400}{72}$$
$$b = 1075$$

774 is 72% of 1075 employees.

(d) a is 97.5; p is 12.5; b is unknown.

$$\frac{a}{b} = \frac{p}{100}$$
$$\frac{97.5}{b} = \frac{12.5}{100}$$
$$12.5 \cdot b = 97.5 \cdot 100$$
$$\frac{12.5 \cdot b}{12.5} = \frac{9750}{12.5}$$
$$b = 780$$

97.5 miles is 12.5% of the 780 miles.

5. (a) The percent, p, of the loss is 52% and the amount, a, of the total loss is 182 tons.

$$\frac{a}{b} = \frac{p}{100}$$
$$\frac{182}{b} = \frac{52}{100}$$
$$52 \cdot b = 182 \cdot 100$$
$$\frac{52 \cdot b}{52} = \frac{18,200}{52}$$
$$b = 350$$

The total number of tons in the crop was 350 tons.

(b) The percent, p, is 8% and the amount, a, of the total weight is 450 pounds.

$$\frac{a}{b} = \frac{p}{100}$$
$$\frac{450}{b} = \frac{8}{100}$$
$$\frac{8 \cdot b}{8} = \frac{45,000}{8}$$
$$b = 5625$$

The total weight of the alloy is 5625 pounds.

6. (a) a is 7; b is 28; p is unknown.

$$\frac{a}{b} = \frac{p}{100}$$
$$\frac{7}{28} = \frac{p}{100}$$
$$\frac{1}{4} = \frac{p}{100} \quad \text{Lowest terms}$$
$$\frac{4 \cdot p}{4} = \frac{100}{4}$$
$$p = 25$$

$7 is 25% of $28.

Section 6.5 Using Proportions to Solve Percent Problems

(b) a is 30; b is 150; p is unknown.

$$\frac{a}{b} = \frac{p}{100}$$

$$\frac{30}{150} = \frac{p}{100}$$

$$\frac{1}{5} = \frac{p}{100} \quad \text{Lowest terms}$$

$$\frac{5 \cdot p}{5} = \frac{100}{5}$$

$$p = 20$$

20% of 150 athletes is 30 athletes.

(c) a is 1026; b is 2280; p is unknown.

$$\frac{a}{b} = \frac{p}{100}$$

$$\frac{1026}{2280} = \frac{p}{100}$$

$$2280 \cdot p = 1026 \cdot 100$$

$$\frac{2280 \cdot p}{2280} = \frac{102{,}600}{2280}$$

$$p = 45$$

45% of the 2280 court trials in 1026 trials.

(d) a is 72; b is 18; p is unknown.

$$\frac{a}{b} = \frac{p}{100}$$

$$\frac{72}{18} = \frac{p}{100}$$

$$\frac{18 \cdot p}{18} = \frac{7200}{18}$$

$$p = 400$$

72 sales is 400% of 18 sales.

7. (a) a is 578; b is 850; p is unknown.

$$\frac{a}{b} = \frac{p}{100}$$

$$\frac{578}{850} = \frac{p}{100}$$

$$\frac{850 \cdot p}{850} = \frac{57{,}800}{850}$$

$$p = 68$$

$578 is 68% of $850.

(b) a is 32.3; b is 38; p is unknown.

$$\frac{a}{b} = \frac{p}{100}$$

$$\frac{32.3}{38} = \frac{p}{100}$$

$$\frac{38 \cdot p}{38} = \frac{3230}{38}$$

$$p = 85$$

32.3 miles per gallon is 85% of 38 miles per gallon.

8. (a) a is 450; b is 300; p is unknown.

$$\frac{a}{b} = \frac{p}{100}$$

$$\frac{450}{300} = \frac{p}{100}$$

$$\frac{3}{2} = \frac{p}{100} \quad \text{Lowest terms}$$

$$\frac{2 \cdot p}{2} = \frac{300}{2}$$

$$p = 150$$

450 students is 150% of 300 students.

(b) a is 600; b is 480; p is unknown.

$$\frac{a}{b} = \frac{p}{100}$$

$$\frac{600}{480} = \frac{p}{100}$$

$$\frac{5}{4} = \frac{p}{100} \quad \text{Lowest terms}$$

$$\frac{4 \cdot p}{4} = \frac{500}{4}$$

$$p = 125$$

600 units 125% of 480 units.

6.5 Section Exercises

3. 35% of 2340 volunteers

$$0.35 \cdot 2340 = 819$$
$$a = 819 \text{ volunteers}$$

7. 125% of 108 folders

$$1.25 \cdot 108 = 135$$
$$a = 135 \text{ folders}$$

11. 2% of $164

$$0.02 \cdot 164 = 3.28$$
$$a = \$3.28$$

15. 15.5% of 275 pounds

$$0.155 \cdot 275 = 42.625$$
$$a = 42.625 \text{ pounds}$$

19. a is 40; p is 25; b is unknown.

$$\frac{a}{b} = \frac{p}{100}$$
$$\frac{40}{b} = \frac{25}{100}$$
$$\frac{40}{b} = \frac{1}{4} \quad \textit{Lowest terms}$$
$$b = 40 \cdot 4$$
$$b = 160$$

40 printers is 25% of 160 printers.

23. a is 495; p is 90; b is unknown.

$$\frac{a}{b} = \frac{p}{100}$$
$$\frac{495}{b} = \frac{90}{100}$$
$$90 \cdot b = 495 \cdot 100$$
$$\frac{90 \cdot b}{90} = \frac{49,500}{90}$$
$$b = 550$$

495 successful students is 90% of 550 students.

27. a is 350; p is 12.5; b is unknown.

$$\frac{a}{b} = \frac{p}{100}$$
$$\frac{350}{b} = \frac{12.5}{100}$$
$$12.5 \cdot b = 35,000$$
$$\frac{12.5 \cdot b}{12.5} = \frac{35,000}{12.5}$$
$$b = 2800$$

$12\frac{1}{2}\%$ of 2800 is 350.

31. a is 13; b is 25; p is unknown.

$$\frac{a}{b} = \frac{p}{100}$$
$$\frac{13}{25} = \frac{p}{100}$$
$$25 \cdot p = 13 \cdot 100$$
$$\frac{25 \cdot p}{25} = \frac{1300}{25}$$
$$p = 52$$

13 tables is 52% of 25 tables.

35. a is 9; b is 600; p is unknown.

$$\frac{a}{b} = \frac{p}{100}$$
$$\frac{9}{600} = \frac{p}{100}$$
$$600 \cdot p = 9 \cdot 100$$
$$\frac{600 \cdot p}{600} = \frac{900}{600}$$
$$p = 1.5$$

9 rolls is 1.5% of 600 rolls.

39. a is 46; b is 500; p is unknown.

$$\frac{a}{b} = \frac{p}{100}$$
$$\frac{46}{500} = \frac{p}{100}$$
$$500 \cdot p = 46 \cdot 100$$
$$\frac{500 \cdot p}{500} = \frac{4600}{500}$$
$$p = 9.2$$

500 wheels is 9.2% of 46 wheels.

43. a is unknown; b is \$110; p is 18.

$$\frac{a}{b} = \frac{p}{100}$$
$$\frac{a}{110} = \frac{18}{100}$$
$$100 \cdot a = 18 \cdot 110$$
$$\frac{100 \cdot a}{100} = \frac{1980}{100}$$
$$a = 19.8$$

The amount withheld is \$19.80.

47. a is unknown; b is 550; p is 40.

$$\frac{a}{b} = \frac{p}{100}$$
$$\frac{a}{550} = \frac{40}{100}$$
$$\frac{a}{550} = \frac{2}{5}$$
$$5 \cdot a = 2 \cdot 550$$
$$\frac{5 \cdot a}{5} = \frac{1100}{5}$$
$$a = 220$$

The number of students who will receive scholarships is 220.

51. a is \$117,000; b is \$755,000; p is unknown.

$$\frac{a}{b} = \frac{p}{100}$$

$$\frac{117{,}000}{755{,}000} = \frac{p}{100}$$

$$755{,}000 \cdot p = 100 \cdot 117{,}000$$

$$\frac{755{,}000 \cdot p}{755{,}000} = \frac{11{,}700{,}000}{755{,}000}$$

$$p = 15.496689$$

$$p \approx 15.5$$

$\approx 15.5\%$ of the total sales will be spent on delivery.

55. a is $2{,}618{,}000$; b is $2{,}380{,}000$; p is unknown.

$$\frac{a}{b} = \frac{p}{100}$$

$$\frac{2{,}618{,}000}{2{,}380{,}000} = \frac{p}{100}$$

$$\frac{1309}{1190} = \frac{p}{100} \quad \text{Lowest terms}$$

$$\frac{1190 \cdot p}{1190} = \frac{1309 \cdot 100}{1190}$$

$$p = 110$$

110% of the goal has been reached.

59. The graph shows that *March* had sales of 7% which is the lowest for the flu season months.

63. p is 20; b is 3100; a is unknown.

$$\frac{a}{b} = \frac{p}{100}$$

$$\frac{a}{3100} = \frac{20}{100}$$

$$\frac{a}{3100} = \frac{1}{5} \quad \text{Lowest terms}$$

$$\frac{5 \cdot a}{5} = \frac{3100}{5}$$

$$a = 620$$

Add the application fee.

$$\$620 + \$25 = \$645$$

The total charge is \$645.

67.
```
        38.04    ← 2 decimals
     ×   0.52    ← 2 decimals
        76 08
       19 02 0
       19.78 08  ← 4 decimals
```

71. $306 \div 0.085$

```
              3 600
    0.085∧)306.000∧    Move the decimal
           255          point three places
           51 0         to the right; write
           51 0         3 0's
              0
              0
              0
              0
              0
```

6.6 The Percent Equation

6.6 Margin Exercises

1. Use amount = percent · base.
   Write the percent as a decimal.

   (a) 28% of 1050 garments

   $$a = 0.28 \cdot 1050$$
   $$a = 294$$

   28% of 1050 garments is 294 garments.

   (b) 19% of 360 pages

   $$a = 0.19 \cdot 360$$
   $$a = 68.4$$

   19% of 360 pages is 68.4 pages.

   (c) 125% of \$84

   $$a = 1.25 \cdot 84$$
   $$a = 105$$

   125% of \$84 is \$105.

   (d) 145% of \$580

   $$a = 1.45 \cdot 580$$
   $$a = 841$$

   145% of \$580 is \$841.

   (e) 0.5% of 600 samples

   $$a = 0.005 \cdot 600$$
   $$a = 3$$

   0.5% of 600 samples is 3 samples.

(f) 0.25% of 160 pounds

$$a = 0.0025 \cdot 160$$
$$a = 0.4$$

0.25% 160 pounds is 0.4 pound.

2. Use amount = percent · base.
Write the percent as a decimal.

(a) 24 is 15% of what number?

$$24 = 0.15 \cdot b$$
$$\frac{24}{0.15} = \frac{0.15 \cdot b}{0.15}$$
$$160 = b$$

24 patients is 15% of 160 patients.

(b) 22.5 is 18% of what number?

$$22.5 = 0.18 \cdot b$$
$$\frac{22.5}{0.18} = \frac{0.18 \cdot b}{0.18}$$
$$125 = b$$

22.5 boxes is 18% of 125 boxes.

(c) 270 is 45% of what number?

$$270 = 0.45 \cdot b$$
$$\frac{270}{0.45} = \frac{0.45 \cdot b}{0.45}$$
$$600 = b$$

270 lab tests is 45% of 600 lab tests.

(d) $5\frac{1}{2}$% of what number is 66?

$$66 = 0.055 \cdot b \quad 5\tfrac{1}{2}\% = 0.055$$
$$\frac{66}{0.055} = \frac{0.055 \cdot b}{0.055}$$
$$1200 = b$$

$5\frac{1}{2}$% of 1200 policies is 66 policies.

3. Use amount = percent·base.
Use p for percent.

(a) The amount is 18 and the base is 90.

$$18 = p \cdot 90$$
$$\frac{18}{90} = \frac{p \cdot 90}{90}$$
$$0.2 = p$$
$$0.2 = 20\% \quad \text{Write decimal as percent}$$

20% of 90 pallets is 18 pallets.

(b) The amount is 68 and the base is 170.

$$68 = p \cdot 170$$
$$\frac{68}{170} = \frac{p \cdot 170}{170}$$
$$0.4 = p$$
$$0.4 = 40\% \quad \text{Write decimal as percent}$$

68 cartons is 40% of 170 cartons.

(c) The amount is 644 and the base is 460.

$$644 = p \cdot 460$$
$$\frac{644}{460} = \frac{p \cdot 460}{460}$$
$$1.4 = p$$
$$1.4 = 140\% \quad \text{Write decimal as percent}$$

644 orders is 140% of 460 orders.

(d) The amount is 3 and the base is 375.

$$3 = p \cdot 375$$
$$\frac{3}{375} = \frac{p \cdot 375}{375}$$
$$0.008 = p$$
$$0.008 = 0.8\% \quad \text{Write decimal as percent}$$

3 sacks is 0.8% of 375 sacks.

6.6 Section Exercises

3. amount = percent · base
$$a = 0.65 \cdot 1300 \quad 65\% = 0.65$$
$$a = 845$$

65% of 1300 species is 845 species.

7. amount = percent · base
$$a = 1.4 \cdot 500 \quad 140\% = 1.4$$
$$a = 700$$

700 tablets is 140 percent of 500 tablets.

11. amount = percent · base
$$a = 0.008 \cdot 520 \quad 0.8\% = 0.008$$
$$a = 4.16$$

$4.16 is 0.8% of $520.

Section 6.7 Applications of Percent

15. $amount = percent \cdot base$
$$130 = 0.40 \cdot b \quad 40\% = 0.40$$
$$\frac{130}{0.40} = \frac{0.40 \cdot b}{0.40}$$
$$325 = b$$

40% of 325 salads is 130 salads.

19. $amount = percent \cdot base$
$$135 = 0.125 \cdot b \quad 12\tfrac{1}{2}\% = 0.125$$
$$\frac{135}{0.125} = \frac{0.125}{0.125} \cdot b$$
$$1080 = b$$

$12\tfrac{1}{2}\%$ of 1080 people is 135 people.

23. $amount = percent \cdot base$
$$70 = p \cdot 140$$
$$\frac{70}{140} = \frac{p \cdot 140}{140}$$
$$0.5 = p$$
$$0.5 = 50\%$$

70 truckloads is 50% of 140 truckloads.

27. $amount = percent \cdot base$
$$330 = p \cdot 264$$
$$\frac{330}{264} = \frac{p \cdot 264}{264}$$
$$1.25 = p$$
$$1.25 = 125\%$$

125% of $264 is $330.

31. $amount = percent \cdot base$
$$999 = p \cdot 740$$
$$\frac{999}{740} = \frac{p \cdot 740}{740}$$
$$1.35 = p$$
$$1.35 = 135\%$$

999 is 135% of 740.

35. 79% of 104.2 million homes

$$amount = percent \cdot base$$
$$a = 0.79 \cdot 104.2$$
$$a \approx 82.3$$

The number of homes that have WD-40 in them is ≈ 82.3 million homes.

39. Six cans is what percent of 123 cans?

$$amount = percent \cdot base$$
$$6 = p \cdot 123$$
$$\frac{6}{123} = \frac{p \cdot 123}{123}$$
$$0.049 \approx p$$
$$0.049 \approx 4.9\%$$

$\approx 4.9\%$ of the cans contained this level of mercury.

43. 220,917 is 46.2% of what number?

$$amount = percent \cdot base$$
$$220,917 = 0.462 \cdot b$$
$$\frac{220,917}{0.462} = \frac{0.462}{0.462} \cdot b$$
$$478,175 \approx b$$

That year $\approx 478,175$ Mustangs were sold.

47. Find the sales tax.

$$amount = percent \cdot base$$
$$a = 0.0775 \cdot 559 \quad 7\tfrac{3}{4}\% = 0.0775$$
$$a \approx 43.32$$

Add the sales tax to the purchase price.

$$\$559 + \approx \$43.32 \approx \$602.32$$

Subtract the trade-in.

$$\approx \$602.32 - \$125 \approx \$477.32$$

The total cost to the customer is $\approx \$477.32$.

51. 72 jockeys is 18% of what number of jockeys?
p is 18; b is unknown; a is 72.

6.7 Applications of Percent

6.7 Margin Exercises

1. Use the sales formula:
   $amount\ of\ sales\ tax$
   $= rate\ of\ tax \cdot cost\ of\ item.$

   (a) The cost of the radio is $59. The sales tax rate is 6%.

   $$amount\ of\ sales\ tax = 6\% \cdot \$59$$
   $$= 0.06 \cdot \$59$$
   $$= \$3.54$$

   The total cost is $\$59 + \$3.54 = \$62.54$.

(b) The cost of the camcorder is $495. The sales tax rate is 6%.

$$\text{amount of tax} = 6\% \cdot \$495$$
$$= 0.06 \cdot \$495$$
$$= \$29.70$$

The total cost is $495 + \$29.70 = \$524.70$.

(c) The cost of the sofa and chair is $1287. The tax rate is 6%.

$$\text{amount of sales tax} = 6\% \cdot \$1287$$
$$= 0.06 \cdot \$1287$$
$$= \$77.22$$

The total cost is $1287 + \$77.22 = \$1364.22$.

(d) The cost of the automobile is $21,400. The tax rate is 6%.

$$\text{amount of sales tax} = 6\% \cdot \$21,400$$
$$= 0.06 \cdot \$21,400$$
$$= \$1284$$

The total cost is $21,400 + \$1284 = \$22,684$.

2. Use the sales tax formula.
$$\text{sales tax} = \text{rate of tax} \cdot \text{cost of item}.$$

(a) The tax on a $380 desk is $19.

$$\$19 = r \cdot \$380$$
$$\frac{19}{380} = \frac{r \cdot 380}{380}$$
$$0.05 = r$$
$$0.05 = 5\%$$

The tax rate is 5%.

(b) The tax on a $12 pair of running shorts is $0.78.

$$\$0.78 = r \cdot \$12$$
$$0.78 = r \cdot 12$$
$$\frac{0.78}{12} = \frac{r \cdot 12}{12}$$
$$0.065 = r$$
$$0.065 = 6.5\% \text{ or } 6\tfrac{1}{2}\%$$

The tax rate is 6.5% or $6\tfrac{1}{2}\%$.

(c) The tax on a $12,320 refrigeration case is $862.40.

$$\$862.40 = r \cdot \$12,320$$
$$\frac{862.4}{12,320} = \frac{r \cdot 12,320}{12,320}$$
$$0.07 = r$$
$$0.07 = 7\%$$

The tax rate is 7%.

3. Commission formula
$$\text{amount of commission}$$
$$= \text{rate or percent of commission}$$
$$\cdot \text{ amount of sales}$$

(a) Rate of commission is 7%; sales are $48,350.

$$\text{amount} = 7\% \cdot \$48,350$$
$$= 0.07 \cdot \$48,350$$
$$= \$3384.50$$

Freida earned a commission of $3384.50 for selling office products.

(b) Rate of commission is 3%; sales are $62,500.

$$\text{amount} = 3\% \cdot \$62,500$$
$$= 0.03 \cdot \$62,500$$
$$= \$1875$$

Angie earned a commission of $1875 for selling appliances.

4. Use the percent proportion.
(a) A commission of $450 and sales worth $22,500: $a = 450$; $b = 22,500$.

$$\frac{a}{b} = \frac{p}{100}$$
$$\frac{450}{22,500} = \frac{p}{100}$$
$$22,500 \cdot p = 450 \cdot 100$$
$$\frac{22,500 \cdot p}{22,500} = \frac{45,000}{22,500}$$
$$p = 2$$

The rate of commission is 2%.

Section 6.7 Applications of Percent

(b) A commission of $2898 and sales worth $32,200:
$a = 2898$; $b = 32,200$.

$$\frac{a}{b} = \frac{p}{100}$$

$$\frac{2898}{32,200} = \frac{p}{100}$$

$$32,200 \cdot p = 2898 \cdot 100$$

$$\frac{32,200 \cdot p}{32,200} = \frac{289,800}{32,200}$$

$$p = 9$$

The rate of commission is 9%.

5. (a) 35% discount on a leather recliner priced at $950

$$\begin{aligned} \text{amount of discount} &= \text{rate of discount} \\ &\quad \cdot \text{original price} \\ &= 0.35 \cdot \$950 \\ &= \$332.50 \end{aligned}$$

$$\begin{aligned} \text{sale price} &= \text{original price} \\ &\quad - \text{amount of discount} \\ &= \$950 - \$332.50 \\ &= \$617.50 \end{aligned}$$

The sale price for the Easy-Boy leather recliner is $617.50.

(b) 40% discount on a swimsuit priced at $34

$$\begin{aligned} \text{amount of discount} &= 0.40 \cdot \$34 \\ &= \$13.60 \end{aligned}$$

$$\begin{aligned} \text{sale price} &= \$34 - \$13.60 \\ &= \$20.40 \end{aligned}$$

6. (a) Production increased from 9400 units to 12,690 units.

increase $= 12,690 - 9400 = 3290$

$$\frac{\text{increase}}{\text{original}} = \frac{p}{100} \quad \begin{array}{l} \textit{Percent} \\ \textit{proportion} \end{array}$$

$$\frac{3290}{9400} = \frac{p}{100}$$

$$9400 \cdot p = 3290 \cdot 100$$

$$\frac{9400 \cdot p}{9400} = \frac{329,000}{9400}$$

$$p = 35$$

The percent of increase is 35%.

(b) Flu cases rose from 496 cases to 620 cases.

increase $= 620 - 496 = 124$

$$\frac{124}{496} = \frac{p}{100}$$

$$496 \cdot p = 124 \cdot 100$$

$$\frac{496 \cdot p}{496} = \frac{12,400}{496}$$

$$p = 25$$

The percent of increase is 25%.

7. (a) The number of employees decreased from 380 to 285.

decrease $= 380 - 285 = 95$

$$\frac{\text{decrease}}{\text{original}} = \frac{p}{100}$$

$$\frac{95}{380} = \frac{p}{100}$$

$$380 \cdot p = 95 \cdot 100$$

$$\frac{380 \cdot p}{380} = \frac{9500}{380}$$

$$p = 25$$

The percent of decrease is 25%.

(b) The number of workers decreased from 4850 to 3977.

decrease $= 4850 - 3977 = 873$

$$\frac{873}{4850} = \frac{p}{100}$$

$$4850 \cdot p = 873 \cdot 100$$

$$\frac{4850 \cdot p}{4850} = \frac{87,300}{4850}$$

$$p = 18$$

The percent of decrease is 18%.

6.7 Section Exercises

3. sales tax $=$ rate of tax $\cdot$ cost of item
$$\$2.04 = r \cdot \$68$$
$$\frac{2.04}{68} = \frac{r \cdot 68}{68}$$
$$0.03 = r$$
$$0.03 = 3\% \quad \textit{tax rate}$$

The tax rate is 3% and the total cost is $70.04 ($68 + $2.04).

7. $\text{sales tax} = \text{rate of tax} \cdot \text{cost of item}$
$\phantom{\text{sales tax}} = 5\tfrac{1}{2}\% \cdot \$220$
$\phantom{\text{sales tax}} = 0.055 \cdot \$220$
$\phantom{\text{sales tax}} = \$12.10 \quad \textit{sales tax}$

Sales tax is $12.10 and total cost is $232.10 ($220 + $12.10).

11. $\text{commission} = \text{rate of commission} \cdot \text{sales}$
$\$1200 = p \cdot \$4800$
$\dfrac{1200}{4800} = \dfrac{p \cdot 4800}{4800}$
$0.25 = p$
$0.25 = 25\% \quad \textit{rate of commission}$

The rate of commission is 25%.

15. $\text{commission} = \text{rate of commission} \cdot \text{sales}$
$\phantom{\text{commission}} = 10\% \cdot \$45,250$
$\phantom{\text{commission}} = 0.10 \cdot \$45,250$
$\phantom{\text{commission}} = \$4525 \quad \textit{amount of commission}$

The amount of commission is $4525.

19. $\text{discount} = \text{rate of discount} \cdot \text{original price}$
$\$54 = p \cdot \$180$
$\dfrac{54}{180} = \dfrac{p \cdot 180}{180}$
$0.3 = p$
$0.3 = 30\% \quad \textit{rate of discount}$

The rate of discount is 30% and the sale price is $126 ($180 − $54).

23. $\text{discount} = \text{rate of discount} \cdot \text{original price}$
$\phantom{\text{discount}} = 10\% \cdot \$37.50$
$\phantom{\text{discount}} = 0.10 \cdot \$37.50$
$\phantom{\text{discount}} = \$3.75 \quad \textit{amount of discount}$

The amount of discount is $3.75 and the sale price is $33.75 ($37.50 − $3.75).

27. $\text{sales tax} = \text{rate of tax} \cdot \text{cost of item}$
$\phantom{\text{sales tax}} = 5\% \cdot \$1050$
$\phantom{\text{sales tax}} = 0.05 \cdot \$1050$
$\phantom{\text{sales tax}} = \$52.50$

The sales tax is $52.50.

31. $\text{sales tax} = \text{rate of tax} \cdot \text{cost of item}$
$\$99 = p \cdot \$1980$
$\dfrac{99}{1980} = \dfrac{p \cdot 1980}{1980}$
$0.05 = p$
$0.05 = 5\%$

The rate of sales tax is 5%.

35. The decrease in accidents is $1276 - 989 = 287$ accidents.

$\dfrac{\text{decrease}}{\text{original}} = \dfrac{p}{100}$
$\dfrac{287}{1276} = \dfrac{p}{100}$
$1276 \cdot p = 287 \cdot 100$
$\dfrac{1276 \cdot p}{1276} = \dfrac{28,700}{1276}$
$p \approx 22.5$

The percent of decrease is ≈ 22.5%.

39. She paid a commission of $459 on sales of $7650. Use percent proportion.

$\dfrac{a}{b} = \dfrac{p}{100}$
$\dfrac{459}{7650} = \dfrac{p}{100}$
$7650 \cdot p = 459 \cdot 100$
$\dfrac{7650 \cdot p}{7650} = \dfrac{45,900}{7650}$
$p = 6$

The rate of commission is 6%.

43. The stock decreased $35.50 − $33.50 = $2.00 per share.

$\dfrac{\text{decrease}}{\text{original}} = \dfrac{p}{100}$
$\dfrac{2}{35.50} = \dfrac{p}{100}$
$35.50 \cdot p = 2 \cdot 100$
$\dfrac{35.50 \cdot p}{35.50} = \dfrac{200}{35.50}$
$p \approx 5.6$

The percent of decrease in price is ≈ 5.6%.

47. $sales\ commission = rate\ of\ commission \cdot sales$
$$= 6\% \cdot \$129,605$$
$$= 0.60 \cdot \$129,605$$
$$= \$7776.30$$

$commission\ for\ agent = 55\% \cdot \$7776.30$
$$= 0.55 \cdot \$7776.30$$
$$\approx \$4276.97$$

The agent receives $\approx \$4276.97$.

51. $amount = percent \cdot base$
$$a = 10\% \cdot 780$$
$$a = 0.10 \cdot 780$$
$$a = 78$$

10% of 780 brackets is 78 brackets.

55. $6\frac{1}{4}\%$ of what number is 50?
$$50 = 6\frac{1}{4} \cdot b \quad 6\frac{1}{4} = 0.0625$$
$$50 = 0.0625 \cdot b$$
$$\frac{50}{0.0625} = \frac{0.0625 \cdot b}{0.0625}$$
$$800 = b$$

$6\frac{1}{4}\%$ of 800 is 50.

6.8 Simple Interest

6.8 Margin Exercises

1. (a) $500 at 4% for 1 year
$$I = p \cdot r \cdot t$$
$$= 500 \cdot (0.04) \cdot 1$$
$$= 20$$

The interest is $20.

(b) $1850 at 6% for 1 year
$$I = p \cdot r \cdot t$$
$$= 1850 \cdot (0.06) \cdot 1$$
$$= 111$$

The interest is $111.

2. (a) $340 at 5% for $3\frac{1}{2}$ years
$$I = p \cdot r \cdot t$$
$$= 340 \cdot (0.05) \cdot (3.5)$$
$$= 59.5$$

The interest is $59.50.

(b) $2450 at 8% for $3\frac{1}{4}$ years
$$I = p \cdot r \cdot t$$
$$= 2450 \cdot (0.08) \cdot (3.25)$$
$$= 637$$

The interest is $637.

(c) $14,200 at 6% for $2\frac{3}{4}$ years
$$I = p \cdot r \cdot t$$
$$= 14,200 \cdot (0.06) \cdot (2.75)$$
$$= 2343$$

The interest is $2343.

3. (a) $1500 at 7% for 4 months
$$I = p \cdot r \cdot t$$
$$= 1500 \cdot (0.07) \cdot \frac{4}{12} \quad \begin{array}{l}4\ months \\ = \frac{4}{12}\ year\end{array}$$
$$= 105 \cdot \frac{1}{3} \quad Lowest\ terms$$
$$= \frac{105}{3} = 35$$

The interest is $35.

(b) $25,000 at $10\frac{1}{2}\%$ for 3 months
$$I = p \cdot r \cdot t$$
$$= 25,000 \cdot (0.105) \cdot \frac{3}{12}$$
$$= 2625 \cdot \frac{1}{4} \quad Lowest\ terms$$
$$= \frac{2625}{4} = 656.25$$

The interest is $656.25.

4. (a) $2500 at $7\frac{1}{2}\%$ for 6 months
$$I = p \cdot r \cdot t$$
$$= 2500 \cdot (0.075) \cdot \frac{6}{12}$$
$$= 187.5 \cdot \frac{1}{2} \quad Lowest\ terms$$
$$= \frac{187.5}{2} = 93.75$$

The interest is $93.75.

$amount\ due = principal + interest$
$$= \$2500 + \$93.75$$
$$= \$2593.75$$

The total amount due is $2593.75.

(b) $10,800 at 6% for 4 years

$$\begin{aligned} I &= p \cdot r \cdot t \\ &= 10,800 \cdot (0.06) \cdot 4 \\ &= 648 \cdot 4 \\ &= 2592 \end{aligned}$$

The interest is $2592.

$$\begin{aligned} amount\ due &= principal + interest \\ &= \$10,800 + \$2592 \\ &= \$13,392 \end{aligned}$$

The total amount due is $13,392.

(c) $4300 at 10% for $2\frac{1}{2}$ years

$$\begin{aligned} I &= p \cdot r \cdot t \\ &= 4300 \cdot (0.10) \cdot 2.5 \\ &= 430 \cdot 2.5 \\ &= 1075 \end{aligned}$$

The interest is $1075.

$$\begin{aligned} amount\ due &= principal + interest \\ &= \$4300 + \$1075 \\ &= \$5375 \end{aligned}$$

The total amount due is $5375.

6.8 Section Exercises

3. $600 at 6% for 4 years

$$\begin{aligned} I &= p \cdot r \cdot t \\ &= 600 \cdot (0.06) \cdot 4 \\ &= 144 \end{aligned}$$

The interest is $144.

7. $2300 at $8\frac{1}{2}$% for $2\frac{1}{2}$ years

$$\begin{aligned} I &= p \cdot r \cdot t \\ &= 2300 \cdot (0.085) \cdot 2.5 \\ &= 488.75 \end{aligned}$$

The interest is $488.75.

11. $200 at 6% for 6 months

$$\begin{aligned} I &= p \cdot r \cdot t \\ &= 200 \cdot (0.06) \cdot \frac{6}{12} \\ &= 12 \cdot \frac{1}{2} \quad \text{Lowest terms} \\ &= \frac{12}{2} = 6 \end{aligned}$$

The interest is $6.

15. $820 at 8% for 24 months

$$\begin{aligned} I &= p \cdot r \cdot t \\ &= 820 \cdot (0.08) \cdot 2 \quad \begin{array}{l} 24\ months \\ = 2\ years \end{array} \\ &= 65.6 \cdot 2 \\ &= 131.2 \end{aligned}$$

The interest is $131.20.

19. $15,000 at $7\frac{1}{4}$% for 7 months

$$\begin{aligned} I &= p \cdot r \cdot t \\ &= 15,000 \cdot (0.0725) \cdot \frac{7}{12} \\ &= 1087.5 \cdot \frac{7}{12} \\ &= \frac{7612.5}{12} \approx 634.38 \end{aligned}$$

The interest is $\approx$ $634.38.

23. $740 at 6% for 9 months

$$\begin{aligned} I &= p \cdot r \cdot t \\ &= 740 \cdot (0.06) \cdot \frac{9}{12} \\ &= 44.4 \cdot \frac{3}{4} \quad \text{Lowest terms} \\ &= \frac{133.2}{4} = 33.3 \end{aligned}$$

The interest is $33.30.

$$\begin{aligned} amount\ due &= principal + interest \\ &= \$740 + \$33.30 \\ &= \$773.30 \end{aligned}$$

The total amount due is $773.30.

27. $2450 at 7% for 6 months

$$\begin{aligned} I &= p \cdot r \cdot t \\ &= 2450 \cdot (0.07) \cdot \frac{6}{12} \quad \tfrac{6}{12} = 0.5 \\ &= 171.5 \cdot 0.5 \\ &= 85.75 \end{aligned}$$

The interest is $85.75.

$$\begin{aligned} amount\ due &= principal + interest \\ &= \$2450 + \$85.75 \\ &= \$2535.75 \end{aligned}$$

The total amount due is $2535.75

Section 6.9 Compound Interest

31. The answer should include:
Amount of principal—This is the amount of money borrowed or loaned.
Interest rate—This is the percent used to calculate the interest.
Time of loan—The length of time that money is loaned or borrowed is an important factor in determining interest.

35. $50,000 at 9% for 18 months

$$\begin{aligned} I &= p \cdot r \cdot t \\ &= 50{,}000 \cdot (0.09) \cdot \frac{8}{12} \\ &= 4500 \cdot 1.5 \\ &= 6750 \end{aligned}$$

The bank will earn $6750.

39. $7840 at $5\frac{1}{2}$% for 9 months

$$\begin{aligned} I &= p \cdot r \cdot t \\ &= 7840 \cdot (0.055) \cdot \frac{9}{12} \\ &= 431.2 \cdot 0.75 \\ &= 323.4 \end{aligned}$$

Norell will earn $323.40

43. $11,500 at $8\frac{3}{4}$% for $\frac{3}{4}$ year

$$\begin{aligned} I &= p \cdot r \cdot t \\ &= 11{,}500 \cdot (0.0875) \cdot 0.75 \\ &= 1006.25 \cdot 0.75 \\ &= 754.6875 \\ &\approx 754.69 \end{aligned}$$

The total amount in the account is $\approx \$12{,}254.69$ ($11,500 + \approx $754.69).

47. $\dfrac{4}{5} = \dfrac{4 \cdot 12}{5 \cdot 12} = \dfrac{48}{60}$

51. $\dfrac{15}{19} = \dfrac{15 \cdot 4}{19 \cdot 4} = \dfrac{60}{76}$

6.9 Compound Interest

6.9 Margin Exercises

1. (a) $500 at 4% for 2 years

Year	Interest
1	$500 \cdot 0.04 \cdot 1 = \$20$
	$\$500 + \$20 = \$520$
	Compound amount
2	$\$520 \cdot 0.04 \cdot 1 = \$20.80$
	$\$520 + \$20.80 = \$540.80$
	Compound amount

The compound amount is $540.80.

(b) $1200 at 3% for 3 years

Year	Interest
1	$\$1200 \cdot 0.03 \cdot 1 = \$36$
	$\$1200 + \$36 = \$1236$
	Compound amount
2	$\$1236 \cdot 0.03 \cdot 1 = \$37.08$
	$\$1236 + \$37.08 = \$1273.08$
	Compound amount
3	$\$1273.08 \cdot 0.03 \cdot 1 \approx \$38.19$
	$\$1273.08 + \approx \$38.19 \approx \$1311.27$
	Compound amount

The compound amount is $\approx \$1311.27$.

2. (a) $1500 at 5% for 3 years

$100\% + 5\% = 105\% = 1.05$
$1500 \cdot 1.05 \cdot 1.05 \cdot 1.05 \approx \$1736.44$

The compound amount is $\approx \$1736.44$.

(b) $900 at 3% for 2 years

$100\% + 3\% = 103\% = 1.03$
$900 \cdot 1.03 \cdot 1.03 = \$954.81$

The compound amount is $954.81.

(c) $2900 at 6% for 4 years

$100\% + 6\% = 106\% = 1.06$
$2900 \cdot 1.06 \cdot 1.06 \cdot 1.06 \cdot 1.06 \approx \$3661.18$

The compound amount is $\approx \$3661.18$.

3. Read from the compound interest table.

(a) $1 at 4% for 12 years: $\approx \$1.60$

(b) $1 at 3% for 5 years: $\approx \$1.16$

(c) $1 at $5\frac{1}{2}$% for 8 years: $\approx \$1.53$

4. Use the table and multiply to find the compound amount. Then subtract the original deposit from the compound amount to find the interest.

   (a) $5000 at 6% for 12 years

   $$\begin{aligned} compound\ amount &= \$5000 \cdot 2.0122 \\ &= \$10,061 \quad \text{6\% and} \\ & \quad\quad\quad\quad\quad\quad\quad \text{12 periods} \\ interest &= \$10,061 - \$5000 \\ &= \$5061 \end{aligned}$$

   (b) $14,100 at $3\frac{1}{2}$% for 10 years

   $$\begin{aligned} compound\ amount & \\ = \$14,100 \cdot 1.4106 & \quad 3\tfrac{1}{2}\%\ and \\ = \$19,889.46 & \quad 10\ periods \\ interest &= \$19,889.46 - \$14,100 \\ &= \$5789.46 \end{aligned}$$

   (c) $25,600 at 8% for 11 years

   $$\begin{aligned} compound\ amount & \\ = \$25,600 \cdot 2.3316 & \quad 8\tfrac{1}{2}\%\ and\ 11 \\ = \$59,688.96 & \quad periods \\ interest &= \$59,688.96 - \$25,600 \\ &= \$34,088.96 \end{aligned}$$

6.9 Section Exercises

3. $500 at 4% for 3 years

Year	Interest
1	$500 \cdot 0.04 \cdot 1 = \$20$
	$500 + \$20 = \$520$
	Compound Interest
2	$520 \cdot 0.04 \cdot 1 = \$20.80$
	$520 + \$20.80 = \$540.80$
	Compound Interest
3	$540.80 \cdot 0.04 \cdot 1 \approx \$21.63$
	$540.80 + \$21.63 = \$562.43$
	Compound Interest

   The compound amount is $562.43.

7. $800 at 4% for 3 years

   $100\% + 4\% = 104\% = 1.04$
   $\$800 \cdot 1.04 \cdot 1.04 \cdot 1.04 \approx \$899.89$

   The compound amount is $\approx \$899.89$.

11. $1180 at 7% for 8 years

    $100\% + 7\% = 107\% = 1.07$
    $\$1180 \cdot 1.07 \cdot 1.07 \cdot 1.07 \cdot 1.07 \cdot 1.07$
    $\cdot 1.07 \cdot 1.07 \cdot 1.07 \approx \$2027.46$.

    The compound amount is $\approx \$2027.46$.

15. $1000 at 6% for 4 years

    6% column, row 4 of the table gives 1.2625. Multiply.

    $$\$1000 \cdot 1.2625 = \$1262.50$$
    $$\qquad\qquad\qquad\qquad compound\ amount$$
    $$\$1262.50 - \$1000 = \$262.50$$
    $$\qquad\qquad\qquad\qquad interest$$

19. $8428.17 at $4\frac{1}{2}$% for 6 years

    4.50% column, row 6 of the table gives 1.3023. Multiply.

    $$\$8428.17 \cdot 1.3023 \approx \$10,976.01$$
    $$\qquad\qquad\qquad\qquad compound\ amount$$
    $$\approx \$10,976.01 - \$8428.17 \approx \$2547.84 \quad interest$$

23. $5280 at 8% compounded annually for 5 years
    8% column, row 5 of the table gives 1.4693. Multiply.

    $$\$5280 \cdot 1.4693 \approx \$7757.90$$
    $$\qquad\qquad\qquad\qquad compound\ amount$$

27. (a) $10,000 at 6% compounded annually for 2 years

    6% column, row 2 from the table is 1.1236.

    $$\$10,000 \cdot 1.1236 = \$11,236$$

    $31,236 ($11,236 + $20,000) at 6% compounded annually for 3 years

    6% column, row 3 from the table is 1.1910.

    $$\$31,236 \cdot 1.1910 \approx \$37,202.08$$
    $$\qquad\qquad compound\ amount$$

    (b) $\approx \$37,202.08 - \$10,000 - \$20,000$
    $\approx \$7202.08 \quad interest$

31. | | |
    |---|---|
    | $19.3 + (6.7 - 5.2) \cdot 58$ | *Parentheses* |
    | $19.3 + 1.5 \cdot 58$ | *Multiply* |
    | $19.3 + 87 = 106.3$ | *Add* |

Chapter 6 Review Exercises

1. $25\% = 0.25$
Drop the percent sign and move the decimal point 2 places to the left.

2. $180\% = 1.8$
Drop the percent sign and move the decimal point 2 places to the left.

3. $12.5\% = 0.125$
Drop the percent sign and move the decimal point 2 places to the left.

4. $0.085 = 0.00085$
Drop the percent sign and move the decimal point 2 places to the left.

5. $2.65 = 265\%$
Move the decimal point 2 places to the right and attach percent sign.

6. $0.02 = 2\%$
Move the decimal point 2 places to the right and attach percent sign.

7. $0.875 = 87.5\%$
Move the decimal point 2 places to the right and attach percent sign.

8. $0.002 = 0.2\%$
Move the decimal 2 places to the right and attach percent sign.

9. $12\% = \frac{12 \div 4}{100 \div 4} = \frac{3}{25}$

10. $37.5\% = \frac{37.5}{100} = \frac{37.5 \cdot 10}{100 \cdot 10} = \frac{375 \div 125}{1000 \div 125} = \frac{3}{8}$

11. $250\% = \frac{250}{100} = \frac{250 \div 50}{100 \div 50} = \frac{5}{2} = 2\frac{1}{2}$

12. $0.25\% = \frac{0.25}{100} = \frac{25}{10{,}000} = \frac{1}{400}$

13. $\frac{3}{4} = \frac{p}{100}$

$4 \cdot p = 3 \cdot 100$ *Cross products are equivalent*

$\frac{4 \cdot p}{4} = \frac{300}{4}$

$p = 75$

$\frac{3}{4} = 75\%$

14. $\frac{5}{8} = \frac{p}{100}$

$8 \cdot p = 5 \cdot 100$ *Cross products are equivalent*

$\frac{8 \cdot p}{8} = \frac{500}{8}$

$p = 62.5$

$\frac{5}{8} = 62.5\%$ or $62\frac{1}{2}\%$

15. $3\frac{1}{4} = 3\frac{25}{100} = 3.25 = 325\%$

16. $\frac{1}{200} = \frac{p}{100}$

$200 \cdot p = 100$

$\frac{200 \cdot p}{200} = \frac{100}{200}$

$p = 0.5$

$\frac{1}{200} = 0.5\%$

17. $\frac{1}{8}$

$$\begin{array}{r} 0.125 \\ 8\overline{)1.000} \\ \underline{8} \\ 20 \\ \underline{16} \\ 40 \\ \underline{40} \\ 0 \end{array}$$

$\frac{1}{8} = 0.125$

18. $\frac{1}{8} = \frac{p}{100}$

$8 \cdot p = 100$

$\frac{8 \cdot p}{8} = \frac{100}{8}$

$p = 12.5$

$\frac{1}{8} = 12.5\%$

19. $0.15 = \frac{15}{100} = \frac{3}{20}$

20. $0.15 = 15\%$

21. $180\% = \frac{180}{100} = \frac{9}{5} = 1\frac{4}{5}$

22. $180\% = 1.80 = 1.8$

23. $\dfrac{a}{b} = \dfrac{p}{100}$ $a = 50, p = 5$

$\dfrac{50}{b} = \dfrac{5}{100}$

$5 \cdot b = 50 \cdot 100$

$\dfrac{5 \cdot b}{5} = \dfrac{5000}{5}$

$b = 1000$

24. $\dfrac{a}{b} = \dfrac{p}{100}$ $b = 960, p = 10$

$\dfrac{a}{960} = \dfrac{10}{100}$

$100 \cdot a = 960 \cdot 10$

$\dfrac{100 \cdot a}{100} = \dfrac{9600}{100}$

$a = 96$

25. 40% of 150 bulbs is 60 bulbs.

percent — 40
base — 150
amount — 60

26. 73 brooms is what percent of 90 brooms?

percent — unknown
base — 90
amount — 73

27. Find 28% of 320 cabinets.

percent — 28
base — 320
amount — unknown

28. 209 ratchets is 32% of what number of ratchets?

percent — 32
base — unknown
amount — 209

29. A golfer lost 3 of his 8 golf balls. What percent were lost?

percent — unknown
base — 8
amount — 3

30. What number is 88% of 1280 keys?

percent — 88
base — 1280
amount — unknown

31. b is 450; p is 12; a is unknown.

$\dfrac{a}{b} = \dfrac{p}{100}$

$\dfrac{a}{450} = \dfrac{12}{100}$

$100 \cdot a = 450 \cdot 12$

$\dfrac{100 \cdot a}{100} = \dfrac{5400}{100}$

$a = 54$

12% of 450 telephones is 54 telephones.

32. b is 1450; p is 60; a is unknown.

$\dfrac{a}{b} = \dfrac{p}{100}$

$\dfrac{a}{1450} = \dfrac{60}{100}$

$100 \cdot a = 60 \cdot 1450$

$\dfrac{100 \cdot a}{100} = \dfrac{87,000}{100}$

$a = 870$

60% of 1450 reference books is 870 reference books.

33. b is 4800; p is 0.9; a is unknown.

$\dfrac{a}{b} = \dfrac{p}{100}$

$\dfrac{a}{4800} = \dfrac{0.9}{100}$

$100 \cdot a = 0.9 \cdot 4800$

$\dfrac{100 \cdot a}{100} = \dfrac{4320}{100}$

$a = 43.2$

0.9% 4800 miles is 43.2 miles.

34. b is 1400; p is 0.2; a is unknown.

$\dfrac{a}{b} = \dfrac{p}{100}$

$\dfrac{a}{1400} = \dfrac{0.2}{100}$

$100 \cdot a = 0.2 \cdot 1400$

$\dfrac{100 \cdot a}{100} = \dfrac{280}{100}$

$a = 2.8$

0.2% of 1400 kilograms is 2.8 kilograms.

Chapter 6 Review Exercises

35. a is 35; p is 7; b is unknown.

$$\frac{a}{b} = \frac{p}{100}$$

$$\frac{35}{b} = \frac{7}{100}$$

$$7 \cdot b = 35 \cdot 100$$

$$\frac{7 \cdot b}{7} = \frac{3500}{7}$$

$$b = 500$$

35 athletes is 7% of 500 athletes.

36. a is 174; p is 15; b is unknown.

$$\frac{a}{b} = \frac{p}{100}$$

$$\frac{174}{b} = \frac{15}{100}$$

$$15 \cdot b = 174 \cdot 100$$

$$\frac{15 \cdot b}{15} = \frac{17{,}400}{15}$$

$$b = 1160$$

174 capsules is 15% of 1160 capsules.

37. a is 338.8; p is 140; b is unknown.

$$\frac{a}{b} = \frac{p}{100}$$

$$\frac{338.8}{b} = \frac{140}{100}$$

$$b \cdot 140 = 338.8 \cdot 100$$

$$\frac{b \cdot 140}{140} = \frac{33{,}880}{140}$$

$$b = 242$$

333.8 meters is 140% of 242 meters.

38. a is 425; p is 2.5; b is unknown.

$$\frac{a}{b} = \frac{p}{100}$$

$$\frac{425}{b} = \frac{2.5}{100}$$

$$2.5 \cdot b = 425 \cdot 100$$

$$\frac{2.5 \cdot b}{2.5} = \frac{42{,}500}{2.5}$$

$$b = 17{,}000$$

2.5% of 17,000 cases is 425 cases.

39. a is 345; b is 690; p is unknown.

$$\frac{a}{b} = \frac{p}{100}$$

$$\frac{345}{690} = \frac{p}{100}$$

$$690 \cdot p = 100 \cdot 345$$

$$\frac{690 \cdot p}{690} = \frac{34{,}500}{690}$$

$$p = 50$$

345 lamps is 50% of 690 lamps.

40. a is 75; b is 1850; p is unknown.

$$\frac{a}{b} = \frac{p}{100}$$

$$\frac{75}{1850} = \frac{p}{100}$$

$$1850 \cdot p = 75 \cdot 100$$

$$\frac{1850 \cdot p}{1850} = \frac{7500}{1850}$$

$$p \approx 4.1$$

$\approx$ 4.1% of 1850 reams is 75 reams.

41. a is 36; b is 380; p is unknown.

$$\frac{a}{b} = \frac{p}{100}$$

$$\frac{36}{380} = \frac{p}{100}$$

$$380 \cdot p = 100 \cdot 36$$

$$\frac{380 \cdot p}{380} = \frac{3600}{380}$$

$$p \approx 9.5$$

$\approx$ 9.5% of 380 pairs is 36 pairs.

42. a is 200; b is 650; p is unknown.

$$\frac{a}{b} = \frac{p}{100}$$

$$\frac{200}{650} = \frac{p}{100}$$

$$650 \cdot p = 200 \cdot 100$$

$$\frac{650 \cdot p}{650} = \frac{20{,}000}{650}$$

$$p \approx 30.8$$

$\approx$ 30.8% of 650 cans is 200 cans.

43. p = 3%; b = 20 million; a is unknown.
Use the percent proportion.
$$\frac{a}{b} = \frac{p}{100}$$
$$\frac{a}{20} = \frac{3}{100}$$
$$100 \cdot a = 20 \cdot 3$$
$$\frac{100 \cdot a}{100} = \frac{60}{100}$$
$$a = \frac{6}{10} = 0.6$$

0.6 million or 600,000 patients were referred to chiropractors by medical doctors.

44. a = 1000; b = 9600; p is unknown.
Use the percent proportion.
$$\frac{a}{b} = \frac{p}{100}$$
$$\frac{1000}{9600} = \frac{p}{100}$$
$$9600 \cdot p = 1000 \cdot 100$$
$$\frac{9600 \cdot p}{9600} = \frac{100,000}{9600}$$
$$p \approx 10.4$$

≈ 10.4% of the birds are in danger of extinction.

45. amount = percent · base
$$a = 0.11 \cdot 236 \quad 11\% = 0.11$$
$$a = 25.96$$

11% of $236 is $25.96.

46. amount = percent · base
$$a = 1.25 \cdot 64$$
$$a = 80$$

125% of 64 dumpsters is 80 dumpsters.

47. amount = percent · base
$$0.128 = p \cdot 32$$
$$\frac{0.128}{32} = \frac{p \cdot 32}{32}$$
$$0.004 = p$$
$$0.004 = 0.4\%$$

0.128 ounces is 0.4% of 32 ounces.

48. amount = percent · base
$$304.5 = p \cdot 174$$
$$\frac{304.5}{174} = \frac{p \cdot 174}{174}$$
$$1.75 = p$$
$$1.75 = 175\%$$

304.5 meters is 175% of 174 meters.

49. amount = percent · base
$$33.6 = 0.28 \cdot b$$
$$\frac{33.6}{0.28} = \frac{0.28 \cdot b}{0.28}$$
$$120 = b$$

33.6 miles is 28% of 120 miles.

50. amount = percent · base
$$46 = 0.08 \cdot b$$
$$\frac{46}{0.08} = \frac{0.08 \cdot b}{0.08}$$
$$575 = b$$

$46 is 8% of $575.

51. sales tax = rate of tax · cost of item
$$= 4\% \cdot \$210$$
$$= 0.04 \cdot \$210$$
$$= \$8.40$$

The sales tax is $8.40 and the total cost is $218.40 ($210 + $8.40).

52. sales tax = rate of tax · cost of item
$$\$58.50 = r \cdot \$780$$
$$\frac{58.50}{780} = \frac{r \cdot 780}{780}$$
$$0.075 = r$$
$$0.075 = 7\frac{1}{2}\%$$

The tax rate is $7\frac{1}{2}\%$ and the total cost is $838.50 ($780 + $58.50).

53. commission = rate of commission · sales
$$= 11\% \cdot \$2800$$
$$= 0.11 \cdot \$2800$$
$$= \$308 \quad \text{amount of commission}$$

The amount of the commission is $308.

54. commission = rate of commission · sales
$$\$3265 = r \cdot \$65,300$$
$$\frac{3265}{65,300} = \frac{r \cdot 65,300}{65,300}$$
$$0.05 = r$$
$$0.05 = 5\% \quad \text{rate of commission}$$

The rate of commission is 5%.

Chapter 6 Review Exercises

55. $\text{discount} = \text{rate of discount} \cdot \text{original price}$
$= 10\% \cdot \$37.50$
$= 0.1 = \$37.50$
$= \$3.75 \quad \text{amount of discount}$

The amount of discount is $3.75 and the sale price is $33.75 ($37.50 − $3.75).

56. $\text{discount} = \text{rate of discount} \cdot \text{original price}$
$\$63 = r \cdot \$252$
$\dfrac{63}{252} = \dfrac{r \cdot 252}{252}$
$0.25 = r$
$0.25 = 25\% \quad \text{rate of discount}$

The rate of discount is 25% and the sale price is $189 ($252 − $63).

57. $100 at 5% for 1 year
$I = p \cdot r \cdot t$
$= 100 \cdot (0.05) \cdot 1$
$= 5$

The interest is $5.

58. $960 at 6% for $1\frac{1}{4}$ years
$I = p \cdot r \cdot t$
$= 960 \cdot (0.06) \cdot 1.25 \quad 1\frac{1}{4} = 1.25$
$= 57.6 \cdot 1.25$
$= 72$

The interest is $72.

59. $300 at 8% for 6 months
$I = p \cdot r \cdot t$
$= 300 \cdot (0.08) \cdot 0.5 \quad \frac{6}{12} = 0.5$
$= 12$

The interest is $12.

60. $1280 at $7\frac{1}{2}\%$ for 18 months
$I = p \cdot r \cdot t$
$= 1280 \cdot (0.075) \cdot 1.5 \quad 18 \text{ months} = 1.5 \text{ years}$
$= 144$

The interest is $144.

61. $350 at $4\frac{1}{2}\%$ for 3 years
$I = p \cdot r \cdot t$
$= 350 \cdot (0.045) \cdot 3$
$= 47.25$

The total amount due is $397.25 ($350 + $47.25).

62. $1530 at 6% for 9 months
$I = p \cdot r \cdot t$
$= 1530 \cdot (0.06) \cdot 0.75 \quad 9 \text{ months} = 0.75 \text{ years}$
$= \$68.85$

The total amount due is $1598.85 ($1530 + $68.85).

63. $2000 at 5% for 10 years

5% column, row 10 of the table gives 1.6289. Multiply.

$\$2000 \cdot 1.6289 = \$3257.80$
$\quad\quad\quad\quad\quad\quad\quad \text{compound amount}$
$\$3257.80 - \$2000 = \$1257.80$
$\quad\quad\quad\quad\quad\quad\quad \text{compound interest}$

64. $1530 at 4% for 5 years

4% column, row 5 of the table gives 1.2167. Multiply.

$\$1530 \cdot 1.2167 \approx \$1861.55$
$\quad\quad\quad\quad\quad\quad\quad \text{compound amount}$
$\$1861.55 - \$1530 = \$331.55$
$\quad\quad\quad\quad\quad\quad\quad \text{compound interest}$

65. $3600 at 6% for 6 years

8% column, row 3 of the table gives 1.2597. Multiply.

$\$3600 \cdot 1.2597 = \$4534.92$
$\quad\quad\quad\quad\quad\quad\quad \text{compound amount}$
$\$4534.92 - \$3600 = \$934.92$
$\quad\quad\quad\quad\quad\quad\quad \text{compound interest}$

66. $11,400 at 6% for 6 years

6% column, row 6 of the table gives 1.4185.

$\$11,400 \cdot 1.4185 = \$16,170.90$
$\quad\quad\quad\quad\quad\quad\quad \text{compound amount}$
$\$16,170.90 - \$11,400 = \$4770.90$
$\quad\quad\quad\quad\quad\quad\quad \text{compound interest}$

67. $b = 40$, $p = 30$

$$\frac{a}{b} = \frac{p}{100}$$

$$\frac{a}{40} = \frac{30}{100}$$

$$\frac{a}{40} = \frac{3}{10} \quad \text{Lowest terms}$$

$$a \cdot 10 = 3 \cdot 40$$

$$\frac{a \cdot 10}{10} = \frac{120}{10}$$

$$a = 12$$

68. a is 574, p is 35.

$$\frac{a}{b} = \frac{p}{100}$$

$$\frac{574}{b} = \frac{35}{100}$$

$$b \cdot 35 = 574 \cdot 100$$

$$\frac{b \cdot 35}{35} = \frac{57,400}{35}$$

$$b = 1640$$

69. 24% of 97 meters

$$a = 0.24 \cdot 97$$

$$a = 23.28$$

24% of 97 meters is 23.28 meters.

70. a is 327, b is 218; p is unknown.

$$\frac{a}{b} = \frac{p}{100}$$

$$\frac{327}{218} = \frac{p}{100}$$

$$218 \cdot p = 327 \cdot 100$$

$$\frac{218 \cdot p}{218} = \frac{32,700}{218}$$

$$p = 150$$

$$150 = 150\%$$

327 cars is 150% of 218 cars.

71. 0.6% of $85

$$a = 0.006 \cdot 85$$

$$a = 0.51$$

0.6% of $85 is $0.51.

72. a is 198; p is 40; b is unknown.

$$\frac{a}{b} = \frac{p}{100}$$

$$\frac{198}{b} = \frac{40}{100}$$

$$\frac{198}{b} = \frac{2}{5} \quad \text{Lowest terms}$$

$$b \cdot 2 = 198 \cdot 5$$

$$\frac{b \cdot 2}{2} = \frac{990}{2}$$

$$b = 495$$

198 students is 40% of 495 students.

73. a is 76; b is 190; p is unknown.

$$\frac{a}{b} = \frac{p}{100}$$

$$\frac{76}{190} = \frac{p}{100}$$

$$190 \cdot p = 76 \cdot 100$$

$$\frac{190 \cdot p}{190} = \frac{7600}{190}$$

$$p = 40$$

$$40 = 40\%$$

76 chickens is 40% of 190 chickens.

74. a is 107.242; p is 43; b is unknown.

$$\frac{a}{b} = \frac{p}{100}$$

$$\frac{107.242}{b} = \frac{43}{100}$$

$$43 \cdot b = 107.242 \cdot 100$$

$$\frac{43 \cdot b}{43} = \frac{10,724.2}{43}$$

$$b = 249.4$$

107.242 liters is 43% of 249.4 liters.

75. 75% = 0.75

Drop the percent sign and move the decimal point two places to the left.

76. 200% = 2

Drop the percent sign and move the decimal point two places to the left.

77. 4 = 400%

Attach two zeros so the decimal point can be moved two places to the right. Attach percent sign.

Chapter 6 Review Exercises

78. $4.71 = 471\%$
Move the decimal point two places to the right and attach percent sign.

79. $6.2\% = 0.062$
Drop the percent sign and move the decimal point two places to the left.

80. $0.621 = 62.1\%$
Move the decimal point two places to the right and attach percent sign.

81. $0.375\% = 0.00375$
Drop the percent sign and move the decimal point two places to the left.

82. $0.0006 = 0.06\%$
Move the decimal point two places to the right and attach percent sign.

83. $\dfrac{1}{4} = \dfrac{1 \cdot 25}{4 \cdot 25} = \dfrac{25}{100} = 0.25 = 25\%$

84. $38\% = \dfrac{38}{100} = \dfrac{38 \div 2}{100 \div 2} = \dfrac{19}{50}$

85. $62.5\% = \dfrac{62.5 \cdot 10}{100 \cdot 10} = \dfrac{625 \div 125}{1000 \div 125} = \dfrac{5}{8}$

86. $\dfrac{3}{8} = \dfrac{p}{100}$

$8 \cdot p = 3 \cdot 100$
$8 \cdot p = 300$
$\dfrac{8 \cdot p}{8} = \dfrac{300}{8}$
$p = 37.5 \text{ or } 37\frac{1}{2}$
$\dfrac{3}{8} = 37.5\% \text{ or } 37\frac{1}{2}\%$

87. $32\frac{1}{2}\% = \dfrac{32.5 \cdot 10}{100 \cdot 10} = \dfrac{325}{1000} = \dfrac{325 \div 25}{1000 \div 25} = \dfrac{13}{40}$

88. $\dfrac{1}{5} = \dfrac{p}{100}$

$5 \cdot p = 1 \cdot 100$
$5 \cdot p = 100$
$\dfrac{5 \cdot p}{5} = \dfrac{100}{5}$
$p = 20$
$\dfrac{1}{5} = 20\%$

89. $0.5\% = \dfrac{0.5 \cdot 10}{100 \cdot 10} = \dfrac{5 \div 5}{1000 \div 5} = \dfrac{1}{200}$

90. $2\frac{1}{4} = 2\frac{1 \cdot 25}{4 \cdot 25} = 2\frac{25}{100} = 2.25 = 225\%$

91. $8520 at $5\frac{1}{2}\%$ for 9 months

$$\begin{aligned} I &= p \cdot r \cdot t \\ &= 8520 \cdot 5\frac{1}{2}\% \cdot \dfrac{9}{12} \quad \dfrac{3}{4} = 0.75 \\ &= 8520 \cdot 0.055 \cdot 0.75 \\ &= 351.45 \end{aligned}$$

The interest is $351.45.

92. $1620 at 14% for 18 months

$$\begin{aligned} I &= p \cdot r \cdot t \\ &= 1620 \cdot 14\% \cdot \dfrac{18}{12} \\ &= 1620 \cdot 0.14 \cdot 1.5 \\ &= 340.20 \quad interest \end{aligned}$$

The total amount due is $1960.20 ($1620 + $340.20).

93. a is 5.5; b is $11.5 + 5.5 = 17$; p is unknown.

$$\dfrac{a}{b} = \dfrac{p}{100}$$
$$\dfrac{5.5}{17} = \dfrac{p}{100}$$
$$17 \cdot p = 5.5 \cdot 100$$
$$\dfrac{17 \cdot p}{17} = \dfrac{550}{17}$$
$$p \approx 32.4$$
$$32.4 \approx 32.4\%$$

The capacity of the freezer is $\approx 32.4\%$ of the capacity of the refrigerator.

94. (a) $12,500 at 6% compounded annually for 4 years
$100\% + 6\% = 106\% = 1.06$

$\$12,500 \cdot 1.06 \cdot 1.06 \cdot 1.06 \cdot 1.06 \approx \$15,780.96$
The compound amount is $\approx \$15,780.96$.

(b) The amount of interest is
$\approx \$3280.96 \ (\approx \$15,780.96 - \$12,500)$.

95. Add the two sales.

$$\$105{,}000 + \$145{,}000 = \$250{,}000$$

$$\begin{aligned} amount\ &of\ commission \\ &= rate\ of\ commission \\ &\quad \cdot amount\ of\ sales \\ &= 1\tfrac{1}{2}\% \cdot \$250{,}000 \\ &= 0.015 \cdot \$250{,}000 \\ &= \$3750 \end{aligned}$$

The commission that she earned was $3750.

96. Increase $= 520 - 481 = 39$
Use the percent proportion.

$$\frac{a}{b} = \frac{p}{100}$$

$$\frac{39}{481} = \frac{p}{100}$$

$$481 \cdot p = 39 \cdot 100$$

$$\frac{481 \cdot p}{481} = \frac{3900}{481}$$

$$p \approx 8.1$$

The increase is $\approx 8.1\%$.

97. Decrease $= 32.8 - 28.5 = 4.3$
Use the percent proportion.

$$\frac{a}{b} = \frac{p}{100}$$

$$\frac{4.3}{32.8} = \frac{p}{100}$$

$$32.8 \cdot p = 4.3 \cdot 100$$

$$\frac{32.8 \cdot p}{32.8} = \frac{430}{32.8}$$

$$p \approx 13.1$$

The percent of decrease is 13.1%.

98. a is 200,000; p is 4; b is unknown.

$$\frac{a}{b} = \frac{p}{100}$$

$$\frac{200{,}000}{b} = \frac{4}{100}$$

$$\frac{200{,}000}{b} = \frac{1}{25} \quad \text{Lowest terms}$$

$$b \cdot 1 = 25 \cdot 200{,}000$$

$$b = 5{,}000{,}000$$

Annually, 5,000,000 cars are sold in Japan.

99. $25\% + 30\% + 8\% + 20\% = 83\%$
and $100\% - 83\% = 17\%$, so the couple saves 17% of their earnings.
Walter's yearly income is

$$\$1950 \cdot 12 = \$23{,}400.$$

Their total yearly income is

$$\$51{,}900\ (\$23{,}400 + \$28{,}500).$$

The amount saved is

$$\begin{aligned} 17\%\ \text{of}\ \$51{,}900 &= 0.17 \cdot \$51{,}900 \\ &= \$8823. \end{aligned}$$

100. $\begin{aligned} amount\ &of\ discount \\ &= rate\ of\ discount \\ &\quad \cdot original\ price \\ &= 7\% \cdot \$398 \\ &= 0.07 \cdot \$398 \\ &= \$27.86 \end{aligned}$

The sale price is $370.14 ($398− $27.86).

$$\begin{aligned} sales\ tax &= rate\ of\ tax \cdot cost\ of\ item \\ &= 0.07 \cdot \$370.14 \\ &\approx \$25.91 \end{aligned}$$

The total cost of the FAX machine is

$$\approx \$396.05\ (\$370.14 + \approx \$25.91).$$

Chapter 6 Test

1. $75\% = 0.75$
Drop the percent sign and move the decimal point two places to the left.

2. $0.6 = 60\%$
Move the decimal point two places to the right and attach a percent sign.

3. $1.8 = 180\%$
Move the decimal point two places to the right and attach a percent sign.

4. $0.875 = 87.5\%$ or $87\tfrac{1}{2}\%$
Move the decimal point two places to the right and attach a percent sign.

5. $300\% = 3.00$ or 3
Drop the percent sign and move the decimal point two places to the left.

Chapter 6 Test

6. $0.05\% = 0.0005$
Drop the percent sign and move the decimal point two places to the left.

7. $62.5\% = \dfrac{62.5 \cdot 10}{100 \cdot 10} = \dfrac{625 \div 125}{1000 \div 125} = \dfrac{5}{8}$

8. $0.25\% = \dfrac{0.25 \cdot 100}{100 \cdot 100} = \dfrac{25 \div 25}{10{,}000 \div 25} = \dfrac{1}{400}$

9. $\dfrac{1}{4} = \dfrac{25}{100} = 0.25 = 25\%$

10. $\dfrac{5}{8} = \dfrac{p}{100}$
$8 \cdot p = 5 \cdot 100$
$\dfrac{8 \cdot p}{8} = \dfrac{500}{8}$
$p = 62.5\%$ or $62\tfrac{1}{2}\%$

11. $1\tfrac{3}{4} = 1\tfrac{3 \cdot 25}{4 \cdot 25} = 1\tfrac{75}{100} = 1.75 = 175\%$

12. Use the percent proportion.
a is 16; p is 5; b is unknown.

$\dfrac{a}{b} = \dfrac{p}{100}$

$\dfrac{16}{b} = \dfrac{5}{100}$

$5 \cdot b = 16 \cdot 100$
$\dfrac{5 \cdot b}{5} = \dfrac{1600}{5}$
$b = 320$

16 files is 5% of 320 files.

13. Use the percent proportion.
a is 250; b is 1250; p is unknown.

$\dfrac{a}{b} = \dfrac{p}{100}$

$\dfrac{250}{1250} = \dfrac{p}{100}$

$250 \cdot 100 = p \cdot 1250$
$\dfrac{25{,}000}{1250} = \dfrac{p \cdot 1250}{1250}$
$20 = p$
$20 = 20\%$

$250 is 20% of $1250.

14. Use the percent proportion.
a is 14,625; p is 75; b is unknown.

$\dfrac{a}{b} = \dfrac{p}{100}$

$\dfrac{14{,}625}{b} = \dfrac{75}{100}$

$\dfrac{14{,}625}{b} = \dfrac{3}{4}$ *Lowest terms*

$3 \cdot b = 4 \cdot 14{,}625$
$\dfrac{3 \cdot b}{3} = \dfrac{58{,}500}{3}$
$b = 19{,}500$

The total down payment is $19,500.

15. $sales\ tax = rate\ of\ tax \cdot cost\ of\ item$
$= 6\tfrac{1}{2}\% \cdot \$2680$
$= 0.065 \cdot \$2680$
$= \$174.20$ *sales tax*

The total cost is $2854.20 ($2680 + $174.20).

16. $commission = rate\ of\ commission \cdot sales$
$= 24\% \cdot \$1040$
$= 0.24 \cdot \$1040$
$= \$249.60$

The amount of the commission is $249.60.

17. $1944 - 1440 = 504$, so the increase is 504 students. Use the percent proportion.

$\dfrac{a}{b} = \dfrac{p}{100}$

$\dfrac{504}{1440} = \dfrac{p}{100}$

$1440 \cdot p = 504 \cdot 100$
$\dfrac{1440 \cdot p}{1440} = \dfrac{50{,}400}{1440}$
$p = 35$
$35 = 35\%$

The rate of increase is 35%.

18. A possible answer is:
Amount is the increase in salary.
This year − last year = increase
Base is last year's salary.
Percent of increase is unknown.

$\dfrac{amount\ of\ increase}{last\ year's\ salary} = \dfrac{p}{100}$

19. The interest formula is $I = p \cdot r \cdot t$.
If time is in months, it is expressed as a fraction with 12 as the denominator. If time is expressed

in years, it is placed over 1 as shown as a decimal number.

$$\begin{array}{lll} I & p \cdot r \cdot t & \\ 9\ months & 1000 \cdot 0.05 \cdot \dfrac{9}{12} & = \$37.50 \\ 2\frac{1}{2}\ years & 1000 \cdot 0.05 \cdot 2.5 & = \$125 \end{array}$$

20. amount of discount
 = rate of discount
  · original price
 = 8% · $48
 = 0.08 · $48
 = $3.84

The amount of discount is $3.84. The sale price is $44.16 ($48 − $3.84).

21. amount of discount = 37.5% · $182
     = 0.375 · $182
     = $68.25

The amount of discount is $68.25. The sale price is $113.75 ($182 − $68.25).

22. $3500 at 5% for $1\frac{1}{2}$ years

$$\begin{aligned} I &= p \cdot r \cdot t \\ &= 3500 \cdot (0.05) \cdot 1.5 \\ &= 262.5 \end{aligned}$$

The interest is $262.50.

23. $5200 at 4% for 3 months

$$\begin{aligned} I &= p \cdot r \cdot t \\ &= 5200 \cdot (0.04) \cdot \dfrac{3}{12} \\ &= 208 \cdot 0.25 \\ &= 52 \end{aligned}$$

The interest is $52.

24. $4600 at 12% for 6 months

$$\begin{aligned} I &= p \cdot r \cdot t \\ &= 4600 \cdot (0.12) \cdot \dfrac{6}{12} \\ &= 552 \cdot 0.5 \quad \tfrac{6}{12} = \tfrac{1}{2} = 0.5 \\ &= 276 \quad interest \end{aligned}$$

The total amount due is $4876 ($4600 + $276).

25. (a) $4000 at 6% for 2 years
 6% column, row 2 of the table gives 1.1236.

$$\$4000 \cdot 1.1236 = \$4494.40$$

$9494.40 ($5000 + $4494.40) at 6% for 2 years
6% column, row 2 of the table gives 1.1236.

$$\$9494.40 \cdot 1.1236 \approx \$10{,}668$$

The total amount after four years is ≈ $10,668

(b) The interest is ≈ $1668 ($10,668 − $9000).

Cumulative Review Exercises (Chapters 1-6)

1.
estimate	exact
9000	8702
80	83
+ 500	+ 549
9580	9334

2.
estimate	exact
1	0.68
40	36.531
+ 5	+ 5.3
46	42.511

3.
estimate	exact
60,000	$\overset{9}{\cancel{6}\cancel{1}{,}\cancel{0}\cancel{3}3}$ (5 10 10 13)
− 50,000	− 51,040
10,000	9993

4.
estimate	exact
6	$\overset{5\ 11\ 9\ 9}{\cancel{6}.\cancel{2}\cancel{0}\cancel{0}\cancel{0}}$ (10)
− 3	− 2.7055
3	3.4945

5.
estimate	exact
7000	6538
× 700	× 708
4,900,000	52 304
	4 576 60
	4,628,904

Cumulative Review Exercises (Chapters 1-6)

6. | estimate | exact |
    |---|---|
    | 70 | 71.6 |
    | $\times\ 5$ | $\times\ 4.5$ |
    | 350 | 35 80 |
    | | 286 4 |
    | | 322.2 |

7. | estimate | exact |
    |---|---|
    | 1 000 | 90 2 |
    | 40)$\overline{40,000}$ | 43)$\overline{38,78^86}$ |

8. | estimate | exact |
    |---|---|
    | 250 | 32 0. |
    | 8)$\overline{2000}$ | 7.6$_\wedge$)$\overline{2432.0_\wedge}$ |
    | | 228 |
    | | 152 |
    | | 152 |
    | | 0 0 |
    | | 0 0 |
    | | 0 |

9. | estimate | exact |
    |---|---|
    | 7 | 8.45 |
    | 1)$\overline{7}$ | 0.8$_\wedge$)$\overline{6.7_\wedge 60}$ |
    | | 6 4 |
    | | 3 6 |
    | | 3 2 |
    | | 40 |
    | | 40 |
    | | 0 |

10. $8^2 - 5 \cdot 4$ *Exponent*
    $64 - 5 \cdot 4$ *Multiply*
    $64 - 20 = 44$ *Subtract*

11. $\sqrt{36} + 4 \cdot 8 - 7$ *Square root*
    $6 + 4 \cdot 8 - 7$ *Multiply*
    $6 + 32 - 7$ *Add*
    $38 - 7 = 31$ *Subtract*

12. $9 + 6 \div 3 + 7 \cdot 4$ *Divide*
    $9 + 2 + 7 \cdot 4$ *Multiply*
    $9 + 2 + 28 = 39$ *Add*

13. 2356 rounded to the nearest ten: $\approx$ 2360

    23$\underline{5}$6

    Next digit is 5 or more.
    Tens place changes $(5 + 1 = 6)$. All digits to the right of the underlined place change to 0.

14. 5,678,159 rounded to the nearest hundred thousand: $\approx 5,700,000$

    5,$\underline{6}$78,159

    Next digit is 5 or more.
    Hundred thousands place changes $(6 + 1 = 7)$. All digits to the right of the underlined place change to 0.

15. \$718.499 rounded to the nearest dollar: $\approx$ \$718

    \$718.|499

    Draw cut-off line.
    First digit cut is less than 5 so the part you keep stays the same.

16. \$451.825 rounded to the nearest cent: $\approx$ \$451.83

    \$451.82|5

    Draw cut-off line.
    First digit cut is 5 or more so round up the part you are keeping.

17. $\dfrac{3}{8} + \dfrac{3}{4} = \dfrac{3}{8} + \dfrac{6}{8} = \dfrac{3+6}{8} = \dfrac{9}{8} = 1\dfrac{1}{8}$

18. $\dfrac{1}{2} + \dfrac{2}{3} = \dfrac{3}{6} + \dfrac{4}{6} = \dfrac{3+4}{6} = \dfrac{7}{6} = 1\dfrac{1}{6}$

19. $4\dfrac{5}{8} \ = \ 4\dfrac{5}{8}$
     $+\ 8\dfrac{3}{4} \ = \ 8\dfrac{6}{8}$
     $\phantom{+\ 8\dfrac{3}{4} \ = \ }12\dfrac{11}{8}$

    $12\dfrac{11}{8} = 12 + \dfrac{8}{8} + \dfrac{3}{8} = 13\dfrac{3}{8}$

20. $\dfrac{3}{4} - \dfrac{5}{8} = \dfrac{6}{8} - \dfrac{5}{8} = \dfrac{6-5}{8} = \dfrac{1}{8}$

21. $5\dfrac{1}{2} \ = \ 5\dfrac{3}{6} \ = \ 4\dfrac{9}{6}$
     $-\ 2\dfrac{2}{3} \ = \ 2\dfrac{4}{6} \ = \ 2\dfrac{4}{6}$
     $\phantom{-\ 2\dfrac{2}{3} \ = \ 2\dfrac{4}{6} \ = \ }2\dfrac{5}{6}$

22. $26\dfrac{1}{3} \ = \ 26\dfrac{5}{15} \ = \ 25\dfrac{20}{15}$
     $-\ 17\dfrac{4}{5} \ = \ 17\dfrac{12}{15} \ = \ 17\dfrac{12}{15}$
     $\phantom{-\ 17\dfrac{4}{5} \ = \ 17\dfrac{12}{15} \ = \ }8\dfrac{8}{15}$

23. $\dfrac{7}{8} \cdot \dfrac{2}{3} = \dfrac{7}{\underset{4}{\cancel{8}}} \cdot \dfrac{\overset{1}{\cancel{2}}}{3} = \dfrac{7 \cdot 1}{4 \cdot 3} = \dfrac{7}{12}$

24. $7\dfrac{3}{4} \cdot 3\dfrac{3}{8} = \dfrac{31}{4} \cdot \dfrac{27}{8} = \dfrac{31 \cdot 27}{4 \cdot 8} = \dfrac{837}{32} = 26\dfrac{5}{32}$

25. $36 \cdot \dfrac{4}{5} = \dfrac{36}{1} \cdot \dfrac{4}{5} = \dfrac{36 \cdot 4}{1 \cdot 5} = \dfrac{144}{5} = 28\dfrac{4}{5}$

26. $\dfrac{5}{9} \div \dfrac{5}{8} = \dfrac{\cancel{5}^{1}}{9} \cdot \dfrac{8}{\cancel{5}_{1}} = \dfrac{1 \cdot 8}{9 \cdot 1} = \dfrac{8}{9}$

27. $10 \div \dfrac{2}{5} = \dfrac{\cancel{10}^{5}}{1} \cdot \dfrac{5}{\cancel{2}_{1}} = \dfrac{25}{1} = 25$

28. $2\dfrac{3}{4} \div 7\dfrac{1}{2} = \dfrac{11}{4} \div \dfrac{15}{2} = \dfrac{11}{\cancel{4}_{2}} \cdot \dfrac{\cancel{2}^{1}}{15} = \dfrac{11 \cdot 1}{2 \cdot 15} = \dfrac{11}{30}$

29. $\dfrac{2}{3} \;\text{---}\; \dfrac{3}{4}$

$\dfrac{2}{3} = \dfrac{8}{12},\; \dfrac{3}{4} = \dfrac{9}{12}$

$\dfrac{8}{12} < \dfrac{9}{12},\; \text{so}\; \dfrac{2}{3} < \dfrac{3}{4}.$

30. $\dfrac{5}{12} \;\text{---}\; \dfrac{7}{15}$

$\dfrac{5}{12} = \dfrac{25}{60},\; \dfrac{7}{15} = \dfrac{28}{60}$

$\dfrac{25}{60} < \dfrac{28}{60},\; \text{so}\; \dfrac{5}{12} < \dfrac{7}{15}.$

31. $\dfrac{7}{15} \;\text{---}\; \dfrac{9}{20}$

$\dfrac{7}{15} = \dfrac{28}{60},\; \dfrac{9}{20} = \dfrac{27}{60}$

$\dfrac{28}{60} > \dfrac{27}{60},\; \text{so}\; \dfrac{7}{15} > \dfrac{9}{20}.$

32. $\left(\dfrac{3}{4} - \dfrac{5}{8}\right) \cdot \dfrac{2}{3}$

$\left(\dfrac{6}{8} - \dfrac{5}{8}\right) \cdot \dfrac{2}{3}$ *Parentheses*

$\dfrac{1}{\cancel{8}_{4}} \cdot \dfrac{\cancel{2}^{1}}{3} = \dfrac{1 \cdot 1}{4 \cdot 3} = \dfrac{1}{12}$ *Multiply*

33. $\dfrac{3}{4} \div \left(\dfrac{2}{5} + \dfrac{1}{5}\right)$ *Exponent*

$\dfrac{3}{4} \div \dfrac{3}{5}$ *Invert*

$\dfrac{\cancel{3}^{1}}{4} \cdot \dfrac{5}{\cancel{3}_{1}} = 1\dfrac{1}{4}$ *Multiply*

34. $\left(\dfrac{5}{6} - \dfrac{5}{12}\right) - \left(\dfrac{1}{2}\right)^{2} \cdot \dfrac{2}{3}$

$\left(\dfrac{10}{12} - \dfrac{5}{12}\right) - \left(\dfrac{1}{2}\right)^{2} \cdot \dfrac{2}{3}$ *Parentheses*

$\dfrac{5}{12} - \left(\dfrac{1}{2}\right)^{2} \cdot \dfrac{2}{3}$ *Exponent*

$\dfrac{5}{12} - \dfrac{1}{4} \cdot \dfrac{2}{3}$ *Multiply*

$\dfrac{5}{12} - \dfrac{2}{12} = \dfrac{3}{12} = \dfrac{1}{4}$ *Subtract*

35. $\dfrac{5}{8} = 0.625$

$\begin{array}{r}0.625\\[-2pt]8\overline{)5.000}\\[-2pt]\underline{48}\\[-2pt]20\\[-2pt]\underline{16}\\[-2pt]40\\[-2pt]\underline{40}\\[-2pt]0\end{array}$

36. $\dfrac{4}{5} = \dfrac{4 \cdot 2}{5 \cdot 2} = \dfrac{8}{10} = 0.8$

37. $\dfrac{17}{20} = 0.85$

$\begin{array}{r}0.85\\[-2pt]20\overline{)17.00}\\[-2pt]\underline{16\;0}\\[-2pt]1\;00\\[-2pt]\underline{1\;00}\\[-2pt]0\end{array}$

38. $\dfrac{12}{14} = \dfrac{6}{7} \approx 0.857$

$\begin{array}{r}0.8571\\[-2pt]7\overline{)6.0000}\\[-2pt]\underline{5\;6}\\[-2pt]40\\[-2pt]\underline{35}\\[-2pt]50\\[-2pt]\underline{49}\\[-2pt]10\\[-2pt]\underline{7}\\[-2pt]3\end{array}$

39. 2 hours to 40 minutes

$\dfrac{2 \text{ hours}}{40 \text{ minutes}} = \dfrac{120 \text{ minutes}}{40 \text{ minutes}}$

$= \dfrac{120}{40} = \dfrac{3}{1}$

40. 15 parking places to 12 cars

$\dfrac{15 \text{ parking places}}{12 \text{ cars}} = \dfrac{15}{12}$

$= \dfrac{15 \div 3}{12 \div 3} = \dfrac{5}{4}$

Cumulative Review Exercises (Chapters 1-6)   165

41. $1\frac{5}{8}$ to 13

$$\frac{1\frac{5}{8}}{13} = \frac{\frac{13}{8}}{\frac{13}{1}} = \frac{13}{8} \div \frac{13}{1} = \frac{\cancel{13}^1}{8} \cdot \frac{1}{\cancel{13}_1} = \frac{1}{8}$$

42. $\frac{4}{10} = \frac{36}{90}$

$\quad 4 \cdot 90 = 360 \quad$ *Cross products*
$\quad 10 \cdot 36 = 360 \quad$ *are equal*

True

43. $\frac{64}{144} = \frac{48}{108}$

$\quad 64 \cdot 108 = 6912 \quad$ *Cross products*
$\quad 144 \cdot 48 = 6912 \quad$ *are equal*

True

44. $\frac{1}{4} = \frac{x}{20}$

$\quad 4 \cdot x = 1 \cdot 20$
$\quad \frac{4 \cdot x}{4} = \frac{20}{4}$
$\quad x = 5$

45. $\frac{315}{45} = \frac{21}{x}$

$\quad \frac{7}{1} = \frac{21}{x} \quad$ *Lowest terms*
$\quad 7 \cdot x = 21$
$\quad \frac{7 \cdot x}{7} = \frac{21}{7}$
$\quad x = 3$

46. $\frac{7}{x} = \frac{81}{162}$

$\quad \frac{7}{x} = \frac{1}{2} \quad$ *Lowest terms*
$\quad 7 \cdot 2 = x \cdot 1$
$\quad 14 = x$

47. $\frac{x}{120} = \frac{7.5}{30}$

$\quad \frac{x}{120} = \frac{1}{4} \quad$ *Lowest terms*
$\quad 4 \cdot x = 120$
$\quad \frac{4 \cdot x}{4} = \frac{120}{4}$
$\quad x = 30$

48. $25\% = 0.25$

Drop the percent sign and move the decimal point two places to the left.

49. $7\% = 0.07$

Drop the percent sign and move the decimal point two places to the left.

50. $300\% = 3.00$ or 3

Drop the percent sign and move the decimal point two places to the left.

51. $0.5\% = 0.005$

Drop the percent sign and move the decimal point two places to the left.

52. $0.56 = 56\%$

Move the decimal point two places to the right and attach percent sign.

53. $2.7 = 270\%$

Move the decimal point two places to the right and attach percent sign.

54. $0.023 = 2.3\%$

Move the decimal point two places to the right and attach percent sign.

55. $6\% = 0.06 = \frac{6}{100} = \frac{6 \div 2}{100 \div 2} = \frac{3}{50}$

56. $62.5\% = 0.625 = \frac{625 \div 125}{1000 \div 125} = \frac{5}{8}$

57. $175\% = 1.75 = 1\frac{75}{100} = 1\frac{75 \div 25}{100 \div 25} = 1\frac{3}{4}$

58. $\frac{7}{8} = \frac{p}{100}$

$\quad 8 \cdot p = 700$
$\quad \frac{8 \cdot p}{8} = \frac{700}{8}$
$\quad p = 87.5$

$\frac{7}{8} = 87.5\%$ or $87\frac{1}{2}\%$

59. $\frac{1}{20} = \frac{1 \cdot 5}{20 \cdot 5} = \frac{5}{100} = 0.05 = 5\%$

60. $3\frac{1}{2} = 3\frac{1 \cdot 5}{2 \cdot 5} = 3\frac{5}{10} = 3.5 = 350\%$

61. 45% of 1200 officers

$\quad 0.45 \cdot 1200 = 540$
$\quad\quad\quad\quad\quad a = 540$ officers

62. b is 850; p is $8\frac{1}{2}$; a is unknown.
Use the percent proportion.
$$\frac{a}{b} = \frac{p}{100}$$
$$\frac{a}{850} = \frac{8\frac{1}{2}}{100}$$
$$a \cdot 100 = 8.5 \cdot 850$$
$$\frac{a \cdot 100}{100} = \frac{7225}{100}$$
$$a = 72.25$$

$8\frac{1}{2}\%$ of \$850 is \$72.25.

63. a is 36; p is 20; b is unknown.
$$\frac{a}{b} = \frac{p}{100}$$
$$\frac{36}{b} = \frac{20}{100}$$
$$20 \cdot b = 36 \cdot 100$$
$$\frac{20 \cdot b}{20} = \frac{3600}{20}$$
$$b = 180$$

36 cans is 20% of 180 cans.

64. a is 76.5; p is $4\frac{1}{2}$; b is unknown.
$$\frac{a}{b} = \frac{p}{100}$$
$$\frac{76.5}{b} = \frac{4\frac{1}{2}}{100}$$
$$4.5 \cdot b = 76.5 \cdot 100$$
$$\frac{4.5 \cdot b}{4.5} = \frac{7650}{4.5}$$
$$b = 1700$$

$4\frac{1}{2}\%$ of 1700 miles is 76.5 miles.

65. a is 164; b is 328; p is unknown.
$$\frac{a}{b} = \frac{p}{100}$$
$$\frac{164}{328} = \frac{p}{100}$$
$$\frac{1}{2} = \frac{p}{100} \quad \textit{Lowest terms}$$
$$2 \cdot p = 1 \cdot 100$$
$$\frac{2 \cdot p}{2} = \frac{100}{2}$$
$$p = 50$$
$$50 = 50\%$$

50% of 328 trees is 164 trees.

66. a is 72; b is 180; p is unknown.
$$\frac{a}{b} = \frac{p}{100}$$
$$\frac{72}{180} = \frac{p}{100}$$
$$180 \cdot p = 72 \cdot 100$$
$$\frac{180 \cdot p}{180} = \frac{7200}{180}$$
$$p = 40$$
$$40 = 40\%$$

72 hours is 40% of 180 hours.

67. $sales\ tax = rate\ of\ tax \cdot cost\ of\ item$
$= 4\% \cdot \$53.99$
$= 0.04 \cdot \$53.99$
$\approx \$2.16$

The sales tax is $\approx$ \$2.16 and the total cost is $\approx$ \$56.15 (\$53.99 + $\approx$ \$2.16).

68. $sales\ tax = rate\ of\ tax \cdot cost\ of\ item$
$\$29.90 = r \cdot \$460$
$$\frac{29.90}{460} = \frac{r \cdot 460}{460}$$
$0.065 = r$
$0.065 = 6\frac{1}{2}\%$

The tax rate is $6\frac{1}{2}\%$ and the total cost is \$489.90 (\$460 + \$29.90).

69. $commission = rate\ of\ commission \cdot sales$
$= 5\% \cdot \$14,622$
$= 0.05 \cdot \$14,622$
$= \$731.10$

The amount of commission is \$731.10.

70. $commission = rate\ of\ commission \cdot sales$
$\$5632.50 = r \cdot \$225,300$
$$\frac{5632.5}{225,300} = \frac{r \cdot 225,300}{225,300}$$
$0.025 = r$
$0.025 = 2.5\%$

The rate of commission is 2.5% or $2\frac{1}{2}\%$.

71. $discount = rate\ of\ discount \cdot original\ price$
$= 35\% \cdot \$152$
$= 0.35 \cdot \$152$
$= \$53.20$

Cumulative Review Exercises (Chapters 1-6)

The amount of discount is $53.20 and the sale price is $98.80 ($152 − $53.20).

72. $discount = rate\ of\ discount \cdot original\ price$
$$\$162.75 = r \cdot \$1085$$
$$\frac{162.75}{1085} = \frac{r \cdot 1085}{1085}$$
$$0.15 = r$$
$$0.15 = 15\%$$

The rate of discount is 15% and the sale price is $922.25 ($1085 − $162.75).

73. $714 at 9% for 2 years
$$\begin{aligned} I &= p \cdot r \cdot t \\ &= 714 \cdot 9\% \cdot 2 \\ &= 714 \cdot (0.09) \cdot 2 \\ &= 128.52 \end{aligned}$$

The total amount to be repaid is ≈$842.52 ($714 + $128.52).

74. $18,350 at 11% for 9 months
$$\begin{aligned} I &= p \cdot r \cdot t \\ &= 18,350 \cdot 11\% \cdot \frac{9}{12} \\ &= 18,350 \cdot (0.11) \cdot 0.75 \\ &\approx 1513.88 \end{aligned}$$

The total amount to be repaid is ≈ $19,863.88 (≈ $18,350 + $1513.88).

75. Set up a proportion.
$$\frac{7\ watches}{3\ hours} = \frac{x}{12\ hours}$$
$$3 \cdot x = 7 \cdot 12$$
$$3 \cdot x = 84$$
$$\frac{3 \cdot x}{3} = \frac{84}{3}$$
$$x = 28$$

28 watches can be cleaned in 12 hours.

76. Set up a proportion.
$$\frac{3.5\ ounces}{6\ gallons} = \frac{x}{102\ gallons}$$
$$6 \cdot x = 3.5 \cdot 102$$
$$\frac{6 \cdot x}{6} = \frac{357}{6}$$
$$x = 59.5$$

59.5 ounces of weed killer is needed.

77. The amount of increase in sales is
$$36,000 - 32,000 = 4000.$$

Use the percent proportion.
$$\frac{amount\ of\ increase}{original} = \frac{p}{100}$$
$$\frac{4000}{32,000} = \frac{p}{100}$$
$$32,000 \cdot p = 4000 \cdot 100$$
$$\frac{32,000 \cdot p}{32,000} = \frac{400,000}{32,000}$$
$$p = 12.5$$

The percent of increase in sales in the northeast region is 12.5%.

78. The amount of increase in sales in the midwestern region is 1300 (66,300 − 65,000).
$$\frac{amount\ of\ increase}{original} = \frac{p}{100}$$
$$\frac{1300}{65,000} = \frac{p}{100}$$
$$65,000 \cdot p = 1300 \cdot 100$$
$$\frac{65,000 \cdot p}{65,000} = \frac{130,000}{65,000}$$
$$p = 2$$

The percent of increase in sales in the midwestern region is 2%.

79. The amount of decrease in sales in the southern region is 4500 (82,000 − 77,500).
$$\frac{amount\ of\ decrease}{original} = \frac{p}{100}$$
$$\frac{4500}{82,000} = \frac{p}{100}$$
$$82,000 \cdot p = 4500 \cdot 100$$
$$\frac{82,000 \cdot p}{82,000} = \frac{450,000}{82,000}$$
$$p \approx 5.5\%$$

The percent of decrease in sales in the southern region is ≈ 5.5%.

80. The amount of decrease in sales in the western region is 4400 (54,000 − 49,600).
$$\frac{amount\ of\ decrease}{original} = \frac{p}{100}$$

$$\frac{4400}{54{,}000} = \frac{p}{100}$$

$$54{,}000 \cdot p = 4400 \cdot 100$$

$$\frac{54{,}000}{54{,}000} \cdot p = \frac{440{,}000}{540{,}000}$$

$$p \approx 8.1\%$$

The percent of decrease in sales in the western region is $\approx 8.1\%$.

81. a is $13,440; p is 28; b is unknown.
Use the percent proportion.

$$\frac{a}{b} = \frac{p}{100}$$

$$\frac{13{,}440}{b} = \frac{28}{100}$$

$$28 \cdot b = 13{,}440 \cdot 100$$

$$\frac{28 \cdot b}{28} = \frac{1{,}344{,}000}{28}$$

$$b = 48{,}000$$

Joan received $48,000.

82. (a) $6000 at 5% for 4 years

$$\$100 + 5\% = 105\% = 1.05$$

$$\$6000 \cdot 1.05 \cdot 1.05 \cdot 1.05 \cdot 1.05 \approx \$7293.04$$

The compound amount after 4 years is $\approx \$7293.04$.

(b) The amount of interest earned is
$\approx \$1293.04$ ($\approx \$7293.04 - \$6000$).

Chapter 7

MEASUREMENT

7.1 The English System

7.1 Margin Exercises

1. (a) 1 cup = <u>8</u> fluid ounces

   (b) 1 gallon = <u>4</u> quarts

   (c) 1 week = <u>7</u> days

   (d) 1 yard = <u>3</u> feet

   (e) 1 foot = <u>12</u> inches

   (f) 1 pound = <u>16</u> ounces

   (g) 1 ton = <u>2000</u> pounds

   (h) 1 hour = <u>60</u> minutes

   (i) 1 pint = <u>2</u> cups

   (j) 1 day = <u>24</u> hours

   (k) 1 minute = <u>60</u> seconds

   (l) 1 quart = <u>2</u> pints

   (m) 1 mile = <u>5280</u> feet

2. (a) $5\frac{1}{2}$ feet to inches.
   Because 1 foot = 12 inches,
   $$5\frac{1}{2} \text{ feet} = 5\frac{1}{2} \cdot 12 = \frac{11}{\cancel{2}_1} \cdot \frac{\cancel{12}^6}{1}$$
   $$= \frac{66}{1} = 66 \text{ inches.}$$

   (b) 64 ounces to pounds
   Because 16 ounces = 1 pound
   $$64 \text{ ounces} = \frac{64}{16} = \frac{64 \div 16}{16 \div 16}$$
   $$= 4 \text{ pounds.}$$

   (c) 6 yards to feet
   Because 1 yard = 3 feet,
   $$6 \text{ yards} = 6 \cdot 3 = 18 \text{ feet.}$$

   (d) 2 tons to pounds
   Because 1 ton = 2000 pounds
   $$2 \text{ tons} = 2 \cdot 2000 = 4000 \text{ pounds.}$$

   (e) 35 pints to quarts
   Because 1 pint = 2 quarts,
   $$35 \text{ pints} = \frac{35}{2} = 17\frac{1}{2} \text{ quarts.}$$

   (f) 20 minutes to hours
   Because 60 minutes = 1 hour,
   $$20 \text{ minutes} = \frac{20}{60} = \frac{20 \div 20}{60 \div 20}$$
   $$= \frac{1}{3} \text{ hour.}$$

   (g) 4 weeks to days
   Because 1 week = 7 days,
   $$4 \text{ weeks} = 4 \cdot 7 = 28 \text{ days.}$$

3. (a) 36 inches to feet

   $$\frac{1 \text{ foot}}{\cancel{12} \text{ i}\cancel{nches}_1} \quad \frac{unit}{fraction}$$

   $$\frac{\cancel{36}^3 \text{ i}\cancel{nches}}{1} \cdot \frac{1 \text{ foot}}{\cancel{12} \text{ i}\cancel{nches}_1} = 3 \text{ feet}$$

   (b) 14 feet to inches

   $$\frac{12 \text{ inches}}{1 \text{ foot}} \quad \frac{unit}{fraction}$$

   $$\frac{14 \cancel{feet}}{1} \cdot \frac{12 \text{ inches}}{1 \cancel{foot}} = 168 \text{ inches}$$

   (c) 60 inches to feet

   $$\frac{1 \text{ foot}}{12 \text{ inches}} \quad \frac{unit}{fraction}$$

   $$\frac{\cancel{60}^5 \cancel{inches}}{1} \cdot \frac{1 \text{ foot}}{\cancel{12} \cancel{inches}_1} = 5 \text{ feet}$$

   (d) 4 yards to feet

   $$\frac{3 \text{ feet}}{1 \text{ yard}} \quad \frac{unit}{fraction}$$

   $$\frac{4 \cancel{yards}}{1} \cdot \frac{3 \text{ feet}}{1 \cancel{yard}} = 12 \text{ feet}$$

(e) 39 feet to yards

$\dfrac{1 \text{ yard}}{3 \text{ feet}}$ $\dfrac{unit}{fraction}$

$\dfrac{\overset{13}{\cancel{39}} \cancel{\text{feet}}}{1} \cdot \dfrac{1 \text{ yard}}{\underset{1}{\cancel{3}} \, \cancel{\text{feet}}} = 13 \text{ yards}$

(f) 2 miles to feet

$\dfrac{5280 \text{ feet}}{1 \text{ mile}}$ $\dfrac{unit}{fraction}$

$\dfrac{2 \, \cancel{\text{miles}}}{1} \cdot \dfrac{5280 \text{ feet}}{1 \, \cancel{\text{mile}}} = 10{,}560 \text{ feet}$

4. (a) 16 pints to quarts

$\dfrac{1 \text{ quart}}{2 \text{ pints}}$ $\dfrac{unit}{fraction}$

$\dfrac{\overset{8}{\cancel{16}} \, \cancel{\text{pints}}}{1} \cdot \dfrac{1 \text{ quart}}{\underset{1}{\cancel{2}} \, \cancel{\text{pints}}} = 8 \text{ quarts}$

(b) 16 quarts to gallons

$\dfrac{1 \text{ gallon}}{4 \text{ quarts}}$ $\dfrac{unit}{fraction}$

$\dfrac{\overset{4}{\cancel{16}} \, \cancel{\text{quarts}}}{1} \cdot \dfrac{1 \text{ gallon}}{\underset{1}{\cancel{4}} \, \cancel{\text{quarts}}} = 4 \text{ gallons}$

(c) 3 cups to pints

$\dfrac{1 \text{ pint}}{2 \text{ cups}}$ $\dfrac{unit}{fraction}$

$\dfrac{3 \, \cancel{\text{cups}}}{1} \cdot \dfrac{1 \text{ pint}}{2 \, \cancel{\text{cups}}} = 1\tfrac{1}{2} \text{ pints}$

(d) $2\tfrac{1}{4}$ gallons to quarts

$\dfrac{4 \text{ quarts}}{1 \text{ gallon}}$ $\dfrac{unit}{fraction}$

$\dfrac{2\tfrac{1}{4} \, \cancel{\text{gallons}}}{1} \cdot \dfrac{4 \text{ quarts}}{1 \, \cancel{\text{gallon}}} = \dfrac{9}{\underset{1}{\cancel{4}}} \cdot \dfrac{\overset{1}{\cancel{4}}}{1} = 9 \text{ quarts}$

(e) 48 ounces to pounds

$\dfrac{1 \text{ pound}}{16 \text{ ounces}}$ $\dfrac{unit}{fraction}$

$\dfrac{\overset{3}{\cancel{48}} \, \cancel{\text{ounces}}}{1} \cdot \dfrac{1 \text{ pound}}{\underset{1}{\cancel{16}} \, \cancel{\text{ounces}}} = 3 \text{ pounds}$

(f) $3\tfrac{1}{2}$ tons to pounds

$\dfrac{2000 \text{ pounds}}{1 \text{ ton}}$ $\dfrac{unit}{fraction}$

$\dfrac{3\tfrac{1}{2} \, \cancel{\text{tons}}}{1} \cdot \dfrac{2000 \text{ pounds}}{1 \, \cancel{\text{ton}}} = \dfrac{7}{\underset{1}{\cancel{2}}} \cdot \dfrac{\overset{1000}{\cancel{2000}}}{1}$

$= 7000 \text{ pounds}$

(g) $1\tfrac{3}{4}$ pounds to ounces

$\dfrac{16 \text{ ounces}}{1 \text{ pound}}$ $\dfrac{unit}{fraction}$

$\dfrac{1\tfrac{3}{4} \, \cancel{\text{pounds}}}{1} \cdot \dfrac{16 \text{ ounces}}{1 \, \cancel{\text{pound}}} = \dfrac{7}{\underset{1}{\cancel{4}}} \cdot \dfrac{\overset{4}{\cancel{16}}}{1}$

$= 28 \text{ ounces}$

(h) 4 ounces to pounds

$\dfrac{1 \text{ pound}}{16 \text{ ounces}}$ $\dfrac{unit}{fraction}$

$\dfrac{\overset{1}{\cancel{4}} \, \cancel{\text{ounces}}}{1} \cdot \dfrac{1 \text{ pound}}{\underset{4}{\cancel{16}} \, \cancel{\text{ounces}}} = \dfrac{1}{4} \text{ or } 0.25 \text{ pound}$

5. (a) 4 tons to ounces

$\dfrac{2000 \text{ pounds}}{1 \text{ ton}}$ $\dfrac{16 \text{ ounces}}{1 \text{ pound}}$ $\dfrac{unit}{fractions}$

$\dfrac{4 \, \cancel{\text{tons}}}{1} \cdot \dfrac{2000 \, \cancel{\text{pounds}}}{1 \, \cancel{\text{ton}}} \cdot \dfrac{16 \text{ ounces}}{1 \, \cancel{\text{pound}}}$

$= 4 \cdot 2000 \cdot 16 \text{ ounces}$

$= 128{,}000 \text{ ounces}$

(b) 90 inches to yards

$\dfrac{1 \text{ foot}}{12 \text{ inches}}$ $\dfrac{1 \text{ yard}}{3 \text{ feet}}$ $\dfrac{unit}{fraction}$

$\dfrac{90 \, \cancel{\text{inches}}}{1} \cdot \dfrac{1 \, \cancel{\text{foot}}}{12 \, \cancel{\text{inches}}} \cdot \dfrac{1 \text{ yard}}{3 \, \cancel{\text{feet}}}$

$= \dfrac{\overset{\overset{5}{30}}{\cancel{90}} \cdot 1 \cdot 1}{1 \cdot \underset{2}{\cancel{12}} \cdot \underset{1}{\cancel{3}}} \text{ yards}$

$= \dfrac{5}{2} \text{ yards} = 2\tfrac{1}{2} \text{ yards or } 2.5 \text{ yards}$

Section 7.1 The English System

(c) 3 miles to inches

$$\frac{5280 \text{ feet}}{1 \text{ mile}} \quad \frac{12 \text{ inches}}{1 \text{ foot}} \quad \text{unit fractions}$$

$$\frac{3 \cancel{\text{miles}}}{1} \cdot \frac{5280 \cancel{\text{feet}}}{1 \cancel{\text{mile}}} \cdot \frac{12 \text{ inches}}{1 \cancel{\text{foot}}}$$

$$= 3 \cdot 5280 \cdot 12 \text{ inches}$$
$$= 190,080 \text{ inches}$$

(d) 36 pints to gallons

$$\frac{1 \text{ quart}}{2 \text{ pints}} \quad \frac{1 \text{ gallon}}{4 \text{ quarts}} \quad \text{unit fractions}$$

$$\frac{36 \cancel{\text{pints}}}{1} \cdot \frac{1 \cancel{\text{quart}}}{2 \cancel{\text{pints}}} \cdot \frac{1 \text{ gallon}}{4 \cancel{\text{quarts}}}$$

$$= \frac{\overset{9}{\cancel{36}}}{1} \cdot \frac{1}{2} \cdot \frac{1}{\underset{1}{\cancel{4}}} \text{ gallons}$$

$$= \frac{9}{2} \text{ gallons} = 4\frac{1}{2} \text{ or } 4.5 \text{ gallons}$$

(e) 4 weeks to minutes

$$\frac{7 \text{ days}}{1 \text{ week}} \quad \frac{24 \text{ hours}}{1 \text{ day}} \quad \frac{60 \text{ minutes}}{1 \text{ hour}} \quad \text{unit fractions}$$

$$\frac{4 \cancel{\text{weeks}}}{1} \cdot \frac{7 \cancel{\text{days}}}{1 \cancel{\text{week}}} \cdot \frac{24 \cancel{\text{hours}}}{1 \cancel{\text{day}}} \cdot \frac{60 \text{ minutes}}{1 \cancel{\text{hour}}}$$

$$= 4 \cdot 7 \cdot 24 \cdot 60 \text{ minutes}$$
$$= 40,320 \text{ minutes}$$

(f) $1\frac{1}{2}$ gallons to cups

$$\frac{4 \text{ quarts}}{1 \text{ gallon}} \quad \frac{2 \text{ pints}}{1 \text{ quart}} \quad \frac{2 \text{ cups}}{1 \text{ pint}} \quad \text{unit fractions}$$

$$\frac{1\frac{1}{2} \cancel{\text{gallons}}}{1} \cdot \frac{4 \cancel{\text{quarts}}}{1 \cancel{\text{gallon}}} \cdot \frac{2 \cancel{\text{pints}}}{1 \cancel{\text{quart}}} \cdot \frac{2 \text{ cups}}{1 \cancel{\text{pint}}}$$

$$= 1\frac{1}{2} \cdot 4 \cdot 2 \cdot 2 \text{ cups}$$
$$= 24 \text{ cups}$$

7.1 Section Exercises

3. $\underline{8}$ fluid ounces = 1 cup

7. $\underline{2000}$ pounds = 1 ton

11. 120 seconds to minutes

$$\frac{\overset{2}{\cancel{120}} \cancel{\text{seconds}}}{1} \cdot \frac{1 \text{ minute}}{\underset{1}{\cancel{60}} \cancel{\text{seconds}}} = 2 \text{ minutes}$$

15. 38 to 40 tons to pounds

$$\frac{38 \cancel{\text{tons}}}{1} \cdot \frac{2000 \text{ pounds}}{1 \cancel{\text{ton}}} = 76,000 \text{ pounds}$$

$$\frac{40 \cancel{\text{tons}}}{1} \cdot \frac{2000 \text{ pounds}}{1 \cancel{\text{ton}}} = 80,000 \text{ pounds}$$

An adult sperm whale may weigh 76,000 to 80,000 pounds.

19. 7 pounds to ounces

$$\frac{7 \cancel{\text{pounds}}}{1} \cdot \frac{16 \text{ ounces}}{1 \cancel{\text{pound}}}$$

$$= 7 \cdot 16 \text{ ounces} = 112 \text{ ounces}$$

23. 90 minutes to hours

$$\frac{90 \cancel{\text{minutes}}}{1} \cdot \frac{1 \text{ hour}}{60 \cancel{\text{minutes}}}$$

$$= \frac{90}{60} \text{ hours} = 1\frac{1}{2} \text{ or } 1.5 \text{ hours}$$

27. 24 ounces to pounds

$$\frac{24 \cancel{\text{ounces}}}{1} \cdot \frac{1 \text{ pound}}{16 \cancel{\text{ounces}}}$$

$$= \frac{24}{16} \text{ pounds} = 1\frac{1}{2} \text{ or } 1.5 \text{ pounds}$$

31. 12 hours is what part of a day?

$$\frac{\overset{1}{\cancel{12}} \cancel{\text{hours}}}{1} \cdot \frac{1 \text{ day}}{\underset{2}{\cancel{24}} \cancel{\text{hours}}} = \frac{1}{2} \text{ or } 0.5 \text{ day}$$

35. $4\frac{1}{4}$ gallons to quarts

$$\frac{4\frac{1}{4} \cancel{\text{gallons}}}{1} \cdot \frac{4 \text{ quarts}}{1 \cancel{\text{gallon}}}$$

$$= 4\frac{1}{4} \cdot 4 \text{ quarts}$$

$$= \frac{17}{4} \cdot \frac{4}{1} \text{ quarts}$$

$$= 17 \text{ quarts}$$

39. 6 yards to inches

$$\frac{6 \cancel{\text{yards}}}{1} \cdot \frac{3 \cancel{\text{feet}}}{1 \cancel{\text{yard}}} \cdot \frac{12 \text{ inches}}{1 \cancel{\text{foot}}}$$

$$= 6 \cdot 3 \cdot 12 \text{ inches}$$
$$= 216 \text{ inches}$$

43. 6 days to seconds

$$\frac{6 \cancel{\text{days}}}{1} \cdot \frac{24 \cancel{\text{hours}}}{1 \cancel{\text{day}}} \cdot \frac{60 \cancel{\text{minutes}}}{1 \cancel{\text{hour}}}$$

$$\cdot \frac{60 \text{ seconds}}{1 \cancel{\text{minute}}}$$

$$= 6 \cdot 24 \cdot 60 \cdot 60 \text{ seconds}$$
$$= 518,400 \text{ seconds}$$

47. (a) 1 pound = 16 ounces

(b) 10 quarts = 20 pints
or 10 pints = 20 cups

(c) 120 minutes = 2 hours
or 120 seconds = 2 minutes

(d) 2 feet = 24 inches

(e) 6000 pounds = 3 tons

(f) 35 days = 5 weeks

51. $6\frac{1}{4}$ gallons to fluid ounces

$$\frac{6\frac{1}{4} \text{ g\!a\!l\!l\!o\!n\!s}}{1} \cdot \frac{4 \text{ q\!u\!a\!r\!t\!s}}{1 \text{ g\!a\!l\!l\!o\!n}} \cdot \frac{32 \text{ ounces}}{1 \text{ q\!u\!a\!r\!t}}$$

$= 6\frac{1}{4} \cdot 4 \cdot 32$ ounces

$= 800$ fluid ounces

55. 129,600 seconds to days

$$\frac{129,600 \text{ s\!e\!c\!o\!n\!d\!s}}{1} \cdot \frac{1 \text{ m\!i\!n\!u\!t\!e}}{60 \text{ s\!e\!c\!o\!n\!d\!s}}$$

$$\cdot \frac{1 \text{ h\!o\!u\!r}}{60 \text{ m\!i\!n\!u\!t\!e\!s}} \cdot \frac{1 \text{ day}}{24 \text{ h\!o\!u\!r\!s}}$$

$= \frac{129,600}{60 \cdot 60 \cdot 24}$ days

$= 1.5$ or $1\frac{1}{2}$ days

59. 4 hours ____ 185 minutes
4 hours $= 4 \cdot 60 = 240$ minutes
240 minutes $>$ 185 minutes so,
4 hours $>$ 185 minutes.

7.2 The Metric System—Length

7.2 Margin Exercises

1. The length of a baseball bat, the height of a doorknob from the floor, and a basketball player's arm length are each about 1 meter in length.

2. (a) The woman's height is 168 *cm*.

(b) The man's waist is 90 *cm* around.

(c) Louise ran the 100 *m* dash in the track meet.

(d) A postage stamp is 22 *mm* wide.

(e) Michael paddled his canoe 2 *km* down the river.

(f) The pencil lead is 1 *mm* thick.

(g) A stick of gum is 7 *cm* long.

(h) The highway speed limit is 90 *km* per hour.

(i) The classroom was 12 *m* long.

(j) A penny is about 18 *mm* across.

3. (a) 3.67 m to cm

$$\text{unit fraction} \Big\} \frac{100 \text{ cm}}{1 \text{ m}}$$

$$\frac{3.67 \text{ m\!}}{1} \cdot \frac{100 \text{ cm}}{1 \text{ m\!}} = 3.67 \cdot 100 \text{ cm} = 367 \text{ cm}$$

(b) 92 cm to m

$$\text{unit fraction} \Big\} \frac{1 \text{ m}}{100 \text{ cm}}$$

$$\frac{92 \text{ c\!m\!}}{1} \cdot \frac{1 \text{ m}}{100 \text{ c\!m\!}} = \frac{92}{100} \text{ m} = 0.92 \text{ m}$$

(c) 432.7 cm to m

$$\text{unit fraction} \Big\} \frac{1 \text{ m}}{100 \text{ cm}}$$

$$\frac{432.7 \text{ c\!m\!}}{1} \cdot \frac{1 \text{ m}}{100 \text{ c\!m\!}} = \frac{432.7}{100} \text{ m} = 4.327 \text{ m}$$

(d) 65 mm to cm

$$\text{unit fraction} \Big\} \frac{1 \text{ cm}}{10 \text{ mm}}$$

$$\frac{65 \text{ m\!m\!}}{1} \cdot \frac{1 \text{ cm}}{10 \text{ m\!m\!}} = \frac{65}{10} \text{ cm} = 6.5 \text{ cm}$$

(e) 0.9 m to mm

$$\text{unit fraction} \Big\} \frac{1000 \text{ mm}}{1 \text{ m}}$$

$$\frac{0.9 \text{ m\!}}{1} \cdot \frac{1000 \text{ mm}}{1 \text{ m\!}} = 0.9 \cdot 1000 \text{ mm}$$
$$= 900 \text{ mm}$$

(f) 2.5 cm to mm

$$\text{unit fraction} \Big\} \frac{10 \text{ mm}}{1 \text{ cm}}$$

$$\frac{2.5 \text{ c\!m\!}}{1} \cdot \frac{10 \text{ mm}}{1 \text{ c\!m\!}} = 2.5 \cdot 10 \text{ mm} = 25 \text{ mm}$$

Section 7.2 The Metric System—Length

4. (a) $43.5 \cdot 10 = \underline{435}$
   $43.5_\wedge$ gives $\underline{435}$.

   (b) $43.5 \div 10 = \underline{4.35}$
   $4_\wedge 3.5$ gives $\underline{4.35}$.

   (c) $28 \cdot 100 = \underline{2800}$
   $28.00_\wedge$ gives $\underline{2800}$.

   (d) $28 \div 100 = \underline{0.28}$
   $_\wedge 28.$ gives $\underline{0.28}$.

   (e) $0.7 \cdot 1000 = \underline{700}$
   $0.700_\wedge$ gives $\underline{700}$.

   (f) $0.7 \div 1000 = \underline{0.0007}$
   $_\wedge 000.7$ gives $\underline{0.0007}$.

5. (a) 12.008 km to m
   Count 3 places to the right on the conversion line.

   $12.008_\wedge$ km $= 12,008$ m

   (b) 561.4 m to km
   Count 3 places to the left on the conversion line.

   $_\wedge 561.4$ m $= 0.5614$ km

   (c) 20.7 cm to m
   Count 2 places to the left on the conversion line.

   $_\wedge 20.7$ cm $= 0.207$ m

   (d) 20.7 cm to mm
   Count 1 place to the right on the conversion line.

   $20.7_\wedge$ cm $= 207$ m

   (e) 4.66 m to cm
   Count 2 places to the right on the conversion line.

   $4.66_\wedge$ m $= 466$ cm

   (f) 85.6 mm to cm
   Count 1 place to the left on the conversion line.

   $8_\wedge 5.6$ mm $= 8.56$ cm

6. (a) 9 m to mm
   Count 3 places to the right on the conversion line.

   $9.000_\wedge$ m $= 9000$ mm

   (b) 3 cm to m
   Count 2 places to the left on the conversion line.

   $_\wedge 03.$ cm $= 0.03$ m

   (c) 14.6 km to m
   Count 3 places to the right on the conversion line.

   $14.600_\wedge$ km $= 14,600$ m

   (d) 5 mm to cm
   Count 1 place to the left on the conversion line.

   $_\wedge 5.$ mm $= 0.5$ cm

   (e) 70 m to km
   Count 3 places to the left on the conversion.

   $_\wedge 070.$ m $= 0.07$ km

   (f) 0.8 m to cm
   Count 2 places to the right on the conversion line.

   $0.80_\wedge$ m $= 80$ cm

7.2 Section Exercises

3. milli means $\frac{1}{1000}$ or $\underline{0.001}$ so

   1 mm $= \underline{\frac{1}{1000}}$ or $\underline{0.001}$ m.

7. the width of your hand in centimeters
   The answer varies—about 8 cm.

11. The child was about 91 *cm* tall.

15. Adriana drove 400 *km* on her vacation.

19. A paper clip is about 3 *cm* long.

23. Examples include 35 mm film for cameras, track and field events, metric auto parts, and lead refills for mechanical pencils.

27. 40 mm to m

   $$\frac{40 \cancel{mm}}{1} \cdot \frac{1 \text{ m}}{1000 \cancel{mm}} = \frac{40}{1000} \text{ m}$$
   $$= 0.040 \text{ m or } 0.04 \text{ m}$$

31. 509 cm to

   $$\frac{509 \cancel{cm}}{1} \cdot \frac{1 \text{ m}}{100 \cancel{cm}} = \frac{509}{100} \text{ m} = 5.09 \text{ m}$$

35. 0.91 m to mm
   Count 3 places to the right on the conversion line.

   $0.910_\wedge$ m $= 910$ mm

39. 35 mm to centimeters

Count one place to the left on the conversion line.

35 mm = 3.5 cm

70 mm to centimeters

Count one place to the left on the conversion line.

70 mm = 7 cm

43. $0.875 = \dfrac{875}{1000} = \dfrac{875 \div 125}{1000 \div 125} = \dfrac{7}{8}$

7.3 The Metric System–Capacity and Weight (Mass)

7.3 Margin Exercises

1. The liter would be used to measure the amount of water in the bathtub, gasoline you buy for your car, and water in a pail.

2. (a) I bought 8 *L* of milk at the store.

   (b) The nurse gave me 10 *mL* of cough syrup.

   (c) This is a 100 *L* garbage can.

   (d) It took 10 *L* of paint to cover the bathroom walls.

   (e) My car's gas tank holds 50 *L*.

   (f) I added 15 *mL* of oil to the pancake mix.

   (g) The can of orange soda holds 350 *mL*.

   (h) My friend gave me a 30 *mL* bottle of expensive perfume.

3. (a) 9 L to mL

   $\dfrac{9 \;\cancel{L}}{1} \cdot \dfrac{1000 \text{ mL}}{1 \;\cancel{L}} = 9000 \text{ mL}$

   (b) 0.75 L to mL

   Count 3 places to the right on the conversion line.

   $0.750_\wedge \text{ L} = 750 \text{ mL}$

   (c) 500 mL to L

   $\dfrac{500 \;\cancel{mL}}{1} \cdot \dfrac{1 \text{ L}}{1000 \;\cancel{mL}} = \dfrac{500}{1000} \text{ L} = 0.5 \text{ L}$

   (d) 5 mL to L

   Count 3 places to the left on the conversion line.

   $_\wedge 005. \text{ mL} = 0.005 \text{ L}$

   (e) 2.07 L to mL

   $\dfrac{2.07 \;\cancel{L}}{1} \cdot \dfrac{1000 \text{ mL}}{1 \;\cancel{L}} = 2070 \text{ mL}$

   (f) 3275 mL to L

   Count 3 places to the left on the conversion line.

   $3_\wedge 275. \text{ mL} = 3.275 \text{ L}$

4. A small paper clip, one playing card, and the check you wrote at the grocery store would each weigh about 1 gram.

5. (a) A thumbtack weighs 800 *mg*.

   (b) A teenager weighs 50 *kg*.

   (c) This large cast-iron frying pan weighs 1 *kg*.

   (d) Jerry's basketball weighed 600 *g*.

   (e) Tamlyn takes a 500 *mg* calcium tablet every morning.

   (f) On his diet, Greg can eat 90 *g* of meat for lunch.

   (g) One strand of hair weighs 2 *mg*.

   (h) One banana might weigh 150 *g*.

6. (a) 10 kg to g

   $\dfrac{10 \;\cancel{kg}}{1} \cdot \dfrac{1000 \text{ g}}{1 \;\cancel{kg}} = 10{,}000 \text{ g}$

   (b) 45 mg to g

   $\dfrac{45 \;\cancel{mg}}{1} \cdot \dfrac{1 \text{ g}}{1000 \;\cancel{mg}} = \dfrac{45}{1000} \text{ g} = 0.045 \text{ g}$

   (c) 6.3 kg to g

   Count 3 places to the right on the conversion line.

   $6.300_\wedge \text{ kg} = 6300 \text{ g}$

   (d) 0.077 g to mg

   Count 3 places to the right on the conversion line.

   $0.077_\wedge \text{ g} = 77 \text{ mg}$

   (e) 5630 g to kg

   Count 3 places to the left on the conversion line.

   $5_\wedge 630. \text{ g} = 5.63 \text{ kg}$

   (f) 90 g to kg

   $\dfrac{90 \;\cancel{g}}{1} \cdot \dfrac{1 \text{ kg}}{1000 \;\cancel{g}} = \dfrac{9}{100} \text{ kg} = 0.09 \text{ kg}$

7. **(a)** Gail bought a 4 L can of paint.
Use *capacity* units.

(b) The bag of chips weighed 450 g.
Use *weight* units.

(c) Give the child 5 mL of liquid aspirin.
Use *capacity* units.

(d) The width of the window is 55 cm.
Use *length* units.

(e) Akbar drives 18 km to work.
Use *length* units.

(f) Each computer weighs 5 kg.
Use *weight* units.

(g) A credit card is 55 mm wide.
Use *length* units.

7.3 Section Exercises

3. Dolores can make 10 L of soup in that pot.

7. Lori caught a small sunfish weighing 150 g.

11. The patient received 250 mg of medication each hour.

15. Pam's backpack weighs 5 kg when it is full of books.

19. This is unreasonable since 5 kilograms of Epsom salts would be about 11 pounds with approximately a quart of water.

23. This is reasonable because 350 milligrams would be a little more than 1 tablet which is 325 milligrams.

27. The unit for your answer (g) is in the numerator. The unit being changed (kg) is in the denominator so it will cancel. The unit fraction is

$$\frac{1000 \text{ g}}{1 \text{ kg}}.$$

31. 3000 mL to L

Count 3 places to the left on the conversion line.

$$3{\scriptstyle\wedge}000 \text{ mL} = 3 \text{ L}$$

35. 8 mL to L

$$\frac{8 \text{ mL}}{1} \cdot \frac{1 \text{ L}}{1000 \text{ mL}} = \frac{8}{1000} \text{ L} = 0.008 \text{ L}$$

39. 8000 g to kg

Count 3 places to the left on the conversion line.

$$8{\scriptstyle\wedge}000. \text{ g} = 8 \text{ kg}$$

43. 0.85 g to mg

Count 3 places to the right on the conversion line.

$$0.850 \text{ g} = 850 \text{ mg}$$

47. 598 mg to g

Count 3 places to the left on the conversion line.

$$_{\wedge}598. \text{ mg} = 0.598 \text{ g}$$

51. 3 g to kg

$$\frac{3 \text{ g}}{1} \cdot \frac{1 \text{ kg}}{1000 \text{ g}} = \frac{3}{1000} \text{ kg} = 0.003 \text{ kg}$$

55. The masking tape is 19 mm wide.

59. My waist measurement is 65 cm.

63. 2 liters to milliliters

$$\frac{2 \text{ L}}{1} \cdot \frac{1000 \text{ mL}}{1 \text{ L}} = 2000 \text{ mL}$$

67. Convert 70 mL to liters.

$$\frac{\overset{7}{\cancel{70}} \text{ mL}}{1} \cdot \frac{1 \text{ L}}{\underset{100}{\cancel{1000}} \text{ mL}} = \frac{7}{100} \text{ L} = 0.07 \text{ L}$$

A healthy human heart pumps 0.07 L of blood per beat.

71. There are 1000 milligrams in a gram so 1005 mg is *greater* than 1 g. The difference in weight is

$$1005 \text{ mg} - 1000 \text{ mg} = 5 \text{ mg}$$
$$\text{or} \quad 1.005 \text{ g} - 1 \text{ g} = 0.005 \text{ g}.$$

75. 1 liter to milliliters

Count 3 places to the right on the conversion line.

$$1.000{\scriptstyle\wedge} \text{ L} = 1000 \text{ mL}$$

Each milliliter of helium weighs 0.0002 gram, so to find the weight of 1 liter multiply 0.0002 and 1000.

$$0.0002 \cdot 1000 = 0.2 \text{ gram}$$

7.4 Applications of Metric Measurement

7.4 Margin Exercises

1. (a) Convert 75 cm to meters.

75 cm = 0.75 m

$$\frac{\$0.89}{1 \text{ m}} \cdot \frac{0.75 \text{ m}}{1} = \$0.6675$$

The cost for 75 cm is ≈$0.67.

(b) Convert 1.2 grams to milligrams.

1.200∧ g = 1200 mg

Divide by the number of doses.

$$\frac{1200 \text{ mg}}{3 \text{ doses}} = 400 \text{ mg/dose}$$

Each dose should be 400 mg.

2. (a) Convert centimeters to meters.

2 m 35 cm = 2.35 m
1 m 85 cm = 1.85 m

Add the measurements of the fabric.

one piece   2.35 m
other piece   + 1.85 m
                    4.20 m

Andrea has 4.2 m of fabric.

(b) Convert centimeters to meters.

9 m 20 cm = 9.20 cm

Divide by the number of pieces needed.

$$\frac{9.2 \text{ m}}{8 \text{ scouts}} = \frac{1.15 \text{ m}}{\text{scout}}$$

Each count will get 1.15 m.

7.4 Section Exercises

3. Convert grams to kilograms.

15 g = 0.015 kg

Multiply the amount of fertilizer used for each plant and the number of applications.

0.015 kg · 650 = 9.75 kg

Kendal used 9.75 kg of fertilizer.

7. Convert centimeters to meters. Then add the lengths of the two pieces.

2 m 8 cm =   2.08 m
2 m 95 cm = + 2.95 m
                      5.03 m

Together the boards are 5.03 m.

11. A box of 50 envelopes weighs 255 g. Subtract the packaging weight to find the net weight.

   255 g
− 40 g
   215 g

There are 50 envelopes. Divide to find the weight of one envelope.

$$\frac{215 \text{ g}}{50 \text{ envelopes}} = \frac{4.3 \text{ g}}{\text{envelope}}$$

Convert grams to milligrams.

$$\frac{4.3 \text{ g}}{1} \cdot \frac{1000 \text{ mg}}{1 \text{ g}} = 4300 \text{ mg}$$

15. Convert kilograms to grams.

40 kg = 40,000 g

Divide by the size of the bags sold.

$$\frac{40,000 \text{ g}}{250 \text{ g}} = 160 \text{ bags}$$

Multiply the number of bags sold and the cost per bag.

160 · $2.95 = $472

The amount of profit is

$472 − $113.50 = $358.50.

19.   0.035   ← 3 *decimal places*
   ×   18
      280
       35
   0.630   ← 3 *decimal places*

0.630 = 0.63

7.5 Metric–English Conversions and Temperature

7.5 Margin Exercises

1. 23 meters to yards

$$\frac{23 \text{ meters}}{1} \cdot \frac{1.09 \text{ yards}}{1 \text{ meter}} \approx 25.1 \text{ yards}$$

(b) 40 centimeters to inches

$$\frac{40 \text{ centimeters}}{1} \cdot \frac{0.39 \text{ inch}}{1 \text{ centimeter}} \approx 15.6 \text{ inches}$$

(c) 5 miles to kilometers

$$\frac{5 \text{ miles}}{1} \cdot \frac{1.61 \text{ kilometers}}{1 \text{ mile}} \approx 8.1 \text{ kilometers}$$

(d) 12 inches to centimeters

$$\frac{12 \text{ inches}}{1} \cdot \frac{2.54 \text{ centimeters}}{1 \text{ inch}}$$
$$\approx 30.5 \text{ centimeters}$$

2. (a) 17 kilograms to pounds

$$\frac{17 \text{ kilograms}}{1} \cdot \frac{2.20 \text{ pounds}}{1 \text{ kilograms}} \approx 37.4 \text{ pounds}$$

(b) 5 liters to quarts

$$\frac{5 \text{ liters}}{1} \cdot \frac{1.06 \text{ quarts}}{1 \text{ liter}} \approx 5.3 \text{ quarts}$$

(c) 90 grams to ounces

$$\frac{90 \text{ grams}}{1} \cdot \frac{0.035 \text{ ounce}}{1 \text{ gram}} \approx 3.2 \text{ ounces}$$

(d) 3.5 gallons to liters

$$\frac{3.5 \text{ gallons}}{1} \cdot \frac{3.78 \text{ liters}}{1 \text{ gallon}} \approx 13.2 \text{ liters}$$

(e) 145 pounds to kilograms

$$\frac{145 \text{ pounds}}{1} \cdot \frac{0.45 \text{ kilograms}}{1 \text{ pound}} \approx 65.3 \text{ kilograms}$$

(f) 8 ounces to grams

$$\frac{8 \text{ ounces}}{1} \cdot \frac{28.35 \text{ grams}}{1 \text{ ounce}} \approx 226.8 \text{ grams}$$

3. (a) Set the living room thermostat at:

21°C.

(b) The baby has a fever of:

39°C.

(c) Wear a sweater outside because its:

15°C.

(d) My iced tea is:

5°C.

(e) Time to go swimming! It's

35°C.

(f) Inside a refrigerator (not the freezer) it's:

3°C.

(g) There is a blizzard outside. It's

−20°C.

(h) I need hot water to get these clothes clean. It should be:

55°C.

4. Use $C = \dfrac{5(F - 32)}{9}$.

(a) 59°F

$$C = \frac{5(59 - 32)}{9} = \frac{5 \cdot \overset{3}{\cancel{27}}}{\underset{1}{\cancel{9}}} = 15$$

59°F = 15°C

(b) 41°F

$$C = \frac{5(41 - 32)}{9} = \frac{5 \cdot \overset{1}{\cancel{9}}}{\underset{1}{\cancel{9}}} = 5$$

41°F = 5°C

(c) 212°F

$$C = \frac{5(212 - 32)}{9} = \frac{5 \cdot \overset{20}{\cancel{180}}}{\underset{1}{\cancel{9}}} = 100$$

212°F = 100°C

(d) 98.6°F

$$C = \frac{5(98.6 - 32)}{9} = \frac{5 \cdot \overset{7.4}{\cancel{66.6}}}{\underset{1}{\cancel{9}}} = 37$$

98.6°F = 37°C

5. Use $F = \dfrac{9 \cdot C}{5} + 32$.

   (a) $100°C$

   $$\dfrac{9 \cdot \overset{20}{\cancel{100}}}{\underset{1}{\cancel{5}}} + 32 = 180 + 32 = 212$$

   $100°C = 212°F$

   (b) $25°C$

   $$F = \dfrac{9 \cdot \overset{5}{\cancel{25}}}{\underset{1}{\cancel{5}}} + 32 = 45 + 32 = 77$$

   $25°C = 77°F$

   (c) $80°C$

   $$F = \dfrac{9 \cdot \overset{16}{\cancel{80}}}{\underset{1}{\cancel{5}}} + 32 = 144 + 32 = 176$$

   $80°C = 176°F$

   (d) $5°C$

   $$F = \dfrac{9 \cdot \overset{1}{\cancel{5}}}{\underset{1}{\cancel{5}}} + 32 = 9 + 32 = 41$$

   $5°C = 41°F$

7.5 Section Exercises

For Exercises 3-11, use the *Metric to English* table.

3. 80 meters to feet

   $$\dfrac{80 \; \cancel{\text{meters}}}{1} \cdot \dfrac{3.28 \text{ feet}}{1 \; \cancel{\text{meter}}} \approx 262.4 \text{ feet}$$

7. 150 grams to ounces

   $$\dfrac{150 \; \cancel{\text{grams}}}{1} \cdot \dfrac{0.035 \text{ ounce}}{1 \; \cancel{\text{gram}}} \approx 5.3 \text{ ounces}$$

11. 28.6 liters to quarts

    $$\dfrac{28.6 \; \cancel{\text{liters}}}{1} \cdot \dfrac{1.06 \text{ quarts}}{1 \; \cancel{\text{liter}}} \approx 30.3 \text{ quarts}$$

15. A snowy day
    $28°F$ is reasonable. $28°C$ is a temperature for a summer day.

19. Oven temperature
    $150°C$ is equivalent to $300°F$ so this is a reasonable oven temperature.

23. $60°F$

    $$C = \dfrac{5(60-32)}{9} = \dfrac{5 \cdot 28}{9} = \dfrac{140}{9} \approx 15.6$$

    $60°F \approx 16°C$

27. $8°C$

    $$F = \dfrac{9 \cdot 8}{5} + 32 = \dfrac{72}{5} + 32 = 14.4 + 32 = 46.4$$

    $8°C \approx 46°F$

31. $136°F$

    $$C = \dfrac{5(136-32)}{9} = \dfrac{5 \cdot 104}{9} = \dfrac{520}{9} \approx 57.8$$

    $136°F \approx 58°C$

35. Convert liters to gallons.

    $$4 \text{ L} \approx 4 \cdot 0.26 = 1.04 \text{ gallons}$$

    Multiply by the cost per gallon.

    $$\$9.20 \cdot 1.04 = \$9.568$$

    The cost is $\approx \$9.57$ (liters converted to gallons).

39. $9^2 = 9 \cdot 9 = 81$

Chapter 7 Review Exercises

1. 1 pound = <u>16</u> ounces
2. <u>3</u> feet = 1 yard
3. 1 ton = <u>2000</u> pounds
4. <u>24</u> hours = 1 day
5. 1 hour = <u>60</u> minutes
6. 1 cup = <u>8</u> fluid ounces
7. <u>4</u> quarts = 1 gallon
8. <u>5280</u> feet = 1 mile
9. <u>12</u> inches = 1 foot
10. 1 week = <u>7</u> days
11. <u>60</u> seconds = 1 minute
12. 1 pint = <u>2</u> cups

Chapter 7 Review Exercises

13. 4 feet to inches

$$\frac{4 \cancel{\text{feet}}}{1} \cdot \frac{12 \text{ inches}}{1 \cancel{\text{foot}}} = 4 \cdot 12 \text{ inches}$$
$$= 48 \text{ inches}$$

14. 15 yards to feet

$$\frac{15 \cancel{\text{yards}}}{1} \cdot \frac{3 \text{ feet}}{1 \cancel{\text{yard}}} = 45 \text{ feet}$$

15. 64 ounces to pounds

$$\frac{\overset{4}{\cancel{64}} \cancel{\text{ounces}}}{1} \cdot \frac{1 \text{ pound}}{\underset{1}{\cancel{16}} \cancel{\text{ounces}}} = 4 \text{ pounds}$$

16. 6000 pounds to tons

$$\frac{\overset{3}{\cancel{6000}} \cancel{\text{pounds}}}{1} \cdot \frac{1 \text{ ton}}{\underset{1}{\cancel{2000}} \cancel{\text{pounds}}} = 3 \text{ tons}$$

17. 150 minutes to hours

$$\frac{\overset{5}{\cancel{150}} \cancel{\text{minutes}}}{1} \cdot \frac{1 \text{ hour}}{\underset{2}{\cancel{60}} \cancel{\text{minutes}}}$$
$$= \frac{5 \cdot 1}{2} \text{ hours} = 2\frac{1}{2} \text{ or } 2.5 \text{ hours}$$

18. 11 cups to pints

$$\frac{11 \cancel{\text{cups}}}{1} \cdot \frac{1 \text{ pint}}{2 \cancel{\text{cups}}}$$
$$= \frac{11 \cdot 1}{2} \text{ pints} = 5\frac{1}{2} \text{ or } 5.5 \text{ pints}$$

19. 18 hours to days

$$\frac{\overset{3}{\cancel{18}} \cancel{\text{hours}}}{1} \cdot \frac{1 \text{ day}}{\underset{4}{\cancel{24}} \cancel{\text{hours}}}$$
$$= \frac{3 \cdot 1}{4} \text{ day} = \frac{3}{4} \text{ or } 0.75 \text{ day}$$

20. 9 quarts to gallons

$$\frac{9 \cancel{\text{quarts}}}{1} \cdot \frac{1 \text{ gallon}}{4 \cancel{\text{quarts}}}$$
$$= \frac{9 \cdot 1}{4} \text{ gallons} = 2\frac{1}{4} \text{ or } 2.25 \text{ gallons}$$

21. $6\frac{1}{2}$ feet to inches

$$\frac{6\frac{1}{2} \cancel{\text{feet}}}{1} \cdot \frac{12 \text{ inches}}{1 \cancel{\text{foot}}} = 78 \text{ inches}$$

22. $1\frac{3}{4}$ pounds to ounces

$$\frac{1\frac{3}{4} \cancel{\text{pounds}}}{1} \cdot \frac{16 \text{ ounces}}{1 \cancel{\text{pound}}} = 28 \text{ ounces}$$

23. 7 gallons to cups

$$\frac{7 \cancel{\text{gallons}}}{1} \cdot \frac{4 \cancel{\text{quarts}}}{1 \cancel{\text{gallon}}} \cdot \frac{2 \cancel{\text{pints}}}{1 \cancel{\text{quart}}} \cdot \frac{2 \text{ cups}}{1 \cancel{\text{pint}}}$$
$$= 7 \cdot 4 \cdot 2 \cdot 2 \text{ cups}$$
$$= 112 \text{ cups}$$

24. 4 days to seconds

$$\frac{4 \cancel{\text{days}}}{1} \cdot \frac{24 \cancel{\text{hours}}}{1 \cancel{\text{day}}} \cdot \frac{60 \cancel{\text{minutes}}}{1 \cancel{\text{hour}}}$$
$$\cdot \frac{60 \text{ seconds}}{1 \cancel{\text{minute}}}$$
$$= 4 \cdot 24 \cdot 60 \cdot 60 \text{ seconds}$$
$$345{,}600 \text{ seconds}$$

25. My thumb is 20 mm wide.

26. Her waist measurement is 66 cm.

27. The two towns are 40 km apart.

28. A basketball court is 30 m long.

29. The height of the picnic bench is 45 cm.

30. The eraser on the end of my pencil is 5 mm long.

31. 5 m to cm
Count 2 places to the right on the metric conversion line.
$$5.00_\wedge \text{ m} = 500 \text{ cm}$$

32. 8.5 km to m

$$\frac{8.5 \cancel{\text{km}}}{1} \cdot \frac{1000 \text{ m}}{1 \cancel{\text{km}}} = 8500 \text{ m}$$

33. 85 mm to cm
Count 1 place to the left on the metric conversion line.
$$8_\wedge 5. \text{ mm} = 8.5 \text{ cm}$$

34. 370 cm to m

$$\frac{\overset{3.7}{\cancel{370}} \cancel{\text{cm}}}{1} \cdot \frac{1 \text{ m}}{\underset{1}{\cancel{100}} \cancel{\text{cm}}} = 3.7 \text{ m}$$

35. 70 m to km
Count 3 places to the left on the metric conversion line.
$$70 \text{ m} = 0.07 \text{ km}$$

36. 0.93 m to mm

$$\frac{0.93 \text{ m}}{1} \cdot \frac{1000 \text{ mm}}{1 \text{ m}} = 0.93 \cdot 1000 \text{ mm}$$
$$= 930 \text{ mm}$$

37. The eye dropper holds 1 mL.

38. I can heat 3 L of water in this pan.

39. Loretta's hammer weighed 650 g.

40. Yongshu's suitcase weighed 20 kg when it was packed.

41. My fish tank holds 80 L of water.

42. I'll buy the 500 mL bottle of mouthwash.

43. Mara took a 200-mg antibiotic pill.

44. This piece of chicken weighs 100 g.

45. 5000 mL to L
Count 3 places to the left on the metric conversion line.
$$5_\wedge 000. \text{ mL} = 5 \text{ L}$$

46. 8 L to mL
Count 3 places to the right on the metric conversion line.
$$8.000_\wedge \text{ L} = 8000 \text{ mL}$$

47. 4.58 g to mg

$$\frac{4.58 \text{ g}}{1} \cdot \frac{1000 \text{ mg}}{1 \text{ g}} = 4.58 \cdot 1000 \text{ mg}$$
$$= 4580 \text{ mg}$$

48. 0.7 kg to g

$$\frac{0.7 \text{ kg}}{1} \cdot \frac{1000 \text{ g}}{1 \text{ kg}} = 0.7 \cdot 1000 \text{ g}$$
$$= 700 \text{ g}$$

49. 6 mg to g
Count 3 places to the left on the metric conversion line.
$$_\wedge 006. \text{ mg} = 0.006 \text{ g}$$

50. 35 mL to L
Count 3 places to the left on the metric conversion line.
$$_\wedge 035. \text{ mL} = 0.035 \text{ L}$$

51. Convert milliliters to liters.

$$\frac{180 \text{ mL}}{1} \cdot \frac{1 \text{ L}}{1000 \text{ mL}} = \frac{180}{1000} \text{ L} = 0.18 \text{ L}$$

Multiply 0.18 L by the number of guests.

$$0.18 \text{ L} \cdot 175 = 31.5 \text{ L}$$

For 175 guests 31.5 L of punch are needed.

52. Convert kilograms to grams.

$$10 \text{ kg} = 10,000 \text{ g}$$

Set up a proportion.

$$\frac{10,000 \text{ g}}{28 \text{ people}} = \frac{x}{1}$$
$$28 \cdot x = 10,000 \cdot 1$$
$$\frac{28 \cdot x}{28} = \frac{10,000}{28}$$
$$x = \frac{10,000}{28}$$
$$\approx 357$$

Jason is allowing ≈ 357 g of turkey for each person.

53. Convert grams to kilograms.
Using the metric conversion line

$$4 \text{ kg } 750 \text{ g} = 4.75 \text{ kg}.$$

Subtract the weight loss from his original weight.

$$\begin{array}{r} 92.00 \text{ kg} \\ -4.75 \text{ kg} \\ \hline 87.25 \text{ kg} \end{array}$$

Yerald weighs 87.25 kg.

54. Convert to kilograms.
Using the metric conversion line

$$2 \text{ kg } 20 \text{ g} = 2.02 \text{ kg}.$$

Multiply by the price per kilogram.

$$\begin{array}{r} \$1.49 \quad \leftarrow 2 \text{ decimals} \\ \times 2.02 \quad \leftarrow 2 \text{ decimals} \\ \hline 298 \\ 2\ 980 \\ \hline \$3.0098 \quad \leftarrow \overline{4 \text{ decimals}} \end{array}$$

Young-Mi paid $\approx \$3.01$ for the onions.

Chapter 7 Review Exercises

55. 6 m to yards

$$\frac{6 \cancel{m}}{1} \cdot \frac{1.09 \text{ yards}}{1 \cancel{m}} \approx 6.5 \text{ yards}$$

56. 30 cm to inches

$$\frac{30 \cancel{cm}}{1} \cdot \frac{0.39 \text{ inches}}{1 \cancel{cm}} \approx 11.7 \text{ inches}$$

57. 108 km to miles

$$\frac{108 \cancel{km}}{1} \cdot \frac{0.62 \text{ miles}}{1 \cancel{km}} \approx 67.0 \text{ miles}$$

58. 800 miles to km

$$\frac{800 \cancel{miles}}{1} \cdot \frac{1.61 \text{ km}}{1 \cancel{mile}} \approx 1288 \text{ km}$$

59. 23 quarts to L

$$\frac{23 \cancel{quarts}}{1} \cdot \frac{0.95 \text{ liters}}{1 \cancel{quart}} \approx 21.9 \text{ liters}$$

60. 41.5 L to quarts

$$\frac{41.5 \cancel{L}}{1} \cdot \frac{1.06 \text{ quarts}}{1 \cancel{L}} \approx 44.0 \text{ quarts}$$

61. Water freezes 0°C.

62. Water boils at 100°C.

63. Normal body temperature is about 37°C.

64. Comfortable room temperature is about 20°C.

65. 77°F

$$C = \frac{5(77-32)}{9} = \frac{5(\overset{5}{\cancel{45}})}{\underset{1}{\cancel{9}}} = 25$$

77°F = 25°C

66. 92°F

$$C = \frac{5(92-32)}{9}$$
$$= \frac{5(\overset{20}{\cancel{60}})}{\underset{3}{\cancel{9}}} = \frac{100}{3} \approx 33.3$$

92°F ≈ 33°C

67. 6°C

$$\begin{aligned} F &= \frac{9 \cdot 6}{5} + 32 \\ &= \frac{54}{5} + 32 \\ &= 10.8 + 32 \\ &= 42.8 \end{aligned}$$

6°C ≈ 43°F

68. 40°C

$$F = \frac{9 \cdot \overset{8}{\cancel{40}}}{\underset{1}{\cancel{5}}} + 32 = 72 + 32 = 104$$

40°C = 104°F

69. I added 1 *L* of oil to my car.

70. The box of books weighed 15 *kg*.

71. Larry's shoe is 30 *cm* long.

72. Jan used 15 *mL* of shampoo on her hair.

73. My fingernail is 10 *mm* wide.

74. I walked 2 *km* to school.

75. The tiny bird weighed 15 *g*.

76. The new library building is 18 *m* wide.

77. The cookie recipe uses 250 *mL* of milk.

78. Renee's pet mouse weighs 30 *g*.

79. One postage stamp weighs 90 *mg*.

80. I bought 30 L of gas for my car.

81. 10.5 cm to mm
Count 1 place to the right on the metric conversion line.
$$10.5 \text{ cm} = 105 \text{ mm}$$

82. 45 minutes to hours

$$\frac{\overset{3}{\cancel{45}} \cancel{\text{minutes}}}{1} \cdot \frac{1 \text{ hour}}{\underset{4}{\cancel{60}} \cancel{\text{minutes}}}$$
$$= \frac{3}{4} \text{ or } 0.75 \text{ hour}$$

83. 90 inches to feet

$$\frac{\overset{15}{\cancel{90}} \cancel{\text{inches}}}{1} \cdot \frac{1 \text{ foot}}{\underset{2}{\cancel{12}} \cancel{\text{inches}}}$$
$$= \frac{15}{2} \text{ feet} = 7\tfrac{1}{2} \text{ or } 7.5 \text{ feet}$$

84. 1.3 m to cm
Count 2 places to the right on the metric conversion line.
$$1.30_\wedge \text{ m} = 130 \text{ cm}$$

85. 25°C to Fahrenheit
$$F = \frac{9 \cdot \overset{5}{\cancel{25}}}{\underset{1}{\cancel{5}}} + 32 = 45 + 32 = 77$$
$$25°C = 77°F$$

86. $3\frac{1}{2}$ gallons to quarts
$$\frac{3\frac{1}{2} \cancel{\text{gallons}}}{1} \cdot \frac{4 \text{ quarts}}{1 \cancel{\text{gallon}}} = 3\frac{1}{2} \cdot 4 \text{ quarts}$$
$$= 14 \text{ quarts}$$

87. 700 mg to g
Count 3 places to the left on the metric conversion line.
$$_\wedge 700. \text{ mg} = 0.7 \text{ g}$$

88. 0.81 L to mL
Count 3 places to the right on the metric conversion line.
$$0.810 \text{ L} = 810 \text{ mL}$$

89. 5 pounds to ounces
$$\frac{5 \cancel{\text{pounds}}}{1} \cdot \frac{16 \text{ ounces}}{1 \cancel{\text{pound}}}$$
$$= 5 \cdot 16 \text{ ounces}$$
$$= 80 \text{ ounces}$$

90. 60 kg to g
$$\frac{60 \cancel{\text{kg}}}{1} \cdot \frac{1000 \text{ g}}{1 \cancel{\text{kg}}} = 60 \cdot 1000 \text{ g} = 60{,}000 \text{ g}$$

91. 1.8 L to mL
Count 3 places to the right on the metric conversion line.
$$1.800_\wedge \text{ L} = 1800 \text{ mL}$$

92. 86°F to Celsius
$$C = \frac{5(86-32)}{9} = \frac{5 \cdot \overset{6}{\cancel{54}}}{\underset{1}{\cancel{9}}} = 30$$
$$86°F = 30°C$$

93. 0.36 m to cm
Count 2 places to the right on the metric conversion line.
$$0.36_\wedge \text{ m} = 36 \text{ cm}$$

94. 55 mL to L
Count 3 places to the left on the metric conversion line.
$$_\wedge 055. \text{ mL} = 0.055 \text{ L}$$

95. Convert centimeters to meters.
$$\begin{array}{l} 2 \text{ m } 4 \text{ m} = 2 + 0.04 \text{ m} = 2.04 \text{ m} \\ 78 \text{ cm} = \underline{-\ 0.78 \text{ m}} \\ 1.26 \text{ m} \end{array}$$

The board is 1.26 m long.

96. Convert centimeters to meters.
$$3 \text{ m } 70 \text{ cm} = 3 + 0.70 \text{ m} = 3.7 \text{ m}$$

Multiply the length of the fabric by the cost per yard.

$$\begin{array}{r} \$12.99 \quad \leftarrow 2 \text{ decimal places} \\ \times 3.7 \quad \leftarrow 1 \text{ decimal place} \\ \hline 9\ 093 \\ 38\ 97 \\ \hline \$48.063 \quad \leftarrow 3 \text{ decimal places} \end{array}$$

The cost of the fabric is ≈$48.06.

97. Convert ounces to grams.
$$\frac{4 \cancel{\text{ounces}}}{1} \cdot \frac{28.35 \text{ grams}}{1 \cancel{\text{ounce}}} \approx 113 \text{ grams}$$

350°F to Celsius
$$\begin{aligned} C &= \frac{5(350-32)}{9} = \frac{5 \cdot 318}{9} \\ &= \frac{1590}{9} \\ &\approx 117°C \end{aligned}$$

Use ≈ 113 grams of rice and a baking temperature of ≈ 177°C.

98. Convert kilograms to pounds.
$$\frac{80.9 \cancel{\text{kilograms}}}{1} \cdot \frac{2.20 \text{ pounds}}{1 \cancel{\text{kilogram}}}$$
$$\approx 178.0 \text{ pounds}$$

Convert meters to feet.
$$\frac{1.83 \text{ meters}}{1} \cdot \frac{3.28 \text{ feet}}{1 \text{ meter}}$$
$$\approx 6.0 \text{ feet}$$

Jalo weighed ≈ 178.0 pounds and is ≈ 6.0 feet tall.

Chapter 7 Test

1. 9 gallons to quarts

   $$\frac{9 \cancel{\text{gallons}}}{1} \cdot \frac{4 \text{ quarts}}{1 \cancel{\text{gallon}}} = 36 \text{ quarts}$$

2. 45 feet to yards

   $$\frac{45 \cancel{\text{feet}}}{1} \cdot \frac{1 \text{ yard}}{3 \cancel{\text{feet}}} = \frac{45}{3} \text{ yards}$$
   $$= 15 \text{ yards}$$

3. 135 minutes to hours

   $$\frac{\overset{27}{\cancel{135}} \cancel{\text{minutes}}}{1} \cdot \frac{1 \text{ hour}}{\underset{12}{\cancel{60}} \cancel{\text{minutes}}}$$
   $$= \frac{27}{12} \text{ hours} = 2.25 \text{ or } 2\tfrac{1}{4} \text{ hours}$$

4. 9 inches to feet

   $$\frac{\overset{3}{\cancel{9}} \cancel{\text{inches}}}{1} \cdot \frac{1 \text{ foot}}{\underset{4}{\cancel{12}} \cancel{\text{inches}}} = \frac{3}{4} \text{ or } 0.75 \text{ foot}$$

5. $3\tfrac{1}{2}$ pounds to ounces

   $$\frac{3\tfrac{1}{2} \cancel{\text{pounds}}}{1} \cdot \frac{16 \text{ ounces}}{1 \cancel{\text{pound}}} = 56 \text{ ounces}$$

6. 5 days to minutes

   $$\frac{5 \cancel{\text{days}}}{1} \cdot \frac{24 \cancel{\text{hours}}}{1 \cancel{\text{day}}} \cdot \frac{60 \text{ minutes}}{1 \cancel{\text{hour}}}$$
   $$= \frac{5 \cdot 24 \cdot 60}{1} \text{ minutes}$$
   $$= 7200 \text{ minutes}$$

7. My husband weighs 75 *kg*.

8. I hiked 5 *km* this morning.

9. She bought 125 *mL* of cough syrup.

10. This apple weighs 180 *g*.

11. This page is 21 *cm* wide.

12. My watch band is 10 *mm* long.

13. I bought 10 *L* of soda for the picnic.

14. The bracelet is 16 *cm* long.

15. 250 cm to meters
    Count 2 places to the left on the metric conversion line.
    $$2_\wedge 50. \text{ cm} = 2.5 \text{ m}$$

16. 4.6 km to meters

    $$\frac{4.6 \cancel{\text{km}}}{1} \cdot \frac{1000 \text{ m}}{1 \cancel{\text{km}}} = 4.6 \cdot 1000 \text{ m}$$
    $$= 4600 \text{ m}$$

17. 5 mm to centimeters
    Count 1 place to the left on the metric conversion line.
    $$_\wedge 5. \text{ mm} = 0.5 \text{ cm}$$

18. 325 mg to grams

    $$\frac{325 \cancel{\text{mg}}}{1} \cdot \frac{1 \text{ g}}{1000 \cancel{\text{mg}}} = \frac{325}{1000} = 0.325 \text{ g}$$

19. 16 L to milliliters
    Count 3 places to the right on the metric conversion line.
    $$16.000_\wedge \text{ L} = 16,000 \text{ mL}$$

20. 0.4 kg to g

    $$\frac{0.4 \cancel{\text{kg}}}{1} \cdot \frac{1000 \text{ g}}{1 \cancel{\text{kg}}} = 0.4 \cdot 1000 \text{ g}$$
    $$= 400 \text{ g}$$

21. 10.55 m to centimeters
    Count 2 places to the right on the metric conversion line.
    $$10.55_\wedge \text{ m} = 1055 \text{ cm}$$

22. 95 mL to liters
    Count 3 places to the left on the metric conversion line.
    $$_\wedge 095 \text{ mL} = 0.095 \text{ L}$$

23. Convert grams to kilograms.

    $$10 \text{ kg } 60 \text{ g} = 10 \text{ kg} + .060 \text{ kg} = 10.06 \text{ kg}$$
    $$3 \text{ kg } 740 \text{ g} = 3 \text{ kg} + .740 \text{ kg} = 3.74 \text{ kg}$$

    Subtract.

    $$\begin{array}{r} 10.06 \text{ kg} \\ - 3.74 \text{ kg} \\ \hline 6.32 \text{ kg} \end{array}$$

    The dog is 6.32 kg heavier.

24. Convert centimeters to meters.

$$1 \text{ m } 35 \text{ cm} = 1 + 0.35 \text{ cm} = 1.35 \text{ m}$$

Multiply the amount of braid needed for each pillow by the number of pillows.

$$\begin{array}{r} 1.35 \text{ m} \\ \times 5 \\ \hline 6.75 \text{ m} \end{array}$$

Denise should buy 6.75 m of braid.

25. The water is almost boiling.
On the Celsius scale water boils at 100° so,

$$95°\text{C} \text{ would be } almost \text{ } boiling.$$

26. The tomato plants may freeze tonight.

$$0°\text{C} \text{ } Water \text{ } freezes \text{ } at \text{ } 0°\text{C}.$$

27. 6 feet to meters

$$\frac{6 \text{ feet}}{1} \cdot \frac{0.30 \text{ meter}}{1 \text{ foot}} \approx 1.8 \text{ meters}$$

28. 125 pounds to kilograms

$$\frac{125 \text{ pounds}}{1} \cdot \frac{0.45 \text{ kilograms}}{1 \text{ pound}}$$

$$\approx 56.3 \text{ kilograms}$$

29. 50 liters to gallons

$$\frac{50 \text{ liters}}{1} \cdot \frac{0.26 \text{ gallon}}{1 \text{ liter}} \approx 13 \text{ gallons}$$

30. 8.1 kilometers to miles

$$\frac{8.1 \text{ kilometers}}{1} \cdot \frac{0.62 \text{ mile}}{1 \text{ kilometer}} \approx 5.0 \text{ miles}$$

31. 74°F to Celsius

$$C = \frac{5(74 - 32)}{9} = \frac{5(42)}{9}$$

$$= \frac{210}{9} \approx 23.3$$

$$74°\text{F} \approx 23°\text{C}$$

32. 2°C to Fahrenheit

$$F = \frac{9 \cdot 2}{5} + 32 = \frac{18}{5} + 32$$

$$= 3.6 + 32 = 35.6$$

$$2°\text{C} \approx 36°\text{F}$$

33. Possible answers: Use the same system as the rest of the world; easier system for children to learn.

34. Possible answers: People like to use the system they're familiar with; the cost for new signs, scales, etc.

Cumulative Review Exercises (Chapters 1-7)

1. estimate   exact

$$\begin{array}{r} 100 \\ 3 \\ + 70 \\ \hline 173 \end{array} \qquad \begin{array}{r} 107.500 \quad Write \text{ } 0's \\ 2.548 \\ + 68.790 \\ \hline 178.838 \end{array}$$

2. estimate   exact

$$\begin{array}{r} 30,000 \\ - 800 \\ \hline 29,200 \end{array} \qquad \begin{array}{r} \overset{299}{\cancel{3}\cancel{0},\cancel{0}\cancel{0}\cancel{0}}\overset{}{^{10}}\overset{}{^{17}} \\ - 829 \\ \hline 30,178 \end{array}$$

3. estimate   exact

$$\begin{array}{r} 90,000 \\ \times 200 \\ \hline 18,000,000 \end{array} \qquad \begin{array}{r} 92,075 \\ \times 183 \\ \hline 276\,225 \\ 7\,366\,00 \\ 9\,207\,5 \\ \hline 16,849,725 \end{array}$$

4. exact   exact

$$\begin{array}{r} 60 \\ \times 5 \\ \hline 300 \end{array} \qquad \begin{array}{r} 56.52 \leftarrow 2 \text{ } decimal \text{ } places \\ \times 4.7 \leftarrow 1 \text{ } decimal \text{ } place \\ \hline 39\,564 \\ 226\,08 \\ \hline 265.644 \leftarrow 3 \text{ } decimal \text{ } places \end{array}$$

5. estimate   exact

$$\begin{array}{r} 500 \\ 40\overline{)20,000} \end{array} \qquad \begin{array}{r} 530 \\ 37\overline{)19,610} \\ \underline{18\,5} \\ 1\,11 \\ \underline{1\,11} \\ 00 \\ \underline{0} \\ 0 \end{array}$$

Cumulative Review Exercises (Chapters 1-7)

6. *estimate*   *exact*

$$8)\overline{40}^{\,5} \qquad 8.3_\wedge)\overline{38.1_\wedge 8}^{\,4.6}$$
$$\underline{33\;2}$$
$$4\;9\;8$$
$$\underline{4\;9\;8}$$
$$0$$

7. *estimate*   *exact*

$$\begin{array}{r}2\\+\;4\\\hline 6\end{array} \qquad \begin{array}{r}1\frac{7}{10}=1\frac{7}{10}\\+\;3\frac{4}{5}=3\frac{8}{10}\\\hline 4\frac{15}{10}\end{array}$$

$$4\tfrac{15}{10}=5\tfrac{5}{10}=5\tfrac{1}{2}$$

8. *estimate*   *exact*

$$\begin{array}{r}6\\-\;1\\\hline 5\end{array} \qquad \begin{array}{r}5\frac{1}{2}=5\frac{7}{14}\\-\;1\frac{2}{7}=1\frac{4}{14}\\\hline 4\frac{3}{14}\end{array}$$

9. *exact*

$$3\tfrac{1}{6}\cdot 4\tfrac{2}{3}=\frac{19}{\cancel{6}_{3}}\cdot\frac{\cancel{14}^{7}}{3}=\frac{133}{9}=14\tfrac{7}{9}$$

estimate $3\cdot 5=15$

10. *exact*

$$2\tfrac{1}{4}\div\frac{9}{10}=\frac{\cancel{9}^{1}}{\cancel{4}_{2}}\cdot\frac{\cancel{10}^{5}}{\cancel{9}_{1}}=\frac{5}{2}=2\tfrac{1}{2}$$

estimate $2\div 1=2$

11. $3-2\tfrac{5}{16}=2\tfrac{16}{16}-2\tfrac{5}{16}=\tfrac{11}{16}$

12. $7+484{,}099+3939$

$$\begin{array}{r}7\\484{,}099\\+\;\;\;\;3\;939\\\hline 488{,}045\end{array}$$

13. $12\cdot 2\tfrac{2}{9}=\dfrac{\cancel{12}^{4}}{1}\cdot\dfrac{20}{\cancel{9}_{3}}=\dfrac{80}{3}=26\tfrac{2}{3}$

14. $0.86\div 0.066\approx 13.0$

$$0.066_\wedge)\overline{0.860_\wedge 00}^{\,13.02}$$
$$\underline{66}$$
$$200$$
$$\underline{198}$$
$$2\;0$$
$$\underline{0}$$
$$2\;00$$
$$\underline{1\;98}$$
$$2$$

15. $\dfrac{3}{8}+\dfrac{5}{6}=\dfrac{9}{24}+\dfrac{20}{24}=\dfrac{29}{24}=1\tfrac{5}{24}$

16. $8-0.9207$

$$\begin{array}{r}7\;\overset{9}{\cancel{10}}\overset{9}{\cancel{10}}\overset{9}{\cancel{10}}10\\\cancel{8}.\cancel{0}\;\cancel{0}\;\cancel{0}\;\cancel{0}\\-\;0\,.\,9\,2\,0\,7\\\hline 7\,.\,0\,7\,9\,3\end{array}$$

17. $3\tfrac{3}{4}\div 6$

$$3\tfrac{3}{4}\div 6=\frac{15}{4}\div\frac{6}{1}=\frac{\cancel{15}^{5}}{4}\cdot\frac{1}{\cancel{6}_{2}}=\frac{5}{8}$$

18.
$$47)\overline{14{,}467}^{\,307\;\;\text{R}\;38}$$
$$\underline{14\;1}$$
$$36$$
$$\underline{\;\;0}$$
$$367$$
$$\underline{329}$$
$$38$$

19. $(2.54)(0.003)$

$$\begin{array}{r}2.54\;\;\leftarrow 2\;decimals\\\times\;\;0.003\;\;\leftarrow 3\;decimals\\\hline 0.00762\;\;\leftarrow 5\;decimals\end{array}$$

20.
$$\begin{array}{ll}24-12\div 6\cdot 8+(25-25) & \textit{Parentheses}\\24-12\div 6\cdot 8+0 & \textit{Divide}\\24-2\cdot 8+0 & \textit{Multiply}\\24-16+0 & \textit{Subtract}\\8+0=8 & \textit{Add}\end{array}$$

21.
$$\begin{array}{ll}3^2+2^5\cdot\sqrt{64} & \textit{Exponents}\\9+32\cdot\sqrt{64} & \textit{Square root}\\9+32\cdot 8 & \textit{Multiply}\\9+256=265 & \textit{Add}\end{array}$$

22. 307.19 is three hundred seven and nineteen hundredths.

23. Eighty-two ten-thousandths is 0.0082.

24. 0.67   = 0.6700
     0.067 = 0.0670
     0.6   = 0.6000
     0.6007 = 0.6007
From smallest to largest:

$$0.067, \ 0.6, \ 0.6007, \ 0.67$$

25. $\dfrac{7}{8}$

$$\begin{array}{r} 0.875 \\ 8\overline{)7.000} \\ \underline{6\ 4} \\ 60 \\ \underline{56} \\ 40 \\ \underline{40} \\ 0 \end{array}$$

$\dfrac{7}{8} = 0.875$ *decimal*

26. $\dfrac{7}{8} = 0.875 = 87.5\%$ or $87\dfrac{1}{2}\%$

27. $0.05 = \dfrac{5}{100} = \dfrac{1}{20}$

28. $0.05 = 5\%$

29. $350\% = \dfrac{350}{100} = \dfrac{35}{10} = 3\dfrac{5}{10} = 3\dfrac{1}{2}$

30. $350\% = 3{\scriptstyle\wedge}50. = 3.5$

31. \$44 to \$4

The ratio is $\dfrac{44}{4} = \dfrac{44 \div 4}{4 \div 4} = \dfrac{11}{1}$.

32. 20 minutes to 3 hours

$$\begin{aligned} 3 \text{ hours} &= 3 \cdot 60 \text{ minutes} \\ &= 180 \text{ minutes} \end{aligned}$$

20 minutes to 180 minutes

$$\dfrac{20}{180} = \dfrac{20 \div 20}{180 \div 20} = \dfrac{1}{9}$$

33. 350 English students to 200 math students

$$\dfrac{350}{200} = \dfrac{350 \div 50}{200 \div 50} = \dfrac{7}{4}$$

34.

size	cost per unit
package of 16	$\dfrac{\$3.87}{16} \approx \$0.242$
package of 22	$\dfrac{\$5.96}{22} \approx \$0.271$
package of 36	$\dfrac{\$11.69}{36} \approx \$0.325$

The best buy is 16 diapers for \$3.87.

35. $\dfrac{x}{16} = \dfrac{3}{4}$

$4 \cdot x = 3 \cdot 16$ *Cross products are equivalent*

$\dfrac{4 \cdot x}{4} = \dfrac{48}{4}$

$x = 12$

36. $\dfrac{0.9}{0.75} = \dfrac{2}{x}$

$0.9 \cdot x = 2 \cdot 0.75$
$0.9 \cdot x = 1.5$
$\dfrac{0.9 \cdot x}{0.9} = \dfrac{1.5}{0.9}$
$x \approx 1.67$

37. Use the percent proportion.
a is 4; b is 80; p is unknown.

$\dfrac{a}{b} = \dfrac{p}{100}$

$\dfrac{4}{80} = \dfrac{p}{100}$

$p \cdot 80 = 4 \cdot 100$
$p \cdot 80 = 400$
$\dfrac{p \cdot 80}{80} = \dfrac{400}{80}$
$p = 5$

\$4 is 5% of \$80.

38. Use the percent proportion.
a is 36; p is 120; b is unknown.

$\dfrac{a}{b} = \dfrac{p}{100}$

$\dfrac{36}{b} = \dfrac{120}{100}$

$120 \cdot b = 36 \cdot 100$
$120 \cdot b = 3600$
$\dfrac{120 \cdot b}{120} = \dfrac{3600}{120}$
$b = 30$

36 hours is 120% of 30 hours.

39. $2\frac{1}{2}$ feet to inches

$$\frac{2\frac{1}{2}\ \cancel{feet}}{1}\cdot\frac{12\text{ inches}}{1\ \cancel{foot}}$$

$$= 2\tfrac{1}{2}\cdot 12\text{ inches} = 30\text{ inches}$$

40. 105 seconds to minutes

$$\frac{\overset{21}{\cancel{105}}\ \cancel{seconds}}{1}\cdot\frac{1\text{ minute}}{\underset{12}{\cancel{60}}\ \cancel{seconds}}$$

$$= \frac{21}{12}\text{ minutes}$$

$$= 1\tfrac{3}{4}\text{ or } 1.75\text{ minutes}$$

41. 2.8 *m* to centimeters

Count 2 places to the right on the metric conversion line.

$$2.80_{\wedge}\text{ m} = 280\text{ cm}$$

42. 65 mg to grams

$$\begin{aligned}\frac{65\ \cancel{mg}}{1}\cdot\frac{1\text{ gram}}{1000\ \cancel{mg}} &= \frac{65}{1000}\text{ g}\\ &= 0.065\text{ g}\end{aligned}$$

43. 198 km to miles

$$\begin{aligned}198\text{ km} &\approx 19\cdot 0.62\text{ miles}\\ &\approx 122.76\text{ miles}\end{aligned}$$

44. 50°F to Celsius

$$\begin{aligned}C &= \frac{5(F-32)}{9}\\ &= \frac{5(50-32)}{9}\\ &= \frac{5(\overset{2}{\cancel{18}})}{\underset{1}{\cancel{9}}} = 10\end{aligned}$$

50°F = 10°C

45. Ron bought the tube of toothpaste weighing 100 *g*.

46. The teacher's desk is 140 *cm* long.

47. The hallway is 3 *m* wide.

48. Joe's hammer weighed 1 *kg*.

49. Ann took a 500-*mg* tablet of Vitamin C.

50. Tia added 125 *mL* of milk to her cereal.

51. John has a slight fever.
38°C is reasonable. Body temperature is about 37°C or 98.6°F.

52. You will need a light jacket outside.
12°C is reasonable. 45°C would be too hot and 0°C would be very cold.

53.

$$\begin{aligned}\textit{amount of sales tax} &= \textit{rate of tax}\\ &\quad\cdot\textit{cost of item}\\ &= 0.075\cdot \$64.95\\ &\approx \$4.87\end{aligned}$$

The sales tax is ≈ \$4.87 and the total cost of the camera is \$69.82 (\$64.95 + \$4.87).

54. 24 prints for \$10.25
Set up a proportion.

$$\begin{aligned}\frac{\$10.25}{24} &= \frac{x}{1}\\ 24\cdot x &= \$10.25\cdot 1\\ \frac{24\cdot x}{24} &= \frac{\$10.25}{24}\\ x &\approx 0.427\end{aligned}$$

The cost per print is ≈ \$0.43.

55. Convert grams to kilograms.

$$650\text{ g} = 0.650\text{ kg} = 0.65\text{ kg}$$

Multiply the amount purchased by the cost per kilogram.

```
  $14.98   ← 2 decimals
×   0.65   ← 2 decimals
    7490
   8 988
  9.7370   ← 4 decimals
```

Mark paid ≈ \$9.74 for the candy.

56. Set up a proportion.

$$\begin{aligned}\frac{1\text{ cm}}{12\text{ km}} &= \frac{7.8\text{ cm}}{x}\\ x\cdot 1 &= 7.8\cdot 12\\ x &= 93.6\end{aligned}$$

The distance is 93.6 kilometers.

57. \$8750 at 9% for $3\frac{1}{2}$ years

$$\begin{aligned}I &= p\cdot r\cdot t\\ &= \$8750\cdot 0.09\cdot 3.5\\ &= \$2756.25\end{aligned}$$

The interest is $2756.25 and the total amount due is $11,506.25 ($8750 + ($2756.25).

58. Use the percent proportion.
a is 31; b is 35; p is unknown.

$$\frac{a}{b} = \frac{p}{100}$$
$$\frac{31}{35} = \frac{p}{100}$$
$$35 \cdot p = 31 \cdot 100$$
$$35 \cdot p = 3100$$
$$\frac{35 \cdot p}{35} = \frac{3100}{35}$$
$$p \approx 88.57$$

The percent of the problems that were correct is $\approx 86.6\%$.

59. Add to find the total weight of the people.

$88 + 88 + 240 + 189 + 127 + 165 + 143 + 219 + 116 + 124 = 1499$

Subtract the total weight from the weight limit.

$$1500 - 1499 = 1$$

The total weight is 1 pound under the limit.

60. Add the amounts needed for the recipes.

$$\begin{array}{rl} 2\frac{1}{4} &= 2\frac{1}{4} \\ 1\frac{1}{2} &= 1\frac{2}{4} \\ +\ \frac{3}{4} &= \frac{3}{4} \\ \hline & 3\frac{6}{4} = 4\frac{2}{4} = 4\frac{1}{2} \text{ cups} \end{array}$$

Find the total amount of brown sugar.

$$\begin{array}{r} 2\frac{1}{3} \\ +\ 2\frac{1}{3} \\ \hline 4\frac{2}{3} \text{ cups} \end{array}$$

Subtract the amount to be used from the total amount.

$$\begin{array}{rl} 4\frac{2}{3} &= 4\frac{4}{6} \\ -\ 4\frac{1}{2} &= 4\frac{3}{6} \\ \hline & \frac{1}{6} \end{array}$$

The Jackson family will have $\frac{1}{6}$ cup more than the amount needed.

61. $\begin{aligned} \textit{amount of discount} &= \textit{rate of discount} \\ &\quad \cdot \textit{original price} \\ &= 30\% \cdot \$189 \\ &= 0.30 \cdot \$189 \\ &\quad \$56.70 \end{aligned}$

The amount of discount is $56.70 and the sale price is $132.30 ($189−$56.70).

62. Convert grams to kilograms.

$$115 \text{ g} = 0.115 \text{ kg}$$
$$450 \text{ g} = 0.45 \text{ kg}$$

Find the total weight of the bags.

$$\begin{array}{r} 48 \\ \times\ 0.115 \\ \hline 240 \\ 48 \\ 4\ 8 \\ \hline 5.520 \end{array}$$

Add the weight of the carton.

$$\begin{array}{r} 0.45 \text{ kg} \\ +\ 5.52 \text{ kg} \\ \hline 5.97 \text{ kg} \end{array}$$

The total weight is 5.97 kg.

63. Set up a proportion.

$$\frac{6 \text{ rows}}{5 \text{ cm}} = \frac{x}{100 \text{ cm}}$$
$$5 \cdot x = 6 \cdot 100$$
$$5 \cdot x = 600$$
$$\frac{5 \cdot x}{5} = \frac{600}{5}$$
$$x = 120$$

Akuba will knit 120 rows.

64. $\frac{3}{8}$ of 5600 students

$$\frac{3}{8} \cdot 5600 = \frac{3}{\cancel{8}} \cdot \frac{\cancel{5600}^{700}}{1}$$
$$= 2100$$

The survey showed that 2100 students work 20 hours or more per week.

Chapter 8

GEOMETRY

8.1 Basic Geometric Terms

8.1 Margin Exercises

1. **(a)** The figure has two endpoints so it is a line segment.

   (b) The figure starts at point S and goes on forever in one direction so it is a ray.

   (c) The figure goes on forever in both directions so it is a line.

   (d) The figure has two endpoints so it is a line segment.

2. **(a)** The lines cross at E so they are intersecting.

   (b) The lines never intersect (cross) so they are parallel.

   (c) The lines never intersect (cross) so they are parallel.

3. **(a)** The angle is named $\angle CQD, \angle 3$, or $\angle DQC$.

   (b) Darken lines $\overleftrightarrow{WT}$ and $\overleftrightarrow{TZ}$.

   See the answer art in the margin exercise of the textbook.

   (c) The angle can be named $\angle 1, \angle R, \angle MRN$, and $\angle NRM$.

4. **(a)** The angle measures exactly 90° and there is a small square at the vertex so it is a right angle.

   (b) The angle measures exactly 180° so it is a straight angle.

   (c) The right angle measures between 90° and 180° so it is obtuse.

   (d) The angle measures between 0° and 90° so it is acute.

5. The lines in (b) show perpendicular lines, because they intersect at right angles. The lines in (a) show intersecting lines. They cross but not at right angles.

8.1 Section Exercises

3. The figure has two endpoints so it is a *line segment* named $\overline{GF}$ or $\overline{FG}$.

7. The lines are *perpendicular* because they intersect at right angles.

11. The lines intersect so they are *not* parallel. At their intersection they *do not* form a right angle so they are not perpendicular. The lines are *intersecting*.

15. The angle can be named $\angle CRT$ or $\angle TRC$.

19. The angle is a *right angle*, as indicated by the small square at the vertex. Right angles measure exactly 90°.

23. Two rays in a straight line measure 180°. An angle that measures 180° is called a *straight angle*.

27. $\angle UST$ is 90° is true.

31. $\overleftrightarrow{QU}$ and $\overleftrightarrow{TS}$ are parallel is false. $\overleftrightarrow{QU}$ and $\overleftrightarrow{TS}$ are perpendicular because they intersect at right angles.

35. $(90 - 37) + 15$ *Parentheses*
    $53 + 15 = 68$ *Add*

8.2 Angles and Their Relationships

8.2 Margin Exercises

1. $\angle AOB$ and $\angle BOC$ are complementary angles because $45° + 45° = 90°$. $\angle COD$ and $\angle DOE$ are complementary angles because $70° + 20° = 90°$.

2. **(a)** The complement of 35° is 55°, because $90° - 35° = 55°$.

   (b) The complement of 80° is 10°, because $90° - 80° = 10°$.

3. $\angle CRF$ and $\angle BRF$ are supplementary because $127° + 53° = 180°$.
   $\angle CRE$ and $\angle ERB$ are supplementary because $53° + 127° = 180°$.
   $\angle BRF$ and $\angle BRE$ are supplementary because $53° + 127° = 180°$.

189

∠CRE and ∠CRF are supplementary because
53° + 127° = 180°.

4. **(a)** The supplement of 175° is 5° because
180° − 5° = 175°.

  (b) The supplement of 30° is 150° because
180° − 30° = 150°.

5. ∠BOC ≅ ∠AOD because they each measure 150°.
∠AOB ≅ ∠DOC because they each measure 30°.

6. ∠SPB and ∠MPD are vertical angles because they do not share a common side and the angles are formed by intersecting lines.
∠BPD and ∠SPM are also vertical angles.

7. **(a)** ∠VOR
∠VOR and ∠SOP are vertical angles so they are congruent and have the same measure of degrees. The measure of ∠SOP is 38° so the measure of ∠VOR is 38°.

  (b) ∠POQ
∠POQ and ∠TOV are vertical angles so they are congruent and have the same measure of degrees. The measure of ∠TOV is 52° so the measure of ∠POQ is 52°.

  (c) ∠QOR
∠QOR and ∠SOT are vertical angles so they are also congruent and have the same measure of degrees.
The measure of ∠SOT is 90° so the measure of ∠QOR is 90°.

8.2 Section Exercises

3. The pairs of supplementary angles are:
∠HNE and ∠ENF because

    77° and 103° = 180°;

    ∠HNG and ∠GNF because

    103° and 77° = 180°;

    ∠HNE and ∠HNG because

    77° and 103° = 180°;

    ∠ENF and ∠GNF because

    103° and 77° = 180°.

7. The complement of 86° is 4° because

    90° − 86° = 4°.

11. The supplement of 90° is 90° because

    180° − 90° = 90°.

15. Because ∠COE and ∠GOH are vertical angles, they are also congruent. This means they have the same measure of degrees.

    ∠COE measures 63° so

    ∠GOH measures 63°.

19. Two angles are complementary if their sum is 90°. Two angles are supplementary if their sum is 180°. Drawings will vary. See examples in the answer section of the textbook.

23. No, because obtuse angles are > 90° so their sum would be > 180°.

27. 2 · 3 + 2 · 4   Multiply
     6 + 8 = 14   Add

8.3 Rectangles and Squares

8.3 Margin Exercises

1. (a), (b), and (e) are figures with four sides that intersect to form 90° angles, so they are rectangles. (c) and (d) do not have four sides. (f) and (g) have four sides, but they do not intersect to form right angles.

2. **(a)** The length of the rectangle is 17 cm and the width is 10 cm.

    $P = 2 \cdot length + 2 \cdot width$
    $ = 2 \cdot 17 \text{ cm} + 2 \cdot 10 \text{ cm}$
    $ = 34 \text{ cm} + 20 \text{ cm}$
    $ = 54 \text{ cm}$

  (b) The length is 10.5 ft and the width is 7 ft.

    $P = 2 \cdot length + 2 \cdot width$
    $ = 2 \cdot 10.5 \text{ ft} + 2 \cdot 7 \text{ ft}$
    $ = 21 \text{ ft} + 14 \text{ ft}$
    $ = 35 \text{ ft}$

Section 8.3 Rectangles and Squares

(c) 6 m wide and 11 m long

$$\begin{aligned} P &= 2 \cdot length + 2 \cdot width \\ &= 2 \cdot 11 \text{ m} + 2 \cdot 6 \text{ m} \\ &= 22 \text{ m} + 12 \text{ m} \\ &= 34 \text{ m} \end{aligned}$$

(d) 0.9 km by 2.8 km

$$\begin{aligned} P &= 2 \cdot length + 2 \cdot width \\ &= 2 \cdot 2.8 \text{ km} + 2 \cdot 0.9 \text{ km} \\ &= 5.6 \text{ km} + 1.8 \text{ km} \\ &= 7.4 \text{ km} \end{aligned}$$

3. (a) The length is 9 ft and the width is 4 ft.

$$\begin{aligned} A &= length \cdot width \\ &= 9 \text{ ft} \cdot 4 \text{ ft} \\ &= 36 \text{ ft}^2 \end{aligned}$$

(b) A rectangle that is 6 m long and 0.5 m wide

$$\begin{aligned} A &= length \cdot width \\ &= 6 \text{ m} \cdot 0.5 \text{ m} \\ &= 3 \text{ m}^2 \end{aligned}$$

(c) 8.2 cm by 41.2 cm

$$\begin{aligned} A &= length \cdot width \\ &= 41.2 \text{ cm} \cdot 8.2 \text{ cm} \\ &= 337.84 \text{ cm}^2 \end{aligned}$$

4. (a) Each side measures 2 ft.

$$\begin{aligned} P &= 4 \cdot s & A &= s \cdot s \\ &= 4 \cdot 2 \text{ ft} & &= 2 \text{ ft} \cdot 2 \text{ ft} \\ &= 8 \text{ ft} & &= 4 \text{ ft}^2 \end{aligned}$$

(b) 10.5 cm on each side

$$\begin{aligned} P &= 4 \cdot s & A &= s \cdot s \\ &= 4 \cdot 10.5 \text{ cm} & &= 10.5 \text{ cm} \cdot 10.5 \text{ cm} \\ &= 42 \text{ cm} & &= 110.25 \text{ cm}^2 \end{aligned}$$

(c) 2.1 miles on a side

$$\begin{aligned} P &= 4 \cdot s & A &= s \cdot s \\ &= 4 \cdot 2.1 \text{ mi} & &= 2.1 \text{ mi} \cdot 2.1 \text{ mi} \\ &= 8.4 \text{ mi} & &= 4.41 \text{ mi}^2 \end{aligned}$$

5. The cost of the carpet is $19.95 per square yard.

(a) The length is 6.5 yd and the width is 5 yd.

$$\begin{aligned} A &= length \cdot width \\ &= 6.5 \text{ yd} \cdot 5 \text{ yd} \\ &= 32.5 \text{ yd}^2 \end{aligned}$$

The cost of the carpet is

$$\frac{32.5 \text{ yd}^2}{1} \cdot \frac{\$19.95}{1 \text{ yd}^2} \approx \$648.38.$$

(b) First change the measurements from feet to yards.

$$\frac{21 \text{ ft}}{3} = 7 \text{ yd} \quad \frac{9 \text{ ft}}{3} = 3 \text{ yd} \quad \frac{12 \text{ ft}}{3} = 4 \text{ yd}$$

Next, break up the room into two pieces.

$$\begin{aligned} Area\ of\ rectangle &= length \cdot width \\ &= 7 \text{ yd} \cdot 4 \text{ yd} \\ &= 28 \text{ yd}^2 \end{aligned}$$

$$\begin{aligned} Area\ of\ square &= s \cdot s \\ &= 3 \text{ yd} \cdot 3 \text{ yd} \\ &= 9 \text{ yd}^2 \end{aligned}$$

$$\begin{aligned} Total\ area &= 28 \text{ yd}^2 + 9 \text{ yd}^2 \\ &= 37 \text{ yd}^2 \end{aligned}$$

The cost of the carpet is

$$\frac{37 \text{ yd}^2}{1} \cdot \frac{\$19.95}{1 \text{ yd}^2} = \$738.15.$$

(c) A classroom that is 24 ft long and 18 feet wide

Change feet to yards.

$$\frac{24 \text{ ft}}{3} = 8 \text{ yd} \quad \frac{18 \text{ ft}}{3} = 6 \text{ yd}$$

$$\begin{aligned} Area &= length \cdot width \\ &= 8 \text{ yd} \cdot 6 \text{ yd} \\ &= 48 \text{ yd}^2 \end{aligned}$$

The cost of the carpet is

$$\frac{48 \text{ yd}^2}{1} \cdot \frac{\$19.95}{1 \text{ yd}^2} = \$957.60.$$

8.3 Section Exercises

3. $P = 4 \cdot s$ $\qquad A = s \cdot s$
    $= 4 \cdot 0.9 \text{ km}$ $\qquad = 0.9 \text{ km} \cdot 0.9 \text{ km}$
    $= 3.6 \text{ km}$ $\qquad = 0.81 \text{ km}^2$

7. 14 m by 0.5 m

    $P = 2 \; length \cdot 2 \cdot width$
    $ = 2 \cdot 14 \text{ m} + 2 \cdot 0.5 \text{ m}$
    $ = 28 \text{ m} + 1 \text{ m}$
    $ = 29 \text{ m}$

    $A = length \cdot width$
    $ = 14 \text{ m} \cdot 0.5 \text{ m}$
    $ = 7 \text{ m}^2$

11. A square 3 mi wide

    $P = 4 \cdot s$ $\qquad A = s \cdot s$
    $= 4 \cdot 3 \text{ mi}$ $\qquad = 3 \text{ mi} \cdot 3 \text{ mi}$
    $= 12 \text{ mi}$ $\qquad = 9 \text{ mi}^2$

15. $P = 28 \text{ m} + 17 \text{ m} + 12 \text{ m} + 4 \text{ m} + 4 \text{ m}$
    $ + 4 \text{ m} + 12 \text{ m} + 17 \text{ m}$
    $ = 98 \text{ m}$

    Break up the figure into a rectangle and a square.

    $A = 17 \text{ m} \cdot 28 \text{ m}$
    $ = 476 \text{ m}^2$

    $A = 4 \text{ m} \cdot 4 \text{ m}$
    $ = 16 \text{ m}^2$

    Total area $= 476 \text{ m}^2 + 16 \text{ m}^2$
    $\phantom{\text{Total area }} = 492 \text{ m}^2$

19. Find the area of the room.

    $A = length \cdot width$
    $ = 25 \text{ ft} \cdot 20 \text{ ft}$
    $ = 500 \text{ ft}^2$

    The cost for the tile is

    $$\frac{500 \cancel{ft^2}}{1} \cdot \frac{\$0.72}{1 \cancel{ft^2}} = \$360.$$

23. Perimeter is the distance around the outside edges of a shape; area is the surface inside the shape measured in square units. Drawings will vary.

27. 50 cm to m

    $$\frac{\overset{1}{\cancel{50}} \, \cancel{cm}}{1} \cdot \frac{1 \text{ m}}{\underset{2}{\cancel{100}} \, \cancel{cm}} = \frac{1}{2} \text{ m} = 0.5 \text{ m}$$

31. 2700 in to yd

    $$\frac{\overset{\overset{75}{225}}{\cancel{2700}} \, \cancel{in}}{1} \cdot \frac{1 \, \cancel{ft}}{\underset{1}{\cancel{12}} \, \cancel{in}} \cdot \frac{1 \text{ yd}}{\underset{1}{\cancel{3}} \, \cancel{ft}} = 75 \text{ yd}$$

8.4 Parallelograms and Trapezoids

8.4 Margin Exercises

1. (a) $P = 15 \text{ m} + 27 \text{ m} + 15 \text{ m} + 27 \text{ m} = 84 \text{ m}$

    (b) $P = 6.91 \text{ km} + 10.3 \text{ km} + 6.91 \text{ km} + 10.3 \text{ km}$
    $ = 34.42 \text{ km}$

2. (a) base: 50 ft, height: 42 ft

    $A = b \cdot h$
    $ = 50 \text{ ft} \cdot 42 \text{ ft}$
    $ = 2100 \text{ ft}^2$

    (b) base: 3.8 cm, height: 2.3 cm

    $A = b \cdot h$
    $ = 3.8 \text{ cm} \cdot 2.3 \text{ cm}$
    $ = 8.74 \text{ cm}^2$

    (c) base: $12\frac{1}{2}$ m, height: $4\frac{3}{4}$ m

    $A = b \cdot h$
    $ = 12\frac{1}{2} \text{ m} \cdot 4\frac{3}{4} \text{ m}$
    $ = 12.5 \text{ m} \cdot 4.75 \text{ m}$
    $ = 59.375 \text{ m}^2 \text{ or } 59\frac{3}{8} \text{ m}^2$

3. (a) $P = 9.8 \text{ in} + 6.3 \text{ in} + 6.9 \text{ in} + 5.6 \text{ in}$
    $ = 28.6 \text{ in}$

    (b) $P = 1.28 \text{ km} + 0.85 \text{ km} + 1.7 \text{ km} + 2 \text{ km}$
    $ = 5.83 \text{ km}$

    (c) $P = 39.7 \text{ cm} + 29.2 \text{ cm} + 74.9 \text{ cm} + 16.4 \text{ cm}$
    $ = 160.2 \text{ cm}$

4. (a) height: 30 ft, short base: 40 ft, long base: 60 ft

    $A = \frac{1}{2} \cdot h \cdot (b + B)$

Section 8.4 Parallelograms and Trapezoids

$$A = \frac{1}{2} \cdot 30 \text{ ft} \cdot (40 \text{ ft} + 60 \text{ ft})$$
$$= \frac{1}{\cancel{2}} \cdot 30 \text{ ft} \cdot (\cancel{100}^{50} \text{ ft})$$
$$= 1500 \text{ ft}^2$$

(b) height: 11 cm, short base: 14 cm, long base: 19 cm

$$A = \frac{1}{2} \cdot h \cdot (b + B)$$
$$= \frac{1}{2} \cdot 11 \text{ cm} \cdot (14 \text{ cm} + 19 \text{ cm})$$
$$= \frac{1}{2} \cdot 11 \text{ cm} \cdot (33 \text{ cm})$$
$$= 0.5 \cdot 363 \text{ cm} \quad \tfrac{1}{2} = 0.5$$
$$= 181.5 \text{ cm}^2$$

(c) height: 4.7 m, short base: 9 m, long base: 10.5 m

$$A = 0.5 \cdot 4.7 \text{ m} \cdot (9 \text{ m} + 10.5 \text{ m})$$
$$= 0.5 \cdot 4.7 \text{ m} \cdot 19.5 \text{ m}$$
$$= 45.825 \text{ m}^2$$

5. (a) Break up the figure into two pieces, a parallelogram and a trapezoid.
Area of parallelogram

$$A = b \cdot h$$
$$= 8 \text{ m} \cdot 5 \text{ m}$$
$$= 40 \text{ m}^2$$

Area of trapezoid

$$A = \frac{1}{2} \cdot h \cdot (b + B)$$
$$= \frac{1}{2} \cdot 4 \text{ m} \cdot (8 \text{ m} + 14 \text{ m})$$
$$= \frac{1}{2} \cdot 4 \text{ m} \cdot (22 \text{ m})$$
$$= 44 \text{ m}^2$$

Total area = 40 m² + 44 m² = 84 m²

(b) Break up the figure into two pieces.
Area of square

$$A = s \cdot s$$
$$= 5 \text{ yd} \cdot 5 \text{ yd}$$
$$= 25 \text{ yd}^2$$

Area of trapezoid

$$A = \frac{1}{2} \cdot h \cdot (b + B)$$
$$= \frac{1}{2} \cdot 5 \text{ yd} \cdot (5 \text{ yd} + 10 \text{ yd})$$
$$= 0.5 \cdot 5 \text{ yd} \cdot 15 \text{ yd} \quad \tfrac{1}{2} = 0.5$$
$$= 37.5 \text{ yd}^2$$

Total area = 25 yd² + 37.5 yd²
          = 62.5 yd²

6. (a) Floor (a) area is 84 m².

$$\text{Cost} = \frac{84 \; \cancel{m^2}}{1} \cdot \frac{\$18.50}{1 \; \cancel{m^2}}$$
$$= \$1554$$

(b) Floor (b) area is 62.5 yd².

$$\text{Cost} = \frac{62.5 \; \cancel{yd^2}}{1} \cdot \frac{\$28}{1 \; \cancel{yd^2}}$$
$$= \$1750$$

8.4 Section Exercises

3. $P = 4 \cdot 51.8 \text{ m}$
    $= 207.2 \text{ m}$

7. $A = b \cdot h$
    $= 31 \text{ mm} \cdot 25 \text{ mm}$
    $= 775 \text{ mm}^2$

11. $A = \frac{1}{2} \cdot h \cdot (b + B)$
    $= 0.5 \cdot 42 \text{ cm} \cdot (61.4 \text{ cm} + 86.2 \text{ cm})$
    $= 0.5 \cdot 42 \text{ cm} \cdot (147.6 \text{ cm})$
    $= 3099.6 \text{ cm}^2$

15. Perimeter is the distance around the edges of a figure. Height is not part of the perimeter. Square units are used for area, not perimeter.

$$P = 2.5 \text{ cm} + 2.5 \text{ cm} + 2.5 \text{ cm} + 2.5 \text{ cm}$$
$$= 10 \text{ cm}$$

19. Break up the figure into 3 parts.
Top figure

$$A = s \cdot s$$
$$= 96 \text{ ft} \cdot 96 \text{ ft}$$
$$= 9216 \text{ ft}^2$$

Middle figure

$$A = b \cdot h$$
$$= 96 \text{ ft} \cdot 72 \text{ ft}$$
$$= 6912 \text{ ft}^2$$

Bottom figure

$$A = s \cdot s$$
$$= 96 \text{ ft} \cdot 96 \text{ ft}$$
$$= 9216 \text{ ft}^2$$

Total area $= 9216 \text{ ft}^2 + 6912 \text{ ft}^2 + 9216 \text{ ft}^2$
$= 25,344 \text{ ft}^2$

23. $25 \cdot 1\frac{3}{7} \cdot \frac{28}{75} = \frac{\cancel{25}^1}{1} \cdot \frac{10}{\cancel{7}_1} \cdot \frac{\cancel{28}^4}{\cancel{75}_3} = \frac{40}{3} = 13\frac{1}{3}$

8.5 Triangles

8.5 Margin Exercises

1. (a) $P = 31 \text{ mm} + 16 \text{ mm} + 25 \text{ m}$
$= 72 \text{ mm}$

(b) $P = 25.9 \text{ m} + 16.2 \text{ m} + 11.7 \text{ m}$
$= 53.8 \text{ m}$

(c) $P = 6\frac{1}{2} \text{ yd} + 9\frac{3}{4} \text{ yd} + 11\frac{1}{4} \text{ yd}$
$= 6\frac{2}{4} \text{ yd} + 9\frac{3}{4} \text{ yd} + 11\frac{1}{4} \text{ yd}$
$= 26\frac{6}{4} \text{ yd} = 27\frac{1}{2} \text{ yd or } 27.5 \text{ yd}$

2. (a) base: 32 m, height 20 m

$$A = \frac{1}{2} \cdot b \cdot h$$
$$= \frac{1}{2} \cdot 32 \text{ m} \cdot 20 \text{ m}$$
$$= 320 \text{ m}^2$$

(b) base: 2.1 cm, height: 1.7 cm

$$A = 0.5 \cdot b \cdot h$$
$$= 0.5 \cdot 2.1 \text{ cm} \cdot 1.7 \text{ cm}$$
$$= 1.785 \text{ cm}^2$$

(c) base: 6 in, height: 4.5 in

$$A = 0.5 \cdot b \cdot h$$
$$= 0.5 \cdot 6 \text{ in} \cdot 4.5 \text{ in}$$
$$= 13.5 \text{ in}^2$$

(d) base: $9\frac{1}{2}$ ft, height: 7 ft

$$A = 0.5 \cdot b \cdot h$$
$$= 0.5 \cdot 9.5 \text{ ft} \cdot 7 \text{ ft}$$
$$= 33.25 \text{ ft}^2 \text{ or } 33\frac{1}{4} \text{ ft}^2$$

3. Find the area of the entire figure which is a square.

$$A = s \cdot s$$
$$= 25 \text{ m} \cdot 25 \text{ m}$$
$$= 625 \text{ m}^2$$

Find the area of the unshaded parts which are triangles.

$$A = \frac{1}{2} \cdot b \cdot h$$
$$= \frac{1}{2} \cdot 25 \text{ m} \cdot 10 \text{ m}$$
$$= 125 \text{ m}^2$$

Subtract to find the area of the shaded part.

entire area	unshaded triangle	unshaded triangle
625 m² −	125 m² −	125 m²

$= 375 \text{ m}$ *shaded part*

4. The shaded part is 375 m². The cost of the carpet is $27 per square meter.

$$\frac{375 \text{ m}^2}{1} \cdot \frac{\$27}{1 \text{ m}^2} = \$10,125$$

The cost for carpeting is $10,125.
The unshaded part is 125 m² + 125 m².
The cost for the vinyl floor covering is $18 per square meter.

$$\frac{125 \text{ m}^2}{1} \cdot \frac{\$18}{1 \text{ m}^2} = \$2250$$

The cost for the vinyl floor covering is $4500 ($2250 + $2250).

Total cost $= \$10,125 + \$2250 + \$2250$
$= \$14,625$

5. (a) *Step 1* $48° + 59° = 107°$

Step 2 $180° - 107° = 73°$
$\angle G$ measures 73°.

Section 8.6 Circles

(b) *Step 1* $90° + 55° = 145°$

Step 2 $180° - 145° = 35°$

$\angle C$ measures $35°$.

(c) *Step 1* $60° + 60° = 120°$

Step 2 $180° - 120° = 60°$

$\angle X$ measures $60°$.

8.5 Section Exercises

3. $P = 26.4 \text{ cm} + 18 \text{ cm} + 15.6 \text{ cm}$
 $= 60 \text{ cm}$

7. $A = 0.5 \cdot b \cdot h$
 $= 0.5 \cdot 28.4 \text{ cm} \cdot 21.3 \text{ cm}$
 $= 302.46 \text{ cm}^2$

11. First, find the area of the entire figure.

$$A = l \cdot w$$
$$= 52 \text{ m} \cdot 37 \text{ m}$$
$$= 1924 \text{ m}^2$$

Find the area of the triangle.

$$A = \frac{1}{2} \cdot b \cdot h$$
$$= \frac{1}{2} \cdot 52 \text{ m} \cdot 28 \text{ m}$$
$$= 728 \text{ m}^2$$

Shaded area $= 1924 \text{ m}^2 - 728 \text{ m}^2$
$= 1196 \text{ m}^2$

15. *Step 1* $72° + 60° = 132°$

Step 2 $180° - 132° = 48°$

The unlabeled angle measures $48°$.

19. $A = \frac{1}{2} \cdot b \cdot h$
 $= \frac{1}{2} \cdot 3\frac{1}{2} \text{ ft} \cdot 4\frac{1}{2} \text{ ft}$
 $= \frac{1}{2} \cdot \frac{7}{2} \text{ ft} \cdot \frac{9}{2} \text{ ft}$
 $= \frac{63}{8} \text{ ft}^2$
 $= 7\frac{7}{8} \text{ ft}^2$ or 7.875 ft^2

To make the flap, $7\frac{7}{8}$ ft² or 7.875 ft² of canvas is needed.

23. (a) Area of one side of the house

$$A = \frac{1}{2} \cdot b \cdot h$$
$$= \frac{1}{2} \cdot 8 \text{ m} \cdot 8 \text{ m}$$
$$= 32 \text{ m}^2$$

(b) Area of one roof section

$$A = 0.5 \cdot b \cdot h$$
$$= 0.5 \cdot 3 \text{ m} \cdot 9 \text{ m}$$
$$= 13.5 \text{ m}^2$$

27. $0.8 \cdot 0.8$

0.8 ← *1 decimal place*
$\times \ 0.8$ ← *1 decimal place*
0.64 ← *2 decimal places*

8.6 Circles

8.6 Margin Exercises

1. (a) diameter: 40 ft

$$r = \frac{d}{2} = \frac{40 \text{ ft}}{2} = 20 \text{ ft}$$

(b) diameter: 11 cm

$$r = \frac{d}{2} = \frac{11 \text{ cm}}{2} = 5.5 \text{ cm}$$

(c) radius: 32 yd

$$d = 2 \cdot r = 2 \cdot 32 \text{ yd} = 64 \text{ yd}$$

(d) radius: 9.5 m

$$d = 2 \cdot r = 2 \cdot 9.5 \text{ m} = 19 \text{ m}$$

2. (a) diameter: 150 ft

$$C = \pi \cdot d$$
$$\approx 3.14 \cdot 150 \text{ ft}$$
$$\approx 471 \text{ ft}$$

(b) radius: 7 inches

$$C = 2 \cdot \pi \cdot r$$
$$\approx 2 \cdot 3.14 \cdot 7 \text{ in}$$
$$\approx 44.0 \text{ in}$$

(c) diameter: 0.9 km

$$C = \pi \cdot d$$
$$\approx 3.14 \cdot 0.9 \text{ km}$$
$$\approx 2.8 \text{ km}$$

(d) radius: 4.6 m

$$C = 2 \cdot \pi \cdot r$$
$$\approx 2 \cdot 3.14 \cdot 4.6 \text{ m}$$
$$\approx 28.9 \text{ m}$$

3. (a) radius: 1 cm

$$A = \pi \cdot r \cdot r$$
$$\approx 3.14 \cdot 1 \text{ cm} \cdot 1 \text{ cm}$$
$$\approx 3.1 \text{ cm}^2$$

(b) diameter: 12 m, so $r = 6$ m

$$A = \pi \cdot r \cdot r$$
$$\approx 3.14 \cdot 6 \text{ m} \cdot 6 \text{ m}$$
$$\approx 113.0 \text{ m}^2$$

(c) radius: 1.8 km

$$A = \pi \cdot r \cdot r$$
$$\approx 3.14 \cdot 1.8 \text{ km} \cdot 1.8 \text{ km}$$
$$\approx 10.2 \text{ km}^2$$

(d) diameter: 8.4 cm, so $r = 4.2$ cm

$$A = \pi \cdot r \cdot r$$
$$\approx 3.14 \cdot 4.2 \text{ cm} \cdot 4.2 \text{ cm}$$
$$\approx 55.4 \text{ cm}^2$$

4. (a) radius: 24 m
Area of circle

$$A = \pi \cdot r \cdot r$$
$$\approx 3.14 \cdot 24 \text{ m} \cdot 24 \text{ m}$$
$$\approx 1808.6 \text{ m}^2$$

Area of semicircle

$$\frac{1808.6 \text{ m}^2}{2} \approx 904.3 \text{ m}^2$$

(b) diameter: 35.4 ft, so $r = 17.7$ ft
Area of circle

$$A = \pi \cdot r \cdot r$$
$$\approx 3.14 \cdot 17.7 \text{ ft} \cdot 17.7 \text{ ft}$$
$$\approx 983.7306 \text{ ft}^2$$

Area of semicircle

$$\frac{983.7306 \text{ ft}^2}{2} \approx 491.9 \text{ ft}^2$$

(c) radius: 9.8 m
Area of circle

$$A = \pi \cdot r \cdot r$$
$$\approx 3.14 \cdot 9.8 \text{ m} \cdot 9.8 \text{ m}$$
$$\approx 301.5656$$

Area of semicircle

$$A \approx \frac{301.5656 \text{ m}^2}{2} \approx 150.8 \text{ m}^2$$

5. diameter of rug: 3 m
cost for binding: $4.50 per meter

$$C = \pi \cdot d$$
$$\approx 3.14 \cdot 3 \text{ m}$$
$$\approx 9.42 \text{ m}$$

Cost of binding

$$= \frac{9.42 \text{ m}}{1} \cdot \frac{\$4.50}{1 \text{ m}}$$
$$= \$42.39$$

6. diameter: 3 m, so $r = 1\frac{1}{2}$ m
cost for rubber backing: $2 per square meter

$$A = \pi \cdot r \cdot r$$
$$\approx 3.14 \cdot 1\frac{1}{2} \text{ m} \cdot 1\frac{1}{2} \text{ m}$$
$$\approx 7.065 \text{ m}^2$$

Cost for rubber backing

$$= \frac{7.065 \text{ m}^2}{1} \cdot \frac{\$2}{\text{m}^2}$$
$$= \$14.13$$

7. (a) Some possibilities are:

diameter; diagonal
fraction; fracture
parallel; paramedic
percent; per capita
perimeter; periscope
radius; radiate
rectangle; rectify
subtract; submarine

(b) *Peri* in perimeter means around, so perimeter is the distance around the edges of a shape.

8.6 Section Exercises

3. The diameter is 0.7 km so the radius is
$$\frac{d}{2} = \frac{0.7 \text{ km}}{2} = 0.35 \text{ km}.$$

7. diameter: 2.6 m
$$\begin{aligned} C &= \pi \cdot d \\ &\approx 3.14 \cdot 2.6 \text{ m} \\ &\approx 8.2 \text{ m} \end{aligned}$$
radius: $\frac{2.6 \text{ m}}{2} = 1.3 \text{ m}$
$$\begin{aligned} A &= \pi \cdot r \cdot r \\ &\approx 3.14 \cdot 1.3 \text{ m} \cdot 1.3 \text{ m} \\ &\approx 5.3 \text{ m}^2 \end{aligned}$$

11. $d = 7\frac{1}{2}$ ft
$$\begin{aligned} C &= \pi \cdot 7\frac{1}{2} \text{ ft} \\ &\approx 3.14 \cdot 7.5 \text{ ft} \\ &\approx 23.6 \text{ ft} \end{aligned}$$
$r = \frac{7\frac{1}{2}}{2}$ ft = 3.75 ft
$$\begin{aligned} A &= \pi \cdot r \cdot r \\ &\approx 3.14 \cdot 3.75 \text{ ft} \cdot 3.75 \text{ ft} \\ &\approx 44.2 \text{ ft}^2 \end{aligned}$$

15. diameter of tire: 70 cm
The point moves the length of the circumference in one turn.
$$C \approx 3.14 \cdot 70 \text{ cm} \approx 219.8 \text{ cm}$$
The point moves ≈ 219.8 cm.

19. The diameter is $7\frac{1}{2}$ in, so the radius is
$\frac{7\frac{1}{2} \text{ in}}{2} = 3\frac{3}{4}$ in or 3.75 in.
$$\begin{aligned} \text{Area} &= \pi \cdot r \cdot r \\ &\approx 3.14 \cdot 3.75 \text{ in} \cdot 3.75 \text{ in} \\ &\approx 44.15625 \text{ in}^2 \end{aligned}$$
The area of a small pizza is ≈ 44.2 in^2.

23.

Size	Cost per square inch
small	$\frac{\$3.70}{44.2 \text{ in}^2} \approx \$0.084$
medium	$\frac{\$8.95}{132.7 \text{ in}^2} \approx \$0.067$
large	$\frac{\$14.30}{201.0 \text{ in}^2} \approx \$0.071$

The best buy is the medium pizza.

27. Area of the circle
$$\begin{aligned} A &= \pi \cdot r \cdot r \\ &\approx 3.14 \cdot 10 \text{ cm} \cdot 10 \text{ cm} \\ &\approx 314 \text{ cm}^2 \end{aligned}$$
Area of the semicircle
$$\frac{314 \text{ cm}^2}{2} \approx 157 \text{ cm}^2$$
Area of the triangle
$$\begin{aligned} A &= \frac{1}{2} \cdot b \cdot h \\ &= \frac{1}{2} \cdot 20 \text{ cm} \cdot 10 \text{ cm} \\ &= 100 \text{ cm}^2 \end{aligned}$$
The shaded area is
$$\approx 157 \text{ cm}^2 - 100 \text{ cm}^2 \approx 57 \text{ cm}^2.$$

31. The radius is 150 miles.
$$\begin{aligned} A &= \pi \cdot r \cdot r \\ &\approx 3.14 \cdot 150 \text{ mi} \cdot 150 \text{ mi} \\ &\approx 70{,}650 \text{ mi}^2 \end{aligned}$$
There are 70,650 mi^2 in the broadcast area.

35. Find the area of the rectangle with length: 29 ft and width: 16 ft.
$$\begin{aligned} A &= length \cdot width \\ &= 29 \text{ ft} \cdot 16 \text{ ft} \\ &= 464 \text{ ft}^2 \end{aligned}$$
Both semicircles are the same and are equal to a circle. The radius is 8 ft.
$$\begin{aligned} A &= \pi \cdot r \cdot r \\ &\approx 3.14 \cdot 8 \text{ ft} \cdot 8 \text{ ft} \\ &\approx 200.96 \text{ ft}^2 \end{aligned}$$
$$\begin{aligned} \text{Total area} &= 464 \text{ ft}^2 + 200.96 \text{ ft}^2 \\ &= 664.96 \text{ ft}^2 \end{aligned}$$
$$\begin{aligned} \text{Cost of the sod} &= \frac{664.96 \text{ ft}^2}{1} \cdot \frac{\$1.76}{1 \text{ ft}^2} \\ &\approx \$1170.33 \end{aligned}$$

39. $\frac{1}{2} = \frac{1 \cdot 5}{2 \cdot 5} = \frac{5}{10} = 0.5$

43. $\dfrac{2}{3}$

$$\begin{array}{r}0.6666\\3\overline{)2.0000}\\\underline{1\,8}\\20\\\underline{18}\\20\\\underline{18}\\20\\\underline{18}\\2\end{array}$$

$\dfrac{2}{3} \approx 0.667$

8.7 Volume

8.7 Margin Exercises

1. **(a)** length 8 m, width 3 m, height 3 m

$$\begin{aligned}V &= length \cdot width \cdot height\\&= 8\text{ m} \cdot 3\text{ m} \cdot 3\text{ m}\\&= 72\text{ m}^3\end{aligned}$$

(b) length 23.4 cm, width 15.2 cm, height 52.3 cm

$$\begin{aligned}V &= length \cdot width \cdot height\\&= 23.4\text{ cm} \cdot 15.2\text{ cm} \cdot 52.3\text{ cm}\\&= 18,602.064\text{ cm}^3\\&\approx 18,602.1\text{ cm}^3\end{aligned}$$

(c) length $6\tfrac{1}{4}$ ft, width $3\tfrac{1}{2}$ ft, height 2 ft

$$\begin{aligned}V &= length \cdot width \cdot height\\&= 6.25\text{ ft} \cdot 3.5\text{ ft} \cdot 2\text{ ft}\\&= 43\tfrac{3}{4}\text{ ft}^3 \text{ or } 43.75\text{ ft}^3\\&\approx 43.8\text{ ft}^3\end{aligned}$$

2. **(a)** $r = 12$ in

$$\begin{aligned}V &= \tfrac{4}{3} \cdot \pi \cdot r^3\\&\approx \tfrac{4}{3} \cdot 3.14 \cdot 12\text{ in} \cdot 12\text{ in} \cdot 12\text{ in}\\&\approx \dfrac{21,703.68\text{ in}^3}{3}\\&\approx 7234.56\text{ in}^3\\&\approx 7234.6\text{ in}^3\end{aligned}$$

(b) $r = 3.5$ m

$$\begin{aligned}V &= \tfrac{4}{3} \cdot \pi \cdot r^3\\&\approx \tfrac{4}{3} \cdot 3.14 \cdot 3.5\text{ m} \cdot 3.5\text{ m} \cdot 3.5\text{ m}\\&\approx \dfrac{538.51\text{ m}^3}{3}\\&\approx 179.50333\text{ m}^3\\&\approx 179.5\text{ m}^3\end{aligned}$$

(c) $r = 2.7$ cm

$$\begin{aligned}V &= \tfrac{4}{3} \cdot \pi \cdot r^3\\V &\approx \tfrac{4}{3} \cdot 3.14 \cdot 2.7\text{ cm} \cdot 2.7\text{ cm} \cdot 2.7\text{ cm}\\&\approx \dfrac{247.21848\text{ cm}^3}{3}\\&\approx 82.40616\text{ cm}^3\\&\approx 82.4\text{ cm}^3\end{aligned}$$

3. **(a)** $r = 15$ ft

$$\begin{aligned}V &= \dfrac{2 \cdot \pi \cdot r^3}{3}\\&\approx \dfrac{2 \cdot 3.14 \cdot 15\text{ ft} \cdot 15\text{ ft} \cdot 15\text{ ft}}{3}\\&\approx \dfrac{21,195\text{ ft}^3}{3}\\&\approx 7065\text{ ft}^3\end{aligned}$$

(b) $r = 6$ cm

$$\begin{aligned}V &= \dfrac{2 \cdot \pi \cdot r^3}{3}\\&\approx \dfrac{2 \cdot 3.14 \cdot 6\text{ cm} \cdot 6\text{ cm} \cdot 6\text{ cm}}{3}\\&\approx \dfrac{1356.48\text{ cm}^3}{3}\\&\approx 452.16\text{ cm}^3\\&\approx 452.2\text{ cm}^3\end{aligned}$$

(c) $r = 3.7$ mm

$$\begin{aligned}V &= \dfrac{2 \cdot \pi \cdot r^3}{3}\\&\approx \dfrac{2 \cdot 3.14 \cdot 3.7\text{ mm} \cdot 3.7\text{ mm} \cdot 3.7\text{ mm}}{3}\\&\approx \dfrac{318.10084\text{ mm}^3}{3}\\&\approx 106.03361\text{ mm}^3\\&\approx 106.0\text{ mm}^3\end{aligned}$$

Section 8.7 Volume

4. (a) $r = 4$ ft, $h = 12$ ft
$$V = \pi \cdot r \cdot r \cdot h$$
$$\approx 3.14 \cdot 4 \text{ ft} \cdot 4 \text{ ft} \cdot 12 \text{ ft}$$
$$\approx 602.88 \text{ ft}^3$$
$$\approx 602.9 \text{ ft}^3$$

(b) $r = \dfrac{7 \text{ cm}}{2} = 3.5$ cm, $h = 6$ cm
$$V = \pi \cdot r \cdot r \cdot h$$
$$\approx 3.14 \cdot 3.5 \text{ cm} \cdot 3.5 \text{ cm} \cdot 6 \text{ cm}$$
$$\approx 230.79 \text{ cm}^3$$
$$\approx 230.8 \text{ cm}^3$$

(c) $r = 14.5$ yd, $h = 3.2$ yd
$$V = \pi \cdot r \cdot r \cdot h$$
$$\approx 3.14 \cdot 14.5 \text{ yd} \cdot 14.5 \text{ yd} \cdot 3.2 \text{ yd}$$
$$\approx 2112.592 \text{ yd}^3$$
$$\approx 2112.6 \text{ yd}^3$$

5. Volume of cone $= \dfrac{B \cdot h}{3}$

First find the area of the base.
$$B = \pi \cdot r \cdot r$$
$$\approx 3.14 \cdot 2 \text{ ft} \cdot 2 \text{ ft}$$
$$\approx 12.56 \text{ ft}^2$$

Now find the volume of the cone.
$$V = \dfrac{B \cdot h}{3}$$
$$\approx \dfrac{12.56 \text{ ft}^2 \cdot 11 \text{ ft}}{3}$$
$$\approx \dfrac{138.16 \text{ ft}^3}{3}$$
$$\approx 46.053333 \text{ ft}^3$$
$$\approx 46.1 \text{ ft}^3$$

6. base: 10 m by 10 m
height: 8 m
Find the area of the base.
$$B = 10 \text{ m} \cdot 10 \text{ m}$$
$$= 100 \text{ m}^2$$
$$V = \dfrac{B \cdot h}{3}$$
$$= \dfrac{100 \text{ m}^2 \cdot 8 \text{ m}}{3}$$
$$\approx 266.6666 \text{ m}^3$$
$$\approx 266.7 \text{ m}^3$$

8.7 Section Exercises

3. Volume of a sphere
$$V = \dfrac{4}{3} \cdot \pi \cdot r^3$$
$$\approx \dfrac{4 \cdot 3.14 \cdot 22 \text{ m} \cdot 22 \text{ m} \cdot 22 \text{ m}}{3}$$
$$\approx 44{,}579.627 \text{ m}^3$$
$$\approx 44{,}579.6 \text{ m}^3$$

7. Volume of a cylinder
$$V = \pi \cdot r^2 \cdot h$$
$$\approx 3.14 \cdot 5 \text{ ft} \cdot 5 \text{ ft} \cdot 6 \text{ ft}$$
$$\approx 471 \text{ ft}^3$$

11. Volume of a pyramid
Area of the base
$$B = 8 \text{ cm} \cdot 15 \text{ cm}$$
$$= 120 \text{ cm}^2$$
$$V = \dfrac{B \cdot h}{3}$$
$$= \dfrac{120 \text{ cm}^2 \cdot 20 \text{ cm}}{3}$$
$$= 800 \text{ cm}^3$$

15. Use the formula for finding the volume of a sphere.
$$\text{radius} = \dfrac{16.8 \text{ cm}}{2} = 8.4 \text{ cm}$$
$$V = \dfrac{4}{3} \cdot \pi \cdot r^3$$
$$\approx \dfrac{4 \cdot 3.14 \cdot 8.4 \text{ cm} \cdot 8.4 \text{ cm} \cdot 8.4 \text{ cm}}{3}$$
$$\approx 2481.4541 \text{ cm}^3$$
$$\approx 2481.5 \text{ cm}^3$$

The volume of the globe is $\approx 2481.5 \text{ cm}^3$.

19. Volume of a pyramid
Find the area of the base.
$$B = 145 \text{ m} \cdot 145 \text{ m}$$
$$= 21{,}025 \text{ m}^2$$
$$V = \dfrac{B \cdot h}{3}$$
$$= \dfrac{21{,}025 \text{ m}^2 \cdot 93 \text{ m}}{3}$$
$$= 651{,}775 \text{ m}^3$$

The volume of the ancient stone pyramid is $651{,}775 \text{ m}^3$.

23. Volume of the base

$$V = \ell \cdot w \cdot h$$
$$= 11 \text{ cm} \cdot 9 \text{ m} \cdot 3 \text{ cm}$$
$$= 297 \text{ cm}^3$$

Volume of the column

$$V = 9 \text{ cm} \cdot 2 \text{ cm} \cdot 12 \text{ cm}$$
$$= 216 \text{ cm}^3$$

Volume of entire object

$$297 \text{ cm}^3 + 216 \text{ cm}^3 = 513 \text{ cm}^3$$

27. $\sqrt{16} = 4$, because $4 \cdot 4 = 16$.

8.8 Pythagorean Theorem

8.8 Margin Exercises

1. (a) $\sqrt{36} = 6$ because $6 \cdot 6 = 36$.

(b) $\sqrt{25} = 5$ because $5 \cdot 5 = 25$.

(c) $\sqrt{9} = 3$ because $3 \cdot 3 = 9$.

(d) $\sqrt{100} = 10$ because $10 \cdot 10 = 100$.

(e) $\sqrt{121} = 11$ because $11 \cdot 11 = 121$.

2. (a) $\sqrt{11}$
Calculator shows 3.3166248; $\sqrt{11} \approx 3.317$.

(b) $\sqrt{40}$
Calculator shows 6.3245553; $\sqrt{40} \approx 6.325$.

(c) $\sqrt{56}$
Calculator shows 7.4833148; $\sqrt{56} \approx 7.483$.

(d) $\sqrt{196}$
Calculator shows 14.

(e) $\sqrt{147}$
Calculator shows 12.124356; $\sqrt{147} \approx 12.124$.

3. (a) legs: 5 in and 12 in

$$\begin{aligned}hypotenuse &= \sqrt{(leg)^2 + (leg)^2} \\ &= \sqrt{(5)^2 + (12)^2} \\ &= \sqrt{25 + 144} \\ &= \sqrt{169} \\ &= 13 \text{ in}\end{aligned}$$

(b) hypotenuse: 25 cm, leg: 7 cm

$$\begin{aligned}leg &= \sqrt{(hypotenuse)^2 - (leg)^2} \\ &= \sqrt{(25)^2 - (7)^2} \\ &= \sqrt{625 - 49} \\ &= \sqrt{576} \\ &= 24 \text{ cm}\end{aligned}$$

(c) legs: 17 m and 13 m

$$\begin{aligned}hypotenuse &= \sqrt{(leg)^2 + (leg)^2} \\ &= \sqrt{(17)^2 + (13)^2} \\ &= \sqrt{289 + 169} \\ &= \sqrt{458} \\ &\approx 21.400935 \\ &\approx 21.401 \text{ m}\end{aligned}$$

(d) hypotenuse: 20 ft, leg 18 ft

$$\begin{aligned}leg &= \sqrt{(hypotenuse)^2 - (leg)^2} \\ &= \sqrt{(20)^2 - (18)^2} \\ &= \sqrt{400 - 324} \\ &= \sqrt{76} \\ &\approx 8.7177979 \\ &\approx 8.718 \text{ ft}\end{aligned}$$

(e) legs: 8 mm and 5 mm

$$\begin{aligned}hypotenuse &= \sqrt{(leg)^2 + (leg)^2} \\ &= \sqrt{(8)^2 + (5)^2} \\ &= \sqrt{64 + 25} \\ &= \sqrt{89} \\ &\approx 9.4339811 \\ &\approx 9.434 \text{ mm}\end{aligned}$$

4. (a) hypotenuse; 25 ft, leg: 20 ft

$$\begin{aligned}leg &= \sqrt{(25)^2 - (20)^2} \\ &= \sqrt{225} \\ &= 15\end{aligned}$$

The bottom of the ladder is 15 ft from the building.

(b) legs: 11 ft and 8 ft

$$\begin{aligned}hypotenuse &= \sqrt{(11)^2 + (8)^2} \\ &= \sqrt{185} \\ &\approx 13.601471 \\ &\approx 13.601\end{aligned}$$

Section 8.8 Pythagorean Theorem

The ladder is ≈ 13.601 ft long.

(c) Find how high up the ladder will reach on the building.
Use this formula:

$leg = \sqrt{(hypotenuse)^2 - (leg)^2}$.

hypotenuse: 17 ft, leg 10 ft

$$\begin{aligned} leg &= \sqrt{(17)^2 - (10)^2} \\ &= \sqrt{289 - 100} \\ &= \sqrt{189} \\ &\approx 13.747727 \\ &\approx 13.748 \end{aligned}$$

The ladder will reach ≈ 13.748 ft.

8.8 Section Exercises

3. $\sqrt{64} = 8$ because $8 \cdot 8 = 64$.

7. $\sqrt{5}$
Calculator shows 2.236068.
$\sqrt{5} \approx 2.236$

11. $\sqrt{101}$
Calculator shows 10.049876.
$\sqrt{101} \approx 10.050$

15. $\sqrt{1000}$
Calculator shows 31.622777.
$\sqrt{1000} \approx 31.623$

19. legs: 15 ft and 36 ft

$$\begin{aligned} hypotenuse &= \sqrt{(leg)^2 + (leg)^2} \\ &= \sqrt{(15)^2 + (36)^2} \\ &= \sqrt{225 + 1296} \\ &= \sqrt{1521} \\ &= 39 \text{ ft} \end{aligned}$$

23. hypotenuse: 20 mm, leg: 16 mm

$$\begin{aligned} leg &= \sqrt{(hypotenuse)^2 - (leg)^2} \\ &= \sqrt{(20)^2 - (16)^2} \\ &= \sqrt{400 - 256} \\ &= \sqrt{144} \\ &= 12 \text{ mm} \end{aligned}$$

27. legs: 7 yd and 4 yd

$$\begin{aligned} hypotenuse &= \sqrt{(7)^2 + (4)^2} \\ &= \sqrt{49 + 16} \\ &= \sqrt{65} \\ &\approx 8.0622577 \\ &\approx 8.062 \text{ yd} \end{aligned}$$

31. legs: 1.3 m and 2.5 m

$$\begin{aligned} hypotenuse &= \sqrt{(1.3)^2 + (2.5)^2} \\ &= \sqrt{1.69 + 6.25} \\ &= \sqrt{7.94} \\ &\approx 2.8178006 \\ &\approx 2.818 \text{ m} \end{aligned}$$

35. hypotenuse: 21.6 km, leg: 13.2 km

$$\begin{aligned} leg &= \sqrt{(hypotenuse)^2 - (leg)^2} \\ &= \sqrt{(21.6^2) - (13.2)^2} \\ &= \sqrt{466.56 - 174.24} \\ &= \sqrt{292.32} \\ &\approx 17.097368 \\ &\approx 17.097 \text{ km} \end{aligned}$$

39. hypotenuse: 1000 m; leg: 800 m

$$\begin{aligned} leg &= \sqrt{(hypotenuse)^2 - (leg)^2} \\ &= \sqrt{(1000)^2 - (800)^2} \\ &= \sqrt{1,000,000 - 640,000} \\ &= \sqrt{360,000} \\ &= 600 \text{ m} \end{aligned}$$

43. 30 is about halfway between 25 and 36 so $\sqrt{30}$ should be about halfway between 5 and 6, or ≈ 5.5. Using a calculator, $\sqrt{30} \approx 5.477$. Similarly $\sqrt{26}$ should be a little more than $\sqrt{25}$. By calculator it is ≈ 5.099. Also, $\sqrt{35}$ should be a little less than $\sqrt{36}$. By calculator it is ≈ 5.916.

47. $\dfrac{2}{9} = \dfrac{x}{36}$

$9 \cdot x = 2 \cdot 36$ *Cross products are equivalent*

$9 \cdot x = 72$

$\dfrac{9 \cdot x}{9} = \dfrac{72}{9}$

$x = 8$

8.9 Similar Triangles

8.9 Margin Exercises

1. **(a)** Corresponding angles measure the same number of degrees.
   The corresponding angles are angles:
   P and Z, N and X, and M and Y.
   $\overline{PN}$ and $\overline{XZ}$ are opposite corresponding angles M and Y.
   $\overline{PM}$ and $\overline{ZY}$ are opposite corresponding angles N and X.
   $\overline{NM}$ and $\overline{XY}$ are opposite corresponding angles P and Z.

   The corresponding sides are

   $\overline{PN}$ and $\overline{ZX}$, $\overline{PM}$ and $\overline{ZY}$, $\overline{NM}$ and $\overline{XY}$.

   (b) The corresponding angles are angles:

   A and E, B and F, C and G.

   The corresponding sides are

   $\overline{AB}$ and $\overline{EF}$, $\overline{BC}$ and $\overline{GF}$, $\overline{AC}$ and $\overline{EG}$.

2. Find $\overline{EF}$.

   $\dfrac{EF}{CB} = \dfrac{1}{3}$ Ratio from Example 1

   Replace EF with x and CB with 33.

   $$\dfrac{x}{33} = \dfrac{1}{3}$$
   $$3 \cdot x = 33 \cdot 1$$
   $$3 \cdot x = 33$$
   $$\dfrac{3 \cdot x}{3} = \dfrac{33}{3}$$
   $$x = 11$$
   $$\overline{EF} = 11 \text{ m}$$

3. **(a)** Find $\overline{AB}$.
   From Example 2,
   $\dfrac{PR}{AC} = \dfrac{1}{2}$, so $\dfrac{PQ}{AB} = \dfrac{1}{2}$.
   Replace PQ with 3 and AB with x.

   $$\dfrac{3}{x} = \dfrac{1}{2}$$
   $$x \cdot 1 = 3 \cdot 2$$
   $$x = 6$$

   $\overline{AB}$ is 6 ft.
   Find the perimeter.

   $$\begin{aligned} Perimeter &= 14 \text{ ft} + 10 \text{ ft} + 6 \text{ ft} \\ &= 30 \text{ ft} \end{aligned}$$

   (b) Set up a ratio.

   $$\dfrac{PQ}{AB} = \dfrac{10 \text{ m}}{30 \text{ m}} = \dfrac{1}{3} \text{ so,}$$
   $$\dfrac{QR}{CB} = \dfrac{1}{3} \text{ and } \dfrac{PR}{AC} = \dfrac{1}{3}.$$

   Replace QR with x and CB with 18 and write a proportion.

   $$\dfrac{x}{18} = \dfrac{1}{3}$$
   $$3 \cdot x = 18 \cdot 1$$
   $$\dfrac{3 \cdot x}{3} = \dfrac{18}{3}$$
   $$x = 6$$

   $\overline{QR}$ is 6 m.
   The perimeter of triangle PQR is

   $$10 \text{ m} + 8 \text{ m} + 6 \text{ m} = 24 \text{ m}.$$

   Replace PR with 8 and AC with y and write a proportion.

   $$\dfrac{8}{y} = \dfrac{1}{3}$$
   $$y \cdot 1 = 8 \cdot 3$$
   $$y = 24$$

   $\overline{AC}$ is 24 m.

   The perimeter of triangle ABC is
   $30 \text{ m} + 18 \text{ m} + 24 \text{ m} = 72 \text{ m}.$

4. **(a)** Write a proportion.

   $$\dfrac{h}{5} = \dfrac{48}{12}$$
   $$12 \cdot h = 5 \cdot 48$$
   $$12 \cdot h = 240$$
   $$\dfrac{12 \cdot h}{12} = \dfrac{240}{12}$$
   $$h = 20$$

   The flagpole is 20 ft high.

Section 8.9 Similar Triangles

(b) Write a proportion.

$$\frac{h}{7.2} = \frac{12.5}{5}$$
$$5 \cdot h = 7.2 \cdot 12.5$$
$$5 \cdot h = 90$$
$$\frac{5 \cdot h}{5} = \frac{90}{5}$$
$$h = 18$$

The flagpole is 18 m high.

8.9 Section Exercises

3. The triangles do not have the same shape so they are not similar.

7. The corresponding angles are

$$\angle B \text{ and } \angle Q, \angle C \text{ and } \angle R,$$
$$\angle A \text{ and } \angle P.$$

The corresponding sides are

$$\overline{AB} \text{ and } \overline{PQ}$$
$$\overline{BC} \text{ and } \overline{QR}$$
$$\overline{AC} \text{ and } \overline{PR}.$$

11. $\frac{AB}{PQ} = \frac{9 \text{ m}}{6 \text{ m}} = \frac{9}{6} = \frac{3}{2}$

$\frac{AC}{PR} = \frac{12 \text{ m}}{8 \text{ m}} = \frac{12}{8} = \frac{3}{2}$

$\frac{BC}{QR} = \frac{15 \text{ m}}{10 \text{ m}} = \frac{15}{10} = \frac{3}{2}$

15. Set up a ratio of corresponding sides.

$$\frac{6 \text{ cm}}{12 \text{ cm}} = \frac{6}{12} = \frac{1}{2}$$

Write a proportion to find a.

$$\frac{a}{12} = \frac{1}{2}$$
$$2 \cdot a = 12 \cdot 1$$
$$\frac{2 \cdot a}{2} = \frac{12}{2}$$
$$a = 6 \text{ cm}$$

Write a proportion to find b.

$$\frac{7.5}{b} = \frac{1}{2}$$
$$1 \cdot b = 2 \cdot 7.5$$
$$b = 15 \text{ cm}$$

19. Write a proportion to find h.

$$\frac{2}{16} = \frac{3}{h}$$
$$2 \cdot h = 3 \cdot 16$$
$$2 \cdot h = 48$$
$$\frac{2 \cdot h}{2} = \frac{48}{2}$$
$$h = 24 \text{ ft}$$

23. Set up a ratio of corresponding sides to find the length of the missing sides in triangle FGH.

$$\frac{DE}{GH} = \frac{CE}{FH}$$
$$\frac{12}{8} = \frac{12}{x}$$
$$12 \cdot x = 8 \cdot 12$$
$$\frac{12 \cdot x}{12} = \frac{96}{12}$$
$$x = 8$$

Each missing side of triangle FGH is 8 cm.

$$\textit{Perimeter of triangle FGH} = 8 \text{ cm} + 8 \text{ cm} + 8 \text{ cm}$$
$$= 24 \text{ cm}$$

Set up a ratio of corresponding sides to find the height of triangle FGH.

$$\frac{8.4}{12} = \frac{h}{8}$$
$$12 \cdot h = 8 \cdot 8.4$$
$$\frac{12 \cdot h}{12} = \frac{67.2}{12}$$
$$h = 5.6 \text{ cm}$$

$$\textit{Area triangle FGH} = 0.5 \cdot 8 \text{ cm} \cdot 5.6 \text{ cm}$$
$$= 22.4 \text{ cm}^2$$

27. Set up a ratio of corresponding sides.

$$\frac{100 \text{ m}}{220 \text{ m}} = \frac{5}{11}$$

Write a proportion to find n.

$$\frac{50}{n} = \frac{5}{11}$$
$$5 \cdot n = 50 \cdot 11$$
$$5 \cdot n = 550$$
$$\frac{5 \cdot n}{5} = \frac{550}{5}$$
$$n = 110 \text{ m}$$

31. $8 \div 4 + 3 \cdot 2$ *Divide*
     $2 + 3 \cdot 2$ *Multiply*
     $2 + 6 = 8$ *Add*

35. $16 - 5 + 2(6 - 4)$ *Parentheses*
     $16 - 5 + 2(2)$ *Multiply*
     $16 - 5 + 4$ *Subtract*
     $11 + 4 = 15$ *Add*

Chapter 8 Review Exercises

1. The figure is a *line segment* named $\overline{AB}$ or $\overline{BA}$. It is a piece of a line that has two endpoints.

2. The figure is a *line* named $\overleftrightarrow{CD}$ or $\overleftrightarrow{DC}$. It is a straight row of points that go on forever in both directions.

3. The figure is a *ray* named $\overrightarrow{OP}$. It is part of a line that goes on forever in one direction and has only one endpoint.

4. The lines are *parallel* because they do not intersect (never cross).

5. The lines are *perpendicular* because they intersect at right angles.

6. The lines are *intersecting*, but not perpendicular because they do not form a right angle.

7. Angle LMN measures between 0° and 90° so it is an acute angle.

8. Angle AOB measures between 90° and 180° so it is an obtuse angle.

9. Angle P is a straight angle that measures 180°.

10. Angle WOX is a right angle that measures 90°.

11. Because they are vertical angles, these angles are also congruent.

$$\angle 1 \cong \angle 4, \angle 2 \cong 5, \angle 3 \cong \angle 6$$

The pairs of complementary angles are

$$\angle 1 \text{ and } \angle 2, \angle 4 \text{ and } \angle 5,$$
$$\angle 5 \text{ and } \angle 1, \angle 4 \text{ and } \angle 2.$$

12. The congruent angles are

$$\angle 4 \cong \angle 7, \angle 3 \cong 6.$$

The pairs of complementary angles are

$$\angle 1 \text{ and } \angle 2, \angle 3 \text{ and } \angle 4, \angle 6 \text{ and }$$
$$\angle 7, \angle 6 \text{ and } \angle 4, \angle 7 \text{ and } \angle 3.$$

13. $\angle AOB$ and $\angle BOC$,
$\angle BOC$ and $\angle COD$,
$\angle COD$ and $\angle DOA$, and
$\angle DOA$ and $\angle AOB$
are supplementary because the sum of each pair of angles is 180°.

14. $\angle ERH$ and $\angle HRG$,
$\angle HRG$ and $\angle GRF$,
$\angle GRF$ and $\angle FRE$, and
$\angle FRE$ and $\angle ERH$
are supplementary because the sum of each pair of angles is 180°.

15. (a) The complement of 80° is 10° because $80° + 10° = 90°$.

(b) The complement of 45° is 45° because $45° + 45° = 90°$.

(c) The complement of 7° is 83° because $7° + 83° = 90°$.

16. (a) The supplement of 155° is 25° because $155° + 25° = 180°$.

(b) The supplement of 90° is 90° because $90° + 90° = 180°$.

(c) The supplement of 33° is 147° because $33° + 147° = 180°$.

17. $P = 1.5 \text{ m} + 0.92 \text{ m} + 1.5 \text{ m} + 0.92 \text{ m}$
     $= 4.84 \text{ m}$

18. The figure is a square. So all 4 sides have the same measurement.

$$P = 32 \text{ in} + 32 \text{ in} + 32 \text{ in} + 32 \text{ in}$$
$$= 128 \text{ in}$$

19. $P = 4 \cdot s$
     $= 4 \cdot 38 \text{ cm}$
     $= 152 \text{ cm}$

To trim all the edges 152 cm of trim is needed.

20. $P = 2 \cdot length + 2 \cdot width$
     $= 2 \cdot 12 \text{ ft} + 2 \cdot 8\frac{1}{2} \text{ ft}$
     $= 24 \text{ ft} + 17 \text{ ft}$
     $= 41 \text{ ft}$

To surround the garden 41 feet of fencing is needed.

Chapter 8 Review Exercises

21. $A = length \cdot width$
    $= 27 \text{ mm} \cdot 18 \text{ mm}$
    $= 486 \text{ mm}^2$

22. $A = length \cdot width$
    $= 5\frac{1}{2} \text{ ft} \cdot 3 \text{ ft}$
    $= 5.5 \text{ ft} \cdot 3 \text{ ft}$
    $= 16.5 \text{ ft}^2 \text{ or } 16\frac{1}{2} \text{ ft}^2$

23. $A = s^2$
    $= 6.3 \text{ m} \cdot 6.3 \text{ m}$
    $= 39.69$
    $\approx 39.7 \text{ m}^2$

24. a parallelogram

    $P = 11 \text{ cm} + 14 \text{ cm} + 11 \text{ cm} + 14 \text{ cm}$
    $ = 50 \text{ cm}$

    $A = b \cdot h$
    $ = 14 \text{ cm} \cdot 10 \text{ cm}$
    $ = 140 \text{ cm}^2$

25. a trapezoid

    $P = 26 \text{ ft} + 21.1 \text{ ft} + 37 \text{ ft} + 18 \text{ ft}$
    $ = 102.1 \text{ ft}$

    $A = \frac{1}{2} \cdot h \cdot (b + B)$
    $ = \frac{1}{2} \cdot 18 \text{ ft} \cdot (26 \text{ ft} + 37 \text{ ft})$
    $ = \frac{1}{2} \cdot 18 \text{ ft} \cdot 63 \text{ ft}$
    $ = 567 \text{ ft}^2$

26. a trapezoid

    $P = 33.9 \text{ m} + 59.7 \text{ m} + 34.2 \text{ m} + 72.4 \text{ m}$
    $ = 200.2 \text{ m}$

    $A = 0.5 \cdot h \cdot (b + B)$
    $ = 0.5 \cdot 31.4 \text{ m} \cdot (59.7 \text{ m} + 72.4 \text{ m})$
    $ = 0.5 \cdot 31.4 \text{ m} \cdot 132.1 \text{ m}$
    $ \approx 2073.97 \text{ m}^2$
    $ \approx 2074.0 \text{ m}^2$

27. $P = 153 \text{ cm} + 153 \text{ cm} + 212 \text{ cm}$
    $ = 518 \text{ cm}$

    $A = \frac{1}{2} \cdot b \cdot h$
    $ = \frac{1}{2} \cdot 212 \text{ cm} \cdot 102 \text{ cm}$
    $ = 10,812 \text{ cm}^2$

28. $P = 5 \text{ m} + 12.3 \text{ m} + 9.8 \text{ m}$
    $ = 27.1 \text{ m}$

    $A = \frac{1}{2} \cdot b \cdot h$
    $ = \frac{1}{2} \cdot 9.8 \text{ m} \cdot 4.2 \text{ m}$
    $ = 20.58 \text{ m}^2$

29. $P = 8 \text{ ft} + 3\frac{1}{2} \text{ ft} + 8\frac{3}{4} \text{ ft}$
    $ = 8 \text{ ft} + 3.5 \text{ ft} + 8.75 \text{ ft}$
    $ = 20.25 \text{ ft or } 20\frac{1}{4} \text{ ft}$

    $A = \frac{1}{2} \cdot b \cdot h$
    $ = \frac{1}{2} \cdot 8 \text{ ft} \cdot 3\frac{1}{2} \text{ ft}$
    $ = 14 \text{ ft}^2$

30. *Step 1* $70° + 40° = 110°$
    Step 2 $180° - 110° = 70°$
    The unlabeled angle measures 70°.

31. *Step 1* $90° + 66° = 156°$
    Step 2 $180° - 156° = 24°$
    The unlabeled angle measures 24°.

32. radius: 68.9 m
    $$d = 2 \cdot r = 2 \cdot 68.9 \text{ m} = 137.8 \text{ m}$$
    The diameter of the field is 137.8 m.

33. diameter: 3 inches
    $$r = \frac{d}{2} = \frac{3 \text{ in}}{2} = 1\frac{1}{2} \text{ in or } 1.5 \text{ in}$$
    The radius of the juice can is $1\frac{1}{2}$ or 1.5 inches.

34. radius: 1 cm, $d = 2$ cm
    $C = \pi \cdot d$
    $ \approx 3.14 \cdot 2 \text{ cm}$
    $ \approx 6.3 \text{ cm}$

    $A = \pi \cdot r \cdot r$
    $ \approx 3.14 \cdot 1 \text{ cm} \cdot 1 \text{ cm}$
    $ \approx 3.1 \text{ cm}^2$

35. radius: 17.4 m, $d = 34.8$ m

$$\begin{aligned} C &= \pi \cdot d \\ &\approx 3.14 \cdot 34.8 \text{ m} \\ &\approx 109.272 \text{ m} \\ &\approx 109.3 \text{ m} \end{aligned}$$

$$\begin{aligned} A &= \pi \cdot r \cdot r \\ &\approx 3.14 \cdot 17.4 \text{ m} \cdot 17.4 \text{ m} \\ &\approx 950.6664 \text{ m}^2 \\ &\approx 950.7 \text{ m}^2 \end{aligned}$$

36. diameter: 12 in, radius: 6 in

$$\begin{aligned} C &= \pi \cdot d \\ &\approx 3.14 \cdot 12 \text{ in} \\ &\approx 37.68 \text{ in} \\ &\approx 37.7 \text{ in} \end{aligned}$$

$$\begin{aligned} A &= \pi \cdot r \cdot r \\ &\approx 3.14 \cdot 6 \text{ in} \cdot 6 \text{ in} \\ &\approx 113.04 \text{ in}^2 \\ &\approx 113.0 \text{ in}^2 \end{aligned}$$

37. Area of circle
radius: 3.6 m

$$\begin{aligned} A &= \pi \cdot r \cdot r \\ &\approx 3.14 \cdot 3.6 \text{ m} \cdot 3.6 \text{ m} \\ &\approx 40.6944 \text{ m}^2 \end{aligned}$$

Area of semicircle

$$\frac{40.6944 \text{ m}^2}{2} = 20.3472 \text{ m}^2 \approx 20.3 \text{ m}^2$$

38. Break up the rectangle into 2 smaller rectangles. Each rectangle will have a length of 8 inches and a width of 4 inches.

Area of rectangle length · width		Area of rectangle length · width
8 in · 4 in = 32 in²	+	8 in · 4 in = 32 in²

Total area = 32 in² + 32 in² = 64 in²

39. Break up the figure into 3 parts.
a rectangle
with length 24 km and width 12 km

$$A = 24 \text{ km} \cdot 12 \text{ km} = 288 \text{ km}^2$$

a parallelogram
with base 24 km and height 11 km

$$\begin{aligned} A &= b \cdot h \\ &= 24 \text{ km} \cdot 11 \text{ km} \\ &= 264 \text{ km}^2 \end{aligned}$$

a square
with side 11 km

$$\begin{aligned} A &= s \cdot s \\ &= 11 \text{ km} \cdot 11 \text{ km} \\ &= 121 \text{ km}^2 \end{aligned}$$

Total area

$$\begin{array}{rl} 288 \text{ km}^2 & \textit{Rectangle} \\ 264 \text{ km}^2 & \textit{Parallelogram} \\ + \; 121 \text{ km}^2 & \textit{Square} \\ \hline 673 \text{ km}^2 & \end{array}$$

40. Break up the figure into 2 parts.
a rectangle
with length 45 m and width 21 m

$$\begin{aligned} A &= 45 \text{ m} \cdot 21 \text{ m} \\ &= 945 \text{ m}^2 \end{aligned}$$

a triangle
with base 15 m and height 10 m

$$\begin{aligned} A &= \frac{1}{2} \cdot 15 \text{ m} \cdot 10 \text{ m} \\ &= 75 \text{ m}^2 \end{aligned}$$

Total area

$$945 \text{ m}^2 + 75 \text{ m}^2 = 1020 \text{ m}^2$$

41. Break up the figure into 3 parts.
2 rectangles
with length 15 ft and width 6 ft

$$\begin{aligned} A &= length \cdot width \\ &= 15 \text{ ft} \cdot 6 \text{ ft} \\ &= 90 \text{ ft}^2 \end{aligned}$$

a square
7ft by 7 ft

$$\begin{aligned} A &= s \cdot s \\ &= 7 \text{ ft} \cdot 7 \text{ ft} \\ &= 49 \text{ ft}^2 \end{aligned}$$

Total shaded area
$= 90 \text{ ft}^2 + 90 \text{ ft}^2$ *Rectangles*
$+ 49 \text{ ft}^2$ *Square*
$= 229 \text{ ft}^2$

42. Find the area of the trapezoid and subtract the area of the triangle.
Area of trapezoid

$$\begin{aligned} A &= \frac{1}{2} \cdot h \cdot (b + B) \\ &= \frac{1}{2} \cdot 12 \text{ ft} \cdot (11 \text{ ft} + 18 \text{ ft}) \\ &= \frac{1}{2} \cdot 12 \text{ ft} \cdot (29 \text{ ft}) \\ &= 174 \text{ ft}^2 \end{aligned}$$

Area of triangle

$$\begin{aligned} A &= \frac{1}{2} \cdot b \cdot h \\ &= \frac{1}{2} \cdot 12 \text{ ft} \cdot 7 \text{ ft} \\ &= 42 \text{ ft}^2 \end{aligned}$$

Total shaded area

$174 \text{ ft}^2 - 42 \text{ ft}^2 = 132 \text{ ft}^2$

43. Find the area of the rectangle and subtract the area of the two unshaded triangles.
Area of rectangle

$$\begin{aligned} A &= length \cdot width \\ &= (48 \text{ cm} + 48 \text{ cm}) \cdot 74 \text{ cm} \\ &= 96 \text{ cm} \cdot 74 \text{ cm} \\ &= 7104 \text{ cm}^2 \end{aligned}$$

Area of triangle

$$\begin{aligned} A &= \frac{1}{2} \cdot b \cdot h \\ &= \frac{1}{2} \cdot 48 \text{ cm} \cdot 36 \text{ cm} \\ &= 864 \text{ cm}^2 \end{aligned}$$

Total shaded area
$= 7104 \text{ cm}^2 - (864 \text{ cm}^2 + 864 \text{ cm}^2)$
$= 7104 \text{ cm}^2 - 1728 \text{ cm}^2$
$= 5376 \text{ cm}^2$

44. Find the area of the rectangle and subtract the area of the semicircle.

Area of rectangle

$$\begin{aligned} A &= length \cdot width \\ &= 32 \text{ ft} \cdot 21 \text{ ft} \\ &= 672 \text{ ft}^2 \end{aligned}$$

Area of semicircle

$\text{radius} = \frac{d}{2} = \frac{21}{2} = 10.5 \text{ ft}$

$$\begin{aligned} A &= \pi \cdot r \cdot r \\ &\approx 3.14 \cdot 10.5 \text{ ft} \cdot 10.5 \text{ ft} \\ &\approx 346.185 \text{ ft}^2 \end{aligned}$$

$\frac{346.185 \text{ ft}^2}{2} \approx 173.0925 \text{ ft}^2 \approx 173.1 \text{ ft}^2$

Total shaded area

$672 \text{ ft}^2 - \approx 173.1 \text{ ft}^2 \approx 498.9 \text{ ft}^2$

45. Find the area of the rectangle.

$$\begin{aligned} A &= length \cdot width \\ &= 21 \text{ yd} \cdot 14 \text{ yd} \\ &= 294 \text{ yd}^2 \end{aligned}$$

The two semicircles at the ends make one circle.

$$\begin{aligned} A &= \pi \cdot r \cdot r \\ &\approx 3.14 \cdot 7 \text{ yd} \cdot 7 \text{ yd} \\ &\approx 153.86 \text{ yd}^2 \\ &\approx 153.9 \text{ yd}^2 \end{aligned}$$

Total area

$294 \text{ yd}^2 + \approx 153.9 \text{ yd}^2 \approx 447.9 \text{ yd}^2$

46. $V = length \cdot width \cdot height$
$= 4 \text{ in} \cdot 3 \text{ in} \cdot 2\frac{1}{2} \text{ in}$
$= 30 \text{ in}^3$

47. $V = length \cdot width \cdot height$
$= 6 \text{ cm} \cdot 4 \text{ cm} \cdot 4 \text{ cm}$
$= 96 \text{ cm}^3$

48. $V = length \cdot width \cdot height$
$= 30 \text{ mm} \cdot 20 \text{ mm} \cdot 75 \text{ mm}$
$= 45{,}000 \text{ mm}^3$

49. $V = \frac{4}{3} \cdot \pi \cdot r^3$
$\approx \frac{4}{3} \cdot 3.14 \cdot (4 \text{ m})^3$
$\approx \frac{4}{3} \cdot 3.14 \cdot 64 \text{ m}^3$
$\approx 267.94667 \text{ m}^3$
$\approx 267.9 \text{ m}^3$

50. $V = \frac{2}{3} \cdot \pi \cdot r^3$
    $\approx \frac{2}{3} \cdot 3.14 \cdot (6 \text{ ft})^3$
    $\approx \frac{2}{3} \cdot 3.14 \cdot 216 \text{ ft}^3$
    $\approx 452.16 \text{ ft}^3$
    $\approx 452.2 \text{ ft}^3$

51. $V = \pi \cdot r^2 \cdot h$
    $\approx 3.14 \cdot 5 \text{ cm} \cdot 5 \text{ cm} \cdot 7 \text{ cm}$
    $\approx 549.5 \text{ cm}^3$

52. $V = \pi \cdot r^2 \cdot h \quad d = 24 \text{ m}; r = 12 \text{ m}$
    $\approx 3.14 \cdot 12 \text{ m} \cdot 12 \text{ m} \cdot 4 \text{ m}$
    $\approx 1808.64 \text{ m}^3$
    $\approx 1808.6 \text{ m}^3$

53. $V = \frac{1}{3} \cdot \pi \cdot r^2 \cdot h$
    $\approx \frac{1}{3} \cdot 3.14 \cdot 7 \text{ m} \cdot 7 \text{ m} \cdot 10 \text{ m}$
    $\approx 512.86667 \text{ m}^3$
    $\approx 512.9 \text{ m}^3$

54. $V = \frac{1}{3} \cdot B \cdot h \quad B = 3 \text{ yd} \cdot 4 \text{ yd}$
    $\hspace{3.3cm} = 12 \text{ yd}^2$
    $= \frac{1}{3} \cdot 12 \text{ yd}^2 \cdot 4 \text{ yd}$
    $= 16 \text{ yd}^3$

55. $\sqrt{49} = 7$ because $7 \cdot 7 = 49$.

56. $\sqrt{8}$
    Calculator shows 2.8284271.
    $\sqrt{8} \approx 2.828$

57. $\sqrt{3000}$
    Calculator shows 54.772256.
    $\sqrt{3000} \approx 54.772$

58. $\sqrt{144} = 12$ because $12 \cdot 12 = 144$.

59. $\sqrt{58}$
    Calculator shows 7.6157731.
    $\sqrt{58} \approx 7.616$

60. $\sqrt{625} = 25$ because $25 \cdot 25 = 625$.

61. $\sqrt{105}$
    Calculator shows 10.246951.
    $\sqrt{105} \approx 10.247$

62. $\sqrt{80}$
    Calculator shows 8.9442719.
    $\sqrt{80} \approx 8.944$

63. $hypotenuse = \sqrt{(leg)^2 + (leg)^2}$
    $= \sqrt{(15)^2 + (8)^2}$
    $= \sqrt{225 + 64}$
    $= \sqrt{289}$
    $= 17 \text{ in}$

64. $leg = \sqrt{(hypotenuse)^2 - (leg)^2}$
    $= \sqrt{(25)^2 - (24)^2}$
    $= \sqrt{625 - 576}$
    $= \sqrt{49}$
    $= 7 \text{ cm}$

65. $leg = \sqrt{(hypotenuse)^2 - (leg)^2}$
    $= \sqrt{(15)^2 - (11)^2}$
    $= \sqrt{225 - 121}$
    $= \sqrt{104}$
    ≈ 10.198039
    $\approx 10.198 \text{ cm}$

66. $hypotenuse = \sqrt{(leg)^2 + (leg)^2}$
    $= \sqrt{(6)^2 + (4)^2}$
    $= \sqrt{36 + 16}$
    $= \sqrt{52}$
    ≈ 7.2111026
    $\approx 7.211 \text{ in}$

67. $hypotenuse = \sqrt{(leg)^2 + (leg)^2}$
    $= \sqrt{(2.2)^2 + (1.3)^2}$
    $= \sqrt{4.84 + 1.69}$
    $= \sqrt{6.53}$
    ≈ 2.5553865
    $\approx 2.555 \text{ m}$

68. $leg = \sqrt{(hypotenuse)^2 - (leg)^2}$
    $= \sqrt{(12)^2 - (8.5)^2}$
    $= \sqrt{144 - 72.25}$
    $= \sqrt{71.75}$
    ≈ 8.4705372
    $\approx 8.471 \text{ km}$

69. Set up a ratio of corresponding sides.
    $$\frac{40 \text{ ft}}{20 \text{ ft}} = \frac{40}{20} = \frac{2}{1}$$
    Write a proportion to find y.
    $$\frac{y}{15} = \frac{2}{1}$$
    $$y \cdot 1 = 2 \cdot 15$$
    $$y = 30 \text{ ft}$$

Chapter 8 Review Exercises

Write a proportion to find x.

$$\frac{x}{17} = \frac{2}{1}$$
$$x \cdot 1 = 17 \cdot 2$$
$$x = 34 \text{ ft}$$

70. Set up a ratio of corresponding sides.

$$\frac{4 \text{ m}}{6 \text{ m}} = \frac{4}{6} = \frac{2}{3}$$

Write a proportion to find x.

$$\frac{6}{x} = \frac{2}{3}$$
$$2 \cdot x = 3 \cdot 6$$
$$2 \cdot x = 18$$
$$\frac{2 \cdot x}{2} = \frac{18}{2}$$
$$x = 9 \text{ m}$$

Write a proportion to find y.

$$\frac{5}{y} = \frac{2}{3}$$
$$2 \cdot y = 5 \cdot 3$$
$$2 \cdot y = 15$$
$$\frac{2 \cdot y}{2} = \frac{15}{2}$$
$$y = 7.5 \text{ m}$$

71. $\frac{16 \text{ mm}}{12 \text{ mm}} = \frac{4}{3}$ Ratio

Write a proportion to find x.

$$\frac{x}{9} = \frac{4}{3}$$
$$3 \cdot x = 9 \cdot 4$$
$$\frac{3 \cdot x}{3} = \frac{36}{3}$$
$$x = 12 \text{ mm}$$

Write a proportion to find y.

$$\frac{10}{y} = \frac{4}{3}$$
$$y \cdot 4 = 10 \cdot 3$$
$$\frac{y \cdot 4}{4} = \frac{30}{4}$$
$$y = 7.5 \text{ mm}$$

72. a square

$$\begin{aligned} P &= 4 \cdot s \\ &= 4 \cdot 4\tfrac{1}{2} \text{ in} \\ &= 18 \text{ in} \end{aligned}$$

$$\begin{aligned} A &= s \cdot s \\ &= 4\tfrac{1}{2} \text{ in} \cdot 4\tfrac{1}{2} \text{ in} \\ &= 20\tfrac{1}{4} \text{ in}^2 \text{ or } 20.25 \text{ in}^2 \end{aligned}$$

73. a trapezoid

$$\begin{aligned} P &= 2.3 \text{ cm} + 2.5 \text{ cm} + 2.1 \text{ cm} + 3.4 \text{ cm} \\ &= 10.3 \text{ cm} \end{aligned}$$

$$\begin{aligned} A &= 0.5 \cdot h \cdot (b + B) \\ &= 0.5 \cdot 2.1 \text{ cm} \cdot (2.5 \text{ cm} + 3.4 \text{ cm}) \\ &= 0.5 \cdot 2.1 \text{ cm} \cdot 5.9 \text{ cm} \\ &= 6.195 \text{ cm}^2 \end{aligned}$$

74. a circle

$$\begin{aligned} C &= \pi \cdot d \\ &\approx 3.14 \cdot 13 \text{ m} \\ &\approx 40.82 \text{ m} \end{aligned}$$

$$\begin{aligned} A &= \pi \cdot r^2 \quad r = \tfrac{13 \text{ m}}{2} = 6.5 \text{ m} \\ &\approx 3.14 \cdot 6.5 \text{ m} \cdot 6.5 \text{ m} \\ &\approx 132.665 \text{ m}^2 \end{aligned}$$

75. $\begin{aligned}P &= 17 \text{ ft} + 10 \text{ ft} + 17 \text{ ft} + 10 \text{ ft} \\ &= 54 \text{ ft}\end{aligned}$

$$\begin{aligned} A &= b \cdot h \\ &= 10 \text{ ft} \cdot 14 \text{ ft} = 140 \text{ ft}^2 \end{aligned}$$

76. $\begin{aligned} P &= 6\tfrac{1}{4} \text{ yd} + 6 \text{ yd} + 6\tfrac{1}{4} \text{ yd} \\ &= 18.5 \text{ yd or } 18\tfrac{1}{2} \text{ yd}\end{aligned}$

$$\begin{aligned} A &= \tfrac{1}{2} \cdot b \cdot h \\ &= \tfrac{1}{2} \cdot 6 \text{ yd} \cdot 5 \text{ yd} \\ &= 15 \text{ yd}^2 \end{aligned}$$

77. $\begin{aligned}P &= 0.7 \text{ km} + 2.8 \text{ km} + 0.7 \text{ km} + 2.8 \text{ km} \\ &= 7 \text{ km}\end{aligned}$

$A = length \cdot width$
$ = 2.8 \text{ km} \cdot 0.7 \text{ km}$
$ = 1.96 \text{ km}^2$

78. $C = 2 \cdot \pi \cdot r$
$ \approx 2 \cdot 3.14 \cdot 8.5 \text{ m}$
$ \approx 53.38 \text{ m}$

$A = \pi \cdot r^2$
$ \approx 3.14 \cdot 8.5 \text{ m} \cdot 8.5 \text{ m}$
$ \approx 226.865 \text{ m}^2$

79. $P = 24 \text{ mm} + 15 \text{ mm} + 24 \text{ mm} + 15 \text{ mm}$
$ = 78 \text{ mm}$

$A = b \cdot h$
$ = 24 \text{ mm} \cdot 12 \text{ mm}$
$ = 288 \text{ mm}^2$

80. $P = 13 \text{ mi} + 9 \text{ mi} + 16 \text{ mi}$
$ = 38 \text{ mi}$

$A = 0.5 \cdot b \cdot h$
$ = 0.5 \cdot 9 \text{ mi} \cdot 13 \text{ mi}$
$ = 58.5 \text{ mi}^2$

81. $\overleftrightarrow{WX}$ and $\overleftrightarrow{YZ}$ are parallel lines.

82. $\overline{QR}$ is a line segment.

83. $\angle CQD$ is an acute angle.

84. $\overleftrightarrow{PQ}$ and $\overleftrightarrow{NO}$ are intersecting lines.

85. $\angle APB$ is a right angle. Right angles measure 90° so
$\angle APB$ measures 90°.

86. $\overrightarrow{AB}$ is a ray.

87. $\overleftrightarrow{T}$ is a straight angle.
Straight angles measure 180°.

88. $\angle FEG$ is an obtuse angle.

89. $\overleftrightarrow{LM}$ and $\overleftrightarrow{JK}$ are perpendicular lines.

90. The complement of an angle measuring 9° is
$90° - 9° = 81°$.

91. The supplement of an angle measuring 42° is
$180° - 42° = 138°$.

92. Find the unknown length of the horizontal line.
$17 \text{ m} - 1 \text{ m} - 1 \text{ m} = 15 \text{ m}$

$P = 17 \text{ m} + 16 \text{ m} + 1 \text{ m} + 12 \text{ m} + 15 \text{ m}$
$ + 12 \text{ m} + 1 \text{ m} + 16 \text{ m}$
$ = 90 \text{ m}$

Break up the figure into 3 rectangles to find the area.
2 rectangles with
length 12 m and width 1 m

$A = 12 \text{ m} \cdot 1 \text{ m}$
$ = 12 \text{ m}^2$

a rectangle with
length 17 m and
width 16 m -12 m $= 4$ m

$A = 17 \text{ m} \cdot 4 \text{ m}$
$ = 68 \text{ m}^2$

Total area
$12 \text{ m}^2 + 12 \text{ m}^2 + 68 \text{ m}^2 = 92 \text{ m}^2$

93. $P = 72 \text{ cm} + 19 \text{ cm} + 50 \text{ cm} + 19 \text{ cm}$
$ + 72 \text{ cm} + 50 \text{ cm}$
$ = 282 \text{ cm}$

Break up the figure into 2 parallelograms.
a parallelogram with
base 72 cm and height 45 cm

$A = 72 \text{ cm} \cdot 45 \text{ cm}$
$ = 3240 \text{ cm}^2$

a parallelogram with
base 19 cm and height 50 cm

$A = 19 \text{ cm} \cdot 50 \text{ cm}$
$ = 950 \text{ cm}^2$

Total area
$3240 \text{ cm}^2 + 950 \text{ cm}^2 = 4190 \text{ cm}^2$

94. a cylinder
$V = \pi \cdot r^2 \cdot h$
$ \approx 3.14 \cdot 2 \text{ ft} \cdot 2 \text{ ft} \cdot 8 \text{ ft}$
$ \approx 100.48 \text{ ft}^3$
$ \approx 100.5 \text{ ft}^3$

95. a cube

$$V = length \cdot width \cdot height$$
$$= 1\tfrac{1}{2} \text{ in} \cdot 1\tfrac{1}{2} \text{ in} \cdot 1\tfrac{1}{2} \text{ in}$$
$$= 3.375 \text{ in}^3$$
$$\approx 3.4 \text{ in}^3 \text{ or } 3\tfrac{3}{8} \text{ in}^3$$

96. a cube

$$V = length \cdot width \cdot height$$
$$= 3.5 \text{ m} \cdot 3 \text{ m} \cdot 0.7 \text{ m}$$
$$= 7.35 \text{ m}^3$$
$$\approx 7.4 \text{ m}^3$$

97. a pyramid

$$V = \tfrac{1}{3} \cdot B \cdot h \quad B = 11 \text{ cm} \cdot 9 \text{ cm}$$
$$= 99 \text{ cm}^2$$
$$\tfrac{1}{3} \cdot 99 \text{ cm}^2 \cdot 17 \text{ cm}$$
$$= 561 \text{ cm}^3$$

98. a cone

$$V = \tfrac{1}{3} \cdot \pi \cdot r^2 \cdot h$$
$$\approx \tfrac{1}{3} \cdot 3.14 \cdot 9 \text{ cm} \cdot 9 \text{ cm} \cdot 15 \text{ cm}$$
$$\approx \tfrac{3815.1}{3} \text{ cm}^3$$
$$\approx 1271.7 \text{ cm}^3$$

99. a sphere

$$V = \tfrac{4}{3} \cdot \pi \cdot r^3$$
$$\approx \tfrac{4}{3} \cdot 3.14 \cdot 7 \text{ m} \cdot 7 \text{ m} \cdot 7 \text{ m}$$
$$\approx 1436.0267 \text{ m}^3$$
$$\approx 1436.0 \text{ m}^3$$

100.
$$leg = \sqrt{(hypotenuse)^2 - (leg)^2}$$
$$= \sqrt{(14)^2 - (6)^2}$$
$$= \sqrt{196 - 36}$$
$$= \sqrt{160}$$
$$\approx 12.649111$$
$$\approx 12.649 \text{ km}$$

101. *Step 1* $60° + 48° = 108°$

Step 2 $180° - 108° = 72°$

$\angle D$ measures $72°$.

102. Set up a ratio of corresponding sides.

$$\frac{18 \text{ m}}{15 \text{ m}} = \frac{18}{15} = \frac{6}{5}$$

Write a proportion to find x.

$$\frac{x}{10} = \frac{6}{5}$$
$$5 \cdot x = 10 \cdot 6 \quad \textit{Cross products}$$
$$\textit{are equivalent}$$
$$5 \cdot x = 60$$
$$\frac{5 \cdot x}{5} = \frac{60}{5}$$
$$x = 12 \text{ mm}$$

Write a proportion to find y.

$$\frac{16.8}{y} = \frac{6}{5}$$
$$y \cdot 6 = 16.8 \cdot 5$$
$$y \cdot 6 = 84$$
$$\frac{y \cdot 6}{6} = \frac{84}{6}$$
$$y = 14 \text{ mm}$$

103. The *dec* prefix in decade means 10 and the *cent* prefix in century means 100, so divide 200 (two centuries) by 10. The answer is 20 decades.

Chapter 8 Test

1. $\angle LOM$ is an acute angle so the answer is (e).

2. $\angle YOX$ is a right angle so the answer is (a).

3. $\overleftrightarrow{CD}$ is a line so the answer is (b).

4. $\overleftrightarrow{W}$ is a straight angle so the answer is (g).

5. $\overrightarrow{GH}$ is a ray so the answer is (d).

6. Perpendicular lines intersect to form a right angle. Parallel lines never intersect. See examples in the answer section of your textbook.

7. The complement of an angle measuring 81° is

$$90° - 81° = 9°.$$

8. The supplement of an angle measuring 20° is

$$180° - 20° = 160°.$$

9. Vertical angles are congruent angles. The congruent angles are

$\angle 1$ and $\angle 4, \angle 2$ and $\angle 5, \angle 3$ and $\angle 6$.

10. $P = 4 \text{ ft} + 7\frac{1}{2} \text{ ft} + 4 \text{ ft} + 7\frac{1}{2} \text{ ft}$
    $= 23 \text{ ft}$

    $A = length \cdot width$
    $= 7\frac{1}{2} \text{ ft} \cdot 4 \text{ ft}$
    $= 30 \text{ ft}^2$

11. $P = 4 \cdot s$
    $= 4 \cdot 18 \text{ mm}$
    $= 72 \text{ mm}$

    $A = s \cdot s$
    $= 18 \text{ mm} \cdot 18 \text{ mm}$
    $= 324 \text{ mm}^2$

12. $P = 5.9 \text{ m} + 7.2 \text{ m} + 5.9 \text{ m} + 7.2 \text{ m}$
    $= 26.2 \text{ m}$

    $A = b \cdot h$
    $= 7.2 \text{ m} \cdot 4.6 \text{ m}$
    $= 33.12 \text{ m}^2$

13. $P = 29 \text{ cm} + 46 \text{ cm} + 57 \text{ cm} + 37 \text{ cm}$
    $= 169 \text{ cm}$

    $A = \frac{1}{2} \cdot h \cdot (b + B)$
    $= \frac{1}{2} \cdot 37 \text{ cm} \cdot (29 \text{ cm} + 57 \text{ cm})$
    $= \frac{1}{2} \cdot 37 \text{ cm} \cdot 86 \text{ cm}$
    $= 1591 \text{ cm}^2$

14. $P = 11.4 \text{ m} + 8.65 \text{ m} + 12 \text{ m}$
    $= 32.05 \text{ m}$

    $A = 0.5 \cdot b \cdot h$
    $= 0.5 \cdot 12 \text{ m} \cdot 8 \text{ m}$
    $= 48 \text{ m}^2$

15. $P = 9 \text{ yd} + 15\frac{4}{5} \text{ yd} + 13 \text{ yd}$
    $= 37\frac{4}{5} \text{ yd or } 37.8 \text{ yd}$

    $A = \frac{1}{2} \cdot b \cdot h$
    $= \frac{1}{2} \cdot 13 \text{ yd} \cdot 9 \text{ yd}$
    $= 58.5 \text{ yd}^2 \text{ or } 58\frac{1}{2} \text{ yd}^2$

16. *Step* 1 $90° + 35° = 125°$

    Step 2 $180° - 125° = 55°$

    The third angle measures $55°$.

17. diameter = 25 in

    $radius = \frac{d}{2} = \frac{25 \text{ in}}{2}$
    $= 12.5 \text{ in or } 2\frac{1}{2} \text{ in}$

18. radius = 0.9 km

    $C = 2 \cdot \pi \cdot r$
    $\approx 2 \cdot 3.14 \cdot 0.9 \text{ km}$
    $\approx 5.652 \text{ km}$
    $\approx 5.7 \text{ km}$

19. $A = \pi \cdot r^2$ $r = \frac{d}{2} = \frac{16.2 \text{ cm}}{2} = 8.1 \text{ cm}$
    $\approx 3.14 \cdot 8.1 \text{ cm} \cdot 8.1 \text{ cm}$
    $\approx 206.0154 \text{ cm}^2$
    $\approx 206.0 \text{ cm}^2$

20. $A = \frac{\pi \cdot r^2}{2}$
    $\approx \frac{3.14 \cdot 5 \text{ m} \cdot 5 \text{ m}}{2}$
    $\approx \frac{78.5}{2} \text{ m}^2$
    $\approx 39.25 \text{ m}^2$
    $\approx 39.3 \text{ m}^2$

21. $V = length \cdot width \cdot height$
    $= 30 \text{ m} \cdot 18 \text{ m} \cdot 12 \text{ m}$
    $= 6480 \text{ m}^3$

22. Volume of a sphere

    $V = \frac{4}{3} \cdot \pi \cdot r^3$
    $\approx \frac{4}{3} \cdot 3.14 \cdot 2 \text{ ft} \cdot 2 \text{ ft} \cdot 2 \text{ ft}$
    $\approx \frac{100.48}{3} \text{ ft}^3$
    $\approx 33.493333 \text{ ft}^3$
    $\approx 33.5 \text{ ft}^3$

23. Volume of a cylinder

    $V = \pi \cdot r^2 \cdot h$
    $\approx 3.14 \cdot 18 \text{ ft} \cdot 18 \text{ ft} \cdot 5 \text{ ft}$
    $\approx 5086.8 \text{ ft}^3$

24. $hypotenuse = \sqrt{(leg)^2 + (leg)^2}$
    $= \sqrt{(7)^2 + (6)^2}$
    $= \sqrt{49 + 36}$
    $= \sqrt{85}$
    ≈ 9.2195445
    $\approx 9.220 \text{ cm}$

25. Set up a ratio of corresponding sides.

$$\frac{10 \text{ cm}}{15 \text{ cm}} = \frac{10}{15} = \frac{2}{3}$$

Write a proportion to find y.

$$\frac{y}{18} = \frac{2}{3}$$
$$y \cdot 3 = 18 \cdot 2$$
$$\frac{y \cdot 3}{3} = \frac{36}{3}$$
$$y = 12 \text{ cm}$$

Write a proportion to find z.

$$\frac{z}{9} = \frac{2}{3}$$
$$z \cdot 3 = 9 \cdot 2$$
$$\frac{z \cdot 3}{3} = \frac{18}{3}$$
$$z = 6 \text{ cm}$$

26. Linear units like cm are used to measure perimeter, radius, diameter, and circumference. Area is measured in square units like cm² (squares that measure 1 cm on each side). Volume is measured in cubic units like cm³.

Cumulative Review Exercises (Chapters 1-8)

1. *estimate*   *exact*

    ```
        300              319
     60,000           58,028
    +  6 000         +  6 227
    ———————         ————————
     66,300           64,574
    ```

2. *estimate*   *exact*

    ```
        20             20.070
      - 10            - 9.828
     ————             ———————
        10             10.242
    ```

3. *estimate*   *exact*

    ```
         4             3.664
      ×  7           ×   7.3
     ————            ———————
        28            1 0992
                      25 648
                     ———————
                      26.7472
    ```

4. *estimate*   *exact*

    ```
      30,000            28,419
    ×     70          ×     73
    ——————————       ——————————
    2,100,000           85 257
                      1 989 33
                     ——————————
                      2,074,587
    ```

5. *estimate*   *exact*

    ```
       200              20 0.8
      ———              ————————
    3)600           2.8∧)562.2∧4
                         56
                         ——
                          2
                          0
                          —
                          2 2
                            0
                          ———
                          2 2 4
                          2 2 4
                          —————
                              0
    ```

6. *estimate*   *exact*

    ```
        100               94
       ————              ————
    50)5000           52)4888
                         468
                         ———
                         208
                         208
                         ———
                           0
    ```

7. *estimate*   *exact*

    ```
         5           4½   = 4 5/10
       + 5         + 4 9/10 = 4 9/10
       ———         ———————————————
        10           8 14/10 = 9 2/5
    ```

8. *estimate*   *exact*

    ```
        3           3 1/6 = 19/6 = 76/24
      - 2         - 1 7/8 = 15/8 = 45/24
      ———         ——————————————————————
        1                          31/24 = 1 7/24
    ```

9. *exact*

$$3\tfrac{1}{9} \cdot 1\tfrac{5}{7} = \frac{\overset{4}{\cancel{28}}}{\underset{3}{\cancel{9}}} \cdot \frac{\overset{4}{\cancel{12}}}{\underset{1}{\cancel{7}}} = \frac{16}{3} = 5\tfrac{1}{3}$$

estimate $3 \cdot 2 = 6$

10. $3\frac{3}{5} \div 8 = \frac{18}{5} \div \frac{8}{1} = \frac{\cancel{18}^9}{5} \cdot \frac{1}{\cancel{8}_4} = \frac{9}{20}$

11. $1 - 0.0868$

$$\begin{array}{r} \overset{\overset{9}{\cancel{10}}\overset{9}{\cancel{10}}\overset{9}{\cancel{10}}10}{1.\cancel{0}\cancel{0}\cancel{0}\cancel{0}} \\ -\,0.0868 \\ \hline 0.9132 \end{array}$$

12. $\begin{array}{r} 70 \text{ R}79 \\ 81{\overline{)5749}} \\ \underline{567} \\ 79 \\ \underline{0} \\ 79 \end{array}$

13. $10 \div \frac{5}{16} = \frac{10}{1} \div \frac{5}{16} = \frac{\cancel{10}^2}{1} \cdot \frac{16}{\cancel{5}_1} = 32$

14. $(0.006)(0.013)$

$$\begin{array}{r} 0.006 \leftarrow 3 \text{ decimal places} \\ \times 0.013 \leftarrow 3 \text{ decimal places} \\ \hline 18 \\ 6 \\ \hline 0.000078 \leftarrow 6 \text{ decimal places} \end{array}$$

15. $40{,}020 - 915$

$$\begin{array}{r} \overset{3\ \overset{9}{\cancel{10}}\ 10\ 1\ 10}{\cancel{4}\cancel{0}{,}\cancel{0}\cancel{2}\cancel{0}} \\ -915 \\ \hline 39{,}105 \end{array}$$

16. $0.7 \div 0.036 \approx 19.44$

Move the decimal point three places to the right in the dividend and divisor.

$$\begin{array}{r} 19.444 \\ 36{\overline{)700.000}} \\ \underline{36} \\ 340 \\ \underline{324} \\ 16\,0 \\ \underline{14\,4} \\ 1\,60 \\ \underline{1\,44} \\ 160 \\ \underline{144} \\ 16 \end{array}$$

17. $6\frac{1}{6} - 1\frac{3}{4}$

$\begin{aligned} 6\frac{1}{6} &= 6\frac{2}{12} = 5\frac{14}{12} \\ -\,1\frac{3}{4} &= 1\frac{9}{12} = 1\frac{9}{12} \\ &\phantom{= 1\frac{9}{12} =}\,4\frac{5}{12} \end{aligned}$

18. $752.6 + 83 + 0.485$

$$\begin{array}{r} 752.600 \\ 83.000 \\ +0.485 \\ \hline 836.085 \end{array}$$

19. $\begin{array}{ll} 16 - (10 - 2) \div 2 \cdot 3 + 5 & \textit{Parentheses} \\ 16 - 8 \div 2 \cdot 3 + 5 & \textit{Divide} \\ 16 - 4 \cdot 3 + 5 & \textit{Multiply} \\ 16 - 12 + 5 & \textit{Subtract} \\ 4 + 5 = 9 & \textit{Add} \end{array}$

20. $\begin{array}{ll} 2^4 \div \sqrt{64} + 6^2 & \textit{Exponents} \\ 16 \div \sqrt{64} + 36 & \textit{Square root} \\ 16 \div 8 + 36 & \textit{Divide} \\ 2 + 36 = 38 & \textit{Add} \end{array}$

21. 0.0208 is two hundred eight ten-thousandths.

22. Six hundred sixty and five hundredths in numbers is 660.05.

23. From smallest to largest:
$2.55 = 2.550$
$2.505 = 2.5050$
$2.055 = 2.0550$
$2.5005 = 2.5005$
Answer: $2.055, 2.5005, 2.505, 2.55$

24. *Per* means divide and *cent* means 100, so divide by 100 to change a percent to a decimal.

25. $0.02 = \frac{2}{100} = \frac{2 \div 2}{100 \div 2} = \frac{1}{50}$

26. $0.02 = 2\%$

Move the decimal point two places to the right and attach percent sign.

27. $1\frac{3}{4} = 1\frac{75}{100} = 1.75$

28. $1.75 = 175\%$

29. $40\% = 0.4 = \frac{4 \div 2}{10 \div 2} = \frac{2}{5}$

30. $40\% = 0.4$

31. 4 feet to 6 inches

4 feet $= 4 \cdot 12$ inches $= 48$ inches

$\frac{48 \text{ inches}}{6 \text{ inches}} = \frac{48 \div 6}{6 \div 6} = \frac{8}{1}$

Cumulative Review Exercises (Chapters 1-8) 215

32. 21 sunny days to 9 cloudy days

$$\frac{21 \text{ days}}{9 \text{ days}} = \frac{21}{9} = \frac{7}{3}$$

33. $\frac{5}{13} = \frac{x}{91}$

$13 \cdot x = 5 \cdot 91$ *Cross products are equivalent*

$13 \cdot x = 455$

$\frac{13 \cdot x}{13} = \frac{455}{13}$

$x = 35$

34. $\frac{207}{69} = \frac{300}{x}$

$207 \cdot x = 69 \cdot 300$ *Cross products are equivalent*

$207 \cdot x = 20{,}700$

$\frac{207 \cdot x}{207} = \frac{20{,}700}{207}$

$x = 100$

35. $\frac{4.5}{x} = \frac{6.7}{3}$

$6.7 \cdot x = 3 \cdot 4.5$

$6.7 \cdot x = 13.5$

$\frac{6.7 \cdot x}{6.7} = \frac{13.5}{6.7}$

$x \approx 2.0149$

≈ 2.01

36. a is 72; b is 45; p is unknown.
Use the percent proportion.

$$\frac{a}{b} = \frac{p}{100}$$

$$\frac{72}{45} = \frac{p}{100}$$

$45 \cdot p = 72 \cdot 100$

$45 \cdot p = 7200$

$\frac{45 \cdot p}{45} = \frac{7200}{45}$

$p = 160$

72 patients is 160% of 45 patients.

37. a is 18; p is 3; b is unknown.
Use the percent proportion.

$$\frac{a}{b} = \frac{p}{100}$$

$$\frac{18}{b} = \frac{3}{100}$$

$3 \cdot b = 18 \cdot 100$

$3 \cdot b = 1800$

$\frac{3 \cdot b}{3} = \frac{1800}{3}$

$b = 600$

$18 is 3% of $600.

38. $2\frac{1}{4}$ hours to minutes

$$\frac{2\frac{1}{4} \text{ hours}}{1} \cdot \frac{60 \text{ minutes}}{1 \text{ hour}} = 135 \text{ minutes}$$

39. 40 ounces to pounds

$$\frac{40 \text{ ounces}}{1} \cdot \frac{1 \text{ pound}}{16 \text{ ounces}} = \frac{40}{16} \text{ pounds}$$
$$= 2\frac{1}{2} \text{ or } 2.5 \text{ pounds}$$

40. 8 cm to meters
Count 2 places to the left on the metric conversion line.

$$8 \text{ cm} = 0.08 \text{ m}$$

41. 1.8L to mL
Count 3 places to the right on the metric conversion line.

$$1.8 \text{ L} = 1800 \text{ mL}$$

42. Her wristwatch strap is 15 *mm* wide.

43. Jon added 2 *L* of oil to his car.

44. The child weighs 15 *kg*.

45. The bookcase is 90 *cm* high.

46. Water freezes at 0°C and boils at 100°C.

47. a rectangle

$P = 3\frac{1}{2} \text{ in} + 2 \text{ in} + 3\frac{1}{2} \text{ in} + 2 \text{ in}$

$= 11 \text{ in}$

$A = length \cdot width$

$= 3\frac{1}{2} \text{ in} \cdot 2 \text{ in}$

$= 7 \text{ in}^2$

48. a triangle

$$P = 2.1 \text{ m} + 2.1 \text{ m} + 1.7 \text{ m}$$
$$= 5.9 \text{ m}$$

$$A = 0.5 \cdot b \cdot h$$
$$= 0.5 \cdot 2.1 \text{ m} \cdot 1.5 \text{ m}$$
$$= 1.575 \text{ m}^2$$

49. a circle

$$C = 2 \cdot \pi \cdot r$$
$$\approx 2 \cdot 3.14 \cdot 5 \text{ ft}$$
$$\approx 31.4 \text{ ft}$$

$$A = \pi \cdot r \cdot r$$
$$\approx 3.14 \cdot 5 \text{ ft} \cdot 5 \text{ ft}$$
$$\approx 78.5 \text{ ft}^2$$

50. a parallelogram

$$P = 24 \text{ cm} + 14 \text{ cm} + 24 \text{ cm} + 14 \text{ cm}$$
$$= 76 \text{ cm}$$

$$A = base \cdot height$$
$$= 24 \text{ cm} \cdot 11 \text{ cm}$$
$$= 264 \text{ cm}^2$$

51. a trapezoid

$$P = 13 \text{ m} + 10 \text{ m} + 7 \text{ m} + 10.8 \text{ m}$$
$$= 40.8 \text{ m}$$

$$A = 0.5 \cdot h \cdot (b + B)$$
$$= 0.5 \cdot 9.5 \text{ m}(7 \text{ m} + 13 \text{ m})$$
$$= 0.5 \cdot 9.5 \text{ m} \cdot 20 \text{ m}$$
$$= 95 \text{ m}^2$$

52. $P = 10 \text{ yd} + 10 \text{ yd} + 10 \text{ yd} + 10 \text{ yd} + 10 \text{ yd}$
$= 50 \text{ yd}$

Break up the figure into 2 parts.
a square

$$A = s \cdot s$$
$$= 10 \text{ yd} \cdot 10 \text{ yd}$$
$$= 100 \text{ yd}^2$$

a triangle

$$A = \frac{1}{2} \cdot b \cdot h$$
$$= \frac{1}{2} \cdot 10 \text{ yd} \cdot 8.4 \text{ yd}$$
$$= 42 \text{ yd}^2$$

Total area

$$100 \text{ yd}^2 + 42 \text{ yd}^2 = 142 \text{ yd}^2$$

53. $hypotenuse = \sqrt{(leg)^2 + (leg)^2}$
$= \sqrt{(19)^2 + (15)^2}$
$= \sqrt{361 + 225}$
$= \sqrt{586}$
≈ 24.207437
$\approx 24.2 \text{ mm}$

54. Set up a ratio of corresponding sides.

$$\frac{5.5 \text{ ft}}{15 \text{ ft}} = \frac{5.5}{15} = \frac{1.1}{3}$$

Write a proportion to find x.

$$\frac{x}{22} = \frac{1.1}{3}$$
$$3 \cdot x = 1.1 \cdot 22$$
$$\frac{3 \cdot x}{3} = \frac{24.2}{3}$$
$$x \approx 8.0666667$$
$$x \approx 8.1 \text{ ft}$$

55. a is 53; b is 90; p is unknown.

$$\frac{a}{b} = \frac{p}{100}$$
$$\frac{53}{90} = \frac{p}{100}$$
$$90 \cdot p = 53 \cdot 100$$
$$90 \cdot p = 5300$$
$$\frac{90 \cdot p}{90} = \frac{5300}{90}$$
$$p = 58.8$$
$$\approx 59$$

Mei Ling has $\approx 59\%$ of the necessary credits.

56. $15\frac{1}{2}$ ounces of Brand T for $2.99 − $0.30 (coupon)
= $2.69

$$\frac{\$2.69}{15\frac{1}{2} \text{ ounces}} \approx \$0.0174 \text{ per ounce}$$

14 ounces of Brand F for $2.49

$$\frac{\$2.49}{14 \text{ ounces}} \approx \$0.178 \text{ per ounce}$$

18 ounces of Brand H for $3.89 − $0.40 (coupon) = $3.49

$$\frac{\$3.49}{18 \text{ ounces}} \approx \$0.194 \text{ per ounce}$$

The best buy is Brand T at $15\frac{1}{2}$ ounces for $2.99 − $0.30 coupon.

57. Use the formula for the volume of a cylinder.

$$V = \pi \cdot r^2 \cdot h \quad r = \frac{d}{2} = \frac{13 \text{ cm}}{2} = 6.5 \text{ cm}$$
$$\approx 3.14 \cdot 6.5 \text{ cm} \cdot 6.5 \text{ cm} \cdot 17 \text{ cm}$$
$$\approx 2255.305$$
$$\approx 2255.3 \text{ cm}^3$$

58. $amount\ of\ discount = rate\ of\ discount$
$\qquad \cdot original\ price$
$= 65\% \cdot \$44$
$= 0.65 \cdot \$44$
$= \$28.60$

The sale price is $44 − $28.60 = $15.40.

59. First add the amount of canvas material that was used.

$$\begin{array}{r} 1\frac{2}{3} = 1\frac{8}{12} \\ + 1\frac{3}{4} = 1\frac{9}{12} \\ \hline 2\frac{17}{12} = 3\frac{5}{12} \text{ yd} \end{array}$$

Subtract $3\frac{5}{12}$ from the amount of canvas material that Steven bought.

$$\begin{array}{r} 4\frac{1}{2} = 4\frac{6}{12} \\ - 3\frac{5}{12} = 3\frac{5}{12} \\ \hline 1\frac{1}{12} \text{ yd} \end{array}$$

There will be $1\frac{1}{12}$ yd left.

60. $\dfrac{30 \text{ pounds}}{140 \text{ people}} = \dfrac{x}{200 \text{ people}}$

$$140 \cdot x = 30 \cdot 200$$
$$140 \cdot x = 6000$$
$$= \frac{6000}{140}$$
$$\approx 42.857$$
$$\approx 42.9$$

To feed 200 people the cooks will need ≈42.9 pounds of meat.

61. Convert 85 cm to m.

$$85 \text{ cm} = 0.85 \text{ cm}$$

She will need $4 \cdot 0.85$ m = 3.4 m.

62. Draw a sketch of the frame.

Two inches are added to the length on each side, and two inches are added to the width on each side. The width of the frame is 12 inches and the length is 14 inches.

$$P = 12 \text{ in} + 14 \text{ in} + 12 \text{ in} + 14 \text{ in}$$
$$= 52 \text{ in}$$

Chapter 9

BASIC ALGEBRA

9.1 Signed Numbers

9.1 Margin Exercises

1. **(a)** A temperature at the North Pole of 70 degrees below 0 is $-70°$.

   (b) Your checking account is overdrawn by 15 dollars is written $-\$15$.

   (c) The altitude of a place 284 feet below sea level is -284 ft.

2. **(a)** -8 is negative.

   (b) $-\frac{3}{4}$ is negative

   (c) 1 is positive.

   (d) 0 is neither positive nor negative.

3. See the graphs in the margin exercise answers of the textbook.

   (a) $-1, 1, -3, 3$

   (b) $-2, 4, 0, -1, -4$

4. **(a)** $4 > 0$

   Because 4 is to the right of 0 on the number line, 4 is greater than 0.

   (b) $-1 < 0$

   Because -1 is to the left of 0 on the number line, -1 is less than 0.

   (c) $-3 < -1$

   Because -3 is to the left of -1 on the number line, -3 is less than -1.

   (d) $-8 > -9$

   Because -8 is to the right of -9 on the number line, -8 is greater than -9.

   (e) $0 > -3$

   Because 0 is to the right of -3 on the number line, 0 is greater than -3.

5. **(a)** The distance from 0 to 5 is 5, so $|5|$ is 5.

   (b) The distance from 0 to -5 is 5, so $|-5|$ is 5.

   (c) $|-17| = 17$

   (d) $-|-9| = -9$

   $|-9| = 9$ But there is a negative sign outside the absolute value bars. So, -9 is the solution.

   (e) $-|2| = -2$

6. **(a)** The opposite of 4 is $-(4) = -4$.

   (b) The opposite of 10 is $-(10) = -10$.

   (c) The opposite of 49 is $-(49) = -49$.

   (d) The opposite of $\frac{2}{5}$ is $-\left(\frac{2}{5}\right) = -\frac{2}{5}$,

7. **(a)** The opposite of -4 is $-(-4) = 4$.

   (b) The opposite of -10 is $-(-10) = 10$.

   (c) The opposite of -25 is $-(-25) = 25$.

   (d) The opposite of -1.9 is $-(-1.9) = 1.9$.

   (e) The opposite of -0.85 is $-(-0.85) = 0.85$.

   (f) The opposite of of $-\frac{3}{4}$ is $-\left(-\frac{3}{4}\right) = \frac{3}{4}$.

9.1 Section Exercises

3. The price of the stock fell $12.

   -12

7. 24 is positive.

11. 0 is neither.

For Exercises 15-23, see the graphs in the answer section of the textbook.

27. $0 > -2$

   Because 0 is to the right of -2 on a number line, 0 is greater than -2.

31. $1 > 0$

   Because 1 is to the right of 0 on a number line, 1 is greater than 0.

Section 9.2 Addition and Subtraction of Signed Numbers

35. $-75 < -72$

Because -75 is to the left of -72 on a number line, -75 is less than -72.

39. $-115 > -120$

Because -115 is to the right of -120 on a number line, -115 is greater than -120.

43. $|-5| = 5$

The distance from 0 to -5 is 5.

47. $|251| = 251$

The distance from 0 to 251 is 251.

51. $\left|-\frac{1}{2}\right| = \frac{1}{2}$

The distance from 0 to $-\frac{1}{2}$ is $\frac{1}{2}$.

55. $|0.618| = 0.618$

The distance from 0 to 0.618 is 0.618.

59. $-\left|-\frac{5}{2}\right| = -\left(\frac{5}{2}\right) = -\frac{5}{2}$

This is a two step problem. First $\left|-\frac{5}{2}\right| = \frac{5}{2}$. Then $-\left(\frac{5}{2}\right) = -\frac{5}{2}$.

63. $-|4| = -(4) = -4$

Because the negative sign is outside the absolute value bars, the answer is negative.

67. The opposite of -54 is $-(-54) = 54$.

71. The opposite of 163 is -163.

75. The opposite of $-4\frac{1}{2}$ is $-\left(-4\frac{1}{2}\right) = 4\frac{1}{2}$.

79. The opposite -1.4 is $-(-1.4) = 1.4$.

83. Some possible answers are temperatures below zero, loss of points in a game, and an overdrawn checking account.

87. $0 < -(-6)$
$-(-6) = 6$

0 is less than 6, so $0 < -(-6)$ is true.

91. $\frac{3}{4} + \frac{1}{5} = \frac{15}{20} + \frac{4}{20} = \frac{19}{20}$

9.2 Addition and Subtraction of Signed Numbers

9.2 Margin Exercises

1. See the graphs in the margin exercise answers in the textbook.

2. See the graphs in the margin exercise answers in the textbook.

   (a) $3 + (-2) = 1$
   (b) $-4 + 1 = -3$
   (c) $-3 + 7 = 4$
   (d) $-1 + (-4) = -5$

3. (a) $-4 + (-4)$

   Add the absolute values.

   $|-4| = 4; |-4| = 4$
   $4 + 4 = 8$

   Write a negative sign in front of the sum.

   $-4 + (-4) = -8$

   (b) $-3 + (-20)$

   Add the absolute values.

   $|-3| = 3; |-20| = 20$
   $3 + 20 = 23$

   Write a negative sign in front of the sum.

   $-3 + (-20) = -23$

   (c) $-31 + (-5)$

   Add the absolute values.

   $|-31| = 31; |-5| = 5$
   $31 + 5 = 36$

   Write a negative sign in front of the sum.

   $-31 + (-5) = -36$

   (d) $-10 + (-8)$

   Add the absolute values.

   $|-10| = 10; |-8| = 8$
   $10 + 8 = 18$

Write a negative sign in front of the sum.
$$-10 + (-8) = -18$$

(e) $-\dfrac{9}{10} + \left(-\dfrac{3}{5}\right)$

Add the absolute values.
$$\left|-\dfrac{9}{10}\right| = \dfrac{9}{10};\ \left|-\dfrac{3}{5}\right| = \dfrac{3}{5}$$
$$\dfrac{9}{10} + \dfrac{3}{5} = \dfrac{9}{10} + \dfrac{6}{10} = \dfrac{15}{10} = \dfrac{3}{2}$$

Write a negative sign in front of the sum.
$$-\dfrac{9}{10} + \left(-\dfrac{3}{5}\right) = -\dfrac{3}{2}$$

4. (a) $10 + (-2)$

The signs are different so subtract the absolute values.
$$|10| = 10;\ |-2| = 2$$
$$10 - 2 = 8$$

The positive number, 10, has the larger absolute value, so the answer is positive.
$$10 + (-2) = 8$$

(b) $-7 + 8$

The signs are different so subtract the absolute values.
$$|-7| = 7;\ |8| = 8$$
$$8 - 7 = 1$$

The positive number, 8, has the larger absolute value, so the answer is positive.
$$-7 + 8 = 1$$

(c) $-11 + 11$

The signs are different so subtract the absolute values.
$$|-11| = 11;\ |11| = 11$$
$$11 - 11 = 0$$

The numbers have equal absolute values, so the answer is neither positive nor negative.
$$-11 + 11 = 0$$

(d) $23 + (-32)$

The signs are different so subtract the absolute values.
$$|23| = 23;\ |-32| = 32$$
$$32 - 23 = 9$$

The negative number, -32, has the larger absolute value, so the answer is negative.
$$23 + (-32) = -9$$

(e) $-\dfrac{7}{8} + \dfrac{1}{4}$

$$\left|-\dfrac{7}{8}\right| = \dfrac{7}{8};\ \left|\dfrac{1}{4}\right| = \dfrac{1}{4}$$

The signs are different so subtract the absolute values.
$$\dfrac{7}{8} - \dfrac{1}{4} = \dfrac{7}{8} - \dfrac{2}{8} = \dfrac{5}{8}$$

The negative number, $-\dfrac{7}{8}$, has the larger absolute value, so the answer is negative.
$$-\dfrac{7}{8} + \dfrac{1}{4} = -\dfrac{5}{8}$$

5. (a) The additive inverse of 12 is -12. The sum of the number and its inverse is $12 + (-12) = 0$.

(b) The additive inverse of -9 is $-(-9)$ or 9. The sum of the number and its inverse is $(-9) + 9 = 0$.

(c) The additive inverse of 3.5 is -3.5. The sum of the number and its inverse is $3.5 + (-3.5) = 0$.

(d) The additive inverse of $-\dfrac{7}{10}$ is $-\left(-\dfrac{7}{10}\right)$ or $\dfrac{7}{10}$. The sum of the number and its inverse is $\left(-\dfrac{7}{10}\right) + \dfrac{7}{10} = 0$.

(e) The additive inverse of 0 is 0. The sum of the number and its inverse is $0 + 0 = 0$.

6. (a) $-7 - 2$ in words is negative seven minus positive two.

(b) -10 in words is negative ten.

(c) $3 - (-5)$ in words is positive three minus negative five.

(d) 4 in words is positive four.

(e) $-8 - (-6)$ in words is negative eight minus negative six.

(f) $2 - 9$ in words is positive two minus positive nine.

7. (a) $-6 - 5$

Change positive 5 to its opposite (-5) and add.
$$-6 + (-5) = -11$$

Section 9.2 Addition and Subtraction of Signed Numbers

(b) $3 - (-10)$

Change negative 10 to its opposite (+10) and add.

$$3 - (-10) = 3 + (+10) = 13$$

(c) $-8 - (-2)$

Change negative 2 to its opposite (+2) and add.

$$-8 - (-2) = -8 + (+2) = -6$$

(d) $4 - 9$

Change positive 9 to its opposite (−9) and add.

$$4 - 9 = 4 + (-9) = -5$$

(e) $-7 - (-15)$

Change negative 15 to its opposite (+15) and add.

$$-7 - (-15) = -7 + (+15) = 8$$

(f) $-\frac{2}{3} - \left(-\frac{5}{12}\right)$

Change negative $\frac{5}{12}$ to its opposite $\left(+\frac{5}{12}\right)$ and add.

$$-\frac{2}{3} + \left(+\frac{5}{12}\right) = -\frac{8}{12} + \left(+\frac{5}{12}\right)$$
$$= -\frac{3}{12} = -\frac{1}{4}$$

8. (a) $6 - 7 + (-3)$
$6 - (+7) + (-3)$
$-1 + (-3) = -4$

(b) $-2 + (-3) - (-5)$
$-5 - (-5)$
$-5 + (+5) = 0$

(c) $-3 - (-9) - (-5)$
$-3 + (+9) - (-5)$
$6 + (+5) = 11$

(d) $8 - (-2) + (-6)$
$8 + (+2) + (-6)$
$10 + (-6) = 4$

9. (a) $-1 - 2 + 3 - 4$
$-1 + (-2) + 3 - 4$
$-3 + 3 + (-4)$
$0 + (-4) = -4$

(b) $7 - 6 - 5 + (-4)$
$7 + (-6) - 5 + (-4)$
$1 + (-5) + (-4)$
$-4 + (-4) = -8$

(c) $-6 + (-15) - (-19) + (-25)$
$-21 + (+19) + (-25)$
$-2 + (-25) = -27$

(d)
$$\begin{array}{cccc} -19.2 & & & \\ -6.7 & \to -25.9 & & \\ 15.8 & 15.8 & \to -10.1 & \\ 17.1 & 17.1 & 17.1 & \to 7 \\ -5.4 & -5.4 & -5.4 & -5.4 \\ & & & 1.6 \end{array}$$

9.2 Section Exercises

3. $-5 + (-2) = -7$

See the graph in the answer section of the textbook.

7. $-8 + 5$

The signs are different so subtract the absolute values.

$$|-8| = 8; \; |5| = 5$$
$$8 - 5 = 3$$

The negative number, −8, has the larger absolute value, so the answer is negative.

$$-8 + 5 = -3$$

11. $-2 + (-5)$

Add the absolute values.

$$|-2| = 2; \; |-5| = 5$$
$$2 + 5 = 7$$

Write a negative sign in front of the sum, because both numbers are negative.

$$-2 + (-5) = -7$$

15. $4 + (-12) = -8$

19. 13 yards gained (positive) and 17 yards lost (negative)

$$13 + (-17) = -4$$

23. $7.8 + (-14.6)$

The signs are different so subtract the absolute values.

$$|7.8| = 7.8; \; |-14.6| = 14.6$$
$$14.6 - 7.8 = 6.8$$

The negative number, −14.6, has the larger absolute value, so the answer is negative.

$$7.8 + (-14.6) = -6.8$$

27. $-\dfrac{7}{10} + \dfrac{2}{5}$

The signs are different so subtract the absolute values.

$$\left|-\dfrac{7}{10}\right| = \dfrac{7}{10}; \quad \left|\dfrac{2}{5}\right| = \dfrac{2}{5}$$

$$\dfrac{7}{10} - \dfrac{2}{5} = \dfrac{7}{10} - \dfrac{4}{10} = \dfrac{3}{10}$$

The negative number, $-\dfrac{7}{10}$, has the larger absolute value, so the answer is negative.

$$-\dfrac{7}{10} + \dfrac{2}{5} = -\dfrac{3}{10}$$

31. Subtract the smaller absolute value from the larger absolute value. The answer has the same sign as the addend with the larger absolute value. Examples:

$$-6 + 2 = -4 \text{ and } 6 + (-2) = 4$$

35. The additive inverse of -9 is 9.

39. The additive inverse of -6.2 is 6.2.

43. $10 - 12 = 10 + (-12) = -2$

47. $-15 - 10 = -15 + (-10) = -25$

51. $-3 - (-8) = -3 + (+8) = 5$

55. $1 - (-10) = 1 + (+10) = 11$

59. $-16 - (-16) = -16 + (+16) = 0$

63. $\dfrac{1}{2} - \dfrac{9}{10} = \dfrac{5}{10} - \dfrac{9}{10}$

$$= \dfrac{5}{10} + \left(-\dfrac{9}{10}\right)$$

$$= -\dfrac{4}{10} = -\dfrac{2}{5}$$

67. (a) $6 - 9$
    6 *minus* 9

(b) (-9)
    negative 9

(c) $-(-2)$
    the *opposite of negative* 2

71. $4 - (-13) + (-5)$
    $4 + (+13) + (-5)$
    $17 + (-5) = 12$

75. $4 - (-4) - 3$
    $4 + (+4) - 3$
    $8 - 3 = 5$

79. $-5.7 - (-9.4) - 8.1$
    $-5.7 + (+9.4) - 8.1$
    $3.7 - (+8.1) = -4.4$

83. $-3 - (-2 + 4) + (-5)$
    $-3 - (+2) + (-5)$
    $-5 + (-5) = -10$

87. $23 \cdot 46$

$$\begin{array}{r} 23 \\ \times\ 46 \\ \hline 138 \\ 92 \\ \hline 1058 \end{array}$$

91. $1235 \div 5$

$$\begin{array}{r} 247 \\ 5\overline{)1235} \\ \underline{10} \\ 23 \\ \underline{20} \\ 35 \\ \underline{35} \\ 0 \end{array}$$

9.3 Multiplication and Division of Signed Numbers

9.3 Margin Exercises

1. (a) $5 \cdot (-4) = -20$

The product of two numbers with different signs is negative.

(b) $-9 \cdot (15) = -135$

(c) $12 \cdot (-1) = -12$

(d) $-6 \cdot (6) = -36$

(e) $\left(-\dfrac{7}{8}\right)\left(\dfrac{4}{3}\right) = \left(-\dfrac{7}{\underset{2}{\cancel{8}}}\right)\left(\dfrac{\overset{1}{\cancel{4}}}{3}\right) = -\dfrac{7}{6}$

2. (a) $(-5) \cdot (-5) = 25$

The product of two numbers with the same sign is positive.

(b) $(-14)(-1) = 14$

Section 9.3   Multiplication and Division of Signed Numbers

(c) $-7 \cdot (-8) = 56$

(d) $3 \cdot 12 = 36$

(e) $\left(-\dfrac{2}{3}\right)\left(-\dfrac{6}{5}\right)\left(-\dfrac{2}{\cancel{3}_1}\right)\left(-\dfrac{\cancel{6}^2}{5}\right) = \dfrac{4}{5}$

3. (a) $\dfrac{-20}{4} = -5$

The numbers have different signs, so the answer is negative.

(b) $\dfrac{-50}{-5} = 10$

The numbers have the same sign, so the answer is positive.

(c) $\dfrac{44}{2} = 22$

(d) $\dfrac{6}{-6} = -1$

(e) $\dfrac{-15}{-1} = 15$

(f) $\dfrac{-\frac{3}{5}}{\frac{9}{10}} = -\dfrac{3}{5} \div \dfrac{9}{10} = -\dfrac{\cancel{3}^1}{\cancel{5}_1} \cdot \dfrac{\cancel{10}^2}{\cancel{9}_3} = -\dfrac{2}{3}$

(g) $\dfrac{-35}{0}$ is undefined.

9.3   Section Exercises

3. $(-5)(9) = -45$

The numbers have different signs, so the product is negative.

7. $10 \cdot (-5) = -50$

The numbers have different signs, so the product is negative.

11. $-8 \cdot (-4) = 32$

The numbers have the same sign, so the product is positive.

15. $-19 \cdot (-7) = 133$

The numbers have the same sign, so the product is positive.

19. $0 \cdot (-25) = 0$

23. $-10 \cdot \left(\dfrac{2}{5}\right) = -\dfrac{\cancel{10}^2}{1} \cdot \dfrac{2}{\cancel{5}_1} = -2 \cdot 2 = -4$

27. $-\dfrac{7}{5} \cdot \left(-\dfrac{10}{3}\right) = -\dfrac{7}{\cancel{5}_1} \cdot \left(-\dfrac{\cancel{10}^2}{3}\right)$

$= \left(-\dfrac{7}{1}\right) \cdot \left(-\dfrac{2}{3}\right)$

$= \dfrac{14}{3}$

31. $-\dfrac{5}{2} \cdot \left(-\dfrac{7}{10}\right) = -\dfrac{\cancel{5}^1}{2} \cdot \left(-\dfrac{7}{\cancel{10}_2}\right)$

$= \left(-\dfrac{1}{2}\right) \cdot \left(-\dfrac{7}{2}\right)$

$= \dfrac{7}{4}$

35. $(-0.5)(-12) = 6$

39. $-1.25 \cdot (-3.6) = 4.5$

43. $0 \cdot (-58.6) = 0$

47. $\dfrac{30}{-6} = -5$

The numbers have different signs, so the answer is negative.

51. $\dfrac{14}{-1} = -14$

The numbers have different signs, so the answer is negative.

55. $\dfrac{-48}{-12} = 4$

The numbers have the same sign, so the answer is positive.

59. $\dfrac{-573}{-3} = 191$

63. $\dfrac{-30}{-30} = 1$

67. $-\dfrac{2}{3} \div (-2) = -\dfrac{\cancel{2}^1}{3} \cdot \left(-\dfrac{1}{\cancel{2}_1}\right) = \dfrac{1}{3}$

71. $-\dfrac{7}{5} \div \dfrac{3}{10} = -\dfrac{7}{\cancel{5}_1} \cdot \dfrac{\cancel{10}^2}{3} = -\dfrac{14}{3}$

75. $\dfrac{-7.05}{1.5} = -4.7$

The numbers have different signs, so the answer is negative.

79. $(-4) \cdot (-6) \cdot \dfrac{1}{2} = 24 \cdot \dfrac{1}{2} = 12$

83. $\left(-\dfrac{1}{2}\right) \cdot \left(\dfrac{2}{5}\right) \cdot \left(\dfrac{7}{8}\right) = -\dfrac{\overset{1}{\cancel{2}}}{10} \cdot \left(\dfrac{7}{\underset{4}{\cancel{8}}}\right) = -\dfrac{7}{40}$

87. Similar: If the signs match, the result is positive. If the signs are different, the result is negative. Different: Multiplication is commutative, division is not. You can multiply by zero, but dividing by zero is not allowed.

91. $|-8| \div (-4) \cdot |-5|$
$8 \div (-4) \cdot |-5|$
$-2 \cdot 5 = -10$

95. $7 + 6 \div 2 \cdot 4 - 9$ *Divide*
$7 + 3 \cdot 4 - 9$ *Multiply*
$7 + 12 - 9$ *Add*
$19 - 9 = 10$ *Subtract*

9.4   Order of Operations

9.4   Margin Exercises

1. (a) $-9 + (-15) + (-3)$ *Add*
$-24 + (-3)$
-27

(b) $-8 - (-2) + (-6)$
$-8 + (+2) + (-6)$
$-6 + (-6)$
-12

(c) $-2 - (-7) - (-4)$
$-2 + (+7) - (-4)$ *Add*
$5 + (+4)$
9

(d) $3 \cdot (-4) \div (-6)$ *Multiply*
$-12 \div (-6)$ *Divide*
2

(e) $-18 \div 9 \cdot (-4)$ *Divide*
$-2 \cdot (-4)$ *Multiply*
8

2. (a) $10 + 8 \div 2$ *Divide*
$10 + 4$ *Add*
14

(b) $4 - 6 \cdot (-2)$ *Multiply*
$4 - (-12)$
$4 + (+12)$ *Add*
16

(c) $-3 + (-5) \cdot 2 - 1$
$-3 + (-10) - 1$
$-13 - 1$
$-13 + (-1)$
-14

(d) $-6 \div 2 + 3 \cdot (-2)$ *Divide*
$-3 + 3 \cdot (-2)$ *Multiply*
$-3 + (-6)$ *Add*
-9

(e) $7 - 6 \cdot 2 \div (-3)$ *Multiply*
$7 - 12 \div (-3)$ *Divide*
$7 - (-4)$
$7 + (+4)$ *Add*
11

3. (a) $2 + 40 \div (-5 + 3)$ *Parentheses*
$2 + 40 \div (-2)$ *Divide*
$42 + (-20)$ *Add*
-18

(b) $-5 \cdot 5 - (15 + 5)$ *Parentheses*
$-5 \cdot 5 - 20$ *Multiply*
$-25 + (-20)$ *Add*
-45

(c) $(-24 \div 2) + (15 - 3)$ *Parentheses*
$-12 + 12$ *Add*
0

(d) $-3 \cdot (2 - 8) - 5 \cdot (4 - 3)$ *Parentheses*
$-3 \cdot (-6) - 5 \cdot 1$ *Multiply*
$18 - 5$ *Subtract*
13

(e) $3 \cdot 3 - (10 \cdot 3) \div 5$ *Parentheses*
$3 \cdot 3 - 30 \div 5$ *Divide*
$3 \cdot 3 - 6$ *Multiply*
$9 - 6$ *Subtract*
3

(f) $6 - (2 + 7) \div (-4 + 1)$ *Parentheses*
$6 - 9 \div (-3)$ *Divide*
$6 + 3$ *Add*
9

4. (a) $2^3 - 3^2$ *Exponents*
$8 - 9$
$8 + (-9)$ *Add*
-1

Section 9.4 Order of Operations

(b) $4^2 - 3^2 \cdot (5-2)$ *Parentheses*
$4^2 - 3^2 \cdot 3$ *Exponents*
$16 - 9 \cdot 3$ *Multiply*
$16 - 27$
$16 + (-27)$ *Add*
-11

(c) $-18 \div (-3) \cdot 2^3$ *Exponent*
$-18 \div (-3) \cdot 8$ *Divide*
$6 \cdot 8$ *Multiply*
48

(d) $(-3)^3 + (3-8)^2$
$(-3)^3 + (-5)^2$ *Exponents*
$-27 + 25$ *Add*
-2

(e) $\dfrac{3}{8} + \left(-\dfrac{1}{2}\right)^2 \div \dfrac{1}{4}$ *Exponent*
$\dfrac{3}{8} + \left(\dfrac{1}{4}\right) \div \dfrac{1}{4}$ *Divide*
$\dfrac{3}{8} + 1$ *Add*
$\dfrac{3}{8} + \dfrac{8}{8}$
$\dfrac{11}{8}$

5. (a) $\dfrac{-3 \cdot 2^3}{-10 - 6 + 8}$

Do the work in the numerator.
$-3 \cdot 2^3$ *Exponent*
$-3 \cdot 8$
-24 *Numerator*

Do the work in the denominator
$-10 - 6 + 8$
$-10 + (-6) + 8$
$-16 + 8$
-8

Divide. $\dfrac{-24}{-8} = 3$

(b) $\dfrac{(-10)(-5)}{-6 \div 3 \cdot 5}$

Numerator:
$(-10)(-5) = 50$

Denominator:
$-6 \div 3 \cdot 5$
$-2 \cdot 5$
-10

Divide. $\dfrac{50}{-10} = -5$

(c) $\dfrac{6 + 18 \div (-2)}{(1-10) \div 3}$

Numerator:
$6 + 18 \div (-2)$
$6 + (-9)$
-3

Denominator:
$(1-10) \div 3$
$(-9) \div 3$
-3

Divide. $\dfrac{-3}{-3} = 1$

(d) $\dfrac{6^2 - 3^2 \cdot 4}{5 + (3-7)^2}$

Numerator:
$6^2 - 3^2 \cdot 4$
$36 - 9 \cdot 4$
$36 - 36$
0

Denominator:
$5 + (3-7)^2$
$5 + (-4)^2$
$5 + 16$
21

Divide. $\dfrac{0}{21} = 0$

9.4 Section Exercises

3. $-1 + 15 + (-7) \cdot 2$ *Multiply*
$-1 + 15 + (-14)$ *Add*
$14 + (-14)$
0

7. $10 - 7^2$ *Exponent*
$10 - 49$
$10 + (-49)$ *Add*
-39

11. $4^2 + 3^2 + (-8)$ *Exponents*
$16 + 9 + (-8)$ *Add*
$25 + (-8)$
17

15. $(-4)^2 + (-3)^2 + 5$ *Exponents*
    $16 + 9 + 5$ *Add*
    $25 + 5$
    30

19. $-7 + 6 \cdot (8 - 14)$ *Parentheses*
    $-7 + 6 \cdot (-6)$ *Multiply*
    $-7 + (-36)$
    -43

23. $(-5) \cdot (7 - 13) \div (-10)$ *Parentheses*
    $(-5) \cdot (-6) \div (-10)$ *Multiply*
    $30 \div (-10)$ *Divide*
    -3

27. $2 - (-5) \cdot (-3)^2$ *Exponent*
    $2 - (-5) \cdot 9$ *Multiply*
    $2 - (-45)$
    $2 + (+45)$
    47

31. $30 \div (-5) - 36 \div (-9)$ *Divide*
    $-6 - 36 \div (-9)$
    $-6 + 4$
    -2

35. $4 \cdot 3^2 + 7 \cdot (3 + 9) - (-6)$ *Parentheses*
    $4 \cdot 3^2 + 7 \cdot 12 - (-6)$ *Exponent*
    $4 \cdot 9 + 7 \cdot 12 - (-6)$ *Multiply*
    $36 + 84 - (-6)$ *Add*
    $120 + (+6)$
    126

39. $\dfrac{-2 \cdot 4^2 - 4 \cdot (6 - 2)}{-4 \cdot (8 - 13) \div (-5)}$

    Numerator:

    $-2 \cdot 4^2 - 4 \cdot (6 - 2)$ *Parentheses*
    $-2 \cdot 4^2 - 4 \cdot 4$ *Exponent*
    $-2 \cdot 16 - 4 \cdot 4$ *Multiply*
    $-32 - 16$ *Add*
    $-32 + (-16)$
    -48

    Denominator:

    $-4 \cdot (8 - 13) \div (-5)$ *Parentheses*
    $-4 \cdot (-5) \div (-5)$ *Multiply*
    $20 \div (-5)$
    -4

    Divide. $\dfrac{-48}{-4} = 12$

43. $(-4)^2 \cdot (7 - 9)^2 \div 2^3$ *Parentheses*
    $(-4)^2 \cdot (-2)^2 \div 2^3$ *Exponents*
    $16 \cdot 4 \div 8$ *Multiply*
    $64 \div 8$ *Divide*
    8

47. $(-0.75) \cdot (3.6 - 5)^2$ *Parentheses*
    $(-0.75) \cdot (-1.4)^2$ *Exponent*
    $(-0.75) \cdot (1.96)$ *Multiply*
    -1.47

51. $\dfrac{2}{3} \div \left(-\dfrac{5}{6}\right) - \dfrac{1}{2}$ *Invert, cancel*

    $\dfrac{2}{\cancel{3}_1} \cdot \left(-\dfrac{\cancel{6}^2}{5}\right) - \dfrac{1}{2}$ *Multiply*

    $-\dfrac{4}{5} + \left(-\dfrac{1}{2}\right)$

    $-\dfrac{8}{10} + \left(-\dfrac{5}{10}\right)$ *Add*

    $-\dfrac{13}{10}$

55. $\dfrac{3}{5} \cdot \left(-\dfrac{7}{6}\right) - \left(\dfrac{1}{6} - \dfrac{5}{3}\right)$ *Parentheses*

    $\dfrac{3}{5} \cdot \left(-\dfrac{7}{6}\right) - \left(\dfrac{1}{6} - \dfrac{10}{6}\right)$

    $\dfrac{\cancel{3}^1}{5} \cdot \left(-\dfrac{7}{\cancel{6}_2}\right) - \left(-\dfrac{9}{6}\right)$ *Multiply*

    $-\dfrac{7}{10} - \left(-\dfrac{9}{6}\right)$ $\dfrac{9}{6} = \dfrac{3}{2} = \dfrac{15}{10}$

    $-\dfrac{7}{10} - \left(+\dfrac{15}{10}\right)$ $\dfrac{8}{10} = \dfrac{4}{5}$

    $\dfrac{4}{5}$

59. $1.6 \cdot (-0.8) \div (-0.32) \div 2^2$ *Exponent*
    $1.6 \cdot (-0.8) \div (-0.32) \div 4$ *Multiply*
    $-1.28 \div (-0.32) \div 4$ *Divide*
    $4 \div 4$
    1

63. $\dfrac{-9 + 18 \div (-3) \cdot (-6)}{5 - 4 \cdot 12 \div 3 \cdot 2}$

    Numerator:

    $-9 + 18 \div (-3) \cdot (-6)$ *Divide*
    $-9 + (-6) \cdot (-6)$ *Multiply*
    $-9 + 36$ *Add*
    27

Denominator:

$$5 - 4 \cdot 12 \div 3 \cdot 2 \quad \textit{Divide}$$
$$5 - 4 \cdot 4 \cdot 2 \quad \textit{Multiply}$$
$$5 - 16 \cdot 2$$
$$5 - 32$$
$$5 + (-32) \quad \textit{Add}$$
$$-27$$

Divide. $\dfrac{27}{-27} = -1$

67. $|-12| \div 4 + 2 \cdot 3^2 \div 6 \quad \textit{Exponent}$
$|-12| \div 4 + 2 \cdot 9 \div 6 \quad \textit{Absolute value}$
$12 \div 4 + 2 \cdot 9 \div 6$
$3 + 2 \cdot 9 \div 6 \quad \textit{Divide}$
$3 + 18 \div 6 \quad \textit{Multiply}$
$3 + 3 \quad \textit{Divide}$
6

71. $\dfrac{5}{3} - \dfrac{3}{8} \cdot \dfrac{4}{9} = \dfrac{5}{3} - \dfrac{\cancel{3}^{1}}{\cancel{8}_{2}} \cdot \dfrac{\cancel{4}^{1}}{\cancel{9}_{3}}$

$= \dfrac{5}{3} - \dfrac{1}{6}$

$= \dfrac{10}{6} - \dfrac{1}{6} = \dfrac{9}{6} = \dfrac{3}{2}$ or $1\tfrac{1}{2}$

9.5 Evaluating Expressions and Formulas

9.5 Margin Exercises

1. $5x - 3y$

   (a) $x = 1, y = 2$

   Replace x with 1. Replace y with 2.

   $$5x - 3y$$
   $$5(1) - 3(2)$$
   $$5 - 6$$
   $$-1$$

   (b) $x = 3, y = -4$

   Replace x with 3. Replace y with -4.

   $$5x - 3y$$
   $$5(3) - 3(-4)$$
   $$15 + 12$$
   $$27$$

   (c) $x = 0, y = 6$

   Replace x with 0. Replace y with 6.

   $$5x - 3y$$
   $$5(0) - 3(6)$$
   $$0 - 18$$
   $$-18$$

2. $7m - 8n + p$

   (a) $m = 1, n = 2, p = 5$

   Replace m with 1, n with 2, and p with 5.

   $$7m - 8n + p$$
   $$7(1) - 8(2) + 5$$
   $$7 - 16 + 5$$
   $$-9 + 5$$
   $$-4$$

   (b) $m = -4, n = -3, p = -7$

   Replace m with -4, n with -3, and p with -7.

   $$7m - 8n + p$$
   $$7(-4) - 8(-3) + (-7)$$
   $$-28 + 24 + (-7)$$
   $$-4 + (-7)$$
   $$-11$$

   (c) $m = -5, n = 0, p = -1$

   Replace m with -5, n with 0, and p with -1.

   $$7m - 8n + p$$
   $$7(-5) - 8(0) + (-1)$$
   $$-35 - 0 + (-1)$$
   $$-35 + (-1)$$
   $$-36$$

3. $x + 6y$

   (a) $x = 9, y = -3$

   Replace x with 9. Replace y with -3.

   $$x + 6y$$
   $$9 + 6(-3)$$
   $$9 + (-18)$$
   $$-9$$

   (b) $x = -2, y = 1$

   Replace x with -2. Replace y with 1.

   $$x + 6y$$
   $$-2 + 6(1)$$
   $$-2 + 6$$
   $$4$$

(c) $x = 6$, $y = -1$

Replace x with 6. Replace y with -1.

$$x + 6y$$
$$6 + 6(-1)$$
$$6 + (-6)$$
$$0$$

4. $\dfrac{3k + r}{2s}$

(a) $k = 1$, $r = 1$, $s = 2$

Replace k with 1, r with 1, and s with 2.

$$\frac{3k+r}{2s} = \frac{3(1) + 1(1)}{2(2)}$$
$$= \frac{3+1}{4}$$
$$= \frac{4}{4}$$
$$= 1$$

(b) $k = 8$, $r = -2$, $s = -4$

Replace k with 8, r with -2, and s with -4.

$$\frac{3k+r}{2s} = \frac{3(8) + 1(-2)}{2(-4)}$$
$$= \frac{24 + (-2)}{-8}$$
$$= \frac{22}{-8}$$
$$= -\frac{11}{4}$$

(c) $k = -3$, $r = 1$, $s = -2$

Replace k with -3, r with 1, and s with -2.

$$\frac{3k+r}{2s} = \frac{3(-3) + 1(1)}{2(-2)}$$
$$= \frac{-9+1}{-4}$$
$$= \frac{-8}{-4}$$
$$= 2$$

5. (a) $A = \dfrac{1}{2}bh$; $b = 6$ yd, $h = 12$ yd

$$A = \frac{1}{2}(6 \text{ yd})(12 \text{ yd})$$
$$= \frac{1}{\underset{1}{\cancel{2}}}(\overset{3}{\cancel{6}} \text{ yd})(12 \text{ yd})$$
$$= 36 \text{ yd}^2$$

(b) $P = 2\ell + 2w$; $\ell = 10$, $w = 8$

$$P = 2(10) + 2(8)$$
$$= 20 + 16$$
$$= 36$$

(c) $d = rt$; $r = 4$, $t = 80$

$$d = (4)(80) = 320$$

(d) $C = 2\pi r$; $\pi \approx 3.14$, $r = 6$

$$C \approx 2 \cdot 3.14 \cdot 6$$
$$\approx 37.68$$

9.5 Section Exercises

3. $r = 1$, $s = -3$

Replace r with 1. Replace s with -3.

$$2r + 4s$$
$$2(1) + 4(-3)$$
$$2 + (-12)$$
$$-10$$

7. $r = -1$, $s = -7$

Replace r with -1. Replace s with -7.

$$2r + 4s$$
$$2(-1) + 4(-7)$$
$$-2 + (-28)$$
$$-30$$

11. $8x - y$; $x = 1$, $y = 8$

Replace x with 1. Replace y with 8.

$$8x - y$$
$$8(1) - 8$$
$$8 - 8$$
$$0$$

15. $\dfrac{-m + 5n}{2s + 2}$; $m = 4$, $n = -8$, $s = 0$

Replace m with 4, n with -8, and s with 0.

$$\frac{-m + 5n}{2s + 2} = \frac{-4 + 5(-8)}{2(0) + 2}$$
$$= \frac{-4 + (-40)}{0 + 2}$$
$$= \frac{-44}{2}$$
$$= -22$$

Section 9.6 Solving Equations

19. $-c - 5b$; $c = -8$, $b = -4$

Replace c with -8. Replace b with -4.

$$-c - 5b$$
$$-(-8) - 5(-4)$$
$$+8 - (-20)$$
$$8 + (+20)$$
$$28$$

23. $-k - m - 8n$; $k = 6$, $m = -9$, $n = 0$

Replace k with 6, m with -9, and n with 0.

$$-k - m - 8n$$
$$-6 - (-9) - 8(0)$$
$$-6 + (+9) - 0$$
$$3$$

27. $P = 4s$; $s = 7.5$

$$P = 4 \cdot (7.5) = 30$$

31. $A = \pi r^2$; $\pi \approx 3.14$, $r = 5$

Replace π with ≈ 3.14 and r with 5.

$$A = \pi r^2$$
$$\approx 3.14 \cdot 5 \cdot 5$$
$$\approx 78.5$$

35. $V = \frac{1}{3}Bh$; $B = 30$, $h = 60$

$$V = \frac{1}{3} \cdot (30) \cdot (60)$$
$$= 600$$

39. $C = 2\pi r$; $\pi \approx 3.14$, $r = 4$

$$C \approx 2 \cdot (3.14) \cdot 4$$
$$\approx 25.12$$

43. $F = \frac{9C}{5} + 32$; $C = -40$

$$F = \frac{9 \cdot (-40)}{5} + 32$$
$$= -72 + 32$$
$$= -40$$

The formula $F = \frac{9C}{5} + 32$ is used to convert a Celsius temperature to Fahrenheit.

47. $A = \frac{1}{2}h(b + B)$; $h = 7$, $b = 4$, $B = 12$

$$A = \frac{1}{2} \cdot 7(4 + 12)$$
$$= \frac{1}{\cancel{2}} \cdot 7(\cancel{16})^{8}$$
$$= 56$$

The formula $A = \frac{1}{2}h(b + B)$ is used to find the area of a trapezoid.

51. $-\frac{4}{3} \cdot \left(-\frac{3}{4}\right) = -\frac{\cancel{4}^{1}}{\cancel{3}_{1}} \cdot \left(-\frac{\cancel{3}^{1}}{\cancel{4}_{1}}\right) = 1$

9.6 Solving Equations

9.6 Margin Exercises

1. (a) $p + 1 = 8$; 7

Replace p with 7.

$$7 + 1 = 8$$
$$8 = 8 \quad True$$

7 is a solution.

(b) $30 = 5r$; 6

Replace r with 6.

$$30 = 5(6)$$
$$30 = 30 \quad True$$

30 is a solution.

(c) $3k - 2 = 4$; 3

Replace k with 3.

$$3(3) - 2 = 4$$
$$7 = 4 \quad False$$

3 is not a solution.

(d) $23 = 4y + 3$; 5

Replace y with 5.

$$23 = 4(5) + 3$$
$$23 = 23 \quad True$$

23 is a solution.

2. (a)
$$n - 5 = 8$$
$$n - 5 + 5 = 8 + 5$$
$$n = 13$$

Check: $13 - 5 = 8$
$\qquad\qquad 8 = 8 \quad True$

(b)
$$5 = r - 10$$
$$5 + 10 = r - 10 + 10$$
$$15 = r$$

Check: $5 = 15 - 10$
$\qquad\quad 5 = 5 \quad True$

(c)
$$3 = z + 1$$
$$3 - 1 = z + 1 - 1$$
$$2 = z$$

Check: $3 = 2 + 1$
$\qquad\quad 3 = 3 \quad True$

(d)
$$k + 9 = 0$$
$$k + 9 - 9 = 0 - 9$$
$$k = -9$$

Check: $-9 + 9 = 0$
$\qquad\qquad 0 = 0 \quad True$

(e)
$$-2 = y + 9$$
$$-2 + (-9) = y + 9 - 9$$
$$-11 = y$$

Check: $-2 = -11 + 9$
$\qquad\quad -2 = -2 \quad True$

(f)
$$x - 2 = -6$$
$$x - 2 + 2 = -6 + 2$$
$$x = -4$$

Check: $-4 + (-2) = -6$
$\qquad\qquad\quad -6 = -6 \quad True$

3. (a)
$$2y = 14$$
$$\frac{\overset{1}{\cancel{2}} \cdot y}{\underset{1}{\cancel{2}}} = \frac{14}{2}$$
$$y = 7$$

Check: $2y = 14$
$\qquad\quad 2 \cdot 7 = 14$
$\qquad\qquad 14 = 14$

(b)
$$42 = 7p$$
$$\frac{\overset{6}{\cancel{42}}}{\underset{1}{\cancel{7}}} = \frac{7 \cdot p}{7}$$
$$6 = p$$

Check: $42 = 7p$
$\qquad\quad 42 = 7 \cdot 6$
$\qquad\quad 42 = 42 \quad True$

(c)
$$-8a = 32$$
$$\frac{-\overset{1}{\cancel{8}}a}{\underset{1}{-\cancel{8}}} = \frac{32}{-8}$$
$$a = -4$$

Check: $-8(-4) = 32$
$\qquad\qquad 32 = 32 \quad True$

(d)
$$-3r = -15$$
$$\frac{-\overset{1}{\cancel{3}}r}{\underset{1}{-\cancel{3}}} = \frac{-15}{-3}$$
$$r = 5$$

Check: $-3(5) = -15$
$\qquad\qquad -15 = -15 \quad True$

(e)
$$-60 = -6k$$
$$\frac{-60}{-6} = \frac{-\overset{1}{\cancel{6}}k}{\underset{1}{-\cancel{6}}}$$
$$10 = k$$

Check: $-60 = -6k$
$\qquad\quad -60 = -6 \cdot (-10)$
$\qquad\quad -60 = -60 \quad True$

(f)
$$10x = 0$$
$$\frac{\overset{1}{\cancel{10}}x}{\underset{1}{\cancel{10}}} = \frac{0}{10}$$
$$x = 0$$

Check: $10 \cdot 0 = 0$
$\qquad\qquad 0 = 0 \quad True$

4. (a)
$$\frac{a}{4} = 2$$
$$\frac{1}{4}a = 2$$
$$\left(\frac{4}{1}\right) \cdot \left(\frac{1}{4}\right)a = 2 \cdot 4$$
$$a = 8$$

Check: $\frac{a}{4} = 2$
$\qquad\quad \frac{8}{4} = 2$
$\qquad\quad 2 = 2 \quad True$

Section 9.6 Solving Equations

(b)
$$\frac{y}{7} = -3$$
$$\frac{1}{7}y = -3$$
$$\left(\frac{7}{1}\right) \cdot \left(\frac{1}{7}\right)y = -3 \cdot 7$$
$$y = -21$$

Check:
$$\frac{y}{7} = -3$$
$$\frac{-21}{7} = -3$$
$$-3 = -3 \quad True$$

(c)
$$-8 = \frac{k}{6}$$
$$-8 = \frac{1}{6}k$$
$$6 \cdot (-8) = \left(\frac{6}{1}\right) \cdot \left(\frac{1}{6}\right)k$$
$$-48 = k$$

Check:
$$-8 = \frac{k}{6}$$
$$-8 = \frac{-48}{6}$$
$$-8 = -8$$

(d)
$$8 = -\frac{4}{5}z$$
$$\left(-\frac{5}{4}\right) \cdot \left(\frac{8}{1}\right) = \left(-\frac{5}{4}\right) \cdot \left(-\frac{4}{5}\right)z$$
$$-10 = z$$

Check:
$$8 = -\frac{4}{5}z$$
$$8 = \left(-\frac{4}{5}\right) \cdot (-10)$$
$$8 = 8 \quad True$$

(e)
$$-\frac{5}{8}p = -10$$
$$\left(-\frac{8}{5}\right) \cdot \left(-\frac{5}{8}\right)p = (-10) \cdot \left(-\frac{8}{5}\right)$$
$$p = 16$$

Check:
$$-\frac{5}{8}p = -10$$
$$\left(-\frac{5}{8}\right) \cdot (16) = -10$$
$$-10 = -10 \quad True$$

9.6 Section Exercises

3. $4y = 28;\ 7$

Replace y with 7.
$$4(7) = 28$$
$$28 = 28$$

28 is a solution.

7. $p + 5 = 9$

Subtract 5 from both sides.
$$p + 5 - 5 = 9 - 5$$
$$p = 4$$

Check: $p + 5 = 9$
$$4 + 5 = 9$$
$$9 = 9 \quad True$$

The solution is 4.

11. $z - 5 = 3$

Add 5 to both sides.
$$z - 5 + 5 = 3 + 5$$
$$z = 8$$

Check: $z - 5 = 3$
$$8 - 5 = 3$$
$$3 = 3 \quad True$$

The solution is 8.

15. $-5 = n + 3$

Subtract 3 from both sides.
$$-5 + (-3) = n + 3 - 3$$
$$-8 = n$$

Check: $-5 = n + 3$
$$-5 = (-8) + 3$$
$$-5 = -5 \quad True$$

The solution is -8.

19. $-4 + k = 14$

Add 4 to both sides.
$$-4 + 4 + k = 14 + 4$$
$$k = 18$$

Check: $-4 + k = 14$
$$-4 + 18 = 14$$
$$14 = 14 \quad True$$

The solution is 18.

23. $-5 = -2 + r$

Add 2 to both sides.

$$(-5) + 2 = -2 + 2 + r$$
$$-3 = r$$

Check: $-5 = -2 + (-3)$
$-5 = -5$ *True*

The solution is -3.

27. $z - \dfrac{7}{8} = 10$

$$z - \dfrac{7}{8} + \dfrac{7}{8} = 10 + \dfrac{7}{8}$$
$$z = \dfrac{80}{8} + \dfrac{7}{8}$$
$$= \dfrac{87}{8} \text{ or } 10\dfrac{7}{8}$$

Check: $\dfrac{87}{8} - \dfrac{7}{8} = \dfrac{80}{8} = 10$ *True*

The solution is $\dfrac{87}{8}$ or $10\dfrac{7}{8}$.

31. $m - \dfrac{7}{5} = \dfrac{11}{4}$

$$m - \dfrac{7}{5} + \dfrac{7}{5} = \dfrac{11}{4} + \dfrac{7}{5}$$
$$m = \dfrac{55}{20} + \dfrac{28}{20}$$
$$= \dfrac{83}{20}$$

Check: $\dfrac{83}{20} - \dfrac{7}{5} = \dfrac{11}{4}$

$\dfrac{83}{20} - \dfrac{28}{20} = \dfrac{55}{20}$

$\dfrac{55}{20} = \dfrac{55}{20}$ *True*

The solution is $\dfrac{83}{20}$.

35. $3.25 = 4.76 + r$
$3.25 - 4.76 = 4.76 - 4.76 + r$
$-1.51 = r$

Check: $3.25 = 4.76 - 1.51$
$3.25 = 3.25$

The solution is -1.51.

39. $48 = 12r$

Divide both sides by 12.

$$\dfrac{48}{12} = \dfrac{\overset{1}{\cancel{12}} \cdot r}{\underset{1}{\cancel{12}}}$$
$$4 = r$$

Check: $48 = 12r$
$48 = 12(4)$
$48 = 48$ *True*

The solution is 4.

43. $-6k = 36$

Divide both sides by -6.

$$\dfrac{-6k}{-6} = \dfrac{36}{-6}$$
$$k = -6$$

Check: $-6k = 36$
$-6(-6) = 36$
$36 = 36$ *True*

The solution is -6.

47. $-1.2m = 8.4$

Divide both sides by -1.2.

$$\dfrac{-\overset{1}{\cancel{1.2}}m}{\underset{1}{\cancel{-1.2}}} = \dfrac{8.4}{-1.2}$$
$$m = -7$$

Check: $-1.2m = 8.4$
$-1.2(-7) = 8.4$
$8.4 = 8.4$ *True*

The solution is -7.

51. $\dfrac{k}{2} = 17$

$\dfrac{1}{2}k = 17$

Multiply both sides by 2.

$$\dfrac{\overset{1}{\cancel{2}}}{1} \cdot \dfrac{1}{\underset{1}{\cancel{2}}}k = 17 \cdot 2$$
$$k = 34$$

Check: $\dfrac{k}{2} = 17$

$\dfrac{34}{2} = 17$

$17 = 17$ *True*

The solution is 34.

55. $\dfrac{r}{3} = -12$

$\dfrac{1}{3}r = 12$

Section 9.7 Solving Equations with Several Steps

Multiply both sides by 3.

$$\frac{\cancel{3}}{1} \cdot \frac{1}{\cancel{3}} r = -12 \cdot 3$$

$$r = -36$$

Check: $\frac{r}{3} = -12$

$\frac{-36}{3} = -12$

$-12 = -12$ *True*

The solution is -36.

59. $-\dfrac{3}{4} m = -3$

Multiply both sides by $\left(-\dfrac{4}{3}\right)$.

$$-\frac{\cancel{4}}{\cancel{3}} \cdot \left(-\frac{\cancel{3}}{\cancel{4}} m\right) = -3 \cdot \left(-\frac{4}{3}\right)$$

$$m = \frac{12}{3} = 4$$

Check: $-\dfrac{3}{4} m = -3$

$\left(-\dfrac{3}{4}\right) \cdot 4 = -3$

$-3 = -3$ *True*

The solution is 4.

63. $\dfrac{y}{2.6} = 0.5$

Multiply both sides by 2.6.

$$\left(\frac{\cancel{2.6}}{1}\right) \cdot \left(\frac{1}{\cancel{2.6}}\right) y = 0.5(2.6)$$

$$y = 1.3$$

Check: $\dfrac{y}{2.6} = 0.5$

$\dfrac{1.3}{2.6} = 0.5$

$0.5 = 0.5$ *True*

The solution is 1.3.

67. You may add or subtract the same number on both sides of an equation. Many different equations could have -3 as the solution. One possibility is:

$$x + 5 = 2$$
$$x + 5 - 5 = 2 - 5$$
$$x = -3.$$

71.
$$3 = x + 9 - 15$$
$$3 + 15 = x + 9 - 15 + 15$$
$$18 = x + 9$$
$$18 - 9 = x + 9 - 9$$
$$9 = x$$

75. $2\frac{1}{5} \div \left(3\frac{1}{3} - 4\frac{1}{5}\right) = 2\frac{1}{5} \div \left(3\frac{5}{15} - 4\frac{3}{15}\right)$

$$= 2\frac{1}{5} \div \left(\frac{50}{15} - \frac{63}{15}\right)$$

$$= 2\frac{1}{5} \div \left(-\frac{13}{15}\right)$$

$$= \frac{11}{5} \div \left(-\frac{13}{15}\right)$$

$$= \frac{11}{\cancel{5}} \cdot \left(-\frac{\cancel{15}}{13}\right)$$

$$= -\frac{33}{13} \text{ or } -2\frac{7}{13}$$

9.7 Solving Equations with Several Steps

9.7 Margin Exercises

1. (a)
$$2r + 7 = 13$$
$$2r + 7 - 7 = 13 - 7$$
$$2r = 6$$
$$\frac{\cancel{2}r}{\cancel{2}} = \frac{6}{2}$$
$$r = 3$$

Check: Replace r with 3.

$$2(3) + 7 = 13$$
$$13 = 13 \quad True$$

The solution is 3.

(b)
$$20 = 6y - 4$$
$$20 + 4 = 6y - 4 + 4$$
$$24 = 6y$$
$$\frac{24}{6} = \frac{\cancel{6}y}{\cancel{6}}$$
$$4 = y$$

233

Check: Replace y with 4.

$$20 = 6(4) - 4$$
$$20 = 20$$

The solution is 4.

(c)
$$7m + 9 = 9$$
$$7m + 9 - 9 = 9 - 9$$
$$7m = 0$$
$$\frac{7m}{7} = \frac{0}{7}$$
$$m = 0$$

Check: Replace m with 0.

$$7(0) + 9 = 9$$
$$0 + 9 = 9$$
$$9 = 9 \quad True$$

The solution is 0.

(d)
$$-2 = 4p + 10$$
$$-2 + (-10) = 4p + 10 - 10$$
$$-12 = 4p$$
$$\frac{-12}{4} = \frac{\cancel{4}p}{\cancel{4}}$$
$$-3 = p$$

Check: Replace p with -3.

$$-2 = 4(-3) + 10$$
$$-2 = -12 + 10$$
$$-2 = -2 \quad True$$

The solution is -3.

(e)
$$-10z - 9 = 11$$
$$-10z - 9 + 9 = 11 + 9$$
$$-10z = 20$$
$$\frac{-\cancel{10}z}{-\cancel{10}} = \frac{20}{-10}$$
$$z = -2$$

Check: Replace z with -2.

$$-10(-2) - 9 = 11$$
$$20 - 9 = 11$$
$$11 = 11 \quad True$$

The solution is -2.

2. (a) $3(2 + 6) = 3 \cdot 2 + 3 \cdot 6$
$$= 6 + 18$$
$$= 24$$

(b) $8(k - 3)$

Notice that $k - 3$ means $k + (-3)$.

$$8(k - 3) = 8k + 8(-3)$$
$$= 8k + (-24)$$
$$= 8k - 24$$

(c) $-6(r + 5) = -6r + (-6) \cdot 5$
$$= -6r + (-30)$$
$$= -6r - 30$$

(d) $-9(s - 8) = -9s - (-9) \cdot 8$
$$= -9s - (-72)$$
$$= -9s + 72$$

3. (a) $5y + 11y = (5 + 11)y = 16y$

(b) $10a - 28a = (10 - 28)a = -18a$

(c) $3x + 3x - 9x = (3 + 3 - 9)x = -3x$

(d) $k + k = 2k$

(e) $6b - b - 7b = (6 - 1 - 7)b = -2b$

4. (a)
$$3y - 1 = 2y + 7$$
$$3y - 2y - 1 = 2y - 2y + 7$$
$$y - 1 = 7$$
$$y - 1 + 1 = 7 + 1$$
$$y = 8$$

Check: Replace y with 8.

$$3(8) - 1 = 2(8) + 7$$
$$24 - 1 = 16 + 7$$
$$23 = 23 \quad True$$

The solution is 8.

(b)
$$5a + 7 = 3a - 9$$
$$5a - 3a + 7 = 3a - 3a - 9$$
$$2a + 7 = -9$$
$$2a + 7 - 7 = -9 + (-7)$$
$$2a = -16$$
$$\frac{2a}{2} = \frac{-16}{2}$$
$$a = -8$$

Check: Replace a with -8.

$$5(-8) + 7 = 3(-8) - 9$$
$$-40 + 7 = -24 + (-9)$$
$$-33 = -33 \quad True$$

The solution is -8.

(c)
$$3p - 2 = p - 6$$
$$3p - p - 2 = p - p - 6$$
$$2p - 2 = -6$$
$$2p - 2 + 2 = -6 + 2$$
$$2p = -4$$
$$\frac{2p}{2} = \frac{-4}{2}$$
$$p = -2$$

Check: Replace p with -2.

$$3(-2) - 2 = -2 + (-6)$$
$$-6 + (-2) = -2 + (-6)$$
$$-8 = -8 \quad True$$

The solution is -2.

5. (a)
$$-12 = 4(y - 1)$$
$$-12 = 4y - 4$$
$$-12 + 4 = 4y - 4 + 4$$
$$-8 = 4y$$
$$\frac{-8}{4} = \frac{\overset{1}{\cancel{4}}y}{\underset{1}{\cancel{4}}}$$
$$-2 = y$$

Check: Replace y with -2.

$$-12 = 4(-2 - 1)$$
$$-12 = 4(-2) - (4 \cdot 1)$$
$$-12 = -8 + (-4)$$
$$-12 = -12 \quad True$$

The solution is -2.

(b)
$$5(m + 4) = 20$$
$$5m + 20 = 20$$
$$5m + 20 - 20 = 20 - 20$$
$$5m = 0$$
$$m = 0$$

Check: Replace m with 0.

$$5(0 + 4) = 20$$
$$5(4) = 20$$
$$20 = 20 \quad True$$

The solution is 0.

(c)
$$6(t - 2) = 18$$
$$6t - 12 = 18$$
$$6t - 12 + 12 = 18 + 12$$
$$6t = 30$$
$$\frac{6t}{6} = \frac{30}{6}$$
$$t = 5$$

Check: Replace t with 5.

$$6(5 - 2) = 18$$
$$6(3) = 18$$
$$18 = 18 \quad True$$

The solution is 5.

9.7 Section Exercises

3.
$$2 = 8y - 6$$
$$2 + 6 = 8y - 6 + 6$$
$$8 = 8y$$
$$\frac{8}{8} = \frac{8y}{8}$$
$$1 = y$$

Check: Replace y with 1.

$$2 = 8y - 6$$
$$2 = 8(1) - 6$$
$$2 = 2$$

The solution is 1.

7.
$$28 = -9a + 10$$
$$28 - 10 = -9a + 10 - 10$$
$$18 = -9a$$
$$\frac{18}{-9} = \frac{-9a}{-9}$$
$$-2 = a$$

Check: Replace a with -2.

$$28 = -9(-2) + 10$$
$$28 = 18 + 10$$
$$28 = 28 \quad True$$

The solution is -2.

11.
$$-\frac{1}{2}z + 2 = -1$$
$$-\frac{1}{2}z + 2 - 2 = -1 - 2$$
$$-\frac{1}{2}z = -3$$
$$-\frac{2}{1} \cdot \left(-\frac{1}{2}z\right) = -3 \cdot \left(-\frac{2}{1}\right)$$
$$z = 6$$

Check: Replace z with 6.
$$-\frac{1}{2}z + 2 = -1$$
$$-\frac{1}{2}(6) + 2 = -1$$
$$-3 + 2 = -1$$
$$-1 = -1 \quad \textit{True}$$

The solution is 6.

15. $7(p - 8) = 7 \cdot p - 7 \cdot 8$
$= 7p - 56$

19. $-2(y - 3) = -2 \cdot y - (-2) \cdot 3$
$= -2y - (-6)$
$= -2y + 6$

23. $2m + 5m = (2 + 5)m = 7m$

27. $-10a + a = (-10a + 1)a = -9a$

31.
$$4k + 6k = 50$$
$$(4 + 6)k = 50$$
$$10k = 50$$
$$\frac{10k}{10} = \frac{50}{10}$$
$$k = 5$$

Check: Replace k with 5.
$$4k + 6k = 50$$
$$4 \cdot 5 + 6 \cdot 5 = 50$$
$$20 + 30 = 50$$
$$50 = 50 \quad \textit{True}$$

The solution is 5.

35.
$$2b - 6b = 24$$
$$(2 - 6)b = 24$$
$$-4b = 24$$
$$\frac{-4b}{-4} = \frac{24}{-4}$$
$$b = -6$$

Check: Replace b with 6.
$$2b - 6b = 24$$
$$2(-6) - 6(-6) = 24$$
$$-12 - (-36) = 24$$
$$-12 + 36 = 24$$
$$24 = 24 \quad \textit{True}$$

The solution is -6.

39.
$$6p - 2 = 4p + 6$$
$$6p - 2 + 2 = 4p + 6 + 2$$
$$6p = 4p + 8$$
$$6p - 4p = 4p - 4p + 8$$
$$2p = 8$$
$$\frac{2p}{2} = \frac{8}{2}$$
$$p = 4$$

Check: Replace p with 4.
$$6p - 2 = 4p + 6$$
$$6 \cdot 4 - 2 = 4 \cdot 4 + 6$$
$$24 - 2 = 16 + 6$$
$$22 = 22 \quad \textit{True}$$

The solution is 4.

43.
$$-2y + 6 = 6y - 10$$
$$-2y + 6 + 10 = 6y - 10 + 10$$
$$-2y + 16 = 6y$$
$$-2y + 2y + 16 = 6y + 2y$$
$$16 = 8y$$
$$\frac{16}{8} = \frac{8y}{8}$$
$$2 = y$$

Check: Replace y with 2.
$$-2(2) + 6 = 6(2) - 10$$
$$(-4) + 6 = 12 - 10$$
$$2 = 2 \quad \textit{True}$$

The solution is 2.

47.
$$2.5r + 9 = -1$$
$$2.5r + 9 - 9 = -1 + (-9)$$
$$2.5r = -10$$
$$\frac{2.5r}{2.5} = \frac{-10}{2.5}$$
$$r = -4$$

Check: Replace r with -4.

$$2.5(-4) + 9 = -1$$
$$-10 + 9 = -1$$
$$-1 = -1$$

The solution is -4.

51. $\quad -4(t+2) = 12$
$-4t + (-8) = 12$
$-4t - 8 + 8 = 12 + 8$
$-4t = 20$
$$\dfrac{\overset{1}{-\cancel{4}}t}{\underset{1}{-\cancel{4}}} = \dfrac{20}{-4}$$
$t = -5$

Check: Replace t with -5.

$$-4(-5 + 2) = 12$$
$$(-4)\cdot(-5) + (-4)\cdot(2) = 12$$
$$20 + (-8) = 12$$
$$12 = 12$$

The solution is -5.

55. $-2t - 10 = 3t + 5$

Subtract $3t$ from both sides (addition property).

$$-2t - 3t - 10 = 3t - 3t + 5$$
$$-5t - 10 = 5$$

Add 10 to both sides (addition property).

$$-5t - 10 + 10 = 5 + 10$$
$$-5t = 15$$

Divide both sides by -5 (multiplication property).

$$\dfrac{\overset{1}{-\cancel{5}} \cdot t}{\underset{1}{-\cancel{5}}} = \dfrac{15}{-5}$$
$$t = -3$$

59. $\quad 0 = -2(y - 2)$
$0 = -2y + (-2)\cdot(-2)$
$0 = -2y + 4$
$0 + 2y = -2y + 2y + 4$
$2y = 4$
$y = 2$

63. *amount of discount*
 $=$ *rate of discount · original price*
 $= 60\% \cdot \$28$
 $= 0.6 \cdot \$28$
 $= \$16.80$

sale price $=$ *original price − amount of discount*
$\qquad\qquad = \$28 - \$16.80 = \$11.20$

9.8 Applications

9.8 Margin Exercises

1. **(a)** 15 less than a number

 $x - 15$

 (b) 12 more than a number

 $x + 12$ or $12 + x$

 (c) a number increased by 13

 $x + 13$ or $13 + x$

 (d) a number minus 8

 $x - 8$

 (e) -10 plus a number

 $-10 + x$ or $x + (-10)$

 (f) 6 minus a number

 $6 - x$

2. **(a)** double a number

 $2x$

 (b) the product of -8 and a number

 $-8x$

 (c) the quotient of 15 and a number

 $\dfrac{15}{x}$

 (d) one-half of a number

 $\dfrac{1}{2}x$ or $\dfrac{x}{2}$

3. **(a)** Let x = the unknown number.

3 times a number	added to	4	is	19.
↓	↓	↓	↓	↓
$3x$	$+$	4	$=$	19

$$3x + 4 = 19$$
$$3x + 4 - 4 = 19 - 4$$
$$3x = 15$$
$$\frac{\cancel{3}x}{\cancel{3}} = \frac{15}{3}$$
$$x = 5$$

The number is 5.
Check: $3(5) + 4 = 19$
$15 + 4 = 19$
$19 = 19$ *True*

(b) Let $x =$ the unknown number.

$\underbrace{-6 \text{ times a number}}_{-6x}$ $\underset{+}{\text{added to}}$ $\underset{5}{5}$ $\underset{=}{\text{is}}$ $\underset{-13}{-13}.$

$$-6x + 5 = -13$$
$$-6x + 5 - 5 = -13 - 5$$
$$\frac{-\cancel{6}x}{-\cancel{6}} = \frac{-18}{-6}$$
$$x = 3$$

The number is 3.
Check: $-6(3) + 5 = -13$
$-18 + 5 = -13$
$-13 = -13$ *True*

(c) Let $x =$ the amount LuAnn donated. Then
$2x + 10 =$ the amount Susan donated.

$$2x + 10 = 22$$
$$2x + 10 - 10 = 22 - 10$$
$$2x = 12$$
$$\frac{\cancel{2}x}{\cancel{2}} = \frac{12}{2}$$
$$x = 6$$

LuAnn donated $6.
Check: $2(6) + 10 = 22$
$12 + 10 = 22$
$22 = 22$ *True*

4. (a) Let $x =$ the amount made by the daughter
and $x + 12 =$ the amount made by Keonda.

$$x + x + 12 = 182$$
$$2x + 12 = 182$$
$$2x + 12 - 12 = 182 - 12$$
$$2x = 170$$
$$\frac{\cancel{2}x}{\cancel{2}} = \frac{170}{2}$$
$$x = 85$$

The daughter made $85.
Keonda made $85 + $12 = $97.

(b) Let $x =$ the length of the shorter piece and
$x + 3 =$ the length of the longer piece.

$$x + x + 3 = 21$$
$$2x + 3 = 21$$
$$2x + 3 - 3 = 21 - 3$$
$$2x = 18$$
$$\frac{\cancel{2}x}{\cancel{2}} = \frac{18}{2}$$
$$x = 9$$

The length of the shorter piece is 9 m. The length of the longer piece is 9 m + 3 m = 12 m.

5. See the drawing in the margin exercise answers. Use the formula for the perimeter of a rectangle.

$$P = 2 \cdot \ell + 2 \cdot w$$
$$22 = 2 \cdot (x + 3) + 2 \cdot x$$
$$22 = 2x + 6 + 2x$$
$$22 = 4x + 6$$
$$22 - 6 = 4x + 6 - 6$$
$$16 = 4x$$
$$\frac{16}{4} = \frac{4x}{4}$$
$$4 = x$$

The width is 4 m and the length is $x + 3$ or $4 + 3 = 7$ m.

9.8 Section Exercises

3. −5 added to a number

$$-5 + x \text{ or } x + (-5)$$

7. 9 less than a number

$$x - 9$$

11. six times a number

$$6x$$

15. a number divided by 2

$$\frac{x}{2} \text{ or } \frac{1}{2}x$$

19. 10 fewer than seven times a number

$$7x - 10$$

23. A variable is a letter that represents an unknown quantity. Examples: x, w, p
An expression is a combination of letters and numbers. Examples: $6x, w - 5, 2p + 3x$
An equation has an = sign and shows that two expressions are equal.
Examples: $2y = 14;\ x + 5 = 2x;\ 8p - 10 = 54$

27. Let $n =$ the unknown number.

Twice a number	added to	the number	is	−15.
↓	↓	↓	↓	↓
$2n$	$+$	n	$=$	-15

$$2n + n = -15$$
$$3n = -15$$
$$\frac{\cancel{3}n}{\cancel{3}} = \frac{-15}{3}$$
$$n = -5$$

The number is −5.
Check:

$$2n + n = -15$$
$$2 \cdot (-5) + (-5) = -15$$
$$-10 + (-5) = -15$$
$$-15 = -15 \quad True$$

31. Let $\quad p =$ the length of the shorter piece, and
$p + 10 =$ the length of the longer piece.

The length of the shorter piece	and	the length of the longer piece	are	78 cm.
↓	↓	↓	↓	↓
p	$+$	$p + 10$	$=$	78

$$p + p + 10 = 78$$
$$2p + 10 = 78$$
$$2p + 10 - 10 = 78 - 10$$
$$2p = 68$$
$$\frac{\cancel{2}p}{\cancel{2}} = \frac{68}{2}$$
$$p = 34$$

The length of the shorter piece is 34 cm and the length of the longer piece is $34 + 10 = 44$ cm.

Check:

$$34 \text{ cm} + 44 \text{ cm} = 78 \text{ cm} \quad Correct$$

35. See the drawing in the answer section of the textbook.
Let $x =$ the length of the rectangle.

$$P = 2 \cdot \ell + 2 \cdot w$$
$$48 = 2x + 2 \cdot 5$$
$$48 - 10 = 2x + 10 - 10$$
$$38 = 2x$$
$$\frac{38}{2} = \frac{\cancel{2}x}{\cancel{2}}$$
$$19 = x$$

The length is 19 m.
Check:

$$2 \cdot 19 + 2 \cdot 5 = 38 + 10$$
$$48 = 48 \quad Correct$$

39. Let $a =$ Tamu's age.

Four times Tamu's age	less	75	is	a.
↓	↓	↓	↓	↓
$4a$	$-$	75	$=$	a

$$4a - 75 = a$$
$$4a - 75 + 75 = a + 75$$
$$4a = a + 75$$
$$4a - a = a + 75 - a$$
$$3a = 75$$
$$a = 25$$

Tamu is 25 years old.
Check:
$$4(25) - 75 = 25$$
$$100 - 75 = 25$$
$$25 = 25 \quad True$$

43. Let t = the number of years.
$$I = prt$$
$$480 = 800 \cdot (0.12) \cdot t$$
$$480 = 96 \cdot t$$
$$\frac{480}{96} = \frac{\overset{1}{\cancel{96}}}{\underset{1}{\cancel{96}}}t$$
$$5 = t$$

Deposit the money for 5 years.

47. $amount = percent \cdot base$
$= 5\%$ of $\$1830$
$= 0.05 \cdot \$1830$
$= \$91.50$

Each month $91.50 goes into his plan.

Chapter 9 Review Exercises

For Exercises 1-4, see the graphs in the answer section of the textbook.

5. $0 > -2$

Because 0 is to the right of −2 on a number line, 0 is greater than −2.

6. $-5 < 0$

Because −5 is the left of 0 on a number line, −5 is less than 0.

7. $-1 > -4$

Because −1 is to the right of −4 on a number line, −1 is greater than −4.

8. $-9 < -6$

Because −9 is to the left of −6 on a number line, −9 is less than −6.

9. $|8| = 8$

The distance from 0 to 8 on a number line is 8.

10. $|-19| = 19$

The distance from 0 to −19 on a number line is 19.

11. $-|-7| = -7$

This is a two step problem. First $|-7| = 7$. Then $-(7) = -7$.

12. $-|15| = -(15) = -15$

Because the negative sign is outside the absolute value bars, the answer is negative.

13. $-4 + 6$

The signs are different so subtract the absolute values.
$$|-4| = 4; \ |6| = 6$$
$$6 - 4 = 2$$

The positive number, 2, has the larger absolute value, so the answer is positive.
$$-4 + 6 = 2$$

14. $-10 + 3$

The signs are different so subtract the absolute values.
$$|-10| = 10; \ |3| = 3$$
$$10 - 3 = 7$$

The negative number, 10, has the larger absolute value, so the answer is negative.
$$-10 + 3 = -7$$

15. $-11 + (-8)$

Add the absolute values.
$$|-11| = 11; \ |-8| = 8$$
$$11 + 8 = 19$$

Write a negative sign in front of the sum, because both numbers are negative.
$$-11 + (-8) = -19$$

Chapter 9 Review Exercises

16. $-9 + (-24)$

Add the absolute values.
$$|-9| = 9;\ |-24| = 24$$
$$9 + 24 = 33$$

Write a negative sign in front of the sum, because both numbers are negative.
$$-9 + (-24) = -33$$

17. $12 + (-11)$

The signs are different so subtract the absolute values.
$$|12| = 12, |-11| = 11$$
$$12 - 11 = 1$$

The positive number, 12, has the larger absolute value, so the answer is positive.
$$12 + (-11) = 1$$

18. $1 + (-20)$

Subtract the absolute values.
$$|1| = 1;\ |-20| = 20$$
$$20 - 1 = 19$$

The negative number, -20, has the larger absolute value, so the answer is negative.
$$1 + (-20) = -19$$

19. $\dfrac{9}{10} + \left(-\dfrac{3}{5}\right) = \dfrac{9}{10} + \left(-\dfrac{6}{10}\right) = \dfrac{3}{10}$

20. $-\dfrac{7}{8} + \dfrac{1}{2} = -\dfrac{14}{16} + \dfrac{8}{16} = -\dfrac{6}{16} = -\dfrac{3}{8}$

21. $-6.7 + 1.5$

Subtract the absolute values.
$$|-6.7| = 6.7;\ |1.5| = 1.5$$
$$6.7 - 1.5 = 5.2$$

The negative number, -6.7, has the larger absolute value, so the answer is negative.
$$-6.7 + 1.5 = -5.2$$

22. $-0.8 + (-0.7)$

Add the absolute values.
$$|-0.8| = 0.8;\ |-0.7| = 0.7$$
$$0.8 + 0.7 = 1.5$$

Write a negative sign in front of the sum, because both numbers are negative.
$$-0.8 + (-0.7) = -1.5$$

23. The additive inverse of 6 is -6.

24. The additive inverse of -14 is $-(-14)$ or 14.

25. The additive inverse of $-\dfrac{5}{8}$ is $-\left(-\dfrac{5}{8}\right)$ or $\dfrac{5}{8}$.

26. The additive inverse of 3.75 is -3.75.

27. $4 - 10 = 4 + (-10) = -6$

28. $7 - 15 = 7 + (-15) = -8$

29. $-6 - 1 = -6 + (-1) = -7$

30. $-12 - 5 = -12 + (-5) = -17$

31. $8 - (-3) = 8 + (+3) = 11$

32. $2 - (-9) = 2 + (+9) = 11$

33. $-1 - (-14) = -1 + (+14) = 13$

34. $-10 - (-4) = -10 + (+4) = -6$

35. $-40 - 40 = -40 + (-40) = -80$

36. $-15 - (-15) = -15 + (+15) = 0$

37. $\dfrac{1}{3} - \dfrac{5}{6} = \dfrac{2}{6} + \left(-\dfrac{5}{6}\right) = -\dfrac{3}{6} = -\dfrac{1}{2}$

38. $2.8 - (-6.2) = 2.8 + (+6.2) = 9$

39. $-4 \cdot 6 = -24$

The numbers have different signs so the product is negative.

40. $5 \cdot (-4) = -20$

The numbers have different signs so the product is negative.

41. $-3 \cdot (-5) = 15$

The product of two numbers with the same sign is positive.

42. $-8 \cdot (-8) = 64$

43. $\dfrac{80}{-10} = -8$

The numbers have different signs so the answer is negative.

44. $\dfrac{-9}{3} = -3$

45. $\dfrac{-25}{-5} = 5$

The numbers have the same sign so the answer is positive.

46. $\dfrac{-120}{-6} = 20$

47. $(-37)(0) = 0$

48. $(-1)(81) = -81$

49. $\dfrac{0}{-10} = 0$

50. $\dfrac{-20}{0}$ is undefined.

51. $\dfrac{2}{3} \cdot \left(-\dfrac{6}{7}\right) = \dfrac{2}{\cancel{3}_1} \cdot \left(-\dfrac{\cancel{6}^2}{7}\right) = \dfrac{2}{1} \cdot \left(-\dfrac{2}{7}\right) = -\dfrac{4}{7}$

52. $-\dfrac{4}{5} \div \left(-\dfrac{2}{15}\right) = -\dfrac{\cancel{4}^2}{\cancel{5}_1} \cdot \left(-\dfrac{\cancel{15}^3}{\cancel{2}_1}\right) = 6$

53. $-0.5 \cdot (-2.8) = 1.4$

54. $\dfrac{-5.28}{0.8} = -6.6$

Move the decimal place to the right in both the divisor and the dividend.

$$\begin{array}{r} 6.6 \\ 8\overline{)52.8} \\ \underline{48} \\ 4\,8 \\ \underline{4\,8} \\ 0 \end{array}$$

The numbers have different signs, so the answer is negative.

55. $2 - 11 \cdot (-5)$ *Multiply*
    $2 + 55$ *Add*
    57

56. $(-4) \cdot (-8) - 9$ *Multiply*
    $32 - 9$ *Subtract*
    23

57. $48 \div (-2)^3 - (-5)$ *Exponent*
    $48 \div (-8) - (-5)$ *Divide*
    $-6 - (-5)$
    $-6 + (+5)$ *Add*
    -1

58. $-36 \div (-3)^2 - (-2)$ *Exponent*
    $-36 \div 9 - (-2)$ *Divide*
    $-4 - (-2)$
    $-4 + (+2)$ *Add*
    -2

59. $5 \cdot 4 - 7 \cdot 6 + 3 \cdot (-4)$ *Multiply*
    $20 - 42 + (-12)$
    $20 + (-42) + (-12)$ *Add*
    $-22 + (-12)$
    -34

60. $2 \cdot 8 - 4 \cdot 9 + 2 \cdot (-6)$ *Multiply*
    $16 - 36 - 12$
    $16 + (-36) + (-12)$ *Add*
    $-20 + (-12)$
    -32

61. $-4 \cdot 3^3 - 2 \cdot (5 - 9)$ *Parentheses*
    $-4 \cdot 3^3 - 2 \cdot (-4)$ *Exponent*
    $-4 \cdot 27 - 2 \cdot (-4)$ *Multiply*
    $-108 - (-8)$
    $-108 + (+8)$ *Add*
    -100

62. $6 \cdot (-4)^2 - 3 \cdot (7 - 14)$ *Parentheses*
    $6 \cdot (-4)^2 - 3 \cdot (-7)$ *Exponent*
    $6 \cdot 16 - 3 \cdot (-7)$ *Multiply*
    $96 - (-21)$
    $96 + (+21)$ *Add*
    117

63. $\dfrac{3 - (5^2 - 4^2)}{14 + 24 \div (-3)}$

Numerator:

$3 - (5^2 - 4^2)$ *Parentheses*
$3 - (25 - 16)$
$3 - 9$
$3 + (-9)$
-6

Denominator:

$14 + 24 \div (-3)$ *Divide*
$14 + (-8)$
6

Divide. $\dfrac{-6}{6} = -1$

64. $(-0.8)^2 \cdot (0.2) - (-1.2)$ *Exponent*
    $0.64 \cdot (0.2) - (-1.2)$ *Multiply*
    $0.128 + (+1.2)$
    1.328

Chapter 9 Review Exercises

65. $\left(-\dfrac{1}{3}\right)^2 + \dfrac{1}{4} \cdot \left(-\dfrac{4}{9}\right)$ *Exponent*

$\dfrac{1}{9} + \dfrac{1}{\cancel{4}_1} \cdot \left(-\dfrac{\cancel{4}^1}{9}\right)$

$\dfrac{1}{9} + \left(-\dfrac{1}{9}\right)$

0

66. $\dfrac{12 \div (2-5) + 12 \cdot (-1)}{2^3 - (-4)^2}$

Numerator:

$12 \div (2-5) + 12 \cdot (-1)$ *Parentheses*
$12 \div (-3) + 12 \cdot (-1)$ *Divide*
$-4 + 12 \cdot (-1)$ *Multiply*
$-4 + (-12)$
-16

Denominator:

$2^3 - (-4)^2$
$8 - 16$
$8 + (-16)$
-8

Divide. $\dfrac{-16}{-8} = 2$

67. $3k + 5m;\ k = 4,\ m = 3$

Replace k with 4. Replace m with 3.

$3(4) + 5(3)$
$12 + 15$
27

68. $3k + 5m;\ k = -6,\ m = 2$

Replace k with -6. Replace m with 2.

$3(-6) + 5(2)$
$-18 + 10$
-8

69. $2p - q;\ p = -5,\ q = -10$

Replace p with -5. Replace q with -10.

$2(-5) - (-10)$
$-10 + (+10)$
0

70. $2p - q;\ p = 6,\ q = -7$

Replace p with 6. Replace q with -7.

$2(6) - (-7)$
$12 + (+7)$
19

71. $\dfrac{5a - 7y}{2 + m};\ a = 1,\ y = 4,\ m = -3$

Replace a with 1, y with 4, and m with -3.

$\dfrac{5a - 7y}{2 + m} = \dfrac{5(1) - 7(4)}{2 + (-3)}$

$\dfrac{5 - 28}{-1}$

$\dfrac{5 + (-28)}{-1}$

$\dfrac{-23}{-1}$

23

72. $\dfrac{5a - 7y}{2 + m};\ a = 2,\ y = -2,\ m = -26$

Replace a with 2, y with -2, and m with -26.

$\dfrac{5a - 7y}{2 + m} = \dfrac{5(2) - 7(-2)}{2 + (-26)}$

$\dfrac{10 + (+14)}{-24}$

$\dfrac{24}{-24}$

-1

73. $P = a + b + c;\ a = 9,\ b = 12,\ c = 14$

$P = a + b + c$
$= 9 + 12 + 14$
$= 35$

74. $A = \dfrac{1}{2}bh;\ b = 6,\ h = 9$

$= \dfrac{1}{2}(6)(9)$

$= \dfrac{54}{2} = 27$

75. $y + 3 = 0$

Subtract 3 from both sides.

$y + 3 - 3 = 0 - 3$
$y = -3$

Check: $y + 3 = 0$
$-3 + 3 = 0$
$0 = 0$

The solution is -3.

76. $a - 8 = 8$
$a - 8 + 8 = 8 + 8$
$a = 16$

Check: $a - 8 = 8$
$16 - 8 = 8$
$8 = 8$

The solution is 16.

77. $-5 = z - 6$
$-5 + 6 = z - 6 + 6$
$1 = z$

Check: $-5 = z - 6$
$-5 = 1 + (-6)$
$-5 = -5$

The solution is 1.

78. $-8 = -9 + r$
$-8 + 9 = -9 + 9 + r$
$1 = r$

Check: $-8 = -9 + r$
$-8 = -9 + 1$
$-8 = -8$

The solution is 1.

79. $-\frac{3}{4} + x = -2$
$-\frac{3}{4} + x + \frac{3}{4} = -2 + \frac{3}{4}$
$x = -\frac{8}{4} + \frac{3}{4}$
$= -\frac{5}{4}$ or $-1\frac{1}{4}$

Check: $-\frac{3}{4} + x = -2$
$-\frac{3}{4} + \left(-\frac{5}{4}\right) = -2$
$-\frac{8}{4} = -2$
$-2 = -2$

The solution is $-\frac{5}{4}$ or $-1\frac{1}{4}$.

80. $12.92 + k = 4.87$
$12.92 - 12.92 + k = 4.87 + (-12.92)$
$k = -8.05$

Check: $12.92 + k = 4.87$
$12.92 + (-8.05) = 4.87$
$4.87 = 4.87$

The solution is -8.05.

81. $-8r = 56$
$\dfrac{-\overset{1}{\cancel{8}}r}{-\underset{1}{\cancel{8}}} = \dfrac{56}{-8}$
$r = -7$

Check: $-8r = 56$
$(-8)(-7) = 56$
$56 = 56$

The solution is -7.

82. $3p = 24$ Check: $3p = 24$
$\dfrac{3p}{3} = \dfrac{24}{3}$ $3(8) = 24$
      $24 = 24$
$p = 8$

The solution is 8.

83. $\dfrac{z}{4} = 5$
$\dfrac{4}{1} \cdot \dfrac{z}{4} = 5 \cdot 4$
$z = 20$

Check: $\dfrac{z}{4} = 5$
$\dfrac{20}{4} = 5$
$5 = 5$

The solution is 20.

84. $\dfrac{a}{5} = -11$
$\dfrac{5}{1} \cdot \dfrac{a}{5} = -11 \cdot 5$
$a = -55$

Check: $\dfrac{a}{5} = -11$
$\dfrac{-55}{5} = -11$
$-11 = -11$

The solution is -55.

85. $20 = 3y - 7$
$20 + 7 = 3y - 7 + 7$
$27 = 3y$
$\dfrac{27}{3} = \dfrac{3y}{3}$
$9 = y$

Chapter 9 Review Exercises

Check: $20 = 3y - 7$
$20 = 3(9) - 7$
$20 = 20$

The solution is 9.

86. $-5 = 2b + 3$
$-5 - 3 = 2b + 3 - 3$
$-8 = 2b$
$\dfrac{-8}{2} = \dfrac{2b}{2}$
$-4 = b$

Check: $-5 = 2b + 3$
$-5 = 2(-4) + 3$
$-5 = -8 + 3$
$-5 = -5$

The solution is -4.

87. $6(r - 5) = 6 \cdot r - 6 \cdot 5$
$= 6r - 30$

88. $11(p + 7) = 11 \cdot p + 11 \cdot 7$
$= 11p + 77$

89. $-9(z - 3) = -9 \cdot z + (-9) \cdot (-3)$
$= -9z + 27$

90. $-8(x + 4) = (-8) \cdot x + (-8 \cdot 4)$
$= -8x - 32$

91. $3r + 8r = (3 + 8)r$
$= 11r$

92. $10z - 15z = (10 - 15)z$
$= -5z$

93. $3p - 12p + p = (3 - 12 + 1)p$
$= -8p$

94. $-6x - x + 9x = (-6 - 1 + 9)x$
$= 2x$

95. $-4z + 2z = 18$
$-2z = 18$
$\dfrac{-2z}{-2} = \dfrac{18}{-2}$
$z = -9$

Check: $-4(-9) + 2(-9) = 18$
$36 + (-18) = 18$
$18 = 18$ $True$

The solution is -9.

96. $-35 = 9k - 2k$
$-35 = (9 - 2)k$
$\dfrac{-35}{7} = \dfrac{7k}{7}$
$-5 = k$

Check: $-35 = 9k - 2k$
$-35 = 9(-5) - 2(-5)$
$-35 = -45 + (+10)$
$-35 = -35$

The solution is -5.

97. $4y - 3 = 7y + 12$
$4y - 3 - 4y = 7y + 12 - 4y$
$-3 = 3y + 12$
$-3 + (-12) = 3y + 12 - 12$
$-15 = 3y$
$\dfrac{-15}{3} = \dfrac{3y}{3}$
$-5 = y$

Check: $4(-5) + (-3) = 7(-5) + 12$
$-20 + (-3) = -35 + 12$
$-23 = -23$ $True$

The solution is -5.

98. $b + 6 = 3b - 8$
$b + 6 - b = 3b - 8 - b$
$6 = 2b - 8$
$6 + 8 = 2b - 8 + 8$
$14 = 2b$
$\dfrac{14}{2} = \dfrac{2b}{2}$
$7 = b$

Check: $7 + 6 = 3 \cdot 7 - 8$
$13 = 13$ $True$

The solution is 7.

99. $-14 = 2(a - 3)$
$-14 = 2 \cdot a - 2 \cdot 3$
$-14 = 2a - 6$
$-14 + 6 = 2a - 6 + 6$
$-8 = 2a$
$\dfrac{-8}{2} = \dfrac{2a}{2}$
$-4 = a$

Check: $-14 = 2(-4) + 2(-3)$
$-14 = -8 + (-6)$
$-14 = -14$ *True*

The solution is -4.

100. $42 = 7(t+6)$
$42 = 7t + 7(6)$
$42 = 7t + 42$
$42 - 42 = 7t + 42 - 42$
$0 = 7t$
$0 = t$

Check: $42 = 7(0+6)$
$42 = 7 \cdot 0 + 7 \cdot 6$
$42 = 42$

The solution is 0.

101. 18 plus a number

$18 + x$ or $x + 18$

102. half a number

$\frac{1}{2}x$ or $\frac{x}{2}$

103. the sum of four times a number and 6

$4x + 6$ or $6 + 4x$

104. five times a number decreased by 10

$5x - 10$

105. Let $n =$ the number.

$11n - 8n = -9$
$(11 - 8)n = -9$
$3n = -9$
$n = -3$

The number is -3.
Check:

$11n - 8n = -9$
$11(-3) - 8(-3) = -9$
$-33 + (+24) = -9$
$-9 = -9$

106. Let $d =$ the number of additional days.

The cost for 1 day	plus	the cost for each additional day	is	the total cost.
↓	↓	↓	↓	↓
45	+	$35 \cdot d$	=	255

$45 + 35d = 255$
$45 - 45 + 35d = 255 - 45$
$35d = 210$
$\frac{35d}{35} = \frac{210}{35}$
$d = 6$

Scott rented the snowmobile for

$1 + 6 = 7$ days.

Check:

$45 + 35(6) = 255$
$255 = 255$

107. The width is 25 cm and the perimeter is 124 cm.

$P = 2 \cdot \ell + 2 \cdot w$
$124 = 2\ell + 2(25)$
$124 = 2\ell + 50$
$124 - 50 = 2\ell + 50 - 50$
$74 = 2\ell$
$\frac{74}{2} = \frac{2\ell}{2}$
$37 = \ell$

The length of the rectangle is 37 cm.
Check:

$124 = 2(37) + 2(25)$
$124 = 74 + 50$
$124 = 124$

108. Let $a =$ the age of the younger sister, and
$a + 9 =$ the age of the older sister.

Chapter 9 Review Exercises

$$a + a + 9 = 51$$
$$2a + 9 = 51$$
$$2a + 9 - 9 = 51 - 9$$
$$2a = 42$$
$$\frac{2a}{2} = \frac{42}{2}$$
$$a = 21$$

The younger sister is 21 years old and the older sister is $21 + 9 = 30$ years old.

Check: $21 + 21 + 9 = 51$
$51 = 51$

109. $-6 - (-9) = -6 + (+9) = 3$

110. $-8 \cdot (-5) = 40$

111. $-12 + 11 = -1$

112. $\frac{-70}{10} = -7$

113. $-4 \cdot 4 = -16$

114. $5 - 14 = 5 + (-14) = -9$

115. $\frac{-42}{-7} = 6$

116. $16 + (-11) = 5$

117. $-10 - 10 = -10 + (-10) = -20$

118. $\frac{-5}{0}$ is undefined.

119. $-\frac{2}{3} + \frac{1}{9} = -\frac{6}{9} + \frac{1}{9} = -\frac{5}{9}$

120. $0.7(-0.5) = -0.35$

121.
$\|-6\| + 2 - 3 \cdot (-8) - 5^2$	*Exponent*
$\|-6\| + 2 - 3 \cdot (-8) - 25$	*Absolute value*
$6 + 2 - 3 \cdot (-8) - 25$	*Multiply*
$6 + 2 - (-24) - 25$	
$6 + 2 + 24 - 25$	*Add*
$8 + 24 - 25$	
$32 - 25$	*Subtract*
7	

122.
$9 \div \|-3\| + 6 \cdot (-5) + 2^3$	*Exponent*
$9 \div \|-3\| + 6 \cdot (-5) + 8$	*Absolute value*
$9 \div 3 + 6 \cdot (-5) + 8$	*Divide*
$3 + 6 \cdot (-5) + 8$	*Multiply*
$3 + (-30) + 8$	*Add*
$-27 + 8$	
-19	

123.
$$-45 = -5y$$
$$\frac{-45}{-5} = \frac{-5y}{-5}$$
$$9 = y$$

124.
$$b - 8 = -12$$
$$b - 8 + 8 = -12 + 8$$
$$b = -4$$

125.
$$6z - 3 = 3z + 9$$
$$6z - 3 + 3 = 3z + 9 + 3$$
$$6z = 3z + 12$$
$$6z - 3z = 3z + 12 - 3z$$
$$3z = 12$$
$$\frac{3z}{3} = \frac{12}{3}$$
$$z = 4$$

126.
$$-5 = r + 5$$
$$-5 + (-5) = r + 5 - 5$$
$$-10 = r$$

127.
$$-3x = 33$$
$$\frac{-3x}{-3} = \frac{33}{-3}$$
$$x = -11$$

128.
$$2z - 7z = -15$$
$$-5z = -15$$
$$\frac{-5z}{-5} = \frac{-15}{-5}$$
$$z = 3$$

129.
$$3(k - 6) = 6 - 12$$
$$3k - 18 = -6$$
$$3k - 18 + 18 = -6 + 18$$
$$3k = 12$$
$$\frac{3k}{3} = \frac{12}{3}$$
$$k = 4$$

130.
$$6(t + 3) = -2 + 20$$
$$6t + 18 = 18$$
$$6t + 18 - 18 = 18 - 18$$
$$6t = 0$$
$$t = 0$$

131.
$$-10 = \frac{a}{5} - 2$$
$$-10 = \frac{1}{5}a - 2$$
$$-10 + 2 = \frac{1}{5}a - 2 + 2$$
$$-8 = \frac{1}{5}a$$
$$5 \cdot (-8) = \left(\frac{5}{1}\right) \cdot \left(\frac{1}{5}\right) a$$
$$-40 = a$$

132.
$$4 + 8p = 4p + 16$$
$$4 + 8p - 4p = 4p + 16 - 4p$$
$$4 + 4p = 16$$
$$4 + 4p - 4 = 16 - 4$$
$$4p = 12$$
$$\frac{4p}{4} = \frac{12}{4}$$
$$p = 3$$

133. Let $n =$ the number.

Twice a number	decreased by	8	is	the number increased by 7.
↓	↓	↓	↓	↓
$2n$	$-$	8	$=$	$n + 7$

$$2n - 8 = n + 7$$
$$2n - 8 + 8 = n + 7 + 8$$
$$2n = n + 15$$
$$2n - n = n + 15 - n$$
$$n = 15$$

Check: $2(15) - 8 = 15 + 7$
$30 - 8 = 22$
$22 = 22$ True

The number is 15.

134. Let $w =$ the width of the rectangle and
$2w + 3 =$ the length.
$$P = 2 \cdot \ell + 2 \cdot w$$
$$36 = 2(2w + 3) + 2 \cdot w$$
$$36 = 4w + 6 + 2w$$
$$36 = 6w + 6$$
$$36 - 6 = 6w + 6 - 6$$
$$30 = 6w$$
$$\frac{30}{6} = \frac{6w}{6}$$
$$5 = w$$

The length of the rectangle is
$$2(5) + 3 = 10 + 3$$
$$= 13 \text{ inches.}$$

The width is 5 inches.

135. Let $s =$ a zebra's running speed
and
$s + 25 =$ a cheetah's running speed.
$$s + s + 25 = 111$$
$$2s + 25 = 111$$
$$2s + 25 - 25 = 111 - 25$$
$$2s = 86$$
$$s = 43$$

A zebra runs 43 miles per hour, and a cheetah sprints 68 (43 + 25) miles per hour.

136. Let $\ell =$ the length of the longer piece and
$\ell - 6 =$ the length of the shorter piece.
$$\ell + \ell - 6 = 90$$
$$2\ell - 6 = 90$$
$$2\ell - 6 + 6 = 90 + 6$$
$$2\ell = 96$$
$$\frac{2\ell}{2} = \frac{96}{2}$$
$$\ell = 48$$

The length of the longer piece is 48 cm and the length of the shorter piece is 42 (48 − 6) cm.

Chapter 9 Test

1. See the graph in the answer section of the textbook.

2. $-3 < 0; -4 > -8$

3. $|-7| = 7; |15| = 15$

4. $-8 + 7 = -1$

5. $-11 + (-2) = -13$

Chapter 9 Test

6. $6.7 + (-1.4) = 5.3$

7. $8 - 15 = 8 + (-15) = -7$

8. $4 - (-12) = 4 + (+12) = 16$

9. $-\frac{1}{2} - \left(-\frac{3}{4}\right) = -\frac{1}{2} + \left(+\frac{3}{4}\right)$
$= -\frac{2}{4} + \frac{3}{4} = \frac{1}{4}$

10. $8(-4) = -32$

11. $-7(-12) = 84$

12. $-16 \cdot 0 = 0$

13. $\frac{-100}{4} = -25$

14. $\frac{-24}{-3} = 8$

15. $-\frac{1}{4} \div \frac{5}{12} = -\frac{1}{\cancel{4}} \cdot \frac{\cancel{12}^{3}}{5} = -\frac{3}{5}$

16. $-5 + 3 \cdot (-2) - (-12)$ *Multiply*
$-5 + (-6) - (-12)$ *Add*
$-11 - (-12)$
$-11 + (+12)$ *Add*
1

17. $2 - (6 - 8) - (-5)^2$ *Parentheses*
$2 - (-2) - (-5)^2$ *Exponent*
$2 - (-2) - (25)$
$2 + (+2) - 25$ *Add*
$4 + (-25)$
-21

18. $8k - 3m$; $k = -4$, $m = 2$

    Replace k with -4. Replace m with 2.

    $8(-4) - 3(2) = -32 - 6$
    $= -32 + (-6)$
    $= -38$

19. $8k - 3m$; $k = 3$, $m = -1$
    Replace k with 3. Replace m with -1.

    $8(3) - 3(-1) = 24 + 3$
    $= 27$

20. When evaluating, you are given specific values to replace each variable. When solving an equation, you are not given the value of the variable. You must find a value that "works"; that is, when your solution is substituted for the variable, the two sides of the equation are equal.

21. $A = \frac{1}{2} = bh$; $b = 20$, $h = 11$
$= \frac{1}{2} \cdot (20) \cdot (11)$
$= 110$

22. $x - 9 = -4$
$x - 9 + 9 = -4 + 9$
$x = 5$

23. $30 = -1 + r$
$30 + 1 = -1 + r + 1$
$31 = r$

24. $0 = -7y$
$\frac{0}{-7} = \frac{-7y}{-7}$
$0 = y$

25. $\frac{p}{5} = -3$
$\frac{1}{5}p = -3$
$\left(\frac{5}{1}\right) \cdot \left(\frac{1}{5}\right)p = -3 \cdot 5$
$p = -15$

26. $3t - 8t = -25$
$3t + (-8t) = -25$
$-5t = -25$
$\frac{-5t}{-5} = \frac{-25}{-5}$
$t = 5$

27. $3m - 5 = 7m - 13$
$3m - 7m - 5 = 7m - 7m - 13$
$(3 - 7)m - 5 = -13$
$-4m - 5 = -13$
$-4m - 5 + 5 = -13 + 5$
$-4m = -8$
$\frac{-4m}{-4} = \frac{-8}{-4}$
$m = 2$

28.
$$-15 = 3(a-2)$$
$$-15 = 3 \cdot a - 3(-2)$$
$$-15 = 3a + 6$$
$$-15 - 6 = 3a + 6 - 6$$
$$-9 = 3a$$
$$\frac{-9}{3} = \frac{3a}{3}$$
$$-3 = a$$

29. Let $n =$ the number.
$$7n - 23 = 47$$
$$7n - 23 + 23 = 47 + 23$$
$$7n = 70$$
$$\frac{7n}{7} = \frac{70}{7}$$
$$n = 10$$

The number is 10.

Check:
$$7n - 23 = 47$$
$$7(10) - 23 = 47$$
$$70 - 23 = 47$$
$$47 = 47$$

30. Let $\ell =$ the shorter piece and $\ell + 4 =$ the longer piece.
$$\ell + \ell + 4 = 118$$
$$2\ell + 4 = 118$$
$$2\ell + 4 - 4 = 118 - 4$$
$$2\ell = 114$$
$$\frac{2\ell}{2} = \frac{114}{2}$$
$$\ell = 57$$

The length of the shorter piece is 57 cm, and the length of the longer piece is $57 + 4 = 61$ cm.

Check:
$$\ell + \ell + 4 = 118$$
$$57 + 57 + 4 = 118$$
$$118 = 118$$

31. Let $w =$ the width and $4w =$ the length.
$$P = 2 \cdot \ell + 2 \cdot w$$
$$420 = 2(4w) + 2w$$
$$420 = 8w + 2w$$
$$420 = 10w$$
$$\frac{420}{10} = \frac{10w}{10}$$
$$42 = w$$

The length is $4 \cdot 42$ ft or 168 ft. The width is 42 ft.

Check:
$$420 = 2(4w) + 2w$$
$$420 = 2(4 \cdot 42) + 2(42)$$
$$420 = 2(168) + 84$$
$$420 = 336 + 84$$
$$420 = 420$$

32. Hours Marcella spent $+$ hours Tim spent $=$ 19 hours

$h + h - 3 = 19$

Solve the equation.
$$h + h - 3 = 19$$
$$2h - 3 = 19$$
$$2h - 3 + 3 = 19 + 3$$
$$2h = 22$$
$$h = 11$$

Marcella spent 11 hours redecorating their living room and Tim spent 8 $(11 - 3)$ hours.

Check:
$$h + h - 3 = 19$$
$$11 + 11 - 3 = 19$$
$$19 = 19$$

Cumulative Review Exercises (Chapters 1-9)

1. | estimate | exact |
    |---|---|
    | 9 | 8.700 |
    | 1 | 0.902 |
    | + 40 | + 41.000 |
    | 50 | 50.602 |

2. | estimate | exact |
    |---|---|
    | 6 | 6.27 |
    | × 50 | × 49.2 |
    | 300 | 1 254 |
    | | 56 43 |
    | | 250 8 |
    | | 308.484 |

Cumulative Review Exercises (Chapters 1-9)

3. estimate   exact

    $$80\overline{)40{,}000}^{500}$$

    $$78\overline{)39{,}234}^{503}$$
    $$\underline{39\ 0}$$
    $$23$$
    $$\underline{0}$$
    $$234$$
    $$\underline{234}$$
    $$0$$

4. estimate   exact

    $$4 \qquad 3\tfrac{3}{5} = \tfrac{18}{5} = \tfrac{72}{20}$$
    $$\underline{-3} \qquad \underline{-2\tfrac{3}{4}} = \tfrac{11}{4} = \tfrac{55}{20}$$
    $$1 \qquad \phantom{-2\tfrac{3}{4}=\tfrac{11}{4}=\ } \tfrac{17}{20}$$

5. exact

    $$5\tfrac{5}{6} \cdot \tfrac{9}{10} = \tfrac{\cancel{35}^{7}}{\cancel{6}_{2}} \cdot \tfrac{\cancel{9}^{3}}{\cancel{10}_{2}} = \tfrac{21}{4} = 5\tfrac{1}{4}$$

    estimate $6 \cdot 1 = 6$

6. exact

    $$4\tfrac{1}{6} \div 1\tfrac{2}{3} = \tfrac{25}{6} \div \tfrac{5}{3} = \tfrac{\cancel{25}^{5}}{\cancel{6}_{2}} \cdot \tfrac{\cancel{3}^{1}}{\cancel{5}_{1}} = \tfrac{5}{2} = 2\tfrac{1}{2}$$

    estimate $4 \div 2 = 2$

7. $17 - 8.094$

    $$\overset{6\ \overset{9}{\cancel{10}}\overset{9}{\cancel{10}}10}{1\cancel{7}.\cancel{0}\cancel{0}\cancel{0}}$$
    $$\underline{-\ 8.09\ 4}$$
    $$8.90\ 6$$

8. $(1309)(408)$

    $$1309$$
    $$\underline{\times 408}$$
    $$10\ 472$$
    $$\underline{523\ 60}$$
    $$534{,}072$$

9. $4.06 \div 0.072$

    $$0.072_{\wedge}\overline{)4.060_{\wedge}00}^{56.38}$$
    $$\underline{3\ 60}$$
    $$460$$
    $$\underline{432}$$
    $$28\ 0$$
    $$\underline{21\ 6}$$
    $$6\ 40$$
    $$\underline{5\ 76}$$
    $$64$$

    56.38 rounded to the nearest tenth: ≈ 56.4

10. $-12 + 7 = -5$

11. $-5(-8) = 40$

12. $-3 - (-7) = -3 + (+7) = 4$

13. $3.2 + (-4.5) = -1.3$

14. $\dfrac{30}{-6} = -5$

15. $\dfrac{1}{4} - \dfrac{3}{4} = \dfrac{1}{4} + \left(-\dfrac{3}{4}\right) = -\dfrac{2}{4} = -\dfrac{1}{2}$

16. $45 \div \sqrt{25} - 2 \cdot 3 + (10 \div 5) \quad$ Parentheses
    $45 \div \sqrt{25} - 2 \cdot 3 + 2 \quad$ Square root
    $45 \div 5 - 2 \cdot 3 + 2 \quad$ Divide
    $9 - 2 \cdot 3 + 2 \quad$ Multiply
    $9 - 6 + 2 \quad$ Subtract
    $3 + 2 \quad$ Add
    5

17. $-6 - (4 - 5) + (-3)^2 \quad$ Parentheses
    $-6 - (-1) + (-3)^2 \quad$ Exponent
    $-6 - (-1) + 9$
    $-6 + 1 + 9 \quad$ Add
    $-5 + 9$
    4

18. $\dfrac{3}{10} > \dfrac{4}{15}$

    $\dfrac{3}{10} = \dfrac{9}{30}, \ \dfrac{4}{15} = \dfrac{8}{30}$

    $\dfrac{9}{30} > \dfrac{8}{30}$, so $\dfrac{3}{10} > \dfrac{4}{15}$

19. $0.7072 < 0.72$

    because $0.7072 < 0.7200$.

20. $-5 < -2$

    because -5 is to the left of -2 on a number line.

21. $8\% = 0.08 = \dfrac{8 \div 4}{100 \div 4} = \dfrac{2}{25}$

22. $4\tfrac{1}{2} = 4.5 = 450\%$

23. 48 toddlers and 12 infants
$$\dfrac{48}{12} = \dfrac{4}{1}$$

24.
$$\dfrac{x}{12} = \dfrac{1.5}{45}$$
$$\dfrac{x}{12} = \dfrac{\cancel{1.5}^{1}}{\cancel{45}_{30}}$$
$30 \cdot x = 12 \cdot 1$ *Cross products are equivalent*
$$\dfrac{30x}{30} = \dfrac{12}{30}$$
$$x = 0.4$$

25.
$$\dfrac{350}{x} = \dfrac{3}{2}$$
$3 \cdot x = 2 \cdot 350$
$3x = 700$
$$\dfrac{3x}{3} = \dfrac{700}{3}$$
$x \approx 233.33$

26.
$$\dfrac{38}{190} = \dfrac{9}{x}$$
$$\dfrac{\cancel{38}^{1}}{\cancel{190}_{5}} = \dfrac{9}{x}$$
$x = 9 \cdot 5 = 45$

27. b is 3000; p is 0.5; a is unknown.
Use the percent proportion.
$$\dfrac{a}{b} = \dfrac{p}{100}$$
$$\dfrac{a}{3000} = \dfrac{0.5}{100}$$
$100 \cdot a = 3000 \cdot 0.5$
$$\dfrac{100 \cdot a}{100} = \dfrac{1500}{100}$$
$a = 15$

0.5% of 3000 students is 15 students.

28. a is 6.8; b is 12.5; p is unknown.
Use the percent proportion.
$$\dfrac{a}{b} = \dfrac{p}{100}$$
$$\dfrac{6.8}{12.5} = \dfrac{p}{100}$$
$12.5 \cdot p = 6.8 \cdot 100$
$$\dfrac{12.5 \cdot p}{12.5} = \dfrac{680}{12.5}$$
$p = 54.4$

54.4% of 12.5 miles is 6.8 miles.

29. a is 90; p is 180; b is unknown.
Use the percent proportion.
$$\dfrac{a}{b} = \dfrac{p}{100}$$
$$\dfrac{90}{b} = \dfrac{180}{100}$$
$180 \cdot b = 90 \cdot 100$
$$\dfrac{180 \cdot b}{180} = \dfrac{9000}{180}$$
$b = 50$

90 cars is 180% of 50 cars.

30. a is 5.8; b is 145; p is unknown.
Use the percent proportion.
$$\dfrac{a}{b} = \dfrac{p}{100}$$
$$\dfrac{5.8}{145} = \dfrac{p}{100}$$
$145 \cdot p = 5.8 \cdot 100$
$$\dfrac{145 \cdot p}{145} = \dfrac{580}{145}$$
$p = 4$

$5.80 is 4% of $145.

31. $3\tfrac{1}{2}$ gallons to quarts
$$\dfrac{3\tfrac{1}{2} \; \cancel{\text{gallons}}}{1} \cdot \dfrac{4 \text{ quarts}}{1 \; \cancel{\text{gallon}}}$$
$= 3\tfrac{1}{2} \cdot 4$ quarts $= 14$ quarts

32. 72 hours to days
$$\dfrac{72 \; \cancel{\text{hours}}}{1} \cdot \dfrac{1 \text{ day}}{24 \; \cancel{\text{hours}}}$$
$$= \dfrac{72 \cdot 1 \text{ day}}{24} = 3 \text{ days}$$

33. 3.7 L to milliliters
$$\dfrac{3.7 \; \cancel{L}}{1} \cdot \dfrac{1000 \text{ mL}}{1 \; \cancel{L}} = 3.7 \cdot 1000 \text{ mL}$$
$$= 3700 \text{ mL}$$

Cumulative Review Exercises (Chapters 1-9)

34. 40 cm to meters

$$\frac{40 \text{ cm}}{1} \cdot \frac{1 \text{ m}}{100 \text{ cm}} = \frac{40 \text{ m}}{100} = 0.4 \text{ m}$$

35. The building is 15 m high.

36. Rita took 15 mL of cough syrup.

37. Bruce walked 2 km to work.

38. The robin weighs 100 g.

39. Refer to Example 2 in Section 7.5. Normal body temperature is 37°C. A comfortable room temperature is 20°C.

40. $P = 4 \cdot s$
$= 4 \cdot 2\frac{1}{4}$ ft
$= \frac{\cancel{4}^1}{1} \cdot \frac{9}{\cancel{4}_1}$ ft $= 9$ ft

$A = s \cdot s$
$= 2\frac{1}{4}$ ft $\cdot 2\frac{1}{4}$ ft
$= \frac{9}{4}$ ft $\cdot \frac{9}{4}$ ft
$= \frac{81}{16}$ ft^2
$= 5\frac{1}{16}$ ft^2 or 5.0625 ft^2

41. $C = \pi \cdot d$
$\approx 3.14 \cdot 9$ mm
≈ 28.26 mm

$A = \pi r^2$
$\approx 3.14 \cdot 4.5$ mm $\cdot 4.5$ mm
≈ 63.585 mm^2

42. $P = a + b + c$
$= 24$ mi $+ 7$ mi $+ 25$ mi
$= 56$ mi

$A = \frac{1}{2}bh$
$= \frac{1}{2} \cdot 24$ mi $\cdot 7$ mi
$= 84$ mi^2

43. $P = s + s + s + s$
$= 2.4$ cm $+ 1.15$ cm $+ 1.4$ cm $+ 1.5$ cm
$= 6.45$ cm

$A = 0.5 \cdot h(b + B)$
$= 0.5 \cdot 1.15$ cm $(1.4$ cm $+ 2.4$ cm$)$
$= 0.5 \cdot 1.15$ cm $(3.8$ cm$)$
$= 2.185$ cm^2

44. $P = 2 \cdot \ell + 2 \cdot w$
$= 2 \cdot 10$ ft $+ 2 \cdot 8$ ft
$= 20$ ft $+ 16$ ft
$= 36$ ft

$A = bh$
$= 10$ ft $\cdot 7$ ft
$= 70$ ft^2

45. $P = 48$ m $+ 46$ m $+ 22$ m $+ 22$ m
$\quad + 26$ m $+ 24$ m
$= 188$ m

To find the area break the figure into two parts.

a rectangle with length: 48 m, width: 24 m

$A = \ell \cdot w$
$= 48$ m $\cdot 24$ m
$= 1152$ m^2

a square with side: 22 m

$A = s^2$
$= 22$ m $\cdot 22$ m
$= 484$ m^2

Total area

$$1152 \text{ m}^2 + 484 \text{ m}^2 = 1636 \text{ m}^2$$

46. hypotenuse: 20 yd, leg: 15 yd

$\text{leg} = \sqrt{(hypotenuse)^2 - (leg)^2}$
$= \sqrt{(20)^2 - (15)^2}$
$= \sqrt{175} \approx 13.228757$
≈ 13.2 yd

47. Set up a ratio of corresponding sides.

$$\frac{9 \text{ in}}{18 \text{ in}} = \frac{1}{2}$$

Write a proportion to find x.

$$\frac{7}{x} = \frac{1}{2}$$
$$1 \cdot x = 7 \cdot 2$$
$$x = 14 \text{ in}$$

48.
$$-20 = 6 + y$$
$$-20 + (-6) = 6 + y - 6$$
$$-26 = y$$

49.
$$-2t - 6t = 40$$
$$-2t + (-6t) = 40$$
$$-8t = 40$$
$$\frac{-8t}{-8} = \frac{40}{-8}$$
$$t = -5$$

50.
$$3x + 5 = 5x - 11$$
$$3x + 5 + 11 = 5x - 11 + 11$$
$$3x + 16 = 5x$$
$$3x + 16 - 3x = 5x - 3x$$
$$16 = 2x$$
$$\frac{16}{2} = \frac{2x}{2}$$
$$8 = x$$

51.
$$6(p + 3) = -6$$
$$6(p) + 6(3) = -6$$
$$6p + 18 = -6$$
$$6p + 18 - 18 = -6 + (-18)$$
$$6p = -24$$
$$\frac{6p}{6} = \frac{-24}{6}$$
$$p = -4$$

52. Let $n =$ the number.

40	added to	4 times a number	is	0
↓	↓	↓	↓	↓
40	+	4n	=	0

$$40 + 4n = 0$$
$$40 - 40 + 4n = 0 - 40$$
$$4n = -40$$
$$\frac{4n}{4} = \frac{-40}{4}$$
$$n = -10$$

The number is -10.

53. Let $p =$ the money Reggie will receive and
$p + 300 =$ the money Donald will receive.

$$p + p + 300 = 1000$$
$$2p + 300 = 1000$$
$$2p + 300 - 300 = 1000 - 300$$
$$2p = 700$$
$$\frac{2p}{2} = \frac{700}{2}$$
$$p = 350$$

Reggie will receive $350 and Donald will receive $350 + $300 = $650.

54. Make a drawing.

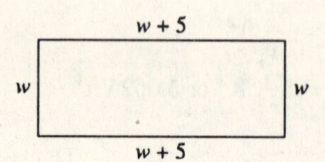

Write an equation.

Let $w =$ the width and
$w + 5 =$ the length.

$$w + w + w + 5 + w + 5 = 82$$
$$4w + 10 = 82$$
$$4w + 10 - 10 = 82 - 10$$
$$4w = 72$$
$$\frac{4w}{4} = \frac{72}{4}$$
$$w = 18$$

The width is 18 cm and the length is 23 (18 + 5) cm.

55. Find the cost for two CDs.

$$\$11.98 + \$11.98 = \$23.96$$

Sales tax

$$= \$23.96 \cdot 6\tfrac{1}{2}\%$$
$$= \$23.96 \cdot 0.065$$
$$\approx \$1.56$$

Total cost

$$\$23.96 + \approx \$1.56 \approx \$25.52$$

56. Multiply $3\tfrac{1}{3}$ cups times $2\tfrac{1}{2}$.

$$3\tfrac{1}{3} \cdot 2\tfrac{1}{2} = \frac{\cancel{10}^{5}}{3} \cdot \frac{5}{\cancel{2}_{1}} = \frac{25}{3} = 8\tfrac{1}{3}$$

He needs $8\tfrac{1}{3}$ cups of tomato sauce.

57. a is 2480; b is 2000; p is unknown.
Use the percent proportion.

$$\frac{a}{b} = \frac{p}{100}$$
$$\frac{2480}{2000} = \frac{p}{100}$$
$$2000 \cdot p = 100 \cdot 2480$$
$$2000p = 248{,}000$$
$$\frac{2000p}{2000} = \frac{248{,}000}{2000}$$
$$p = 124$$

2480 pounds is 124% of 2000 pounds.

58. Convert grams to kilogram.

$$720 \text{ g} = 0.72 \text{ kg}$$

Multiply the weight of the chicken by the cost per kilogram.

$$\begin{array}{r} \$5.97 \\ \times 0.72 \\ \hline 1194 \\ 4\ 179 \\ \hline \$4.2984 \end{array}$$

She paid $\approx \$4.30$ for the chicken.

59. Find the volume of the crate.

$$V = \ell \cdot w \cdot h$$
$$= 2.4 \text{ m} \cdot 1.2 \text{ m} \cdot 1.2 \text{ m}$$
$$= 3.456 \text{ m}^3$$

The crate's volume is

$$4 - 3.456 = 0.554 \text{ m}^3 \text{ less.}$$

60. Use the formula to find the perimeter of a rectangle.

$$P = 2 \cdot length + 2 \cdot width$$
$$35 = 2\ell + 2\left(6\tfrac{1}{2}\right)$$
$$35 = 2\ell + 13$$
$$35 - 13 = 2\ell + 13 - 13$$
$$22 = 2\ell$$
$$11 = \ell$$

The length of the plot is 11 feet.

61. Write a proportion.

$$\frac{25}{14} = \frac{x}{30}$$
$$14 \cdot x = 25 \cdot 30$$
$$14x = 750$$
$$\frac{14x}{14} = \frac{750}{14}$$
$$x \approx 53.571$$

It will take Rich ≈ 54 minutes to read 30 pages.

62. Jackie: $\dfrac{364 \text{ mi}}{14.5 \text{ gal}} \approx 25.1$ mpg

Maya: $\dfrac{406 \text{ mi}}{16.3 \text{ gal}} \approx 24.9$ mpg

Naomi: $\dfrac{300 \text{ mi}}{11.9 \text{ gal}} \approx 25.2$ mpg

Naomi's car had the best gas mileage with ≈ 25.2 miles per gallon.

Chapter 10

STATISTICS

10.1 Circle Graphs

10.1 Margin Exercises

1. **(a)** The circle graphs shows that the greatest number of hours is spent sleeping.

   (b) 6 hours working
   $\underline{-\ 4}$ hours studying
    2 hours

   Two more hours are spent working than studying.

   (c) 4 hours studying
   $$ 6 hours working
   $\underline{+\ 3}$ hours attending class
    13 hours

   13 hours are spent studying, working, and attending classes.

2. **(a)** hours driving to whole day:

   $$\frac{2 \text{ hours}}{24 \text{ hours}} = \frac{1}{12}$$

   (b) hours spent studying to whole day:

   $$\frac{4 \text{ hours}}{24 \text{ hours}} = \frac{1}{6}$$

   (c) hours spent sleeping and doing other to all day:

    7 hours sleeping
   $\underline{+\ 2}$ hours other
    9 hours

   $$\frac{9 \text{ hours}}{24 \text{ hours}} = \frac{3}{8}$$

   (d) hours spent working to whole day:

    6 hours working
   $\underline{+\ 4}$ hours studying
    10 hours

   $$\frac{10 \text{ hours}}{24 \text{ hours}} = \frac{5}{12}$$

3. **(a)** hours spent studying to hours spent working:

   $$\frac{4 \text{ hours}}{6 \text{ hours}} = \frac{2}{3}$$

   (b) hours spent working to hours spent sleeping:

   $$\frac{6 \text{ hours}}{7 \text{ hours}} = \frac{6}{7}$$

   (c) hours spent studying to hours spent driving:

   $$\frac{4 \text{ hours}}{2 \text{ hours}} = \frac{2}{1}$$

   (d) hours spent in class to hours spent for other:

   $$\frac{3 \text{ hours}}{2 \text{ hours}} = \frac{3}{2}$$

4. Use the percent equation:

   $$amount = percent \cdot base.$$

   (a) $b = 12$ billion; $p = 0.03$; find a.

   $$a = 0.03 \cdot 12 \text{ billion}$$
   $$= 0.36 \text{ billion}$$

   The amount spent on CD singles was $0.36 billion or $360,000,000.

   (b) $b = 12$ billion; $p = 0.01$; find a.

   $$a = 0.01 \cdot 12 \text{ billion}$$
   $$= 0.12 \text{ billion}$$

   The amount spent on LP albums and 7-12 inch singles was $0.12 billion or $120,000,000.

   (c) $b = 12$ billion; $p = 0.25$; find a.

   $$a = 0.25 \cdot 12 \text{ billion}$$
   $$= 3 \text{ billion}$$

   The amount spent on cassette albums was $3 billion or $3,000,000,000,

   (d) $b = 12$ billion; $p = 0.05$; find a.

   $$a = 0.05 \cdot 12 \text{ billion}$$
   $$= 0.6 \text{ billion}$$

   The amount spent on cassette singles is $0.6 billion or $600,000,000.

Section 10.1 Circle Graphs

5. See the circle graph in the margin exercise answers of the textbook.

  (a) Under 12 group:
  $$360° \times 25\% = 360° \times 0.25 = 90°$$

  (b) Under 14 group:
  $$360° \times 25\% = 360° \times 0.25 = 90°$$

  (c) Under 16 group:
  $$360° \times 15\% = 360° \times 0.15 = 54°$$

10.1 Section Exercises

3. $\dfrac{\text{cost of materials}}{\text{total cost}} = \dfrac{\$9800}{\$32,000} = \dfrac{49}{160}$

7. History, at 700, has the least number of students.

11. $\dfrac{\text{Computer Science}}{\text{English}} = \dfrac{1800 \text{ students}}{2000 \text{ students}}$
$$= \dfrac{1800}{2000} = \dfrac{9}{10}$$

15. Restrooms are 30% of $1,740,000.
$$a = 0.30 \cdot \$1,740,000$$
$$= \$522,000$$

19. Walkways and curbs are 15% of $1,740,000.
$$a = 0.15 \cdot \$1,740,000$$
$$= \$261,000$$

23. $b = 8740$; $p = 0.02$, find a.
$$a = 0.02 \cdot 8740$$
$$= 174.8$$
$$\approx 175$$

≈ 175 employees miss work 5-6 days because of colds.

27. First find the percent of the total that is to be represented by each item. Next, multiply the percent by 360° to find the size of each sector. Finally, use a protractor to draw each sector.

31. Percent for clothing $= \dfrac{\$420}{\$4200}$
$$= 0.10 = 10\%$$

Degrees of a circle = 10% of 360°
$$= 0.10 \times 360°$$
$$= 36°$$

35. Percent for other $= \dfrac{54°}{360°}$
$$= 0.15 = 15\%$$

Dollar amount = 15% of $4200
$$= 0.15 \times \$4200$$
$$= \$630$$

39. Total amount spent = $32,000

Percent for housing $= \dfrac{\$9600}{\$32,000}$
$$= 0.30 = 30\%$$

Degrees for housing $= (0.30)(360°)$
$$= 108°$$

Percent for food $= \dfrac{\$6400}{\$32,000}$
$$= 0.20 = 20\%$$

Degrees for food $= (0.20)(360°)$
$$= 72°$$

Percent for automobile $= \dfrac{\$4800}{\$32,000}$
$$= 0.15 = 15\%$$

Degrees for automobile $= (0.15)(360°)$
$$= 54°$$

Percent for clothing $= \dfrac{\$3200}{\$32,000}$
$$= 0.10 = 10\%$$

Degrees for clothing $= (0.10)(360°)$
$$= 36°$$

Percent for medical $= \dfrac{\$1600}{\$32,000}$
$$= 0.05 = 5\%$$

Degrees for medical $= (0.05)(360°)$
$$= 18°$$

Percent for savings $= \dfrac{\$1600}{\$32,000}$
$$= 0.05 = 5\%$$

Degrees for savings $= (0.05)(360°)$
$$= 18°$$

Percent for other $= \dfrac{\$4800}{\$32,000}$
$$= 0.15 = 15\%$$

Degrees for other = (0.15)(360°)
= 54°
See the circle graph in the answer section of the textbook.

43. 0.0118   0.01
0.0118 > 0.0100, so
0.0118 > 0.01.

47. 44,272.68   44,272.098
44,272.680 > 44,272.098, so
44,272.68 > 44,272.098.

10.2 Bar Graphs and Line Graphs

10.2 Margin Exercises

1. (a) The bar for 1994 rises to 25, showing that the number of college graduates was

$$25 \times 1000 = 25,000.$$

(b) 1995: $20 \times 1000 = 20,000$

(c) 1997: $30 \times 1000 = 30,000$

(d) 1998: $35 \times 1000 = 35,000$

2. (a) 1st quarter, 1997:

$$4 \times 1000 = 4000$$

1st quarter, 1998:

$$3 \times 1000 = 3000$$

(b) 3rd quarter, 1997:

$$7 \times 1000 = 7000$$

3rd quarter, 1998:

$$8 \times 1000 = 8000$$

(c) 4th quarter, 1997:

$$5 \times 1000 = 5000$$

4th quarter, 1998:

$$4 \times 1000 = 4000$$

(d) The tallest bar rose to 8, showing 8000 installations for the 3rd quarter of 1998.

3. (a) June
The dot is at 5.5 on the vertical axis so
$5.5 \times 10,000 = 55,000.$

(b) May: $3 \times 10,000 = 30,000$

(c) April: $4 \times 10,000 = 40,000$

(d) July: $6 \times 10,000 = 60,000$

4. (a) Thermal-paper machines sold:

1994 : $30 \times 1000 = 30,000$
1996 : $40 \times 1000 = 40,000$
1997 : $20 \times 1000 = 20,000$
1998 : $15 \times 1000 = 15,000$

(b) Plain-paper machines sold:

1994 : $10 \times 1000 = 10,000$
1995 : $20 \times 1000 = 20,000$
1996 : $30 \times 1000 = 30,000$
1997 : $50 \times 1000 = 50,000$

(c) The number of plain-paper machines sold was greater than the number of thermal-paper machines sold when the red line was above the blue line. The first full year in which this happened was 1997.

10.2 Section Exercises

3. The year which had the greatest number of motorcycles stolen was 1996.
In that year 10,500 motorcycles were stolen.

7. May had the greatest number of unemployed workers. The total was 10,000 unemployed workers.

11. The number of unemployed workers increased from 5500 in February of 1997 to 8000 in April of 1997. The increase was 2500 workers.

15. The greatest difference occurred in 1994. The difference was 250,000 (400,000 − 150,000) gallons.

19. The greatest number of burglaries, 600, occurred in April.

23. Two possible explanations are extremely cold or snowy weather and greater police activity.

27. In 1996, the annual sales for Chain Store A were $1,500,000$ $(1500 \cdot 1000)$ compact discs.

31. Probably Chain Store B which had greater sales. Projected sales might range from 4,500,000 compact discs to 5,000,000 compact discs in 1999.

35. The total sales in 1998 were $40,000.

Section 10.4   Mean, Median, and Mode

39. The profit in 1997 was $5000.

43. $b = 59{,}703{,}876$; $p = 0.01$; find a.

$$a = 0.01 \cdot 59{,}703{,}876$$
$$= 597{,}038.76$$
$$\approx 597{,}000$$

Santa Barbara budgeted ≈$597,000 for equipment.

47. $b = 59{,}703{,}876$; $p = 0.2$; find a.

$$a = 0.2 \cdot 59{,}703{,}876$$
$$= 11{,}940{,}775$$
$$\approx 11{,}941{,}000$$

Santa Barbara budgeted ≈$11,941,000 for supplies and services.

10.3   Frequency Distributions and Histograms

10.3   Margin Exercises

1. (a) The least number of sales calls made in a week is 20 calls.

(b) The most common number of sales calls made in a week is 30 calls.

(c) The number of weeks in which 50 calls were made is 4 weeks.

(d) The number of weeks in which 40 calls were made is 6 weeks.

2. (a) Less than 50 calls were made in 35 (13 + 13 + 9) weeks.

(b) In 15 (5 + 4 + 6) weeks, 50 or more calls were made.

3. (a) Less than 60 calls were made in 40 (9 + 13 + 13 + 5) weeks.

(b) In 10 (4 + 6) weeks, 60 or more calls were made.

10.3   Section Exercises

3. The number of members 35 years and under is 13,000 (1000 + 2000 + 4000 + 6000) members.

7. The greatest number of employees are in the $20,000 to $25,000 group.
There are 12 employees in that salary group.

11. The number of employees earning $25,000 or less is 28 (3 + 6 + 7 + 12) employees.

15. 120–129: 2 tally marks and a class frequency of 2

19. 160–169: 1 tally mark and a class frequency of 1

23. 50–74: 6 tally marks and a class frequency of 6

27. 150–174: 1 tally mark and a class frequency of 1

31. 11–15: 11 tally marks and a class frequency of 11

35. 31–35: 4 tally marks and a class frequency of 4

39. $(8 \cdot 6) + (3 \cdot 8) \div 5$
$48 + 24 \div 5$
$48 + 4.8$
52.8

10.4   Mean, Median, and Mode

10.4   Margin Exercises

1. $\text{Mean} = \dfrac{96 + 98 + 84 + 88 + 82 + 92}{6}$

$= \dfrac{540}{6}$

$= 90$

2. (a) $\$25.12 + \$42.58 + \$76.19 + \$32 + \$81.11$
$+ \$26.41 + \$19.76 + \$59.32 + \$71.18 + \$21.03$
$= \$454.70$

$$\text{Mean} = \dfrac{\$454.70}{10} = \$45.47$$

(b) $\$749{,}820 + \$765{,}480 + \$643{,}744 + \$824{,}222$
$+ \$485{,}886 + \$668{,}178 + \$702{,}294 + \$525{,}800$
$= \$5{,}365{,}424$

$$\text{Mean} = \dfrac{\$5{,}365{,}424}{8} = \$670{,}678$$

3.

Value	Frequency	Product
$6	2	$12
$7	3	$21
$8	3	$24
$9	4	$36
$10	6	$60
	18	$153

$$\text{Weighted Mean} = \dfrac{\$153}{18} = \$8.50$$

4.

Credits	Grade	Grade × Credits
3	A = 4	12
1	C = 2	2
3	C = 2	6
3	B = 3	9
3	B = 3	9
13		38

$$\text{Grade Point Average} = \frac{38}{13} \approx 2.92$$

5. Arrange the numbers in numerical order.

$$25, 27, 30, 31, 33, 35, 39, 50, 59$$

The middle number is 33. The median is 33 customers.

6. Arrange in numerical order.

$$121 \text{ ft}, 126 \text{ ft}, 178 \text{ ft}, 189 \text{ ft}, 195 \text{ ft}, 261 \text{ ft}$$

The middle values are 178 and 189. The median is the mean of the two middle values.

$$\text{Mean} = \frac{178 \text{ ft} + 189 \text{ ft}}{2}$$
$$= 183.5 \text{ feet}$$

7. (a) 28, 16, 22, 28, 34

The only number that occurs more than once is 28.
The mode is 28 years.

(b) 312, 219, 782, 312, 219, 426

The numbers 312 and 219 occur twice.
The list is bimodal.
The modes are 312 points and 219 points.

(c) $1706, $1289, $1653, $1892, $1301, $1782

No number occurs more than once.
There is no mode.

10.4 Section Exercises

3. $\text{Mean} = \dfrac{\text{sum of all values}}{\text{number of values}}$

$$= \frac{92 + 51 + 59 + 86 + 68 + 73 + 49 + 80}{8}$$
$$= \frac{558}{8}$$
$$= 69.75$$
$$\approx 69.8$$

7. Sum of all purchases
$= \$75.52 + \$36.15 + \$58.24 + \$21.86$
$+ \$47.68 + \$106.57 + \$82.72$
$+ \$52.14 + \$28.60 + \$72.92$
$= \$582.40.$

Number of sales: 10

$$\text{Mean} = \frac{\$582.40}{10} \approx \$58.24$$

11.

Quiz Scores	Frequency	Product
3	4	(3)(4) = 12
5	2	(5)(2) = 10
9	1	(9)(1) = 9
12	3	(12)(3) = 36
	10	67

$$\text{Weighted Mean} = \frac{\text{Product sum}}{\text{Frequency sum}}$$
$$= \frac{67}{10} = 6.7$$

15. Number of voice mail messages received:

$$9, 12, 14, 15, 23, 24, 28$$

The middle number is 15, so the median is 15 messages.

19. 3, 8, 5, 1, 7, 6, 8, 4

Find the value that occurs most often.
The mode is 8 samples.

23. When the data contains a few very low or a few very high values, the mean will give a poor indication of the average. Consider using the median or mode instead.

27.

Credits	Grades	Grade × Credits
4	B(3)	(4)(3) = 12
2	A(4)	(2)(4) = 8
5	C(2)	(5)(2) = 10
1	F(0)	(1)(0) = 0
3	B(3)	(3)(3) = 9
15		39

$$\text{Grade point average} = \frac{39}{15} = 2.60$$

31. 5, 9, 17, 3, 2, 8, 19, 1, 4, 20

Find the value that occurs most often.
No value occurs most often, so there is no mode.

Chapter 10 Review Exercises

Chapter 10 Review Exercises

1. The largest expense was lodging at $560.

2. Total cost was
$280 + $300 + $560 + $400 + $160 = 1700.

3. $\dfrac{\text{food}}{\text{total cost}} = \dfrac{\$400}{\$1700} = \dfrac{400}{1700} = \dfrac{4}{17}$

   $\dfrac{\text{gasoline}}{\text{total cost}} = \dfrac{\$300}{\$1700} = \dfrac{300}{1700} = \dfrac{3}{17}$

4. $\dfrac{\text{sightseeing}}{\text{total cost}} = \dfrac{\$280}{\$1700} = \dfrac{280}{1700} = \dfrac{14}{85}$

5. $\dfrac{\text{gasoline}}{\text{other}} = \dfrac{\$300}{\$160} = \dfrac{300}{160} = \dfrac{15}{8}$

6. $\dfrac{\text{lodging}}{\text{food}} = \dfrac{\$560}{\$400} = \dfrac{560}{400} = \dfrac{7}{5}$

7. $b = 16{,}500{,}000$; $p = 0.2$; find a.

$$\begin{aligned} a &= 0.2 \cdot 16{,}500{,}000 \\ &= 3{,}300{,}000 \end{aligned}$$

   Ages 12-17 buy 3,300,000 cellular phones.

8. $b = 16{,}500{,}000$; $p = 0.17$; find a.

$$\begin{aligned} a &= 0.17 \cdot 16{,}500{,}000 \\ &= 2{,}805{,}000 \end{aligned}$$

   Ages 45-54 buy 2,805,000 phones.

9. $b = 16{,}500{,}000$; $p = 0.1$; find a.

$$\begin{aligned} a &= 0.1 \cdot 16{,}500{,}000 \\ &= 1{,}650{,}000 \end{aligned}$$

   Ages 55-64 buy 1,650,000 phones.

10. $b = 16{,}500$; $p = 0.12$; find a.

$$\begin{aligned} a &= 0.12 \cdot 16{,}500{,}000 \\ &= 1{,}980{,}000 \end{aligned}$$

    Ages 25-34 buy 1,980,000 phones.

11. Ages 12-17 and 35-44 buy more cellular phones. Perhaps they use a phone more often and need to be reached by phone more often and in different places.

12. Ages 55-64 and 65 and over buy the fewe Perhaps they use the phone less ofter that they do not need to be reached at all times and in different places. Or, t 65 may not have enough income to affor phones.

13. In 1998, the greatest amount of water in occurred in March when there were 8 milli feet of water.

14. In 1997, the least amount of water in th occurred in June when there were 2 million feet of water.

15. In June of 1998, there were 5 million acre-fe water in the lake.

16. In May of 1997, there were 4 million acre-fee water in the lake.

17. From March, 1997 to June, 1997 the water we from 7 to 2 million acre-feet, a decrease of 5 milli acre-feet of water.

18. From April, 1998 to June, 1998 the water wen from 7 to 5 million acre-feet, a decrease of 2 million acre-feet of water.

19. In 1995, Center A purchased $50,000 worth of groceries.

20. In 1997, Center A purchased $20,000 worth of groceries.

21. In 1996, Center B purchased $20,000 worth of groceries.

22. In 1998, Center B purchased $40,000 worth of groceries.

23. The grocery purchases decreased for two years and then moved up slightly.
    Less children are attending the center or fewer children are eating at the child care center.

24. The grocery purchases are increasing. A greater number of children are attending the center or a greater number are eating at the childcare center.

25. Mean
$$= \dfrac{18 + 12 + 15 + 24 + 9 + 42 + 54 + 87 + 21 + 3}{10}$$
$$= \dfrac{285}{10} = 28.5 \text{ digital cameras}$$

Chapter 10 STATISTICS

$$\frac{2? + 22 + 46 + 51 + 48 + 42 + 53 + 42}{10}$$

complaints

Frequency	Product
3	$126
7	$329
2	$106
3	$165
5	$295
20	$1021

Weighted Mean $= \dfrac{\$1021}{20} = \$51.05$

$\approx \$51.10$

Frequency	Product
1	243
3	741
5	1255
7	1785
4	1052
2	542
2	558
24	6176

Weighted Mean $= \dfrac{6176}{24}$

≈ 257.3 points

29. Arrange the numbers in order.

$$13, 28, 35, 37, 39, 43, 54, 68, 75$$

The median is the middle value or 39 claims.

30. Arrange the numbers in order.

$525, $542, $551, $559, $565, $576, $578, $590

There are two numbers in the middle, 559 and 565.
To find the median, find the mean of the two middle scores.

$$\text{Median} = \frac{\$559 + \$565}{2} = \$562$$

31. The mode is the value that occurs most often. The mode is $64.

32. The mode is the value that occurs most often. Two numbers occur twice. The list is bimodal. The modes are 18 and 32 launchings.

33. Degrees for plumbing and electrical
$= 10\%$ of $360°$
$= 0.10 \times 360° = 36°$

34. Percent for work stations
$= \dfrac{\$7840}{\$22,400} = 0.35 = 35\%$

35. Percent for small appliances
$= \dfrac{\$4480}{\$22,400} = 0.20 = 20\%$

36. Percent for interior decoration
$= \dfrac{\$5600}{\$22,400} = 0.25 = 25\%$

37. Degrees for supplies
$= 10\%$ of $360° = 0.10 \times 360° = 36°$

38. See the circle graph in the answer section of the textbook.

39. Mean $= \dfrac{24 + 36 + 26 + 74 + 90}{5}$

$= \dfrac{250}{5} = 50$ years

40. Mean
$= \dfrac{122+135+146+159+128+147+168+139+158}{9}$
$= \dfrac{1302}{9} \approx 144.666 \approx 144.7$ tacks

41. The mode is the value that occurs most often. The mode is 97.

42. The mode is the value that occurs most often. The list is bimodal. There are two modes: 31 and 43 2-bedroom apartments.

43. Arrange the numbers in numerical order.

$1.0, 2.9, 3.2, 4.7, 5.3, 7.1, 8.2, 9.4$

The median is the mean of the two middle numbers.

Mean $= \dfrac{4.7 + 5.3}{2} = 5.0$ hours

44. Arrange the numbers in numerical order.

$1, 2, 3, 7, 9, 14, 15, 18, 21, 28, 46, 59$

The median is the mean of the two middle values.

Median $= \dfrac{14 + 15}{2} = 14.5$ yard sales

Chapter 10 Test

45. 30-39: 4 tally marks and a class frequency of 4

46. 40-49: 1 tally mark and a class frequency of 1

47. 50-59: 6 tally marks and a class frequency of 6

48. 60-69: 2 tally marks and a class frequency of 2

49. 70-79: 13 tally marks and a class frequency of 13

50. 80-89: 7 tally marks and a class frequency of 7

51. 90-99: 7 tally marks and a class frequency of 7

52. See the histogram in the answer section of the textbook.

53.

Value	Frequency	Product
23	2	46
27	5	135
31	4	124
35	6	210
39	5	195
	22	710

Weighted Mean $= \dfrac{710}{22} \approx 32.3$

54.

Value	Frequency	Product
$104	6	624
$112	14	1 568
$115	21	2 415
$119	13	1 547
$123	22	2 706
$127	6	762
$132	9	1 188
	91	10,810

Weighted Mean $= \dfrac{\$10{,}810}{91} \approx \$118.80$

Chapter 10 Test

1. Excavation is 22% of $5,600,000.

$$0.22 \times \$5{,}600{,}000 = \$1{,}232{,}000$$

2. Sidewalks are 18% of $5,600,000.

$$\begin{aligned} a &= 0.18 \times \$5{,}600{,}000 \\ &= \$1{,}008{,}000 \end{aligned}$$

3. Streets and gutters are 30% of $5,600,000.

$$\begin{aligned} a &= 0.30 \times \$5{,}600{,}000 \\ &= \$1{,}680{,}000 \end{aligned}$$

4. Sewer lines are 16% of $5,600,000.

$$\begin{aligned} a &= 0.16 \times \$5{,}600{,}000 \\ &= \$896{,}000 \end{aligned}$$

5. Miscellaneous is 2% of $5,600,000.

$$\begin{aligned} a &= 0.02 \times \$5{,}600{,}000 \\ &= \$112{,}000 \end{aligned}$$

6. Water lines are 12% of $5,600,000.

$$\begin{aligned} a &= 0.12 \times \$5{,}600{,}000 \\ &= \$672{,}000 \end{aligned}$$

7. Degrees for salaries
 $= 30\%$ of $360°$
 $= 0.30 \times 360°$
 $= 108°$

8. Degrees for delivery expense
 $= 10\%$ of $360°$
 $= 0.1 \times 360°$
 $= 36°$

9. Degrees for advertising
 $= 20\%$ of $360°$
 $= 0.2 \times 360°$
 $= 72°$

10. Degrees for rent
 $= 30\%$ of $360°$
 $= 0.3 \times 360°$
 $= 108°$

11. Percent for other
 $= \dfrac{36°}{360°} = 10\%$

12. See the circle graph in the answer section of the textbook.

	Profit	Number of Weeks
13.	$120-$129	3
14.	$130-$139	2
15.	$140-$149	4
16.	$150-$159	3
17.	$160-$169	3
18.	$170-$179	5

19. See the histogram in the answer section of the textbook.

20. Mean
$$= \frac{52 + 61 + 68 + 69 + 73 + 75 + 79 + 84 + 91 + 98}{8}$$
$$= \frac{750}{10} = 75 \text{ books}$$

21. Mean
$$= \frac{22 + 28 + 24 + 27 + 29 + 32 + 33 + 35}{8}$$
$$= \frac{230}{8}$$
$$\approx 28.8 \text{ miles per gallon}$$

22. Mean
$$= \frac{458+432+496+491+500+508+512+396+492+504}{10}$$
$$= \frac{4789}{10} = 478.9 \text{ miles per hour}$$

23. The weighted mean must be used because different classes are worth different numbers of credits.

Credits	Grade	Grade × Credits
3	A	3 · 4 = 12
2	C	2 · 2 = 4
4	B	4 · 3 = 12
9		28

$28 \div 9 \approx 3.11$

24. Arrange the numbers in order from smallest to largest. When there is an odd number of numbers in a list, the median is the middle number.

$$8, 17, \underline{23}, 32, 64$$

The median is 23.

25.

Cost	Frequency	Product
$ 6	7	$ 42
$10	3	$ 30
$11	4	$ 44
$14	2	$ 28
$19	3	$ 57
$24	1	$ 24
	20	$225

Weighted Mean $= \dfrac{\$225}{20} = \$11.25 \approx \$11.30$

26.

Value	Frequency	Product
150	15	2250
160	17	2720
170	21	3570
180	28	5040
190	19	3610
200	7	1400
	107	18,590

Weighted Mean $= \dfrac{18{,}590}{107} \approx 173.7$

27. Arrange the values in order.

$$16, 28, 28, 31, 32, 35, 37, 41$$

The median is the middle score. There two middle scores, 31 and 32. Find the mean of 31 and 32.

Median $= \dfrac{31 + 32}{2} = 31.5$ degrees

28. Arrange the values in order.

$$1.2, 6.3, 8.1, 8.6, 9.3, 10.0, 10.3, 11.4, 22.8$$

The median is the middle score. The median is 9.3 liters.

29. The mode is the value that occurs most often. The mode is 57 meters.

30. The mode is the value that occurs most often. The modes are 103° and 104°.

Cumulative Review Exercises (Chapters 1-10)

1. $72.648 to the nearest cent: $\approx$ $72.65

$$\$72.64|8$$

Draw cut-off line.
First digit cut is 5 or more so round up.

2. $926.499 to the nearest dollar: $\approx$ $926

$$\$926.|499$$

Draw cut-off line.
First digit cut is less than 5 so the part you keep stays the same.

3. 75,696 to the nearest ten: $\approx$ 75,700

75,6$\underline{9}$6 Next digit is 5 or more.

Tens place changes (9 + 1 = 10). All digits to the right of the underlined place change to 0.

Cumulative Review Exercises (Chapters 1-10)

4. 983,168 to the nearest ten thousand: ≈ 980,000

9<u>8</u>3,168 Next digit is less than 5.

Ten thousands place stays the same. All digits to the right of the underlined place change to 0.

5. $3 + 8 \div 4 + 6 \cdot 2$ Divide
    $3 + 2 + 6 \cdot 2$ Multiply
    $3 + 2 + 12$ Add
    17

6. $\sqrt{81} - 4 \cdot 2 + 9$ Square root
    $9 - 4 \cdot 2 + 9$ Multiply
    $9 - 8 + 9$ Subtract
    $1 + 9$ Add
    10

7. $3^2 \cdot 2^4 = 3 \cdot 3 \cdot 2 \cdot 2 \cdot 2 \cdot 2 = 144$

8. $6^2 \cdot 3^2 = 6 \cdot 6 \cdot 3 \cdot 3 = 324$

9.
```
estimate      exact
 60,000      62,318
200,000     159,680
     90          89
+ 20,000    + 22,308
-------     -------
280,090     244,395
```

10.
```
estimate    exact
      3     2.607
    800   796.200
     40    37.960
     50    53.720
+     8   + 8.060
-------   -------
    901   898.547
```

11.
```
estimate      exact
              2 11 10 14 10
300,000      3̷2̷1̷,5̷0̷8
-100,000     - 1 4 7,7 2 5
-------      -----------
200,000        1 7 3,7 8 3
```

12.
```
estimate     exact
             4 15 11 10
   900      8 7 5̷,6̷ 2̷ 0̷
-   60      - 6 3.7 5 7
------      -----------
   840        8 1 1.8 6 3
```

13.
```
estimate      exact
   7000       7064
×   600      ×  635
-------      -----
4,200,000    35 320
             211 92
             4 238 4
             ---------
             4,485,640
```

14.
```
estimate    exact
     60    62.75
×     3   × 2.644
-----     -------
    180    25100
           2 5100
           37 650
           125 50
           --------
           165.91100
```

15.
```
estimate         exact
    500           642
40)20,000      36)23,112
                  21 6
                  ---
                  1 51
                  1 44
                  ----
                    72
                    72
                    --
                     0
```

16.
```
estimate         exact
    15           14.72
 4)60        4.25∧)62.56∧00
  4                42 5
  --               ----
  20               20 06
  20               17 00
  --               -----
   0               3 06 0
                   2 97 5
                   ------
                     8 50
                     8 50
                     ----
                        0
```

17. $\dfrac{3}{4} + \dfrac{3}{8} = \dfrac{6}{8} + \dfrac{3}{8} = \dfrac{6+3}{8} = \dfrac{9}{8} = 1\dfrac{1}{8}$

18. $\dfrac{3}{4} + \dfrac{5}{8} + \dfrac{1}{2} = \dfrac{6}{8} + \dfrac{5}{8} + \dfrac{4}{8} = \dfrac{15}{8} = 1\dfrac{7}{8}$

19. $3\dfrac{2}{3} = 3\dfrac{10}{15}$
   $+ \ 4\dfrac{4}{5} = 4\dfrac{12}{15}$
          $7\dfrac{22}{15} = 8\dfrac{7}{15}$

20. $\dfrac{5}{6} - \dfrac{2}{3} = \dfrac{5}{6} - \dfrac{4}{6} = \dfrac{5-4}{6} = \dfrac{1}{6}$

21. $5\frac{1}{3} = 5\frac{4}{12} = 4\frac{16}{12}$
$\phantom{5\frac{1}{3} =}- 2\frac{3}{4} = 2\frac{9}{12} = 2\frac{9}{12}$
$\phantom{5\frac{1}{3} = 5\frac{4}{12} = }2\frac{7}{12}$

22. $46\frac{3}{4} = 46\frac{15}{20} = 45\frac{35}{20}$
$\phantom{46\frac{3}{4} =}- 15\frac{4}{5} = 15\frac{16}{20} = 15\frac{16}{20}$
$\phantom{46\frac{3}{4} = 46\frac{15}{20} = }30\frac{19}{20}$

23. $\dfrac{7}{8} \cdot \dfrac{4}{5} = \dfrac{7}{\cancel{8}_2} \cdot \dfrac{\cancel{4}^1}{5} = \dfrac{7 \cdot 1}{2 \cdot 5} = \dfrac{7}{10}$

24. $9\dfrac{3}{5} \cdot 4\dfrac{5}{8} = \dfrac{\cancel{48}^6}{5} \cdot \dfrac{37}{\cancel{8}_1} = \dfrac{6 \cdot 37}{5 \cdot 1} = \dfrac{222}{5} = 44\dfrac{2}{5}$

25. $22 \cdot \dfrac{2}{5} = \dfrac{22}{1} \cdot \dfrac{2}{5} = \dfrac{44}{5} = 8\dfrac{4}{5}$

26. $\dfrac{5}{6} \div \dfrac{5}{8} = \dfrac{\cancel{5}^1}{\cancel{6}_3} \cdot \dfrac{\cancel{8}^4}{\cancel{5}_1} = \dfrac{4}{3} = 1\dfrac{1}{3}$

27. $12 \div \dfrac{2}{3} = \dfrac{\cancel{12}^6}{1} \cdot \dfrac{3}{\cancel{2}_1} = \dfrac{18}{1} = 18$

28. $3\dfrac{1}{3} \div 8\dfrac{3}{4} = \dfrac{10}{3} \div \dfrac{35}{4} = \dfrac{\cancel{10}^2}{3} \cdot \dfrac{4}{\cancel{35}_7} = \dfrac{2 \cdot 4}{3 \cdot 7} = \dfrac{8}{21}$

29. $\left(\dfrac{7}{8} - \dfrac{3}{4}\right) \cdot \dfrac{2}{3} = \left(\dfrac{7}{8} - \dfrac{6}{8}\right) \cdot \dfrac{2}{3} = \dfrac{1}{\cancel{8}_4} \cdot \dfrac{\cancel{2}^1}{3} = \dfrac{1}{12}$

30. $\left(\dfrac{5}{6} - \dfrac{1}{3}\right) + \left(\dfrac{1}{2}\right)^2 \cdot \dfrac{3}{4}$
$= \left(\dfrac{5}{6} - \dfrac{2}{6}\right) + \left(\dfrac{1}{2}\right)^2 \cdot \dfrac{3}{4}$
$= \dfrac{3}{6} + \left(\dfrac{1}{2}\right)^2 \cdot \dfrac{3}{4}$
$= \dfrac{3}{6} + \dfrac{1}{4} \cdot \dfrac{3}{4}$
$= \dfrac{3}{6} + \dfrac{3}{16}$
$= \dfrac{24}{48} + \dfrac{9}{48}$
$= \dfrac{33}{48} = \dfrac{11}{16}$

31. $\dfrac{2}{5} = \dfrac{4}{10} = 0.4$

32. $\dfrac{3}{8}$
0.375
$8\overline{)3.000}$
$\underline{2\ 4}$
60
$\underline{56}$
40
$\underline{40}$
0

$\dfrac{3}{8} = 0.375$

33. $\dfrac{3}{4} = \dfrac{3 \cdot 25}{4 \cdot 25} = \dfrac{75}{100} = 0.75$

34. $\dfrac{13}{20} = \dfrac{13 \cdot 5}{20 \cdot 5} = \dfrac{65}{100} = 0.65$

35. $0.218 = 0.2180$
$0.22 = 0.2200$
$0.199 = 0.1990$
$0.207 = 0.2070$
$0.2215 = 0.2215$

From smallest to largest:
$0.199, 0.207, 0.218, 0.22, 0.2215$

36. $0.6319 = 0.6319$
$\dfrac{5}{8} = 0.6250$
$0.608 = 0.6080$
$\dfrac{13}{20} = 0.6500$
$0.58 = 0.5800$

From smallest to largest:
$0.58, 0.608, \dfrac{5}{8}, 0.6319, \dfrac{13}{20}$

37. $2\frac{1}{2}$ inches to 20 inches

$\dfrac{2\frac{1}{2} \text{ inches}}{20 \text{ inches}} = \dfrac{2\frac{1}{2} \div 2\frac{1}{2}}{20 \div 2\frac{1}{2}} = \dfrac{1}{8}$

38. 2 hours to 20 minutes

2 hours = 120 minutes

$\dfrac{120 \text{ minutes}}{20 \text{ minutes}} = \dfrac{120}{20} = \dfrac{6}{1}$

39. $\dfrac{6}{15} = \dfrac{18}{45}$
$6 \cdot 45 = 18 \cdot 15$
$270 = 270 \quad True$

Cumulative Review Exercises (Chapters 1-10) 267

40. $\dfrac{52}{180} = \dfrac{36}{120}$

$36 \cdot 180 = 52 \cdot 120$
$6480 = 6240 \quad False$

41. $\dfrac{1}{4} = \dfrac{x}{12}$

$4 \cdot x = 12 \cdot 1$
$4x = 12$
$\dfrac{4x}{4} = \dfrac{12}{4}$
$x = 3$

42. $\dfrac{14}{x} = \dfrac{364}{104}$

$364 \cdot x = 14 \cdot 104$
$364x = 1456$
$\dfrac{364x}{364} = \dfrac{1456}{364}$
$x = 4$

43. $\dfrac{200}{135} = \dfrac{24}{x}$

$200 \cdot x = 24 \cdot 135$
$200x = 3240$
$\dfrac{200x}{200} = \dfrac{3240}{200}$
$x = 16.2$

44. $\dfrac{x}{208} = \dfrac{6.5}{26}$

$26 \cdot x = 6.5 \cdot 208$
$26x = 1352$
$\dfrac{26x}{26} = \dfrac{1352}{26}$
$x = 52$

45. $35\% = \dfrac{35}{100} = 0.35$

46. $0.025 = \dfrac{25}{1000} = \dfrac{2.5}{100} = 2.5\%$

47. $250\% = \dfrac{250}{100} = 2.50 \text{ or } 2.5$

48. $4.35\% = \dfrac{4.35}{100} = \dfrac{435}{10{,}000} = 0.0435$

49. $2\% = \dfrac{2}{100} = \dfrac{1}{50}$

50. $62\tfrac{1}{2}\% = \dfrac{62\tfrac{1}{2}}{100} = \dfrac{\tfrac{125}{2}}{100} = \dfrac{125}{2} \div \dfrac{100}{1}$

$= \dfrac{125}{2} \cdot \dfrac{1}{100} = \dfrac{125}{200} = \dfrac{125 \div 25}{200 \div 25} = \dfrac{5}{8}$

51. $\dfrac{3}{20} = \dfrac{15}{100} = 15\%$

52. $3\tfrac{1}{4} = 3\tfrac{25}{100} = 3.25 = 325\%$

53. $amount = percent \cdot base$
$a = 0.75 \cdot \$640$
$a = \$480$

75% of $640 is $480.

54. $amount = percent \cdot base$
$a = 0.027 \cdot 3000$
$a = 81$

2.7% of 3000 chairs is 81 chairs.

55. Use the percent proportion.
a is 238; p is 0.085; b is unknown.

$\dfrac{a}{b} = \dfrac{p}{100}$

$8.5 \cdot b = 238 \cdot 100$
$8.5b = 23{,}800$
$\dfrac{8.5b}{8.5} = \dfrac{23{,}800}{8.5}$
$b = 2800$

$8\tfrac{1}{2}\%$ of 2800 people is 238 people.

56. Use the percent proportion.
a is 48; p is 0.15; b is unknown.

$\dfrac{a}{b} = \dfrac{p}{100}$

$\dfrac{48}{b} = \dfrac{15}{100}$

$15 \cdot b = 48 \cdot 100$
$15b = 4800$
$\dfrac{15b}{15} = \dfrac{4800}{15}$
$b = 320$

48 is 15% of 320.

57. Use the percent proportion.
a is 182; b is 520; p is unknown.

$\dfrac{a}{b} = \dfrac{p}{100}$

$\dfrac{182}{520} = \dfrac{p}{100}$

$$520 \cdot p = 182 \cdot 100$$
$$520p = 18,200$$
$$\frac{520 \cdot p}{520} = \frac{18,200}{520}$$
$$p = 35$$

35% of 520 is 182.

58. Use the percent proportion.
a is 13 ; b is 52; p is unknown.
$$\frac{a}{b} = \frac{p}{100}$$
$$\frac{13}{52} = \frac{p}{100}$$
$$52 \cdot p = 13 \cdot 100$$
$$52p = 1300$$
$$\frac{52p}{52} = \frac{1300}{52}$$
$$p = 25$$

13 weeks is 25% of 52 weeks.

59. $\underline{3}$ feet = 1 yard

60. 16 quarts = $\underline{4}$ gallons

61. 5 days = $\underline{120}$ hours

62. $\underline{12,000}$ pounds = 6 tons

63. 5 km to m

Count 3 places to the right on the metric conversion line.
$$5 \text{ km} = 5000 \text{ m}$$

64. 3815 mm to m

Count 3 places to the left on the metric conversion line.
$$3815 \text{ mm to } 3.815 \text{ m}$$

65. 8.3 g to mg
$$\frac{8.3 \text{ g}}{1} \cdot \frac{1000 \text{ mg}}{1 \text{ g}} = 8.3 \cdot 1000 \text{ mg}$$
$$= 8300 \text{ mg}$$

66. 230 g to kg
$$\frac{230 \text{ g}}{1} \cdot \frac{1 \text{ kg}}{1000 \text{ g}} = \frac{230}{1000} \text{ kg} = 0.23 \text{ kg}$$

67. 6 mL to L

Count 3 places to the left on the metric conversion line.
$$6 \text{ mL} = 0.006 \text{ L}$$

68. 0.28 L to mL
$$\frac{0.28 \text{ L}}{1} \cdot \frac{1000 \text{ mL}}{1 \text{ L}} = 0.28 \cdot 1000 \text{ mL}$$
$$= 280 \text{ mL}$$

69. The fuel tank on the chainsaw has a capacity of 750 *mL* of fuel.

70. A nickel weighs 5 *g*.

71. The distance of the run this Saturday is 10 *km*.

72. The heaviest player on the team weighs 108 *kg*.

73. a rectangle 2.8 m by 4.35 m
$$A = \ell \cdot w$$
$$= 2.8 \text{ m} \cdot 4.35 \text{ m}$$
$$= 12.18 \text{ m}^2$$
$$\approx 12.2 \text{ m}^2$$

74. a trapezoid with bases 6.2 cm and 8.4 cm and height 5.3 cm
$$A = \frac{1}{2} \cdot h \cdot (b + B)$$
$$= 0.5 \cdot 5.3 \text{ cm} \cdot (6.2 \text{ cm} + 8.4 \text{ cm})$$
$$= 0.5 \cdot 5.3 \text{ cm} \cdot (14.6 \text{ cm})$$
$$= 38.69 \text{ cm}^2$$
$$\approx 38.7 \text{ cm}^2$$

75. a triangle with base 8.5 ft and height 9 ft
$$A = \frac{1}{2} \cdot b \cdot h$$
$$= 0.5 \cdot 8.5 \text{ ft} \cdot 9 \text{ ft}$$
$$= 38.25 \text{ ft}^2$$
$$\approx 38.3 \text{ ft}^2$$

76. a circle with diameter of 13 cm radius = $\frac{13 \text{ cm}}{2}$ = 6.5 cm
$$A = \pi \cdot r^2$$
$$\approx 3.14 \cdot 6.5 \text{ cm} \cdot 6.5 \text{ cm}$$
$$\approx 132.665 \text{ cm}^2$$
$$\approx 132.7 \text{ cm}^2$$

77. a cylinder with radius 8.6 cm and height 3.8 cm
$$V = \pi \cdot r^2 \cdot h$$
$$\approx 3.14 \cdot 8.6 \text{ cm} \cdot 8.6 \text{ cm} \cdot 3.8 \text{ cm}$$
$$\approx 882.49 \text{ cm}^3$$
$$\approx 882.5 \text{ cm}^3$$

78. a rectangle solid with lengths $5\frac{1}{2}$ m, width 2 m, and height 9 m
$$V = \ell \cdot w \cdot h$$
$$= 5\frac{1}{2} \text{ m} \cdot 2 \text{ m} \cdot 9 \text{ m}$$
$$= 99 \text{ m}^3$$

79. $leg = \sqrt{(hypotenuse)^2 - (leg)^2}$
$= \sqrt{(10)^2 - (6)^2}$
$= \sqrt{100 - 36}$
$= \sqrt{64}$
$= 8$

The length is 8 m.

80. $hypotenuse = \sqrt{(leg)^2 + (leg)^2}$
$= \sqrt{(15)^2 + (8)^2}$
$= \sqrt{225 + 64}$
$= \sqrt{289} = 17$

The hypotenuse is 17 cm.

81. $-10 + (-6) = -16$

82. $-5.7 - (-12.6) = -5.7 + (+12.6) = 6.9$

83. $7 \cdot (-6) = -42$

84. $-14.6 \cdot (-5.7) = 83.22$

85. $\dfrac{-36}{-6} = 6$

86. $\dfrac{-34.04}{14.8} = -2.3$

87. $4x - 3 = 17$
$4x - 3 + 3 = 17 + 3$
$4x = 20$
$\dfrac{4x}{4} = \dfrac{20}{4}$
$x = 5$

88. $-12 = 3(x + 2)$
$-12 = 3x + 6$
$-12 + (-6) = 3x + 6 - 6$
$-18 = 3x$
$\dfrac{-18}{3} = \dfrac{3x}{3}$
$-6 = x$

89. $19x - 12x = 14$
$(19 - 12)x = 14$
$7x = 14$
$\dfrac{7x}{7} = \dfrac{14}{7}$
$x = 2$

90. $3.4x + 6 = 1.4x - 8$
$3.4x + 6 - 6 = 1.4x - 8 - 6$
$3.4x = 1.4x - 14$
$3.4x - 1.4x = 1.4x - 1.4x - 14$
$2x = -14$
$x = -7$

91. Mean
$= \dfrac{16+37+27+31+19+25+15+38+43+19}{10}$
$= \dfrac{270}{10} = 27$ cable hookups

Arrange the values in numerical order.

$15, 16, 19, 19, 25, 27, 31, 37, 38, 43$

The median is the mean of the middle scores.

Median $= \dfrac{25 + 27}{2} = 26$ cable hookups

The mode is the value that occurs most often, 19 cable hookups.

92. Mean
$= \dfrac{20.6+8.6+3.3+5.7+10.6+11.4+4.6+8.7+5.7}{9}$
$= \dfrac{79.2}{9} = 8.8$ tons

Arrange the values in numerical order.

$3.3, 4.6, 5.7, 5.7, 8.6, 8.7, 10.6, 11.4, 20.6$

The median is the middle number, 8.6 tons. The mode is the number that occurs most often, 5.7 tons.

93. Use the percent proportion.
a is 690; b is 1840; p is unknown.
$$\dfrac{a}{b} = \dfrac{p}{100}$$
$$\dfrac{690}{1840} = \dfrac{p}{100}$$
$$1840 \cdot p = 690 \cdot 100$$
$$\dfrac{1840 \cdot p}{1840} = \dfrac{69{,}000}{1840}$$
$$p = 37.5 \text{ or } 37\tfrac{1}{2}$$

Of these cartons 37.5% or $37\frac{1}{2}$% were non-fat cottage cheese.

94. Use the percent proportion.
 a is 78.68; p is 7; b is unknown.
$$\frac{a}{b} = \frac{p}{100}$$
$$\frac{78.68}{b} = \frac{7}{100}$$
$$7 \cdot b = 78.68 \cdot 100$$
$$7b = 7868$$
$$\frac{7b}{7} = \frac{7868}{7}$$
$$b = 1124$$

The cost of the item was $1124.

95. Divide the number of liters of the additive by the number of liters needed for each tank.
$$280\tfrac{1}{2} \div 2\tfrac{3}{4} = \frac{561}{2} \div \frac{11}{4} = \frac{\overset{51}{\cancel{561}}}{\underset{1}{\cancel{2}}} \cdot \frac{\overset{2}{\cancel{4}}}{\underset{1}{\cancel{11}}}$$
$$= \frac{51 \cdot 2}{1 \cdot 1} = 102$$

102 storage tanks can receive the additive.

96. Write a proportion.
$$\frac{19}{25} = \frac{x}{2850}$$
$$25 \cdot x = 19 \cdot 2850$$
$$25 \cdot x = 54,150$$
$$\frac{25 \cdot x}{25} = \frac{54,150}{25}$$
$$x = 2166$$

2166 employees would be expected to be non-smokers.

97. *amount of commission*
 $= 8.5\% \cdot \$48,250$
 $= 0.085 \cdot \$48,250$
 $= \$4101.25$

98. First find the total area.
$$A = \ell \cdot w$$
$$= 45 \text{ yd} \cdot 32 \text{ yd}$$
$$= 1440 \text{ yd}^2$$

Now find the area of the atrium.
$$A = \pi \cdot r^2$$
$$\approx 3.14 \cdot 5 \text{ yd} \cdot 5 \text{ yd}$$
$$\approx 78.5 \text{ yd}^2$$

Subtract the area of the atrium from the total area.
$$1440 \text{ yd}^2 - \approx 78.5 \text{ yd}^2 \approx 1361.5 \text{ yd}^2$$

Multiply the cost of the carpeting by the number of yards needed.
$$\frac{\$43.50}{\cancel{\text{yd}^2}} \cdot \frac{1361.5 \cancel{\text{yd}^2}}{1} \approx \$59,225.25$$

The cost is ≈$59,225.25.

99. Change milliliters to liters.
$$\frac{125 \cancel{\text{mL}}}{1} \cdot \frac{1 \text{ L}}{1000 \cancel{\text{mL}}} = \frac{125}{1000} \text{ L} = 0.125 \text{ L}$$

Multiply the amount of muriatic acid needed for each spa by the number of spas to be serviced.

```
      0.125
   ×    140
      5 000
     12 5
     17.500
```

To service 140 spas 17.5 L of muriatic acid will be needed.

100. $I = p \cdot r \cdot t$
 $= \$3500 \cdot 7\tfrac{1}{2}\% \cdot 6 \text{ months}$
 $= \$3500 \cdot 0.075 \cdot 0.5$
 $= \$131.25$

Total amount due
$$\$3500 + \$131.25 = \$3631.25$$

Appendix B

INDUCTIVE AND DEDUCTIVE REASONING

B.1 Margin Exercises

1. $2, 8, 14, 20, \ldots$
   Find the difference between each pair.
   $$8 - 2 = 6$$
   $$14 - 8 = 6$$
   $$20 - 14 = 6$$
   Note that each number is 6 greater than the previous number. So the next number is $20 + 6$ or 26.

2. $6, 11, 7, 12, 8, 13, \ldots$
   Find the difference between each pair.
   $$11 - 6 = 5$$
   $$7 - 11 = -4$$
   $$8 - 12 = -4$$
   $$13 - 8 = 5$$
   Note that to obtain the next number, either 5 or -4 is added. To obtain the next number, -4 should be added. So, the next number is $13 + (-4)$ or 9.

3. $2, 6, 18, 54, \ldots$
   To see the pattern use division.
   $$6 \div 2 = 3$$
   $$18 \div 6 = 3$$
   $$54 \div 18 = 3$$
   To obtain the next number, 3 is multiplied times the previous number. So, the next number is $(54)(3)$ or 162.

4. The next figure is obtained by rotating the previous figure clockwise. See the answer art in the textbook.

5.   All cars have four wheels.
       All Fords are cars.
       ∴ All Fords have four wheels.
   The statement "All cars have four wheels" is shown by a large circle that represents all items that have 4 wheels with a smaller circle inside that represents cars.

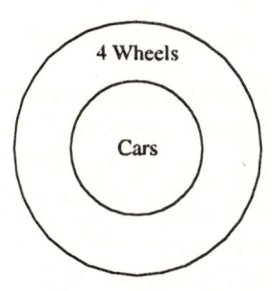

   The statement "All Fords are cars" is represented by adding a third circle representing Fords inside the circle representing cars.

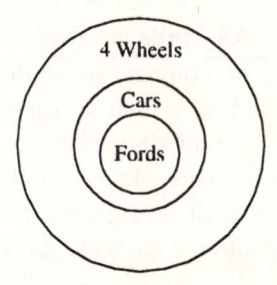

   Since the circle representing Fords is completely inside the circle representing items with 4 wheels, it follows that:
   All Fords have four wheels.
   The conclusion follows from the premises.

6. (a)   All animals are wild
           All cats are animals.
           ∴ All cats are wild.
   "All animals are wild" is represented by a large circle representing wild creatures with a smaller circle inside representing animals.

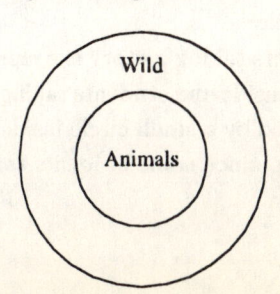

"All cats are animals" is represented by a small circle representing cats, inside the circle representing animals.

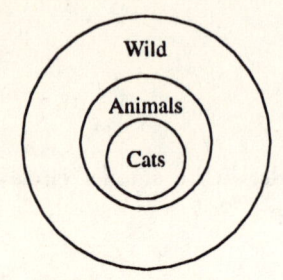

Since the circle representing cats is completely inside the circle representing wild creatures, it follows that;

All cats are wild.

The conclusion follows from the premises.
(Note that correct deductive reasoning may lead to false conclusions if one of the premises is false, in this case, all animals are wild.)

(b)   All students use math.
       All adults use math.
       ∴ All students are students.

A larger circle is used to represent people who use math. A small circle inside the larger circle represents students who use math.
Another small circle inside the larger circle represents adults are students; the circles should overlap.

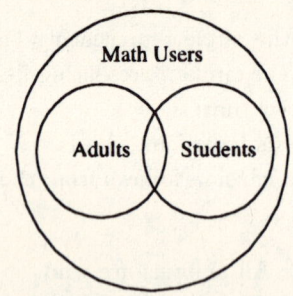

From the diagram, we can see that some adults are not students. Thus, the conclusion does not follow from the premises.

7. All 100 students in the class are represented by a large circle.
Students taking history are represented by a small circle inside and students taking math are also represented by a small circle inside. The small circles overlap since some students take both math and history.

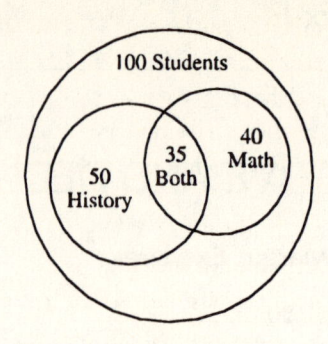

Since 35 students take history and math and 50 take history, 50 − 35, or 15 students take history, but not math. Since 40 students take math, 15 + 40, or 55 students take history, math, or both subjects. Therefore, 100 − 55, or 45 students take neither math nor history.

8. A Chevy, BMW, Cadillac, and Oldsmobile are parked side by side.

   1. The Oldsmobile is on the right side, so write "Oldsmobile" at the right of a line.

      Oldsmobile

   2. The Chevy is between the Oldsmobile and the Cadillac (Fact c). So write "Chevy" between Oldsmobile and Cadillac.

      Cadillac   Chevy   Oldsmobile

   3. The BMW is next to the Cadillac so the BMW must be on the other side of the Cadillac.

      BMW   Cadillac   Chevy   Oldsmobile

   Therefore, the BMW is parked on the left end.

B.1 Exercises

3. 1, 6, 11, 16, 21, ...
Inspect the sequence and note that 5 is added to a term to obtain the next term. So the term immediately following 21 is 21 + 5 = 26.

7. 1, 3, 9, 27, 81, ...
Inspect the sequence and note that 3 is multiplied times a term to obtain the next term. So, the term immediately following 81 is (81)(3) = 243.

11. The first three shapes are unique. The fourth shape is the same as the first shape except that it is reversed, and reversing the position of the second shape gives the fifth shape. So, the next shape will be the reverse of the third shape. See the answer art in the textbook.

15.
All animals are wild.
All lions are animals.
∴ All lions are wild.

The statement "All animals are wild" is shown by a large circle that represents all creatures that are wild with a smaller circle inside that represents animals.

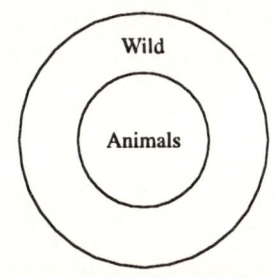

The statement "All lions are animals" is represented by adding a third circle representing lions inside the circle representing animals.

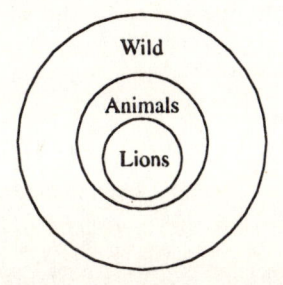

Since the circle representing lions is completely inside the circle representing creatures that are wild, it follows that:

All lions are wild.

19. Use a large circle to represent the 30-day period. Two smaller intersecting circles are placed within the larger circle to represent the days of television watching by the husband and wife. Since they watched 18 days together, place an 18 in the area shared by the two smaller circles. Since the wife watched a total of 25 days, place a 7 in the other region of the circle labeled W.

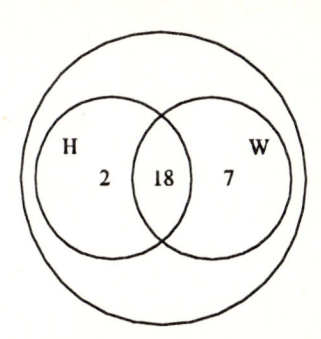

Since the husband watched a total of 20 days, place a 2 in the other region labeled H. The 2, 19 and 7 give a total of 27 days. This results in 3 days for the region outside of the intersecting circle which represents 3 days of neither one watching television.